DIRECT CURRENT

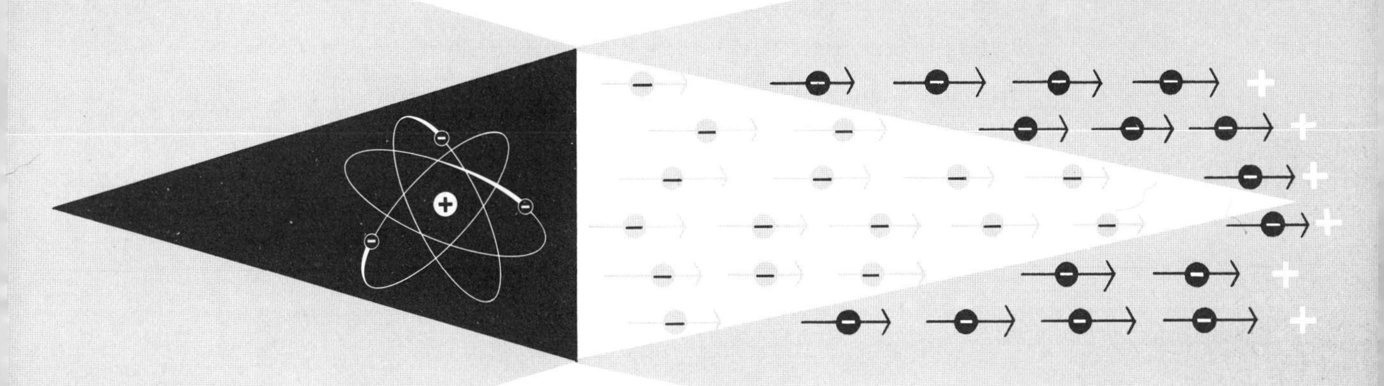

FUNDAMENTALS

ORLA E. LOPER
STATE UNIVERSITY OF NEW YORK
COLLEGE AT OSWEGO

DELMAR PUBLISHERS, MOUNTAINVIEW AVENUE, ALBANY, NEW YORK 12205

DELMAR PUBLISHERS

1963 Edition

Library of Congress Catalog Card Number:
59-12918

PRINTED IN THE UNITED STATES OF AMERICA

Published simultaneously in Canada by
Delmar Publishers — a division of
Van Nostrand Reinhold, Ltd.

Preface

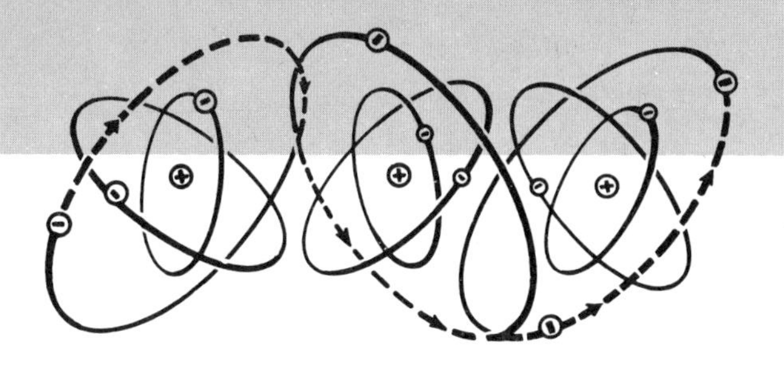

This is the electrical age. Electrical and electronic technology has advanced beyond the wildest dreams of a mere decade ago. The progress has been so rapid in some fields that projects still on the drawing boards have had to be discarded because some new development comes to light, making them obsolete before they are even completed.

Those developments which have come to pass read like the "Science Fiction" of a few years back: Solar batteries power transmitters in orbiting satellites, electronic computers perform mathematical miracles in seconds, nuclear energy has been successfully converted directly to electrical energy without the customary intermediate steam-turbine steps. But these advanced applications are not the only things subject to change. These new uses of electrical energy have made a new approach to electrical instruction all the more necessary.

Not long ago, the direction of electrical current was taught in accordance with Franklin's notion that electricity moved from the positive to the negative terminal. Fifty years ago, teachers could have replaced this notion with the more accurate electron theory. Confirmed by basic experimentation, and reconfirmed in the success of practical devices built in accordance with the concept, this electron-flow idea is essential to a straightforward explanation of electronic devices.

Since the electron theory is a concept basic to all electrical and electronic study this instructional material has been based upon its thorough and continuous explanation. For this reason, atomic structure and the role of the electron form the opening unit of instruction. In succeeding units, the electron is studied in magnetism, in conduction in liquids, gases and vacuum, in the chemical energy of batteries, in thermocouples, piezoelectric materials, photocells, in electromagnetic induction, direct current generators and motors, and finally in heating and lighting --- in all areas, the behavior of the electron remains the center of the presentation of principles. Thus, the foundation is laid for advanced studies in alternating current principles and in basic electronics.

This represents the first of a three-volume series intended to provide an intensive background of fundamentals of direct current, alternating current, and electronics. Each shall have an accompanying manual of selected laboratory experiments. Together they provide basic instructional material for those who require a sound, intensive, technical foundation in electricity and electronics.

William G. Dickson
Editor

Albany, New York

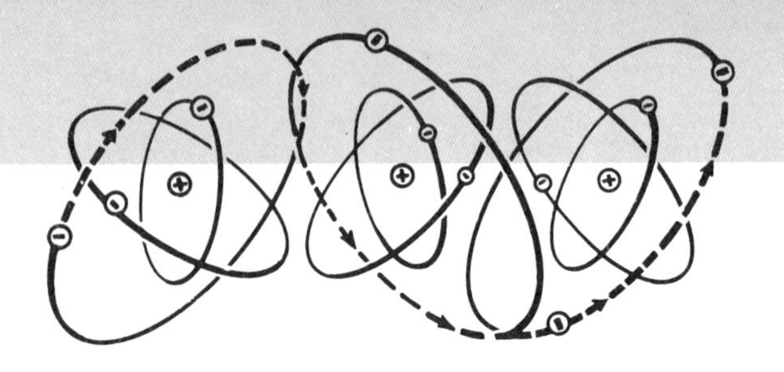

To the Instructor

Basic Electricity I - Fundamentals of Direct Current is the first of a three-volume series designed to provide the foundation for training in the electrical and electronic areas. Along with similar material on alternating current fundamentals and basic electronics, the second and third volumes, it is designed to provide the "floor" upon which advanced studies may be made.

SCOPE The content of Basic Electricity I was determined through analysis of those principles of direct-current electricity which are essential to advancement in electrical technology. Existing courses of study in trade and technical programs were scrutinized to uncover those basic fundamentals common to all such programs, and upon which advanced courses are built. Thus, Basic Electricity I, while it contains a complete and thorough coverage of direct-current fundamentals, is further intended to lead into advanced studies in alternating current and electronics.

ORGANIZATION This instructional material is organized in a logical sequence which proceeds from the simpler concepts to those which are more difficult. It further presents, first, those basic understandings upon which advanced applications are based. As advanced applications are discussed, the basic principles are reviewed so that there is a continuous process of building each new principle upon information which the student has previously mastered. Each unit concludes with a summary of key points and a series of questions designed to review and apply the information of the unit. Many of these review questions are typical of those which are used in the New York State Regents Examinations in Technical Electricity.

CONTENT Beginning with a stimulating discussion of atomic structure and the electron theory, the stage is immediately set for the introduction of the electron as the source of electrical energy. From this beginning, the instructional material continues through electrical measurement, electrostatics, series, parallel, and series-parallel circuits with the essential mathematics involved, resistance factors, power and energy, magnetism and electromagnetism with calculations of magnet-coil windings. The most-used measuring instruments are discussed and their circuits and operation explained. Units on conduction in liquids, gases and vacuum, continue to explain the role of the electron in electrical behavior. Sources of electromotive force are dealt with in the chemical energy of batteries, in thermocouples, piezoelectric materials and photocells, in electromagnetic induction which leads to a thorough presentation of direct current generator principles. The energy stored in a magnetic field, inductance, and inductance calculations are included. Basic principles of deriving mechanical motion from electrical energy lead to a presentation of the principles of D.C. motors and motor calculations. Methods of control are thoroughly discussed. The material concludes with units covering electrical heating devices, lighting, and calculations for the solving of D.C. network problems.

EXPERIMENTS Along with and keyed to this basic text, a series of laboratory experiments has been prepared for student use. These experiments have been thoroughly tested and used in a technical electrical program and have proved their value. Entitled Basic Electricity I Laboratory Experiments, this manual of thirty-five experiments in direct-current electricity is available to those who wish to integrate experimental and classroom study.

TEACHER'S MANUAL A manual containing answers to all problem material in the text has been prepared for the convenience of the instructor.

Contents

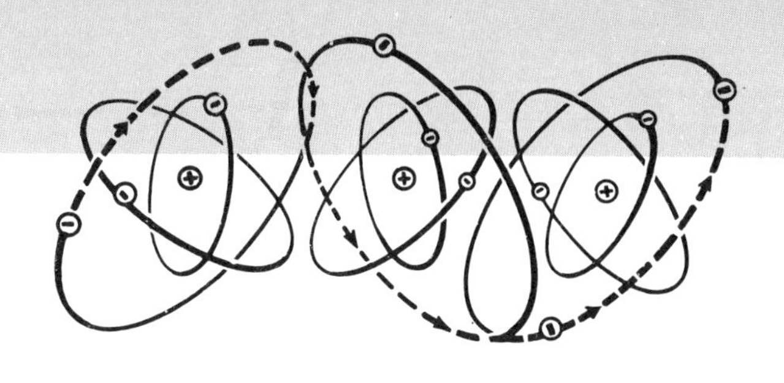

Unit 1 WHAT IS ELECTRICITY?

This question is difficult to answer, because "Electricity" is a broad topic. It's like asking "What is politics?" or "What is life?" – a brief answer doesn't tell much, a long answer makes a book. Sometimes electricity is defined as a form of energy. Electricity does involve making and using energy.

Sometimes electricity is defined as a way in which materials behave. Some people use the term "electricity" as the name for a material that flows through a solid wire; motion of this strange material is called "electric current." It is a lot easier to learn about electricity than it is to define it.

Our knowledge of electricity has been worked out over the years by experimenters in many fields of work: magnetism, batteries, current through gases and through vacuum, studies of metals, and of heat and light. Some of the simplest and most important ideas were discovered fairly recently. So, rather than always taking up ideas in historical order, recently discovered facts will be used in this discussion at once, because they will be a help toward easier understanding.

The first written records of electrical behavior, 2500 years ago, show that the Greeks knew that amber, rubbed on cloth, would attract feathers, cloth fibers, and such light-weight objects. The Greek name for amber was "elektron." From their name for amber came our word "electric", which means, at first, "acting like amber", that is, having the property of attraction.

A hard-rubber comb or the plastic case of a pen acquires the same strange ability after being rubbed on a coat sleeve – the ability of attracting other objects. Long ago, the name "charging" was given to the rubbing process that gives the plastic or hard rubber its ability to attract. After rubbing, the object was called "charged." The "charge" given to the object was thought to be an invisible "load of electricity", whatever that is.

Fig. 1-1

About 300 years ago, a few men began making a systematic study of the behavior of various charged objects. They soon found that repulsion effects were just as important as attraction. Materials could be divided into two groups:

List A	List B
Glass (rubbed on silk)	Hard rubber (rubbed on wool)
Glass (rubbed on wool or cotton)	Block of sulfur (rubbed on wool or fur)
Mica (rubbed on cloth)	Most kinds of rubber (rubbed on cloth)
Asbestos (rubbed on cloth or paper)	Sealing wax (rubbed on silk, wool or fur)
Cat's fur (rubbed with a block of sulfur)	Dry wood (rubbed with glass or mica)
Wool (rubbed with a stick of sealing wax)	Amber (rubbed on cloth)

- Anything from List A attracts anything from List B (charged glass attracts charged rubber).
- Any pair of materials in List A repels each other (charged glass repels charged mica).
- Any pair of materials in List B repels each other (charged rubber repels charged rubber).

From these results appears our first Law of Attraction and Repulsion:

UNLIKE CHARGES ATTRACT, LIKE CHARGES REPEL

Various names were suggested to describe List A and List B. They could have been called by any pair of opposite-sounding names: Up and Down, or Black and White, or Round and Square, or Male and Female. The pair of names finally accepted by scientists was suggested by Benjamin Franklin: "Positive" for List A, and "Negative" for List B.

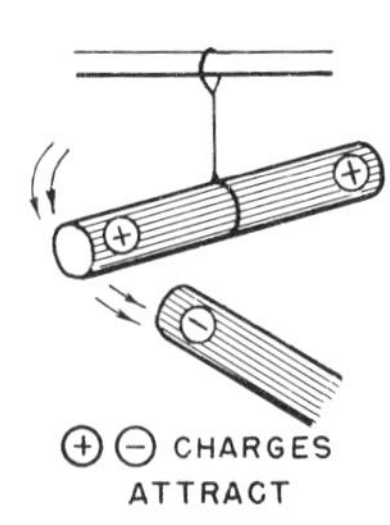

The first-listed material in the groups listed is the one used for a standard of comparison. If an object repels glass which was charged on silk, then that object is "positively charged." If an object repels hard rubber which was charged by rubbing on wool, then that object is called "negatively charged." This is the original definition of the terms "positive" and "negative": Anything that repels charged glass is like charged glass, and is called positive-charged. Anything that repels charged rubber is like charged rubber, and is called negative-charged.

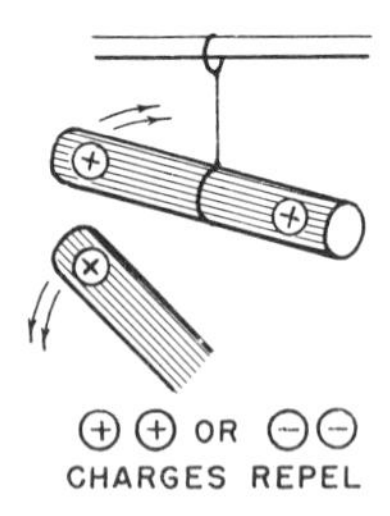

Fig. 1-2

Notice that Lists A and B are insulators. Conductors can be charged also, provided they are on an insulating support. Some metals charge positively, some negatively, depending in part on the presence of surface tarnish, oxide, or dirt.

The frictional movement involved in rubbing the objects together is not of vital importance. Hard rubber simply pressed against wool and removed, without rubbing, will get its negative charge, but not as strongly as if rubbed. The only value of the rubbing is to bring more of the surface area of the rubber and the wool fibers in contact.

For a further understanding of what is occurring in materials when they are electrically charged, we need to review some facts about the internal structure and composition of all materials. Most of these facts about the "structure of matter" have been found out within the last fifty years.

ONE HUNDRED SIMPLE THINGS - ELEMENTS

All of the thousands of kinds of materials that we have consist of various combinations of simple materials called elements. Carbon, oxygen, copper, iron, zinc, tin, chlorine, aluminum, gold, uranium, neon, lead, silver, nitrogen, and hydrogen are elements that most of us have used or heard of. We do not often use the elements silicon, calcium, and sodium in the pure form, so their names may be less familiar. However, these three elements, in combination with oxygen and other elements, make up the largest part of the soil and rocks of our earth, and help form many manufactured products of everyday use.

There are about 100 different kinds of elements in all. Some of them we never hear of, either because they are very scarce, or because people have not yet developed industrial uses for them. Uses are now being developed for germanium, beryllium, and titanium, so their names may sound more familiar ten years from now. In 1890 few people had heard of aluminum; it was then a rare and precious metal.

Everyone has read something about "atoms" in recent years. An atom is the smallest possible speck of an element that can exist. Single atoms are so small that there is no use wondering what one atom looks like — atoms are smaller than the light waves with which we see things.

There are about 30,000,000,000,000,000,000,000 atoms of copper in a one-cent piece, so one atom is a rather small item. A penny is about 6 million atoms thick, that is, an imaginary slicing machine might peel 6 million slices of copper, each slice containing 5 million billion atoms in a layer that is one atom in thickness.

There are about 100 different kinds of atoms, because there are about 100 different elements. The word "atom" is correctly used only as a name for the smallest particle of an element. We can talk about atoms of carbon and atoms of oxygen, and atoms of copper, because these materials are elements.

We do not talk about an atom of water, because there is no such thing. Water is not an element. The smallest possible speck of water is properly called a "molecule." A molecule of water is made of two atoms of hydrogen and one atom of oxygen combined together. Water is a compound of hydrogen and oxygen. The word compound means a material that is composed of two or more different elements combined.

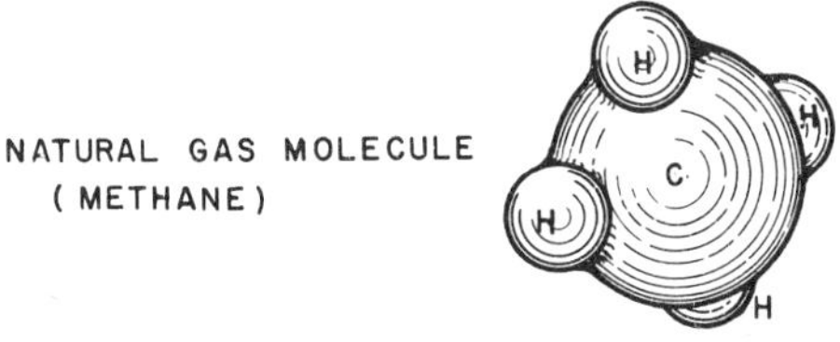

FOUR HYDROGEN ATOMS COMBINED WITH ONE CARBON ATOM

WATER MOLECULE

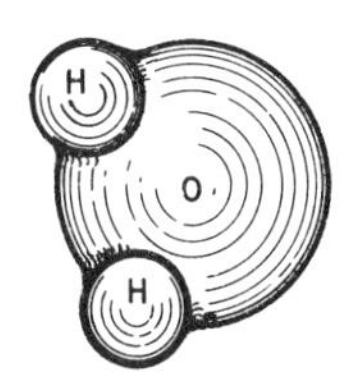

TWO HYDROGEN ATOMS COMBINED WITH ONE OXYGEN ATOM

Fig. 1-3 Molecules

THREE SIMPLE THINGS - ELECTRONS, PROTONS, NEUTRONS

All of these hundred kinds of atoms are found to consist of three kinds of still-smaller particles. These particles are so completely different from any material that we know, that any imaginative picture of them is sure to be inaccurate.

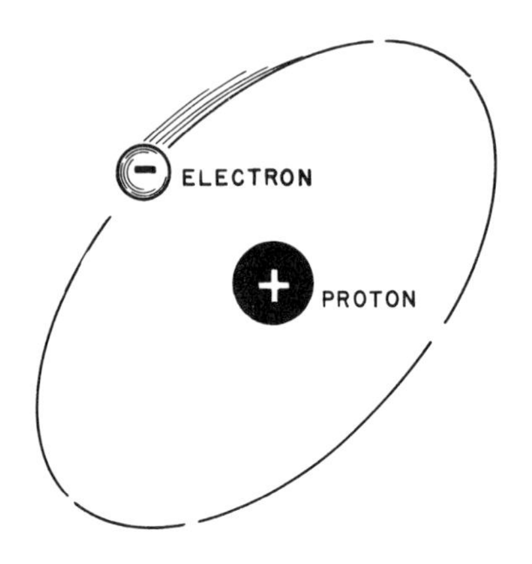

Fig. 1-4 The Hydrogen Atom

Atoms of ordinary hydrogen gas are the simplest in structure of all atoms, consisting of a single positive-charged particle in the center, with one negative-charged particle whizzing around it at high speed. The positive-charged particle has been given the name "proton"; the negative-charged particle is called an "electron."

The diagram (Fig. 1-4) is not drawn to scale as the diameter of the atom is several thousand times greater than the diameter of the particles in it. A more exact sketch would illustrate the electron pinhead-size, revolving in an orbit 150 ft. across, to better show relative dimensions. There is relatively as much open space as in our solar system. But this electron is not properly represented by a pinhead, for it is highly indefinite in shape, a fuzzy wisp that ripples and spins and pulses as it encircles the proton in the center. The electron is too small to have the properties that ordinary materials have. In fact, it certainly is not ordinary material, because the mathematical equation that describes it best is the equation that describes a wave.

The proton that forms the center of the hydrogen atom is smaller than the electron, but 1840 times as heavy. Its most important property is its positive charge.

As we look at diagrams of other atoms, we need two new words to describe them. The nucleus of the atom is the name of the tightly packed heavy central core, in which the atom's protons are assembled. Along with the protons are other particles called neutrons.

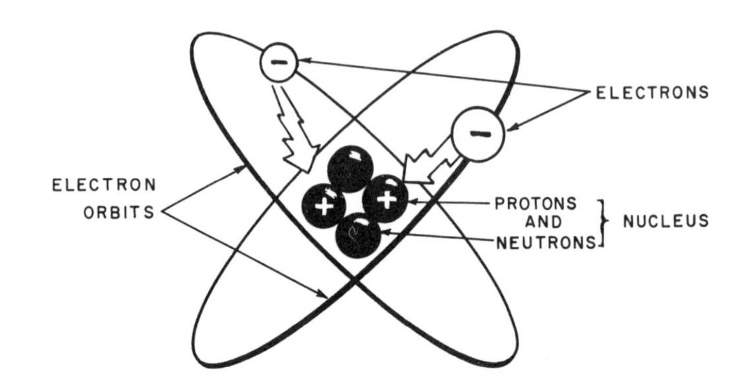

Fig. 1-5 Atomic Structure

The name, neutron, indicates that these heavy particles are electrically neutral; weight is their most important property. A neutron is probably a tightly collapsed combination of an electron and a proton.

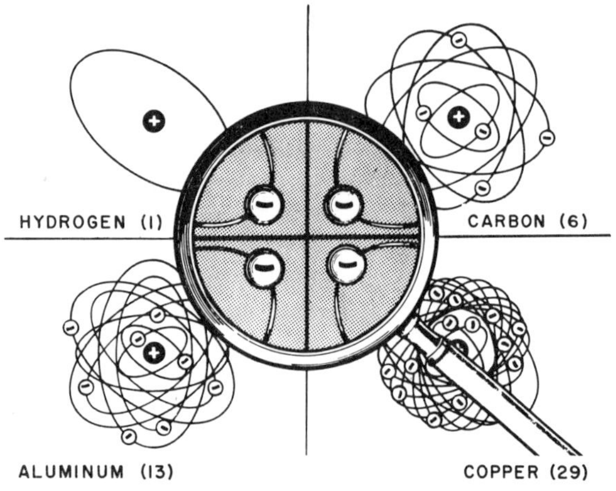

Fig. 1-6 All Electrons Are Identical

It may at first be hard to realize that these three kinds of particles, electrons, protons, and neutrons, make up all of our materials. All electrons are alike, regardless of what material they come from, or exist in. All protons are alike, regardless of what material they form a part. Neutrons, too, are all alike. An atom has no outer skin other than the surface formed by its whirling electrons, a repelling surface comparable to the whirling "surface" that surrounds a child skipping a rope.

The kind of element is determined only by the number of protons in the atom nucleus. If we had some way of assembling 29 protons as tightly as they are packed in an atom's nucleus, we would find that we would need 34 neutrons also, as a sort of "cement" to hold those protons together. This nucleus would attract to itself 29 electrons making an electrically neutral atom (the positive charge of a proton is equally as strong as the negative charge of an electron). This assembly of 29 protons, 29 electrons, and 34 neutrons is an atom of copper. All copper atoms contain 29 protons, and any atom with 29 protons is a copper atom.

In a chunk of ordinary copper, most of the atoms have 29 protons and 34 neutrons in the nucleus, but some have 29 protons and 36 neutrons in the nucleus. These atoms with 36 neutrons are just like the atoms with 34 neutrons in all respects except one: the atoms with 36 neutrons are slightly heavier.

The total of particles in the nucleus (63 or 65 for these two varieties of copper atoms) is the quantity called "Atomic Weight."

The number of protons in the nucleus determines what the element is. The arrangement of electrons around the nucleus determines most of the physical and chemical properties and behavior of the element. The atom's electrons are arranged in distinct layers, or shells, around the nucleus. The innermost ring or shell contains no more than two electrons, the next is limited to 8, the third can have 18, and the fourth, 32.

Referring to the copper atom again, diagrammed at right, its 29 electrons are arranged in four layers: 2 in the shell nearest the nucleus, 8 in the next, and 18 in the third, account for 28 of them. The single 29th electron circulates all alone in the fourth layer. In this position, relatively far from the positive nucleus, and screened from the attracting positive charge by the other electrons, this single electron is not tightly held to the atom, and is fairly free to travel. Inside a piece of copper, these outside single electrons of atoms often change places with one another, sliding from one atom to another with ease. This easy movability of the outside electron of copper atoms accounts for the good electrical conductivity of copper, for electrical conduction in a wire is simply a drift of electrons, sliding from one atom to another along the wire.

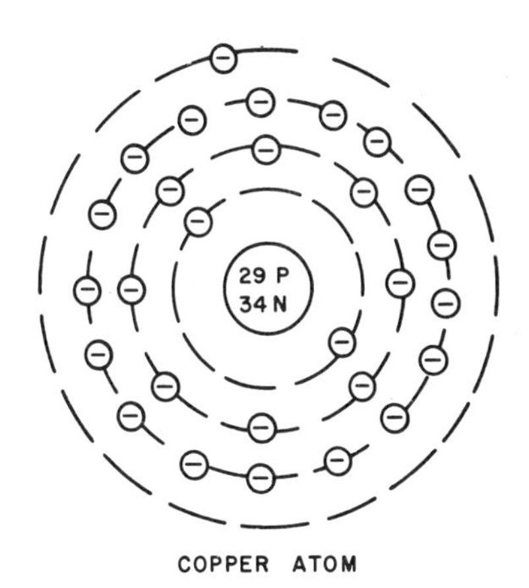

Fig. 1-7

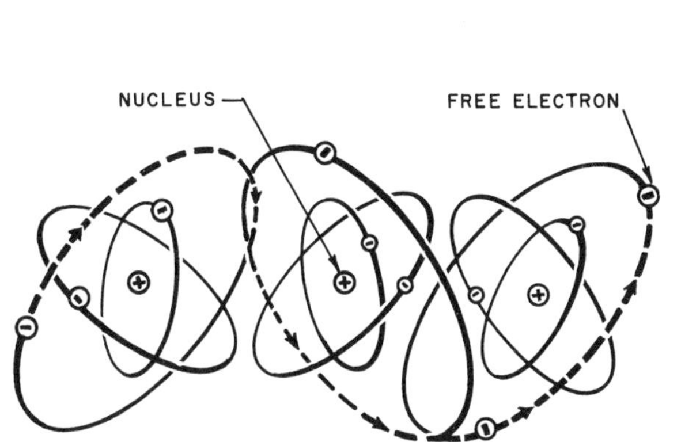

Fig. 1-8

If we had time to examine diagrams of the electron arrangement in all kinds of atoms, we would find that most of them have one or two or three electrons in an outer ring, shielded from the positive nucleus by one or more inner shells of electrons. These elements are all called metals, and are fairly good conductors because one of those outermost electrons is free to wander, provided he can be replaced by a twin-brother electron from a nearby atom.

To contrast with metals, atoms of two nonmetallic elements, sulfur and iodine, are shown. (Both are solids; the iodine used to treat cuts is a little pure iodine dissolved in alcohol.)

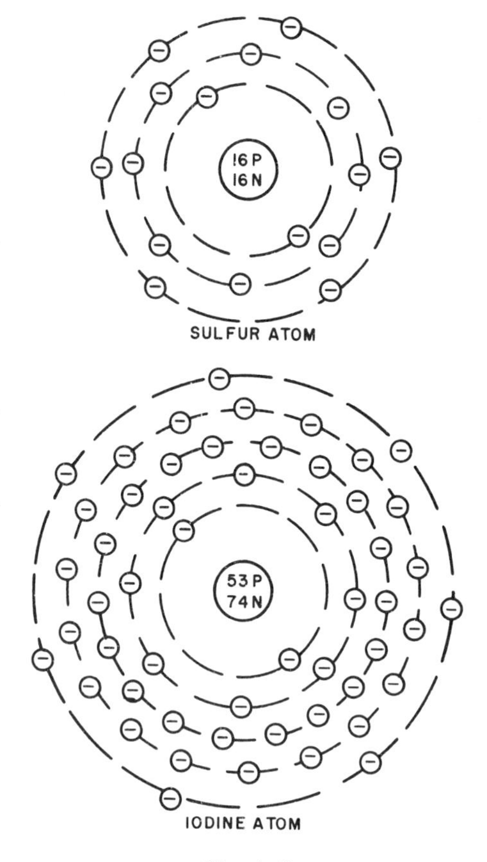

Fig. 1-9

Elements with five or six or seven electrons in their outermost ring are classed as nonmetals. They are not good conductors, for these reasons:

1. Their outside electrons are not as well shielded from the attracting force of the nucleus, because a larger percentage of the atom's electrons is out there in the outside ring, not helping to screen any individual electron from the nucleus' force.

2. Furthermore, a ring of eight electrons has a certain desirable energy-stability about it. This condition is stable enough so that these atoms with 7 or 6 or 5 electrons will readily pick up and hold the 1 or 2 or 3 electrons that can be accommodated in that outer ring, building it up to eight in number. So if, for example, we try to push some electrons through a block of sulfur, we find that our electrons drop into the empty spaces in the outer shell, and are stuck there. In sulfur there are no free electrons, ready to slide over into the next atom and make room for a newcomer.

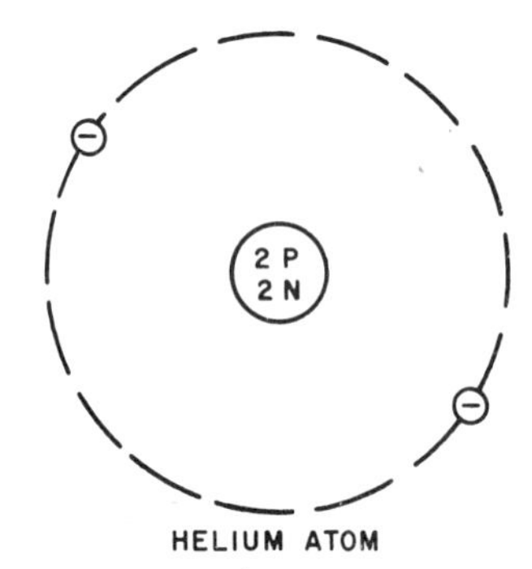

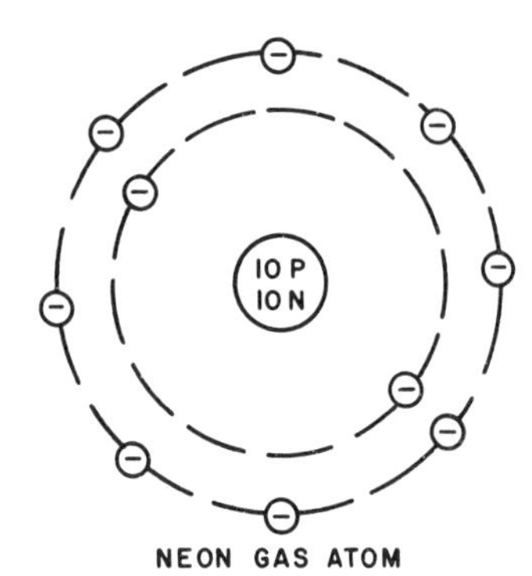

Fig. 1-10

A short look at two other atoms, helium and neon, will complete for now our discussion of atom structure.

Helium has two electrons, but it is not classed as a metal because those electrons are not screened from the nucleus by any other electrons. Neither one of its two electrons is free to wander; they are tightly held.

Neon's eight electrons in its outer ring are tightly held, too. The chemist limits the term "nonmetallic" element to those with 5, 6 or 7 electrons in the outer ring.

He makes another classification for elements like helium and neon, in which the outer ring is filled. These elements are "inert gases." (They are called "inert", chemically, because they do not form combinations with other elements.)

These inert gases can be made conducting, however, by putting the gas, at low pressure, in a situation where the atoms are bombarded with high-speed electrons violently enough so that electrons are jarred entirely loose from the atom. Such is the condition in a neon sign.

To return to the discussion that got us into the atom-structure problem: our purpose was stated as to secure "a further understanding of what is occurring in materials when they are electrically charged." We now have two charged "particles" with which to explain electrical behavior:

Electrons: Negative-charged, lightweight and movable.

Protons: Positive-charged, heavy, stuck down in the center of the atom.

Because protons are immovable in solid materials, all electrical behavior in solid materials is explained by movements of electrons.

Looking back at Lists A and B on Page 2, we find that when a block of sulfur is rubbed with cat's fur, the sulfur and the fur become oppositely charged; the sulfur negative, and the fur positive. All that happened was that some electrons were removed from the fur and transferred to the sulfur. When hard rubber or sealing wax gets a "negative charge" from wool, what it is really getting from the wool is electrons. At the same time we say the wool is getting a "positive charge", but what it is really getting is robbed, some of its electrons having been taken away.

An object becomes positively charged by losing some of its electrons.

An object becomes negatively charged by gaining some electrons.

During these electric-charging operations, relatively few atoms are affected, considering the huge number of atoms in a chunk of material. The addition of a billion electrons to a hard-rubber comb will give it noticeable attraction force, but a billion is a small number in this business. The sleeve on which the comb was rubbed had so many atoms that if only one atom out of every 1,000,000,000,000,000 lost one electron, the billion could be supplied.

This Unit started with the question, "What is electricity?" Electricity is the study of how electrons behave. The absence of a few, or the presence of a few extra, changes the properties of a material. The motion of electrons through a material is electric current.

HOW MUCH CAN WE BELIEVE?

We cannot see electrons directly, and never shall. But scientists can extend and surpass the range of our senses by the use of instruments, just as everyday we use instruments and machines to accomplish tasks that cannot be done by hand and eye alone. Many of these instruments give us, in a way, new senses and new abilities to get information.

"Is this stuff fact or theory? Theories change."

The best evidence of truth, for the practical man, is that everyday devices built in accordance with these theories, actually work. We are as sure of the existence of electrons as we are of stars in the sky. And we have learned how to make electrons travel where we want them to go.

- "Electricity" is explained by the behavior of electrons.
- Like charges repel, unlike charges attract.
- A negative-charged object is one that has gained some extra electrons. It will repel charged hard rubber.
- A positive-charged object is one that has lost some of its electrons. It will repel charged glass.
- All materials can be electrically charged.
- An atom is the smallest chunk of an element; a molecule is the smallest possible portion of a compound. A molecule consists of two or more different kinds of atoms fastened together.
- All atoms consist of various numbers of electrons, protons, and neutrons. The number of protons determines the kind of element.
- Electrons are negative-charged, lightweight, and movable.
- Protons are positive-charged, heavy, and immovable in solids.
- Neutrons are not charged, and are as heavy and immovable in the atom as protons.
- Electrons are arranged in rings or shells in the atom: the number of electrons in the outer ring determines most of the electrical properties of the atom and the element.

REVIEW QUESTIONS

1. a. How were the words "positive charge" and "negative charge" originally defined, in terms of materials?

   b. Using our knowledge of electrons, how are the words "positive charge" and "negative charge" defined?

2. Using electrons, explain what happens to an object when it becomes positively charged. What happens to an object when it becomes negatively charged?

3. State the Law of Attraction and Repulsion.

4. What do each of these words mean: atom, molecule, element, compound, proton, electron, neutron. (There is no point in memorizing definitions of such terms; you should try to understand their meaning so that you can use them correctly.)

5. Tell how atoms of metals differ from atoms of nonmetallic elements, in their electron arrangement. Why are metals good conductors?

6. There is an element called gallium. Its atoms have 31 electrons. From looking at the picture of a copper atom, how would you expect the electrons of an atom of gallium to be arranged? Is gallium a metal?

7. Complete the blanks:

   All materials consist of only about 100 simple substances, called _____. The smallest particles of these simple substances are called _____. Atoms consist of only three kinds of still-smaller particles, called _____, _____, and _____. Of these three, the one of least weight is the _____, the one most readily movable is the _____, the positive-charged particle is the _____, the negative-charged particle is the _____. The particle that is most responsible for electrical behavior of materials is the _____ .

Unit 2 MEASURING ELECTRON MOTION

In dealing with any useful quantity, whether it is vegetables, steel bars, or electrons, a system of measurements has to be set up to keep track of production, transfer, and use of the commodity.

There are three basic measurements involved in the flow of electrons through a wire that deserve explanation now:

1. The rate of flow of electrons
2. The force or pressure that causes them to move
3. Opposition to their movement

RATE OF FLOW

In measuring rate of electron flow, we are concerned with a quantity rate, rather than simple speed. In ordinary electrical devices, the number of electrons passing through each second is the important thing, not their speed in miles per hour. Water pumps are rated in gallons per minute, ventilation fans in cubic feet per minute, grain-handling equipment in bushels per hour — all of these are quantity rates.

In order to establish such a rate, we need a measure of quantity to start with. We could use number of electrons per second, but so many pass by that we would have too huge numbers to use, numbers worse than the number of grains of wheat in Kansas. Just as grains of wheat are lumped together and counted in bushels, we lump together 6,250,000,000,000,000,000 electrons and call this quantity a coulomb of electrons (so named to honor Charles Coulomb, an old-time French scientist). 6,250,000,000,000,000,000 is a large number. If we had that many flies in New York State some summer, and killed them all, they would cover the whole state six feet deep, packed down, 500 flies to the cubic inch.

We measure rate of electron flow in coulombs per second, which compares with measuring the flow of traffic in cars per hour, or with measuring an air current in cubic feet per second, or a water current in gallons per second.

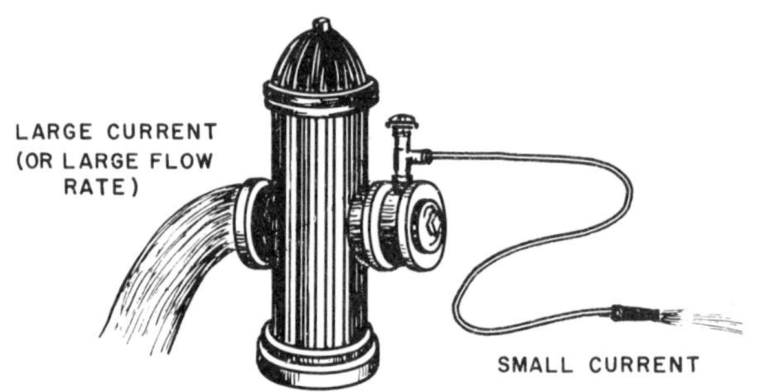

Electron flow is electric current

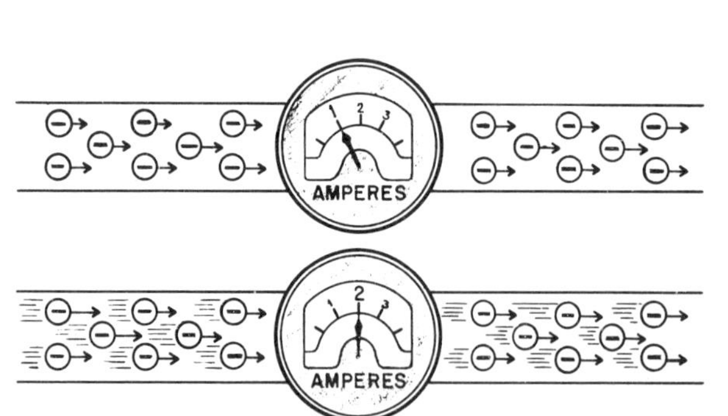

The words "coulombs per second" are seldom heard in conversation, because we use instead one word that means "coulombs per second." That word is ampere, (named for another French scientist). Here's the definition of an ampere:

1 ampere is a flow-rate of 1 coulomb/second

As a side-issue, sometimes people get into discussion of actual "speed of electricity", for purposes of argument rather than purposes of measurement. A more exact term than "speed of electricity" is needed to distinguish between (1) the average speed of individual electrons as they drift through the wire and (2) the speed of the "impulse." We realize that when we turn on a light-switch the light is "on" immediately. In a house wired with No. 12-gage wire, calculation shows that there are so many electrons in the wire that the average speed of individual electrons needs to be only about 3 inches per hour when the current is one ampere. Three inches per hour is the speed that electrons drift through the copper wire, but keep in mind that the wire is full of electrons to begin with, so that when the switch is turned on, they start moving everywhere at once, hence the practically instantaneous "impulse." The actual speed of this impulse depends on the arrangement of the wires, and may be anything from a few thousand miles per second up to 186,000 miles per second, the speed of light, as a theoretical top limit.

In order for electrons to "start moving everywhere at once", and keep moving, a complete conducting path for them must exist. In the open circuit diagram, Fig. 2-1, there is no current anywhere. Electrons cannot move away from the negative post of the battery because there is nowhere for them to go. They will not flow into the lamp because they cannot flow out since the wire is surrounded by insulating air.

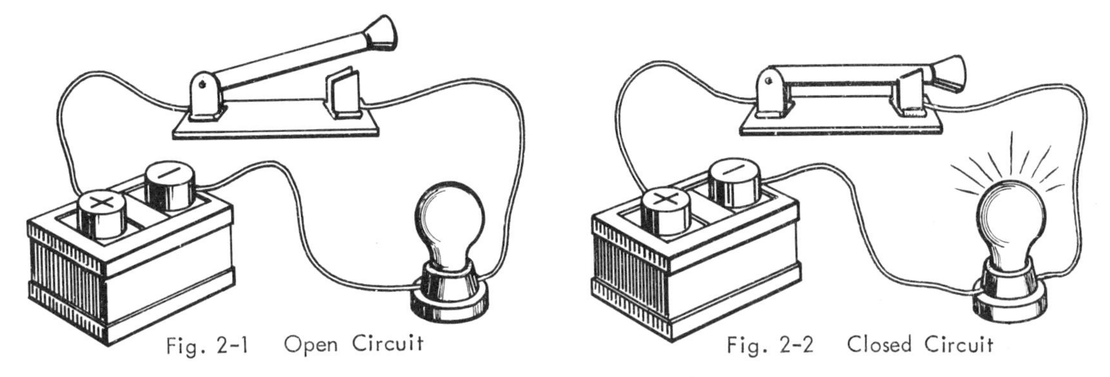

Fig. 2-1 Open Circuit Fig. 2-2 Closed Circuit

As soon as the switch is closed, Fig. 2-2, electrons (negative-charged things, remember) can flow through the lamp, repelled from the negative-charged post of the battery and attracted to the positive-charged post of the battery. In Fig. 2-1, the battery is pushing and pulling on electrons just as hard as it is in Fig. 2-2, but in 2-1 they cannot move. The open-circuit situation is similar to a closed water faucet; the pressure is there, ready to cause flow.

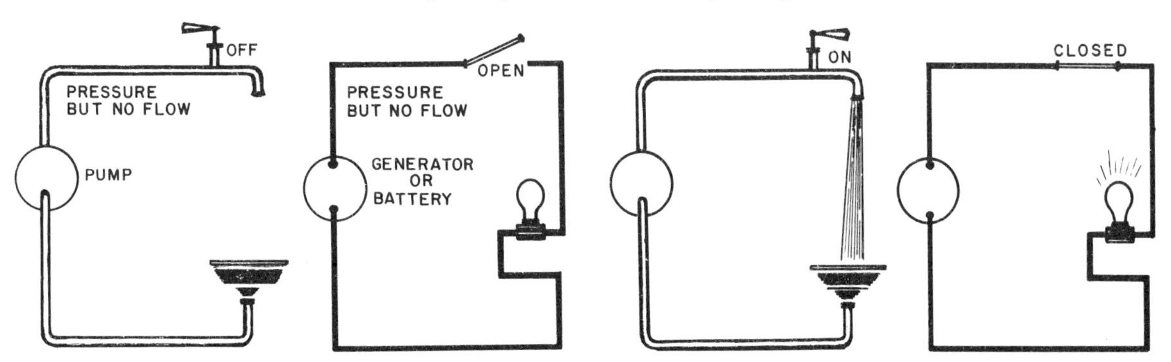

FORCE OR PRESSURE THAT MOVES ELECTRONS

To make electrons move, usefully, they have to be pushed. Of course they do spin around and trade places with other electrons inside a piece of metal, but that is not a particularly useful motion. To use their motion, they must be forced to drift along through the metal in one direction, not just rattle around aimlessly. This force or push that is applied to electrons has been given various names: one is "Electromotive Force."

This electron-moving force, Electromotive Force, e.m.f., can be produced by batteries, by generators, and by other devices. Sometimes this e.m.f. (Electromotive Force) is called "Electrical Pressure", because it is in some ways comparable to water pressure that causes a water current in a pipe, or to air pressure that causes an air current in a ventilation duct.

This e.m.f. or electrical pressure, is measured in "Volts." The term "Voltage" means the same as electrical pressure, or e.m.f. An exact definition of a volt will be taken up later; for now, think of the number of volts as telling the amount of driving force that makes electrons move. Just as greater water pressure will cause more gallons per second of water to run through a pipe, so a greater number of volts of electrical pressure will tend to cause a greater electron current.

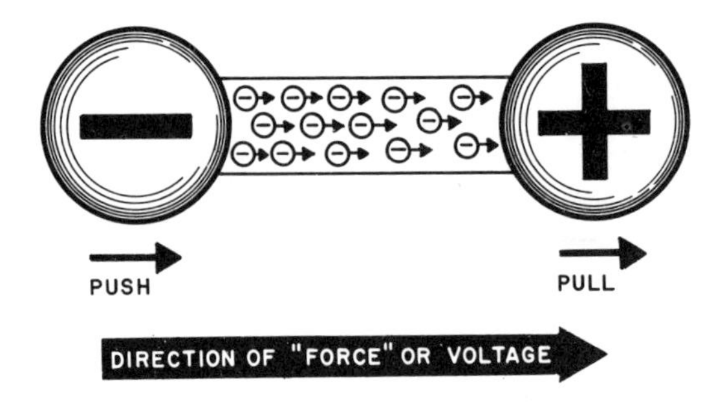

OPPOSITION TO MOVEMENT: RESISTANCE

Like baseballs and rowboats, electrons don't ordinarily keep on moving forward forever, after once given a start. Friction retards the movement of common objects.

Electrons inside a wire have a similar problem. There is a sort of "internal friction" involved in the passage of electrons through a material; this friction-like opposition is called "electrical resistance."

Electrons slide through a copper wire easily, like a boat through water. Electrons move through iron and some metal alloys fairly easily, but not as easily as they do through copper. (To continue the comparison, this is more like rowing a boat through tomato soup.)

There are lots of materials in which electrons can hardly move at all, even if a lot of pressure (high voltage) is applied. One such material is sulfur, discussed in some detail in Unit 1. Trying to move electrons through sulfur or glass or plastic or porcelain is about as effective as trying to row a boat on a concrete road or on plowed ground.

The accompanying list compares the resistance of common materials. Those of highest resistance (so high it is difficult even to measure) are the best insulators; those of lowest resistance are the best conductors, and in between are materials that are poor at conducting and yet haven't quite enough resistance to be called insulators.

INSULATORS

- Waxes and plastics } Best Insulators
- Amber, sulfur, mica }
- Porcelain, oils }
- Glass, cloth, wood
- Ivory, stone
- Alcohol, pure water
- Dry sandy soil
- Faucet water
- Moist soil, human body
- Weak acids
- Strong acids and salts dissolved in water
- Semi-conductors (germanium)
- Carbon, graphite
- Alloys: brass, nichrome
- Metals: iron, tungsten, aluminum, copper, silver } Best Conductors

CONDUCTORS

(See also Pages 18 and 55)

The unit of measure of resistance is named the ohm, (for a German scientist, G. S. Ohm, who found out, 130 years ago, that the current in a wire is proportional to the e.m.f.) One ohm of resistance was defined as just exactly enough resistance so that one volt of applied pressure would cause a current of one ampere through the one ohm. The legal definition of the ampere, volt, and ohm is given in Unit 12.

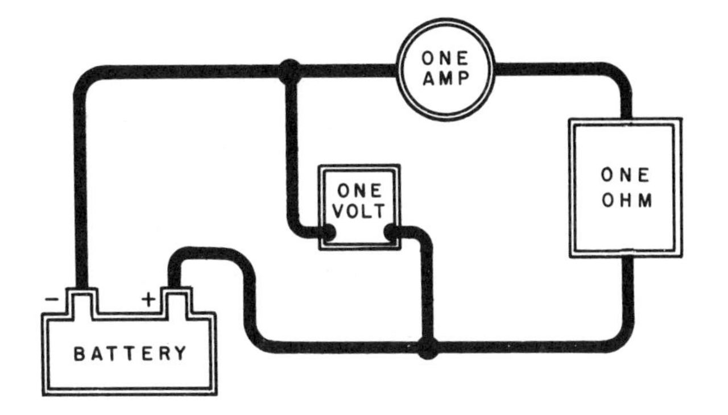

Ohm's Law states that when the voltage (e.m.f.) on a device is increased, there will be more current; also, when the resistance is increased without changing the e.m.f., there will be less current. These ideas combine into one useful formula:

$$\text{Amperes of current} = \frac{\text{Electromotive Force in volts}}{\text{Ohms resistance}}$$

The current is directly proportional to the applied electromotive force, and inversely proportional to the resistance.

For example, if an 8-ohm lamp is connected to a 12-volt battery, current = 12 volts ÷ 8 ohms = 1.5 amps.

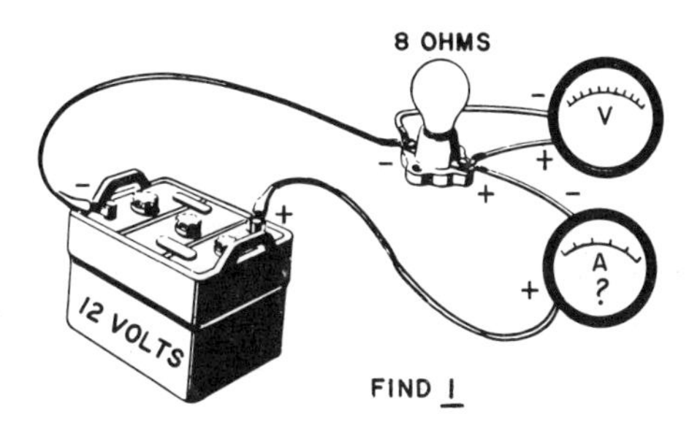

To abbreviate this formula further, it is generally written:

$$I = \frac{E}{R}$$

I (from an old term, "Intensity of Current") represents current in amperes, E represents e.m.f. in volts, and R is resistance in ohms.

The formula may be rearranged in two other useful forms: $E = IR$ and $R = \frac{E}{I}$

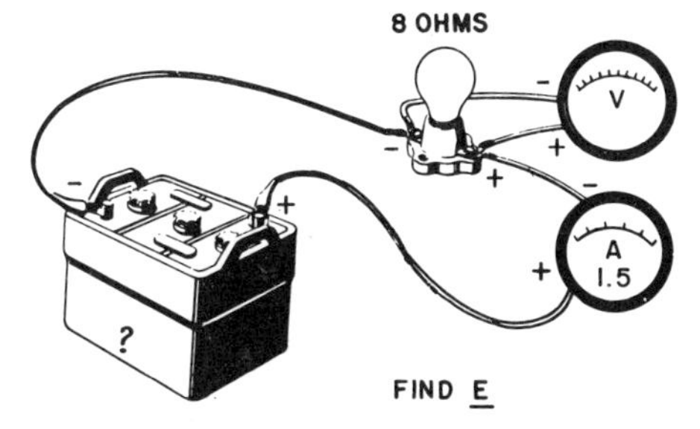

To illustrate using these forms, say we are required to find out how many volts are needed to cause a current of 1.5 amps in an 8-ohm lamp:

Using $E = IR$, $I = 1.5$, $R = 8$

$E = 1.5 \times 8 = 12$ volts, Ans.

Or, if the problem is to find how much resistance will permit a current of 1.5 amps from a 12-volt battery:

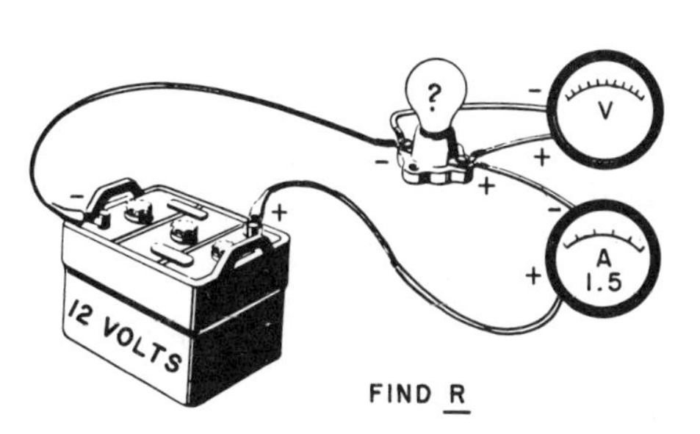

Using $R = \frac{E}{I}$ $E = 12$, $I = 1.5$

$R = \frac{12}{1.5} = 8$ ohms, Ans.

At this point it may be seen that any one of the three formulas tells the relationship between E, I, and R equally well. Rather than memorize three formulas, a better practice in using Ohm's Law is to substitute two known quantities in E = IR and find the third (unknown) quantity by simple algebra.

For example, given E = 120, R = 24, find I:

$$E = IR$$
$$120 = I \text{ times } 24$$

Divide each side of the equation by 24:

$$\frac{120}{24} = \frac{I \times 24}{24}$$

The purpose of dividing by 24 is to cancel out the 24 in I × 24:

$$\frac{120}{24} = \frac{I \times \cancel{24}}{\cancel{24}}$$

This leaves $\frac{120}{24} = I$ $\frac{120}{24} = 5$, and the question is answered, I is 5 amps

A similar process can be used if R is the item to find. Given E = 120 volts, and I = 5 amps, find R:

$$E = IR \qquad 120 = 5R$$

Divide each side of the equation by 5. That will cancel out the 5 that now interferes with our knowing what R equals:

$\frac{120}{5} = \frac{\cancel{5}R}{\cancel{5}}$ $\frac{120}{5} = R$ 24 = R, that is, R is 24 ohms, Ans.

POINTS TO REMEMBER

- Large quantities of electrons are measured in coulombs. A coulomb is a quantity or amount, similar to gallons of gasoline or bushels of grain or pounds of sugar.

- Amperes measure rate of flow of electrons. One ampere is a rate of one coulomb per second.

- Electrons start moving at all points in an electric circuit when the switch is closed so the effect of closing the switch is practically instantaneous, though the average drift-speed of individual electrons is slow.

- Volts measures Electron-moving Force, e.m.f., Electrical Pressure.

- Ohms measures resistance, the opposition of atoms in the material to the passage of electrons.

- E = IR. This is Ohm's Law. E is e.m.f., in volts. I is current in amperes. R is resistance, in ohms.

REVIEW QUESTIONS

1. State Ohm's Law in your own words.

2. In what way is the flow of electrons through a wire similar to the flow of water through a pipe? Use "pressure", "rate of flow" and "resistance" in your answer.

3. Exactly what is measured by each of these units: amperes, coulombs, volts, ohms.

4. What is a "closed circuit"? What is an "open circuit"? Can voltage exist in an "open circuit"? Can current exist in an "open circuit"?

5. What one word means "coulombs per second"?

6. Why do we measure current in coulombs per second instead of in miles per hour or inches per second?

7. Which has more resistance – an electric flatiron or a lamp bulb? (Check your answer after you work out the next set of problems.)

8. Using the Ohm's Law formula, calculate the resistance of each of these devices:

	Volts	Amps
(1) 60-watt lamp bulb	120	0.5
(2) Automobile headlamp	6	4.2
(3) Toaster	120	8.
(4) Electric flatiron	120	10.
(5) Soldering iron	115	2.
(6) 100-watt lamp	120	0.83
(7) Radio-tube filament	35	0.15
(8) 2-cell flashlight bulb	3	0.28
(9) Electric frying pan	115	10.

9. Using the answers obtained in Question 8, calculate what would happen if the 60-watt lamp (No. 1) were connected to a 12-volt automobile battery. What would happen if the automobile headlamp (No. 2) were connected to a 12-volt battery?

10. How much current will there be in a 48-ohm lamp bulb connected to a 120-volt line?

11. How many volts are needed to produce a current of 3 amps in a 4-ohm coil of wire?

12. Calculate volts needed to cause a current of 0.002 amps in a 10,000 ohm resistor.

13. How much current is there in a 60,000-ohm resistor connected to a 6-volt battery?

14. The resistance of a man's thumb may be 12,000 ohms. Calculate current through thumb when the thumb is inserted in a 120-volt lamp socket.

15. 720 coulombs of electrons moved past a point in a wire, taking one minute to do so. Find the current, in amperes.

16. A battery was charged for 24 hours at a 6-amp rate. How many coulombs traveled along the circuit in the 24 hours?

17. The field coil of a certain D.C. motor takes 2 amps on a 220-volt D.C. line. Find its resistance.

18. A spot welder produces 200 amps through a resistance of 0.005 ohms. Find the voltage.

19. Find the current in an 18-ohm electric heater when connected to a 108-volt source.

20. A relay coil with 1,000-ohms resistance is used to operate a large electric switch. In order to operate the relay, the coil must have a current of 0.118 ampere. Find the voltage required to operate the relay.

21. An electromagnet is used to lift scrap iron. The coil has 62.5-ohms resistance, and requires 3.8 amperes. Find the operating voltage.

Unit 3 ELECTRONS SITTING STILL

A more elegant title for this unit is "Electrostatics". The word "static", according to the dictionary, means "at rest, not moving."

A good deal can be learned about electrons when they are sitting still. Of course, electrons are such jumpy things that they won't sit still very well. In jumping from one thing to another, the sparks and arcs they produce are often highly important.

Perhaps the word "static" in a discussion of electricity first reminds one of noise in a radio. During a lightning flash, or any electric spark, vibrating electrons broadcast some energy that is received as snaps and crackles in a radio receiver. The term "static" is now too often applied to any unexplained radio interference, whether of true electrostatic origin or not.

The material to be taken up in this unit is an extension of ideas introduced in Unit 1. "Points to Remember", on Page 8 should be reviewed at this point. These facts are particularly useful:

When any object is being charged negatively, it is receiving some electrons that normally do not belong to it, and they will try to escape. When any object is being charged positively, it is losing some of its electrons. After it has been charged positively, some of its electrons are missing. All that the "positive-charged" object has acquired is a lack of electrons. (Remember that electrons are all alike, regardless of where they come from.) When a positive-charged object has electrons returned to it, it goes back to its original neutral state. The returned electrons do not have to be the same ones that were lost; if a million electrons were lost, and a different million returned, everything is still back to normal.

CONDUCTORS AND INSULATORS

You may have already noticed that the material in Lists A and B on Page 2 are all nonconductors, that is, insulators. For the acquiring of a "static electric charge", insulators work well, because they are materials in which electrons cannot move readily. If a spot on the insulating material has a surplus of electrons, they are stuck there. At some location on the material, there may be a lack of electrons; if so, electrons will find it difficult to slide over and fill the lack.

Materials in which electrons move freely are called conductors. Metals, with their loose electrons in atoms' outer rings, are the best conductors. They can be charged, provided they are insulated from their surroundings by some nonconducting material.

The Best Insulators

Which insulator is best for a certain use depends upon many factors. The table below compares the internal resistance of several insulating materials. The best of these insulators, with resistance of 10^9 and above, must be pure, clean and dry to maintain their resistance. In air of 90% relative humidity, the invisibly thin layer of moisture lets these solids conduct 1000 times as much as they do in air of 50% relative humidity.

Resistance of Insulators in Ohms (Resistance Between Faces of a One-Centimeter Cube of Material)	
10^{15} and up:	Air, diamond, purified waxes (ceresin, paraffin), epoxy resins, fused silica, hard rubber, sulfur, amber, mica, rosin, pure bakelite, shellac, sealing wax, quartz, paraffin oil (mineral oil), carbon tetrachloride.
10^{12} - 10^{15}:	Beeswax, porcelain, glass, liquid hydrocarbons, vegetable oils, synthetic rubber (GRS, BuNa-S, Neoprene), turpentine, vinyls and other plastics.
10^9 - 10^{11} :	Plastic compositions with clay or fiber filler, celluloid, marble, fiber, dry wood, ethyl acetate and similar solvents.
10^6 - 10^8 :	Slate, ivory, alcohols, pure water, Perbunan rubber, solvents such as acetone, benzol, kerosene; glycerine.
10^3 - 10^5 :	Poor insulators, also poor conductors: faucet water, flame, soil, human skin, "conductive rubber".

Another factor is "breakdown voltage", also called "sparking voltage" or "dielectric strength". A layer of air 1/16″ thick may be a good insulator for 3000 volts, but at 6000 volts sparks jump the gap and the air is no longer an insulator. A sheet of good mica may withstand 50,000 volts or more before sparking. The table, right, shows that for a given thickness of insulation, glass or hard rubber, for example, will withstand ten times as much voltage as air before a spark will punch through the insulation.

Other important properties in the consideration of insulators include cost and ease of forming.

Comparative Breakdown Voltages	
Mica	20-60
Glass and fused ceramics	10-50
Hard rubber	10-30
Waxed paper	15-20
Rubber	5-15
Oils	2-7
Air, plain paper	1

USING AN ELECTROSCOPE

Now little more than a toy, this device was once widely used in comparing electric charges, served as a crude voltmeter, and was used in the detection of radio-active minerals. It was an important aid in experiments that led to the discovery of electrons. For everyday use, it has been replaced by devices more accurate and sensitive, but more complex.

To make use of the electroscope, it must first be charged, using a known charge. The charging procedure is simple: First, charge a hard-rubber rod by rubbing it on wool. Then slide the hard-rubber rod along the knob of the electroscope. Electrons from the negative hard rubber are wiped off the rod, on to the electroscope, where they repel each other and scatter all over the metal knob, metal rod, and leaves. The leaves repel each other because both are charged alike, negative in this case, Fig. 3-1.

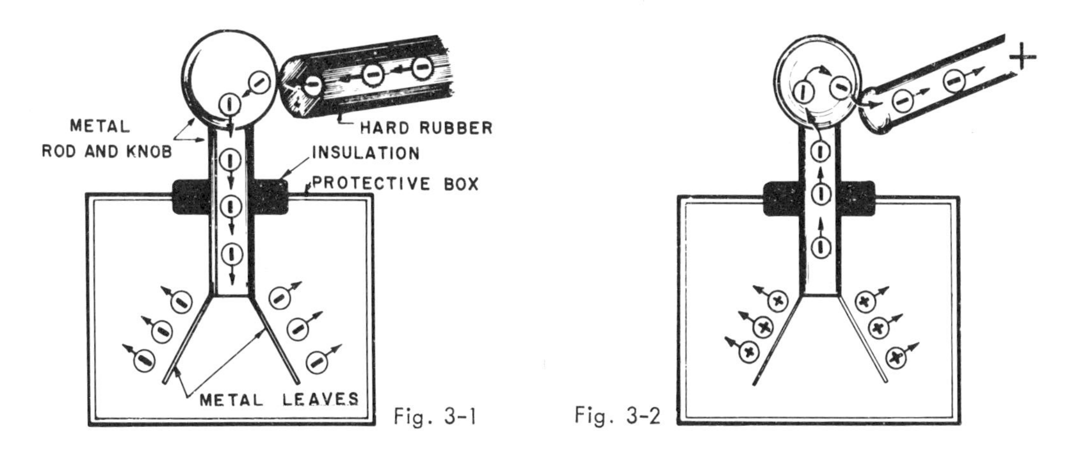

Fig. 3-1 Fig. 3-2

The electroscope could also be charged positively, using a charged glass rod instead of the hard rubber. As the glass rod is wiped along the knob of the originally-neutral electroscope, it will attract electrons from the electroscope. The positive charges (protons) that are left behind are now able to repel each other, and the leaves will again be spread apart, Fig. 3-2.

Identifying an Unknown Charge

A charged electroscope will tell whether an unknown charge is positive or negative. Suppose we charge a pen by rubbing it on a coat-sleeve, and wish to find out if the pen is negative or positive.

Using a hard-rubber rod, we charge the electroscope negatively, as described before. Then the pen is brought slowly toward the top of the electroscope, and we watch for the first motion of the leaves. The leaves may repel farther. If so, why?

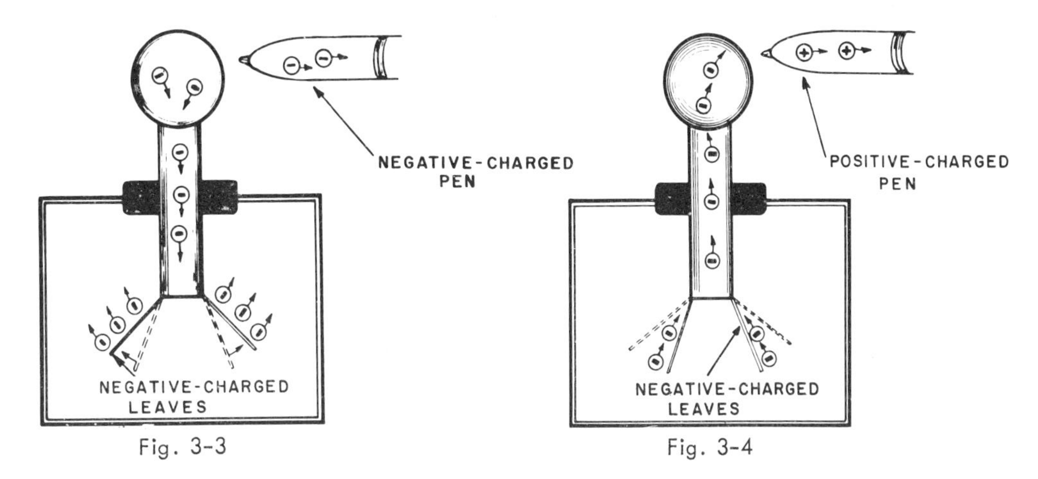

Fig. 3-3 Fig. 3-4

The leaves were negative. If they repel more, they must have become more negative. They can become more negative only by having more electrons forced down to the leaves. And the unknown charge on the pen, therefore, must be negative, because that is the kind of charge that will repel electrons down to the leaves.

If the pen had been charged positively, what would have happened? The positive-charged pen would attract some of the excess electrons up from the leaves toward the knob, so the leaves would at first fall together, as their repelling electrons were removed.

A positive-charged electroscope could be used just as well in identifying unknown charges. Keep in mind that the positive-charged electroscope has relatively few of its electrons removed; there are still lots of them there. When a negative object comes near, it will repel electrons in the electroscope to the leaves, which electrons will neutralize the positive charge there, letting the leaves fall. An approaching positive object would pull more electrons from the leaves, uncovering more positive charges on the leaves, which repel each other more strongly.

In this use of the electroscope, all of the electron motion is within the electroscope itself. The charged pen is not to be brought so close to the knob that any electrons jump the gap.

ELECTROSTATIC INDUCTION

A charged object always affects other objects in its neighborhood, either attracting or repelling electrons that are within the nearby object. The process of the nearby object's acquiring a charge is called "electrostatic induction". Electrostatic induction, along with an unusual combination of circumstances, can cause accidents. For example: On a warm, dry day, a truck drives into the gas station. The driver speaks to the new attendant, Joe. Joe lets go of the iron post, and the truck drives away as Joe steps over to remove the hose from a customer's gas tank. At this point, there is some difficulty involved because the gasoline is on fire. What happened?

Fig. 3-5

A strongly-charged truck, Joe's new rubber-soled shoes, the removal of his hand from the grounded post, electrostatic induction, and a spark in the presence of gasoline fumes, all contributed to this event. Assuming the truck was negative-charged, it repelled electrons from Joe to ground through the post. When Joe let go of the post, he did not at once regain his electrons, being insulated by rubber soles and dry air. When electrons were attracted to his hand at the gasoline tank, the spark ignited gasoline vapor.

Let the electroscope illustrate this induction process. The electroscope represents Joe. The hand touching the electroscope knob represents Joe's connection to ground through the post.

1. Bring a negative-charged rod (truck) near the electroscope.
2. Remove the hand touching the knob.
3. Remove the negative rod.

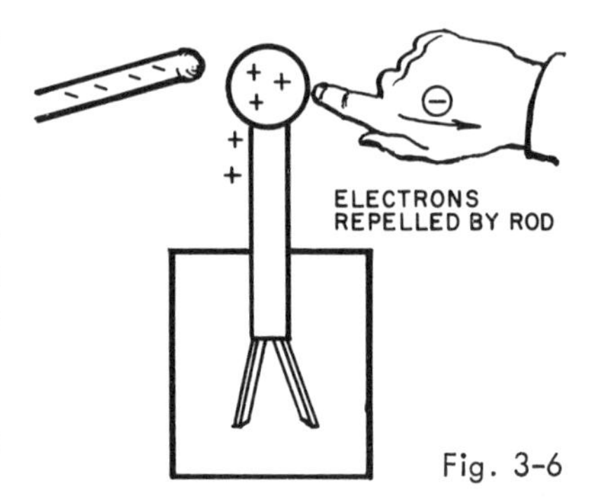

Fig. 3-6

If these steps are performed in correct order, the electroscope will be left in charged condition, shown by its repelling leaves. The fact that the electroscope is positive can be checked by its behavior when the negative rod is slowly brought near it again.

The charge on the electroscope, right, and the charge on Joe are examples of "induced charges."

> An induced charge is caused by the approach of a charged object, without contact with it.

LIGHTNING

Benjamin Franklin showed that lightning is merely a large-scale performance of ordinary electrostatic behavior. (A few people who tried his kite experiment were killed by it.)

The distribution of electric charges in thunderclouds has been mapped but as yet no one knows just how the charges are formed. Most of the lightning flashes occur within the cloud itself. Whether electrons go from cloud to ground or from ground to cloud depends on the part of the storm area that is over some particular spot (notice the diagram below).

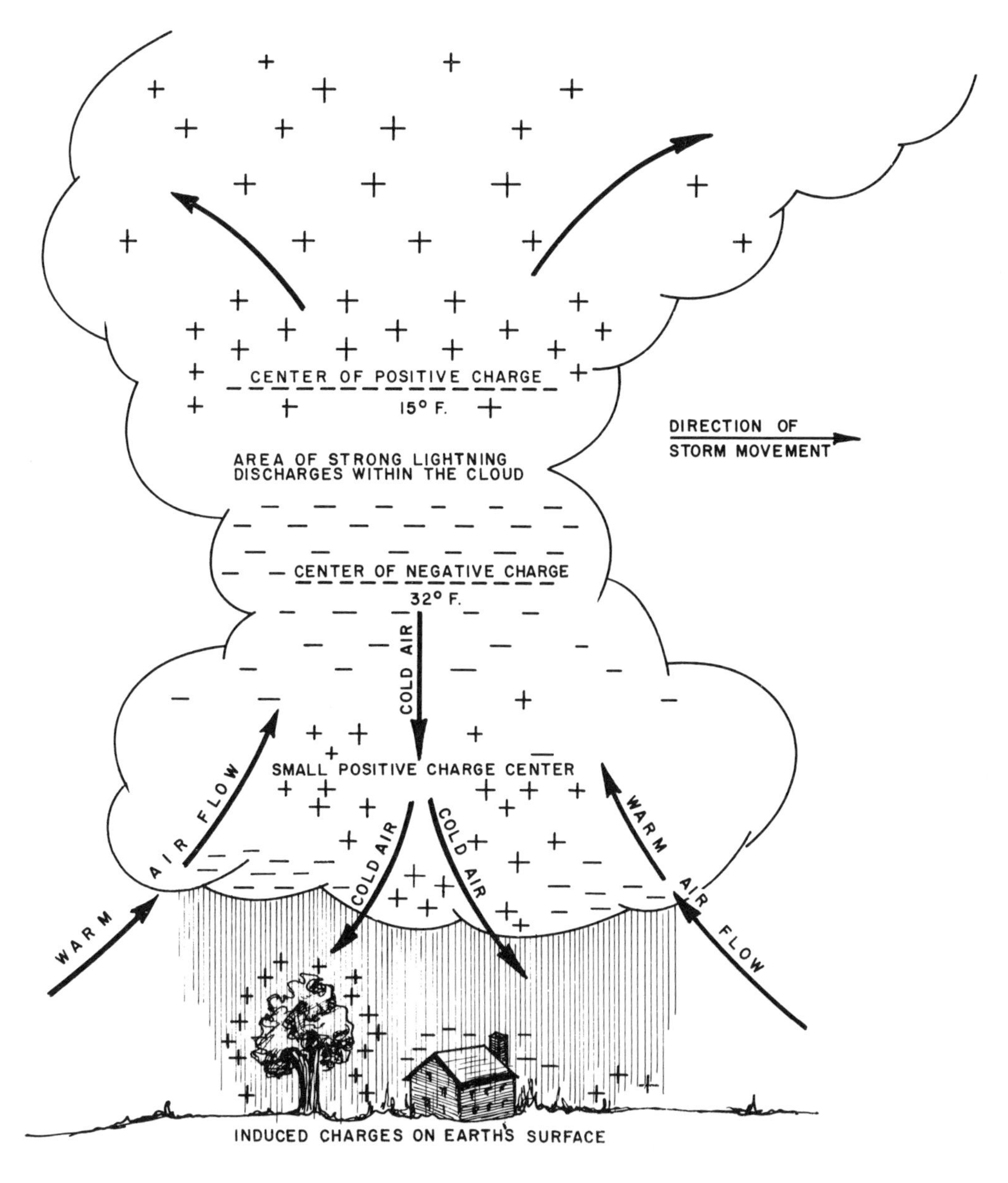

Fig. 3-7

Objects under the small positive-charged area at the center of the storm, like the house, are hit by a rush of electrons from earth to cloud. Objects under the larger negative-charged part of the cloud, like the tree, are hit by electrons driving from the cloud to the earth.

Protection against lightning is provided only by giving it an easy path to ground: one cannot insulate against lightning. Well-grounded lightning rods are effective; ammunition sheds have been protected simply by a steel cable supported along the ridge and grounded at each end. Steel frames of large buildings, grounded during construction, serve as lightning protection for the building. An automobile may be struck by lightning, but its occupants are not harmed, for the steel body shields them, conducting the high-voltage electrons harmlessly past. (Crawling under the car would be definitely unsafe!) A "lightning arrester" for TV and radio antennas is simply a grounded wire brought close to, but not touching, the antenna. Lightning arresters for power lines are materials with specialized resistance properties that permit the high-voltage lightning discharge to pass to ground, but stop the lower-voltage energy of the power line from being grounded.

OTHER NUISANCES

Besides lightning, and the radio interference it causes, static charges are responsible for a variety of nuisances and hazards.

Power belting readily becomes charged. Grounded pulleys, combs or "tinsel bars" close to the belt, conductive belt-dressing, and the use of conductive belt materials are remedies.

Trucks and cars are usually grounded by a wire as they approach a toll gate, to avoid jolts when coins change hands.

Anesthetic gases are combustible. Precautions are taken to avoid static sparks which might cause explosions during surgical operations. Grounded equipment, moist air, and conductive rubber help prevent accumulation of charges.

Prevention of static charges helps prevent dust explosions. Grain dust, flour, wood dust, and cotton lint have produced disastrous explosions.

In printing, sheets of paper may fail to feed into the press or fail to stack properly, if they repel each other or are unduly attracted to nearby objects. When printing is done from a continuous sheet, the sheet may become charged and introduce a fire hazard if combustible solvent vapors are present. Similar problems occur in the cloth and plastic industry. Devices that ground or neutralize these charges include tinsel bars, flames, or a long metal comb connected to an alternating-current power supply.

USEFUL STATIC CHARGES

In mass production paint-spray applications, the paint particles are given a charge after they leave the gun. They are attracted to the object receiving the paint, producing an even coat without waste of paint.

The paint particles, however, have little tendency to go into holes or openings, since the charge there is no greater than that at the outer surface.

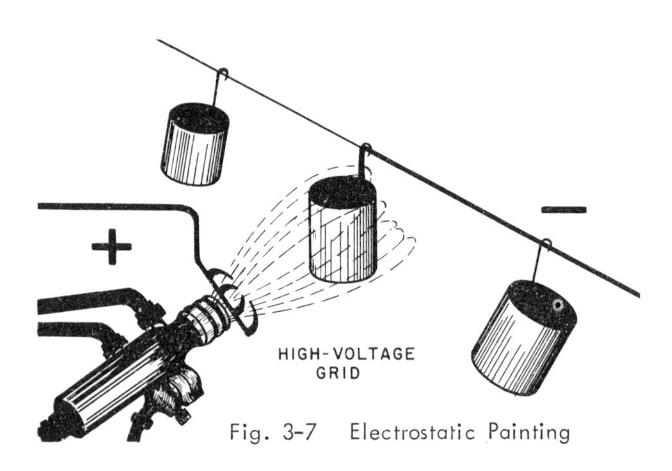

Fig. 3-7 Electrostatic Painting

Sandpaper grit is made to stand up and produce a sharper paper by giving the sand particles a positive charge while the glue-covered, paper backing is negatively charged. As the individual sand grains are charged alike, they repel each other and stand apart.

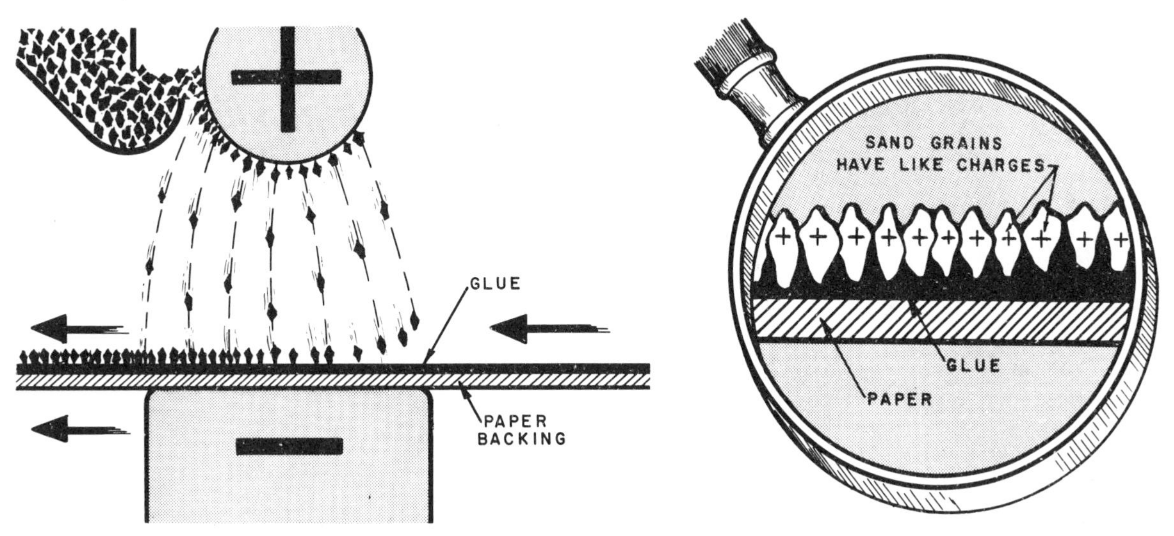

Fig. 3-8 Sandpaper Manufacture

Applying this same principle, smoke "precipitators" charge smoke particles which are then collected on screens where they can no longer blacken the atmosphere. Fiber can be attracted to glue-covered backings to form new types of rugs and fabrics.

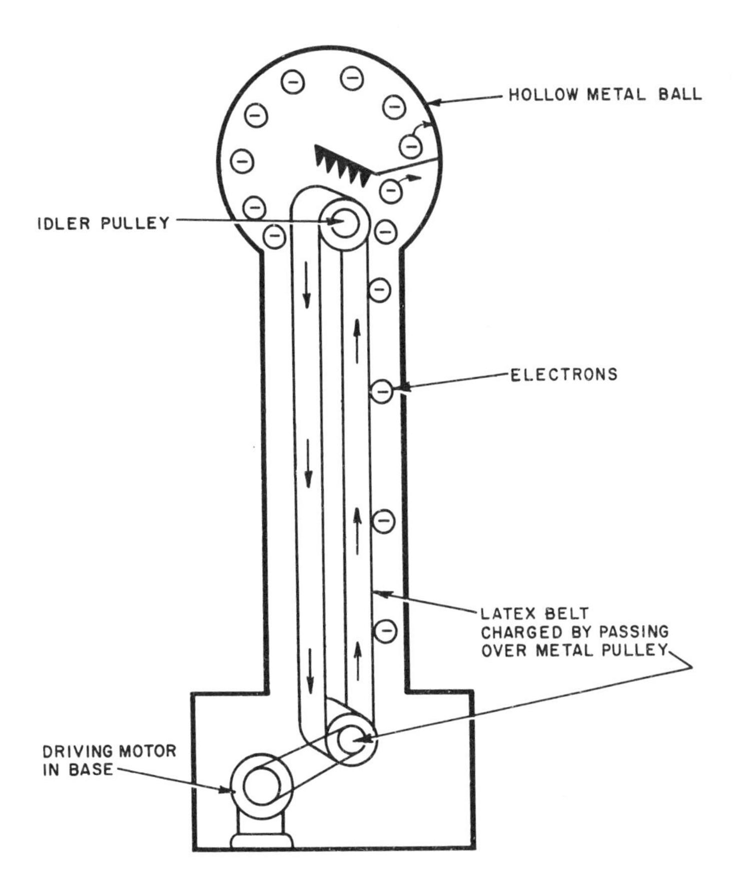

Fig. 3-9 Van de Graaf Generator

ELECTROSTATIC GENERATORS

Many types of "static generators" have been built in past years, which produced, unreliably, tiny currents at high voltage. A recent development is the Van de Graaff generator which is used to create high voltages for accelerating charged particles for "atom-smashing" experiments. It also can be used to test lightning-protection equipment. Small sizes are built for small-scale laboratory work.

The sphere at the top charges up to a few hundred thousand volts, but the number of electrons accumulated there is small enough so that the spark is harmless.

POTENTIAL ENERGY OF ELECTRONS

If an electron is forcibly taken away from one neutral object and put on to another, the electron has gained potential energy. Force had to be used to pull the electron away from A, because the electron is attracted back to A by the positive charge that remains behind. If several electrons are transferred to B, they repel additional electrons. Force has to be used to push electrons on to B. Given the opportunity, electrons will fly back to A from B, producing heat as they return. Or, they could be permitted to return to A through an electric motor, and convert their potential energy to mechanical energy as they pass through the motor.

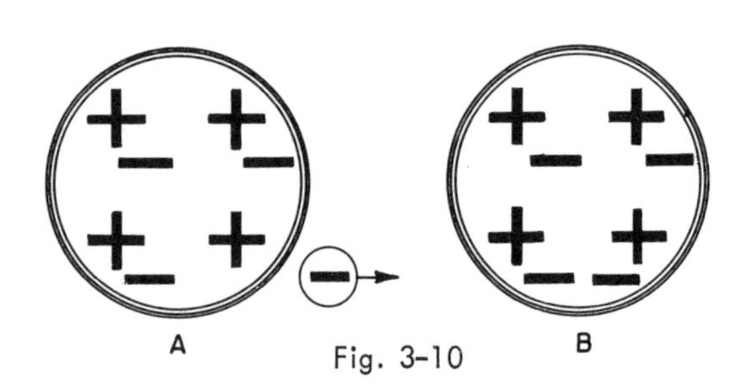

Fig. 3-10

The above behavior may be compared to transfer of water from a pond to a high tank. Water can be taken from the pond and put into the tank, but it does not go there by itself: energy has to be used to carry the water up to the tank. That energy is not wasted: it is the potential energy of the water. Water in the tank, given the opportunity, will run back down to where it came from, doing work on whatever it hits — producing heat by friction, or useful work if it passes over a water wheel.

Each gallon of water in the tank has more potential energy than a gallon of water in the pond. There is a "potential energy difference" between water in the tank and water in the pond.

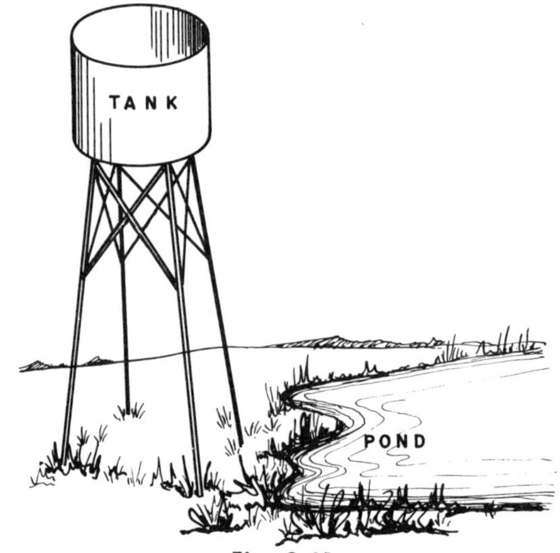

Fig. 3-11

Likewise, there is a "potential energy difference" between electrons in B and electrons in A. To shorten the statement, we say that there is a "potential difference" between B and A.

Potential energy of water can be measured in a unit called a foot-pound. (See Unit 8 for a more detailed discussion of energy and its measurement.) The "potential difference" between tank and pond can be expressed as a number of foot-pounds of energy per gallon of water.

The potential energy of electrons is often measured in a metric-system unit called the "joule." The transfer of each coulomb of electrons from A to B requires the use of a certain number of joules of energy. The potential energy difference between A and B can be expressed as a number of joules of energy per coulomb of electrons. (Comparable to energy per gallon of water.) This cumbersome expression, joules of energy per coulomb, is brought into this discussion because it is the accurate definition of a Volt.

We may continue to think of a volt as a measure of "electrical pressure" or "electromotive force", because these terms may be a little easier to understand. But in case of any question as to the exact meaning of the quantity we measure in volts, it is Potential Difference, the potential energy difference between two points.

Volts = Joules/Coulomb

ELECTRIC LINES OF FORCE

Long years ago, men were puzzled as to just how two objects could exert force on each other when they are at some distance apart, with no material connection between them. Two opposite charged objects attract each other in a vacuum. Light and heat have nothing to do with their attraction.

Fig. 3-12

In our present advanced state of knowledge, the question of how two objects exert force on each other at a distance, with no material connection, is still just as puzzling. We have no evidence for any small particles passing back and forth between them, no threads pulling them together; no sticks to push them apart, if they repel. There is no evidence for any sort of wave passing from one to another.

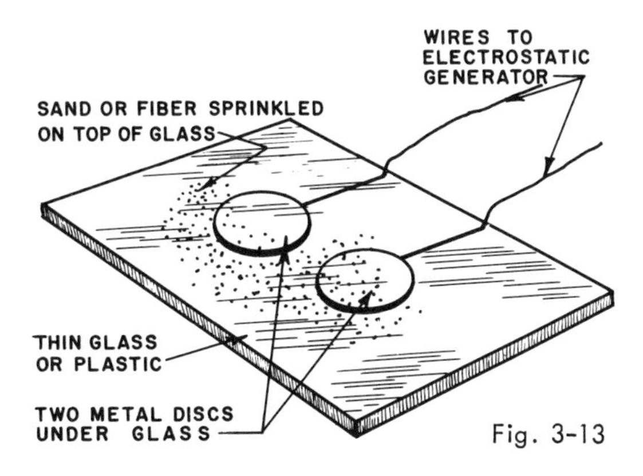

Fig. 3-13

Years ago, this puzzle was "solved" only in imagination, by picturing invisible "lines of force" that pull two opposite charges together, like ropes or rubber bands. The pattern of these imaginary lines may be seen by scattering splinters or dust of some nonconductor between two strongly-charged objects. Sand, short fibers, grass seed, or splintery sawdust can be used. The short fibers become charged by induction, and tend to become aligned in patterns like those illustrated.

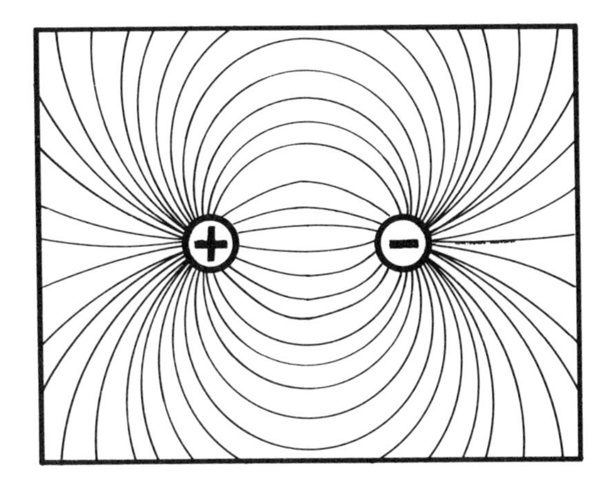

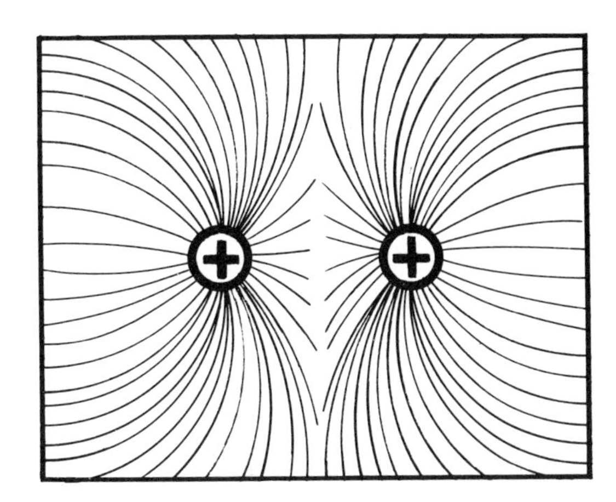

Fig. 3-14

As far as the "lines of force" are concerned, the lines are imaginary, but they graphically represent a very real force.

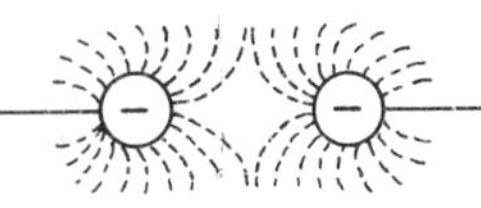

POINTS TO REMEMBER

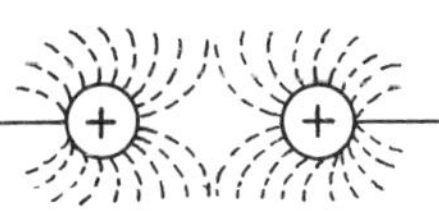

- A negative-charged object has a surplus of electrons; a positive-charged object lacks some electrons.
- A charged electroscope identifies unknown charges.
- Objects may become charged without contact, just by being near a charged object.
- Potential difference is measured in volts. It is the energy difference between electrons in two different locations.
- Charged objects are surrounded by an "electric field", that is, "lines of electric force" extending from the charged object.

REVIEW QUESTIONS

1. What is "static" electricity?
2. Static electricity is more often noticed on which type of material — conductors or insulators? Why?
3. Can conductors be charged?
4. Describe what happens when a positive-charged object comes near (but not touching) a positive-charged electroscope.
5. What happens when a negative-charged object comes near a positive-charged electroscope?
6. What is electrostatic induction?
7. When a negative-charged object approaches a neutral object, what sort of charge is induced on the neutral object?

8. Charged objects are said to possess energy. Explain.

9. "A volt is a joule per coulomb". Explain.

10. What are "electric lines of force"?

11. What is meant by "dielectric strength"?

12. How does a "lightning arrester" stop lightning?

13. State industrial uses of static charges.

14. What industries try to avoid static charges?

Unit 4 USING OHM'S LAW

In Unit 2 you were introduced to three electrical quantities:

Amperes, which measure Intensity of Current (a quantity rate of flow, coulombs per second)

Volts, which measure E.M.F. or Potential Difference (similar to pressure, energy per coulomb)

Ohms, which measure Resistance, the internal opposition that hinders and impedes electron flow

The Ohm's Law formula, $E = I R$, gives the numerical relation between these three quantities, amperes, volts, and ohms. This is the one most useful formula in the study of electric current; it is necessary to practice using it to find any one of the quantities when the other two are known.

Work through the following examples to help become familiar with $E = I R$. Remember, E stands for volts, I for amperes, R for ohms.

(1) Find the potential difference (volts) required to cause a current of one-half ampere in a 60-ohm device:

$$E = I R$$
$$E = 0.5 \times 60$$
$$E = 30 \text{ volts, Ans.}$$

(2) How much potential difference is needed to make a current of five-hundredths of an ampere in a resistor of 2 million ohms?

$$E = I R$$
$$E = 0.05 \times 2{,}000{,}000$$
$$E = 100{,}000 \text{ volts, Ans.}$$

This answer, 100 thousand volts, can be called 100 kilovolts, for the prefix kilo- means thousand. 220 kv means 220 kilovolts, or 220 thousand volts.

Another prefix, mega-, or meg-, means a million. The quantity, 2,000,000 ohms, can be called 2 megohms.

These prefixes, kilo- for thousand, and mega- for million, are also used with other measurements: 10 kilotons = 10,000 tons; 80 megawatts = 80,000,000 watts.

(3) How much current will be caused in a 2-megohm resistor by a potential difference of 120 volts?

$$E = I R$$

$$120 = I \times 2{,}000{,}000$$

(Divide each side of equation by 2,000,000)

$$\frac{120}{2{,}000{,}000} = I$$

$$0.00006 \text{ amp} = I, \quad \text{Ans.}$$

This small quantity, 0.00006 amp, is clumsy to write and inconvenient to read. Fractional prefixes are used to simplify talking about such small amounts.

The prefix milli- means one-thousandth.

One-thousandth of an ampere, 0.001 amp, is one milliampere. The word milliampere is abbreviated m.a., or ma.

Five milliamps, 5 ma., is five-thousandths of an ampere, 0.005 amp. 0.05 amp is five-hundredths of an amp, but it also can be written 0.050 amp, and can be called 50 m.a.

Notice that the decimal point is moved three places in these conversions between amps and milliamps. The answer for Example 3 could be written as 0.06 milliamps. The same quantity, 0.00006 amp, could be written as 0.000060 amp, and read as "sixty-millionths" of an amp, which can introduce another prefix:

The prefix micro- means one-millionth.

One millionth of an ampere is the same thing as one microampere. 0.00006 amps can be called 60 micro-amps. The greek letter μ (pronounced mew) is used as the written abbreviation for micro-.

0.000025 is 25-millionths of an amp, 25 microamps, 25 μa. Moving the decimal point six places converts amps to μa.

(4) A 300-ohm resistor in a radio has a current of 40 ma in it. How much potential difference between the ends of the resistor? (To fit with volts and ohms in the formula, the 40 ma has to be changed to amps, 0.040 amp):

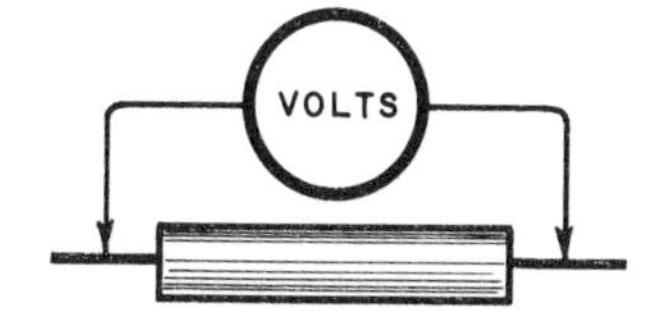

$$E = I R$$

$$E = .040 \times 300$$

$$E = 12 \text{ volts}, \quad \text{Ans.}$$

(5) How much current is produced in a 1.5-megohm resistor by a potential difference of 300 volts? (1.5 megohm has to be rewritten as ohms)

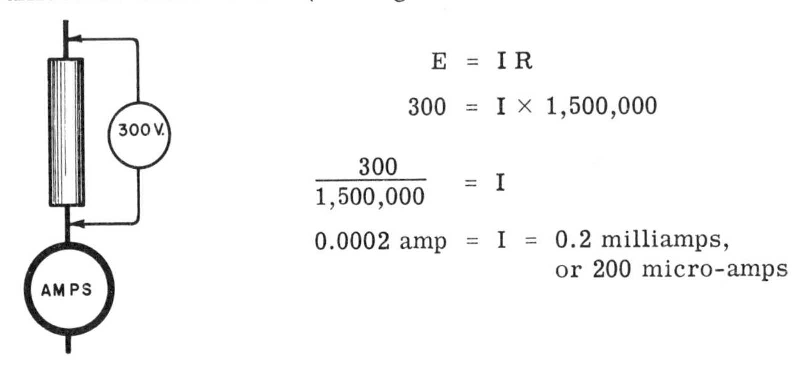

$$E = IR$$

$$300 = I \times 1{,}500{,}000$$

$$\frac{300}{1{,}500{,}000} = I$$

$$0.0002 \text{ amp} = I = 0.2 \text{ milliamps, or } 200 \text{ micro-amps}$$

(6) An electric toaster takes a current of 8 amps on a 120-volt line. How much is its resistance?

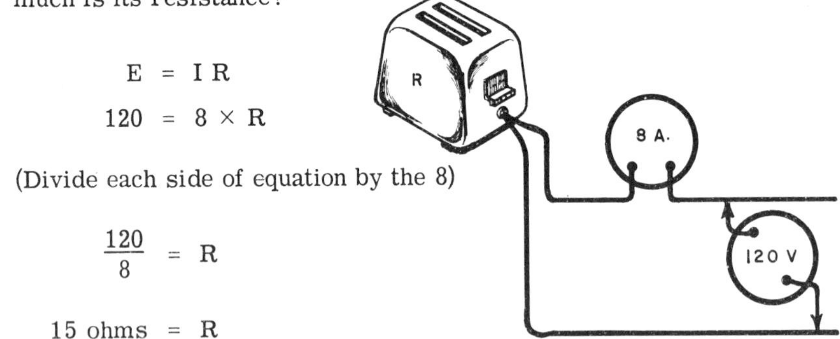

$$E = IR$$

$$120 = 8 \times R$$

(Divide each side of equation by the 8)

$$\frac{120}{8} = R$$

$$15 \text{ ohms} = R$$

Or, this same question could have been answered by using the formula rearranged as

$$R = \frac{E}{I}$$

$$R = \frac{120}{8}$$

$$R = 15 \text{ ohms}$$

(7) How much resistance will pass a current of 4 milliamps at 200 volts?

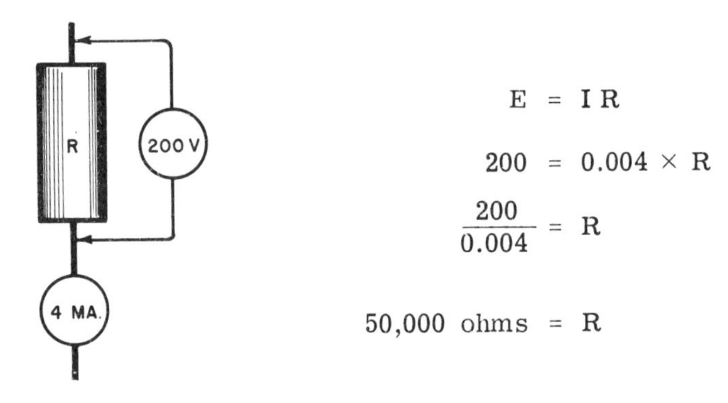

$$E = IR$$

$$200 = 0.004 \times R$$

$$\frac{200}{0.004} = R$$

$$50{,}000 \text{ ohms} = R$$

READING AMMETER AND VOLTMETER SCALES

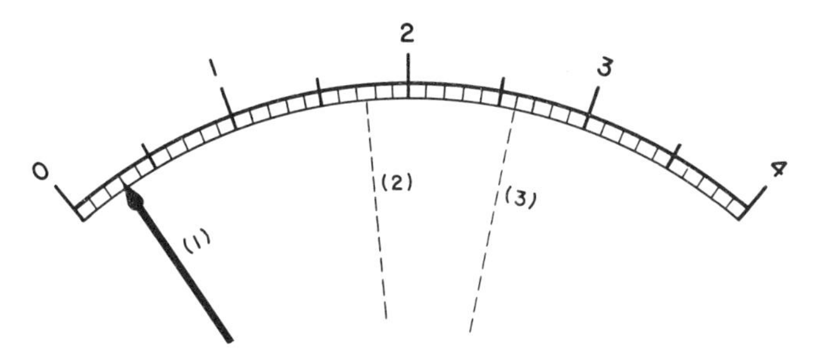

At the left is a portion of an easy-to-read meter scale. Note that the space between whole-number values is divided into ten parts, so that each small division = 0.1 (one-tenth). If the pointer is at position (1), the indicated amount is 0.3. At position (2), the pointer is half-way between 1.7 and 1.8, so the indicated reading is 1.75. At position (3), the pointer is at the 2.6 mark.

One should always take careful notice of the value represented by the small divisions on the scale.

On the meter at the right, each small division is worth 0.2. At position (1), the pointer is at 0.6; position (2) is 3.5; position (3) indicates 5.2.

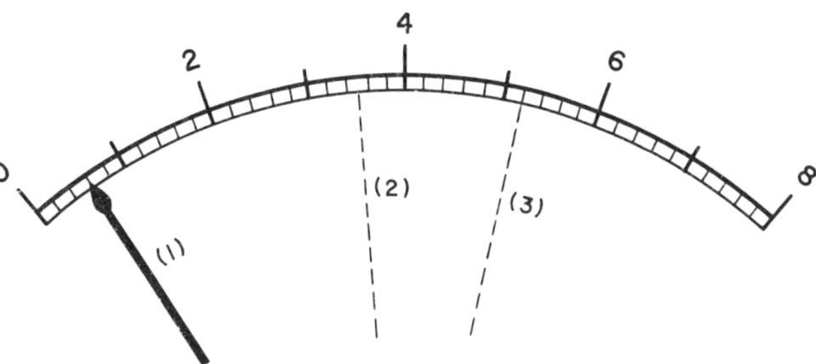

In reading meters, it is customary to state the readings using decimals, rather than common fractions. For example, one should record 8.75 rather than 8 3/4; or 7.4 rather than 7 2/5.

The scale below is shown on an ammeter that has three terminals, marked

When connecting this meter into a circuit, one should first have some notion of how much current there is in the circuit to be measured. If the current is likely to be more than 30 amps, a higher range meter should be used. If the current is presumably less than 30 amps, wires are

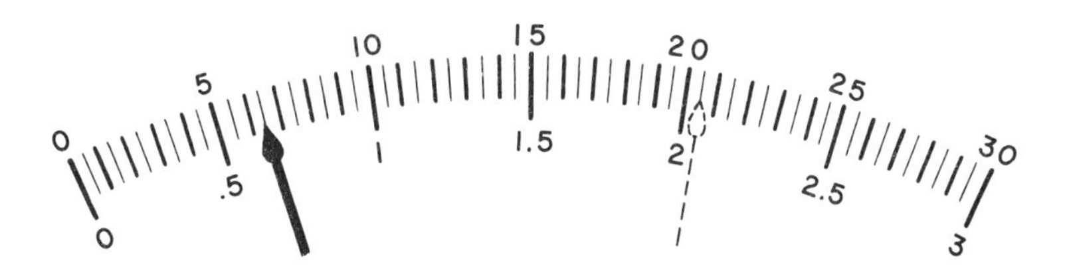

connected to the "High" and the "Plus" terminals, and the results are read from the upper (0-30) set of numbers. The first position of the pointer shows 6.5 amps; the second (dotted line) position shows 20.5 amps.

When connected at the 30-amp terminal, if the meter reads less than 3 amps, the wire should be moved from the "high" to the "low" terminal, permitting a more accurate reading of a small current. When connected to "Low" and "Plus", readings are taken on the 0-3 amp scale. On the low scale, the first pointer position in the sketch shows 0.65 amps; the second, which is halfway between 2.0 and 2.1, shows 2.05 amps.

On the scale below, pointers are shown at 0.08, 0.35, 1.04 and 1.49.

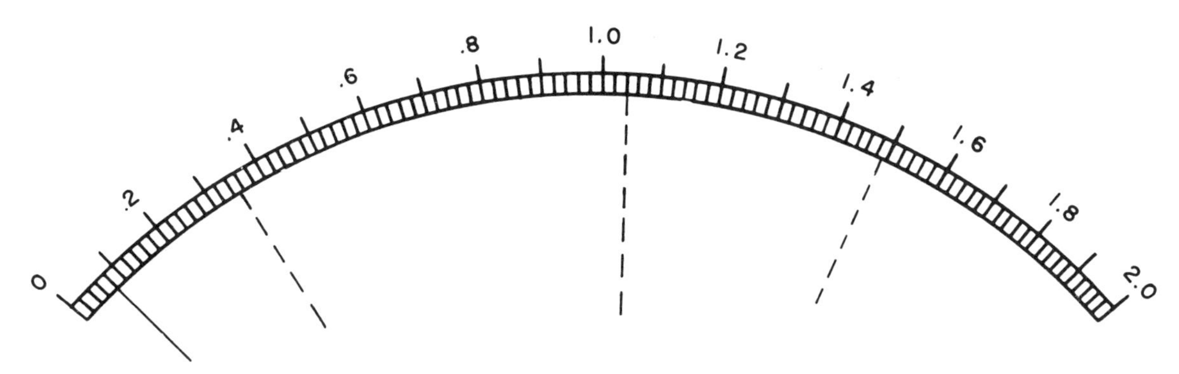

The next scale may represent the scale of a 50-amp ammeter. Note that the small divisions represent intervals of 0.5 amp. The first position of the pointer shows 22 amps. Whether the next one should be called 38 or 38.5, or 38.25, because it is halfway between 38.0 and 38.5,

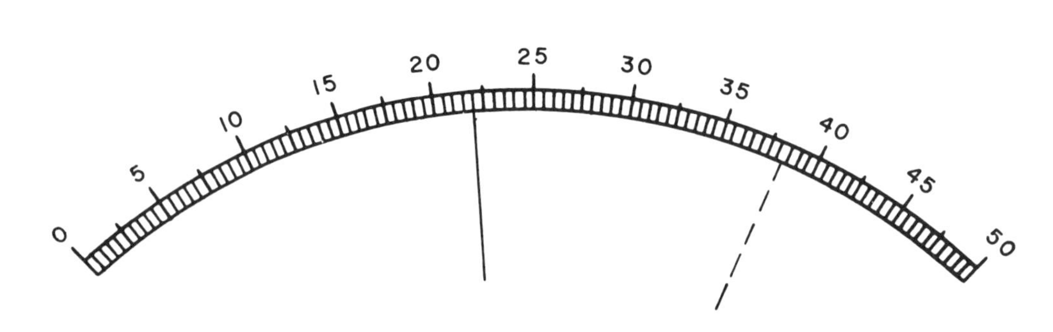

depends on the accuracy of the meter mechanism. If the accuracy of the meter is 2% (meaning 2% of the full-scale reading) then the meter is accurate only to within one ampere, so there is no point in worrying about a half-ampere difficulty in reading the meter. In order to justify reporting 38.25, rather than 38 or 38.5, the meter would need to be 1/2 of 1% accurate, or better.

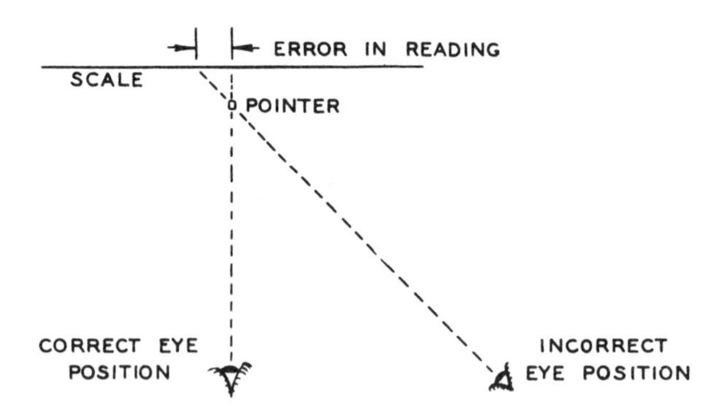

High-accuracy meters have a narrow mirror strip along the scale to help avoid errors caused by failure to view the meter from directly in front of the scale. When using the mirror-scale, one should place his eye in such a position that the image of the pointer disappears behind the pointer itself. Using the ordinary nonmirror plain scale, one should always view the scale so that his "line of sight" is perpendicular to the surface of the scale.

WHAT KILLS PEOPLE - THE VOLTS OR THE AMPS?

Of course, that's an unfair question, because both volts and amps must be available. The current (amps) depends on volts, and on resistance. The greater the volts, the more current will be produced; and the less the resistance, the more current.

The experts don't agree on just how much current is needed to kill someone; there has not been much experimenting along this line. As an average opinion, 0.05 amps through head or chest will kill. (That's only five-hundredths of an ampere, or 50 milliamperes.) Tiny currents are enough to stop the action of nerves that control breathing and heart-beat. Large currents also cause severe surface burns, and severe internal burns too, just as a wire is heated by current through it.

Will 110-volt house wiring kill a person? It has, yet it is possible for one to touch both wires of a 110-volt line under such conditions that the current may be hardly noticeable.

The current depends on the resistance of the person in the circuit, and his electrical resistance has little to do with his physical health or will power.

Fig. 4-1 shows a high-resistance situation. Dry skin has more resistance than moist skin, and a small contact area allows relatively few electrons to move. The current can be calculated from E = I R or I = E ÷ R: I = 120/100,000 I = 0.0012 amps, or 1.2 ma, which is enough to notice, but is not harmful.

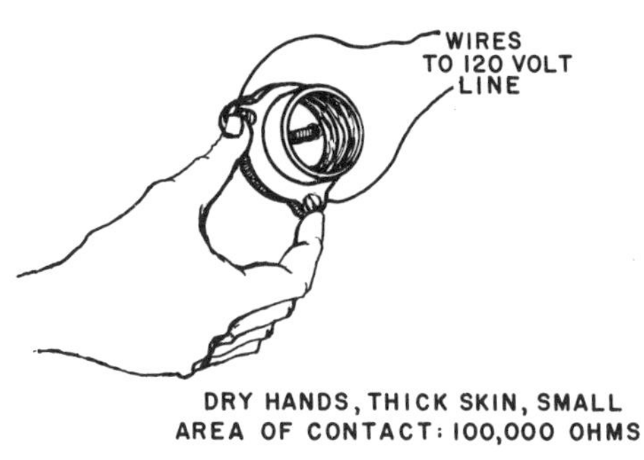

Fig. 4-1

In Fig. 4-2 is shown a low-resistance contact, in which the firm grip over a large area of metal allows plenty of room for lots of electrons to move. It is customary for one of the 120-volt line wires to be connected to the ground at all times. This is a permanent and desirable connection. Not visible on the outside of the electric drill is an accidental and undesirable connection of the other 120-volt wire to the metal housing of the drill. This applies the 120-v potential difference to the man's body. I = 120 ÷ 800 or 0.15 amp, which will put this home craftsman in tomorrow's headlines for the last time.

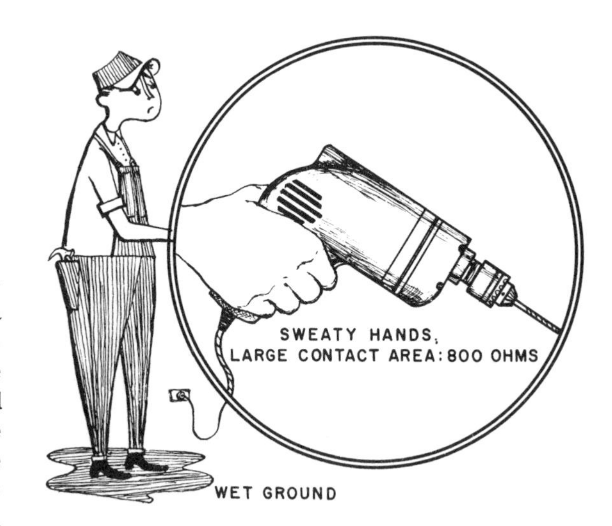

Fig. 4-2 A Low-Resistance Contact

Prevention of such accidents is simple:

The metal case or frame of all power tools and kitchen appliances should be connected to ground by another wire.

This will permit a defective appliance to blow fuses instead of shocking people. If the device is already equipped with a 3-prong grounding plug, USE IT. It is appropriate to check such connections at intervals to see that the grounding connection is complete and effective. (An excellent, thorough discussion of grounding of portable tools is given in a 37-page pamphlet: "Electric Shock - Its Causes and Prevention", U. S. Govt. Printing Office, 1954.)

An automobile battery can put out 150 amperes — why doesn't it hurt to touch the terminals of a car battery? The battery can put 150 amps through a low-resistance wire, but fingers aren't low-resistance wire. It is hard to imagine any condition where body resistance could be so low that 6 or 12 volts would produce noticeable current through one's fingers. But — if you wear a ring, take it off when working on battery clamps. The circuit formed by pliers, ring, and car frame may be less than one-tenth of an ohm.

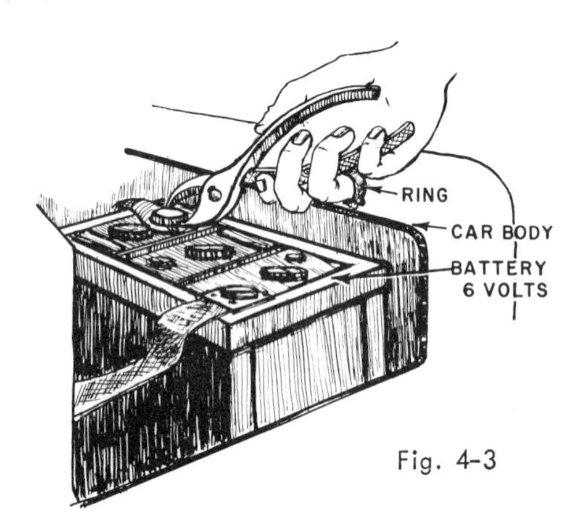

Fig. 4-3

Calculate the current, if R is 0.1 ohm: $I = E \div R = 6 \div .1 = 60$ amps.

The 60 amps through pliers and ring causes no electrical shock; it is some other kind of shock to find you are wearing a red-hot ring.

RESISTORS

A resistor is a piece of material having electrical resistance, and used for the control of current or the production of heat.

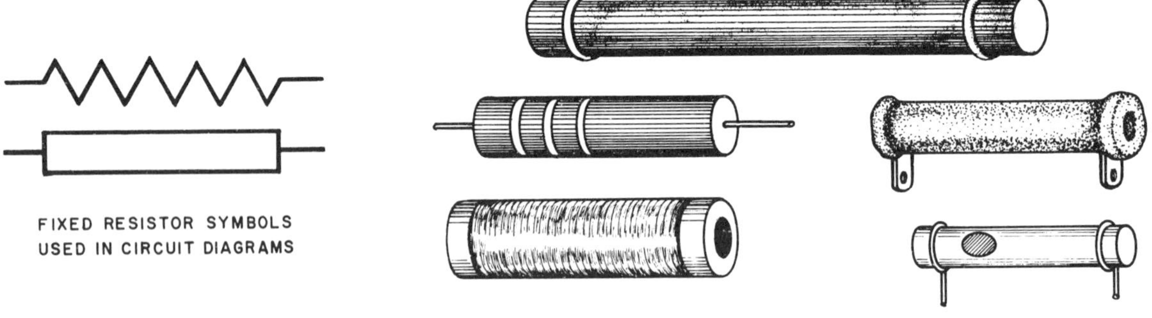

Fig. 4-4 Types of Fixed Resistors

Metals and alloys are commonly used for resistors. The resistor in an incandescent lamp is a coil of fine tungsten wire; nickel-chromium alloy in wire or ribbon form is used as the heating element in toasters, irons, and other resistance-type heating devices. The color-banded resistors in radio and TV receivers, small in size but having a large number of ohms resistance, use a carbon composition as the resistance-material. Fig. 4-4 shows types of fixed resistors, in contrast with those in Fig. 4-5 which are variable or adjustable.

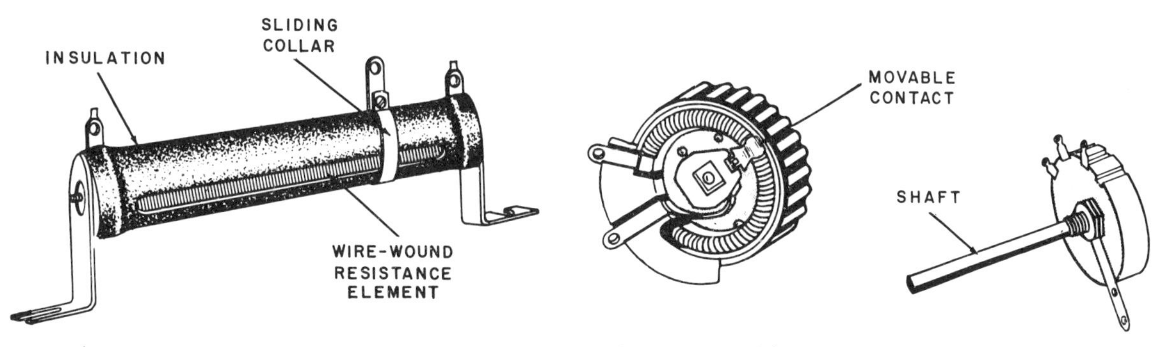

Fig. 4-5 Types of Variable or Adjustable Resistors

A "rheostat" is a variable resistor with only two connections, one fixed and one movable. Variable resistors with three terminals, two at the ends and one movable contact, are now usually called "potentiometers." However, a true potentiometer is a voltage-measuring device (see Unit 12).

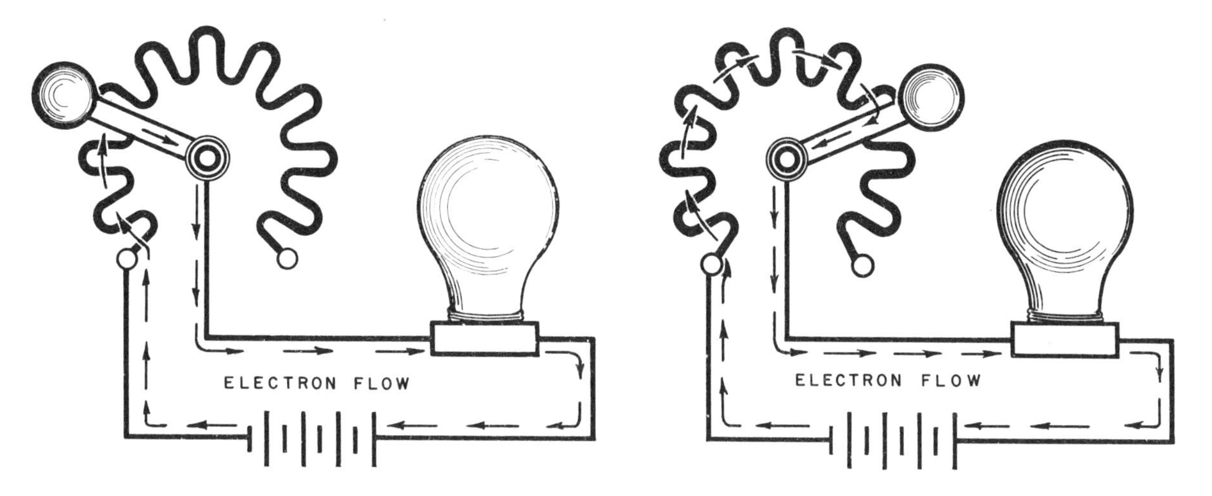

COLOR CODE FOR COMPOSITION RESISTORS

There are two systems of indicating the number of ohms resistance for small resistors, shown in the diagram below. Carbon resistors cannot be made as accurately as wire-wound resistors, and the color code also shows the percentage accuracy of the resistor.

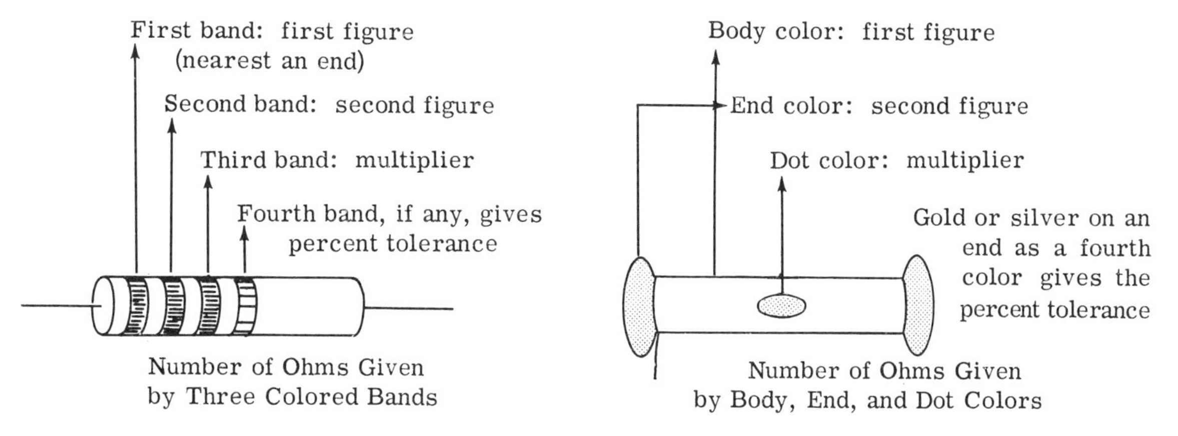

Number of Ohms Given by Three Colored Bands

Number of Ohms Given by Body, End, and Dot Colors

Color	Numerical Meaning 1st and 2nd Figures	Multiplying Value	Percent Tolerance
Black	0	1	
Brown	1	10	
Red	2	100	
Orange	3	1,000	
Yellow	4	10,000	
Green	5	100,000	
Blue	6	1,000,000	
Violet	7	10,000,000	
Gray	8	100,000,000	
White	9	1,000,000,000	
Gold	→	0.1	5%
Silver	→	0.01	10%
	If tolerance is not indicated by color:		20%

Examples:

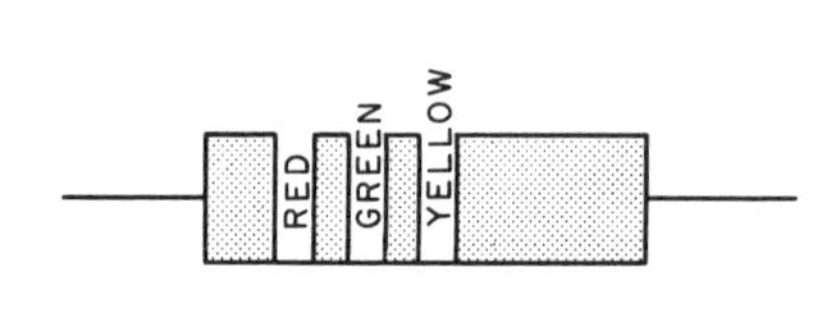

First number, red: 2
Second number, green: 5
Third band, yellow (4) means times 10,000. In other words, put 4 zeros after the first two figures: 2 5 0000
Resistance is 250,000 ohms.
Lack of a fourth color means that the actual ohms may be as much as 20% more or less than the rated value 250,000.

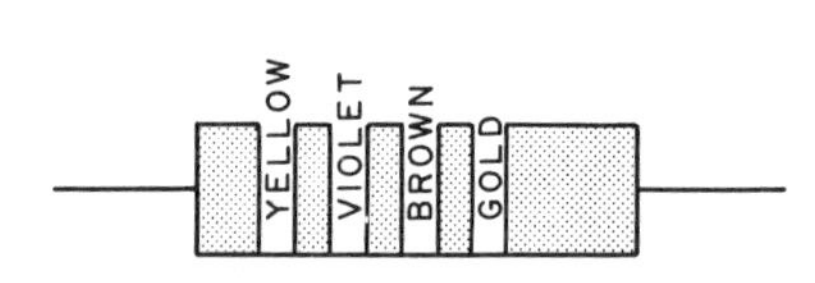

First number, yellow: 4
Second number, violet: 7
Third color, brown: 1. This '1' tells how many zeros to place after the 4 and 7.
Resistance is 470 ohms.
The gold band means that the resistor's actual ohms is within 5% of the 470.

First number, green: 5
Second number, black: 0
Third, green: tells how many zeros to put after the 5 and 0.
5 0 00000 = 5,000,000 ohms
Silver: 10% tolerance: Resistor may measure anywhere between 4,500,000 and 5,500,000 ohms.

First color, red: 2
Second, black: 0
As a third color, gold has a multiplying value of 0.1.
$20 \times 0.1 = 2$ ohms
Resistor is within 5% of 2 ohms.

Body, end, and dot have the same code meaning as the first three stripes on the banded resistors.

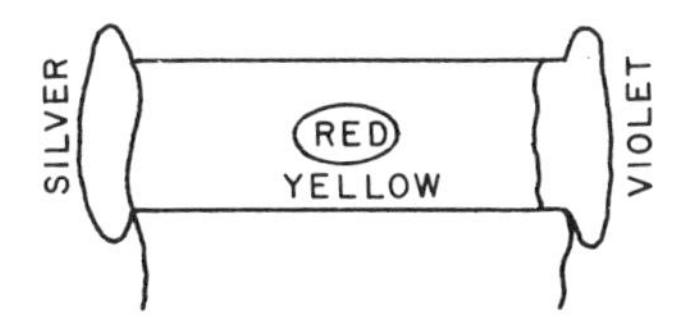

Body color, yellow: 4
Ends, silver and violet. Silver indicates a 10% tolerance and violet is the second figure: 7
Dot, red: 2

4 7 00

Resistor has 4700 ohms, plus or minus 10%

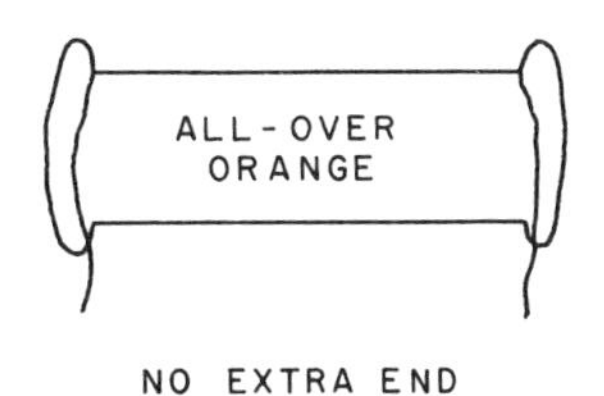

NO EXTRA END OR DOT COLOR

Body color, orange: 3
End color, orange: 3
Dot, orange: 3 zeros

3 3 000, within 20%

What is the resistance value of a resistor with the first three colors: brown, black, black? Brown means 1, black means 0, for the first two figures. The third black has a multiplying value of 1, so the resistance is 10×1 which is 10 ohms. Or, using this third color in the sense of how many zeros to add after the 10, black means none.

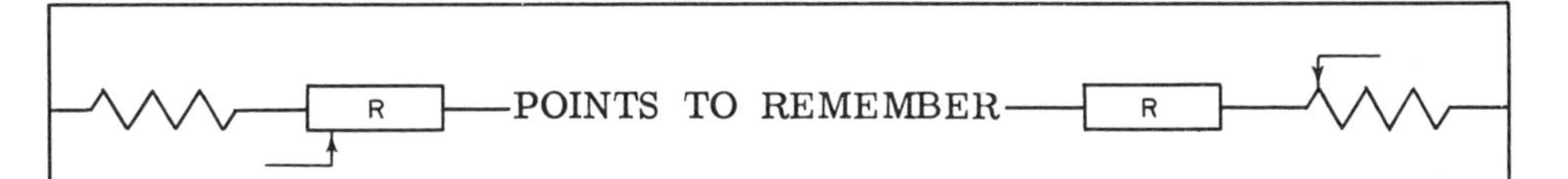

- E = I R, Volts = Amps × Ohms
- A milli-ampere is .001 amp (one-thousandth). A micro-ampere is .000001 amp (a millionth).
- Kilo- means thousand; meg- means million.
- Low-resistance contact with a 115-volt line may be just as fatal as contact with a 4400-volt line.
- Resistors regulate current.
- The resistor color-code is remembered best by using it.

REVIEW QUESTIONS

1. Write .00002 amp as μa, 2,500,000 ohms as megohms, .00002 amp as ma, 250,000 ohms as megohms, 120 μa as amps, 120 ma as amps, 440 v. as kv., .03 ma as μa.

2. Using Ohm's Law, calculate the missing item on each line:

E	I	R
120 v.	50 ma	
3 kv.	60 μa	
250 v.		2 megohms
25 mv. (millivolts)	ma	100 ohms
	10 μa	2 megohms
mv.	10 amps	.0002 ohms

3. Determine ohms rating of resistors color-coded:

   (a) red, red, green
   (b) brown, black, orange
   (c) yellow, violet, black, silver
   (d) blue, gray, brown, gold
   (e) green, black, gold, gold
   (f) Ends: green and silver   Body: red   Dot: orange
   (g) brown all over, except for black dot

4. Quoting from recent Sunday-paper article, alleged to be nonfiction:

   "on the stage . . . a brilliantly lit ballroom scene . . . electric power started to falter . . . trusted master electrician grabbed a cable in each hand and made the connection through his own body. He held on until the first-act curtain fell . . . second-degree burns . . . "

   Any comment?

5. On the next page are shown four full-size meter scales. Take the readings for each of the three positions of the pointer, on each of the scales, and record your readings. Note that meter scale 'C' requires two sets of readings, and that three sets are required for meter scale 'D'. Take these readings as accurately as possible.

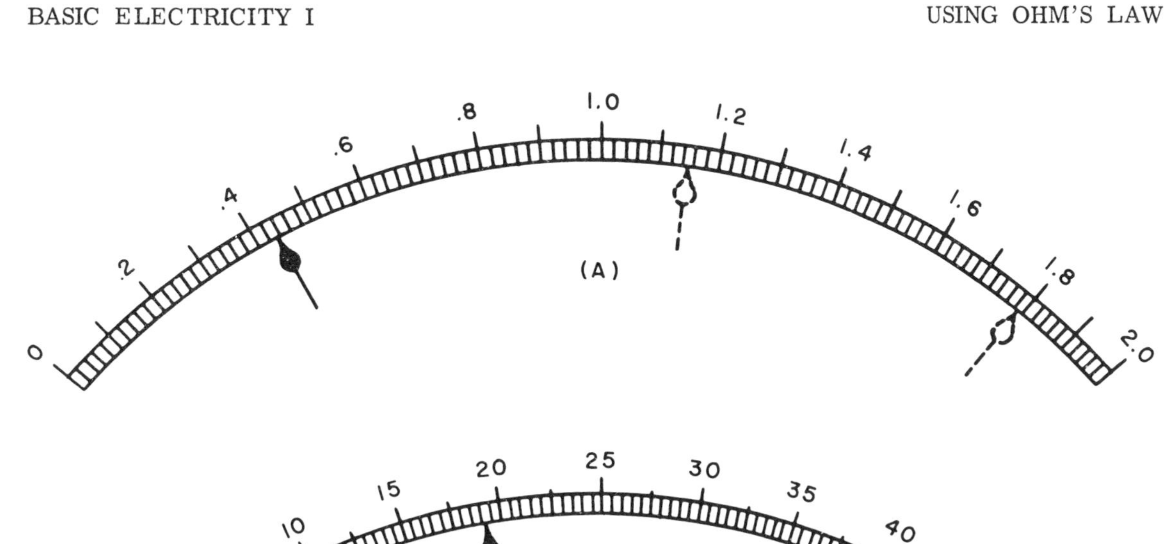

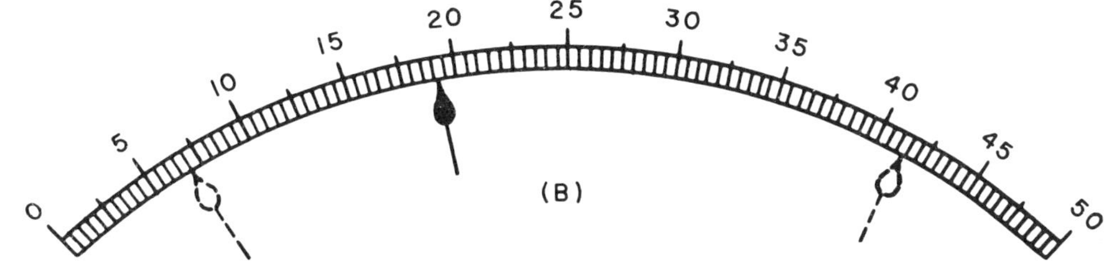

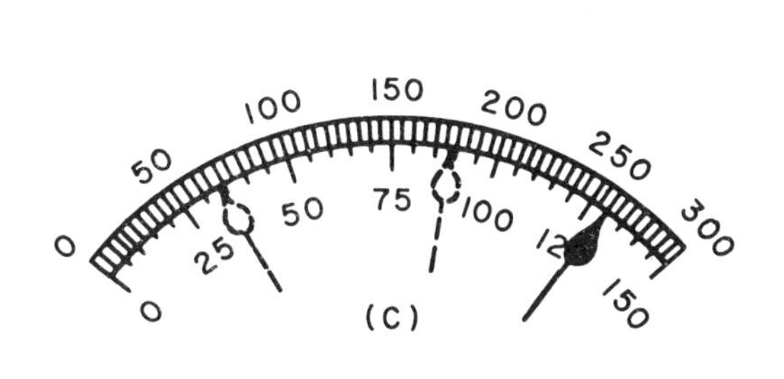

SCALE		FIRST POSITION	SECOND POSITION	THIRD POSITION
A				
B				
C	0-300			
	0-150			
D	250-0-250			
	50-0-50			
	10-0-10			

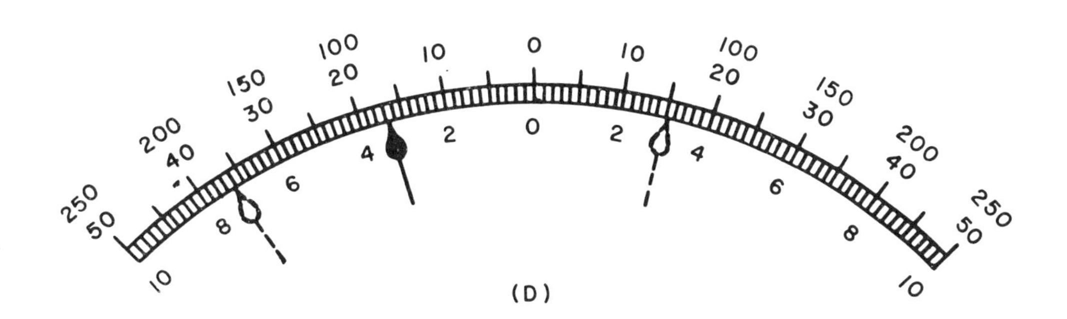

When devices are so connected that there is only one circuit-path for electrons, the devices are said to be in series. Each device necessarily has the same amount of current in it as any other.

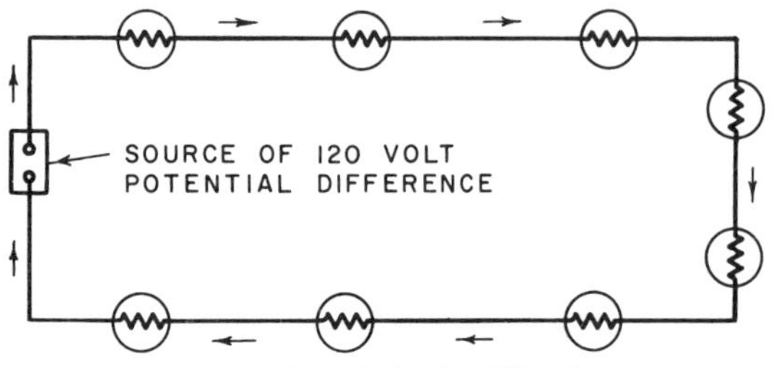

Fig. 5-1 A Series Circuit

Most of us are familiar with a series string of Christmas-tree lights in which all of the lamps fail to light when one lamp burns out. The "burning out" of any one lamp removes its filament from the circuit, having the same effect as opening a switch in the circuit. When electrons cannot flow through one lamp, then they cannot flow through any of the rest of the lamps either. Replacement of the defective lamp permits current through the entire circuit. Each device in series must have the same current as all the rest, because there is only one path for electrons to take.

TOTAL RESISTANCE OF A SERIES CIRCUIT

A single 30-ohm resistor connected to a 120-volt source has a current of 4 amps in it (Ohm's Law).

If we connect two 30-ohm resistors in series, electrons have twice as much opposition to fight through as they complete their circuit; that is, they have to overcome a total resistance of 60 ohms.

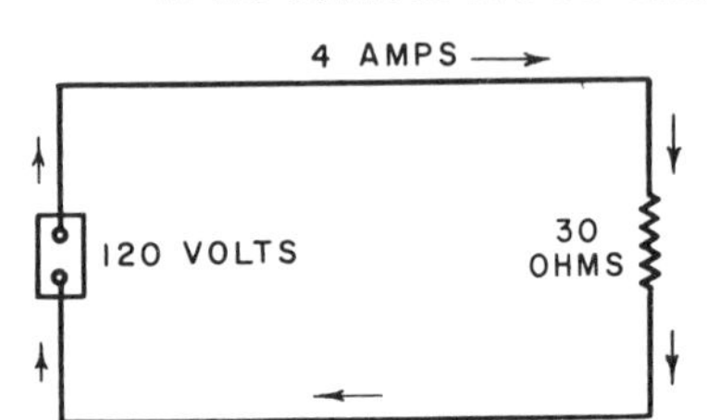

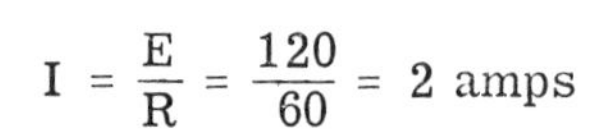

$$I = \frac{E}{R} = \frac{120}{60} = 2 \text{ amps}$$

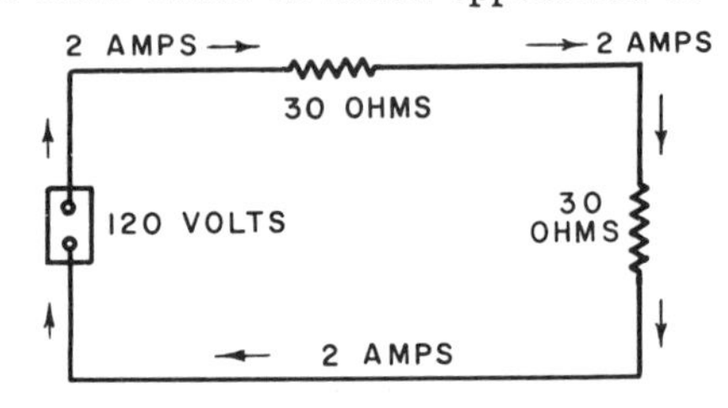

Total resistance of a series circuit is the sum of the individual resistances

Problem: Eight lamps, 30 ohms each, are in series in a Christmas-tree string on 120 volts. (See Fig. 5-1) Find the current.

Ohm's Law is to be used for the whole circuit in this way:

$$\text{Current in the circuit} = \frac{\text{Voltage applied to the whole circuit}}{\text{Total resistance of the whole circuit}}$$

$$I = \frac{120 \text{ volts}}{240 \text{ ohms}} = 0.5 \text{ amp}, \quad \text{Ans.}$$

This 0.5 amp is the current in any one lamp, and it is also the current in the whole circuit. There is only one current in a series circuit.

To find current in a series circuit, use total resistance and line voltage applied to the circuit

Series circuits are common in electrical equipment. The tube-filaments in small radio receivers are usually in series. When one filament burns out, no tubes light. Some TV sets have a few tube-filaments in series. For economy in wiring, incandescent street lamps are usually in series. When a filament is broken, a device in the lamp-holder closes the circuit to permit current to the other street-lamps in the series group.

Current-controlling devices are wired in series with the controlled equipment. A thermostat-switch is in series with the heating-element in an electric iron. Fuses are in series with the equipment they protect. Automatic house-heating equipment has a thermostat, electro-magnet coils, and safety cut-outs in series with a voltage source. Rheostats are placed in series with the coils in large motors to control motor current.

AMPERES, VOLTS, AND OHMS IN SERIES CIRCUITS

Ohm's Law applies to each part of a series circuit, as well as to the entire circuit. Using, as an example, five radio-tube filaments in series, with resistances and line voltage given:

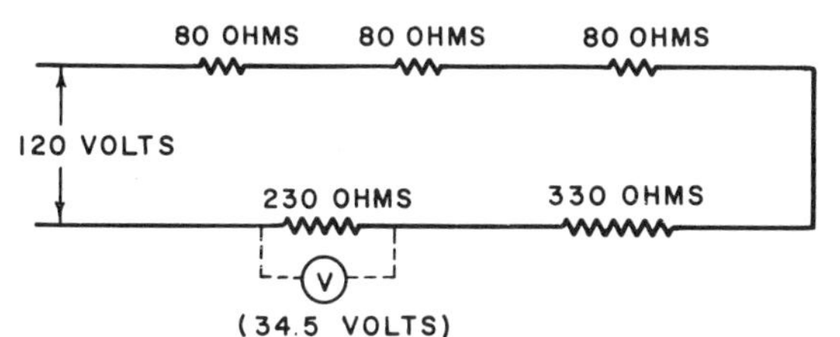

(A) Find current in each resistor.
(B) Find potential difference across each resistor.

(A) is solved as before, using total resistance:

$$I = \frac{E}{R} = \frac{120}{800} = 0.15 \text{ amp, Ans.}$$

(B) To measure potential difference between the ends of the 230-ohm resistor, a voltmeter would be connected to the 230-ohm resistor as shown in the diagram. The meter will read a voltage that is determined only by the 230 ohms and the 0.15 amps through the resistor. Ohm's Law can be applied to this one part of the circuit:

$E = IR$ — Volts on one resistor = Current × Ohms of one resistor

$$E = 0.15 \times 230 = 34.5 \text{ volts}$$

Similarly, we can find the voltage reading across any one of the 80-ohm filaments:

$$E = 0.15 \times 80 = 12 \text{ volts for each 80-ohm filament}$$

Add the potential difference for the 330-ohm filament: $E = 0.15 \times 330 = 49.5$ volts

Do these five separate voltages have any relation to the 120 volts applied to the circuit? Yes, it is no accident that these five voltages, 34.5, 12, 12, 12, and 49.5 add up to 120 volts. These "part voltages" show how energy is apportioned among the series resistors.

Recall, for a moment, the definition of voltage as potential energy per coulomb of electrons. A coulomb of electrons enters the circuit with 120 energy-units. Three resistors use 12 units each, one uses 34.5 units, and one uses 49.5; thus the whole 120 units of energy are converted to heat in the resistors.

The total of individual series voltages equals the applied line voltage.

Just incidentally, some radio receivers use a line-up of tubes numbered 12BA6, 12BE6, 12AT6, 35W4, and 50C5. Does the above problem give you an idea as to what the 12-, 35- and 50- represent in these tube numbers?

Let's look at another example of the use of series circuit principles. With information shown on the diagram, find: (A) current in R_2, (B) potential difference across R_2.

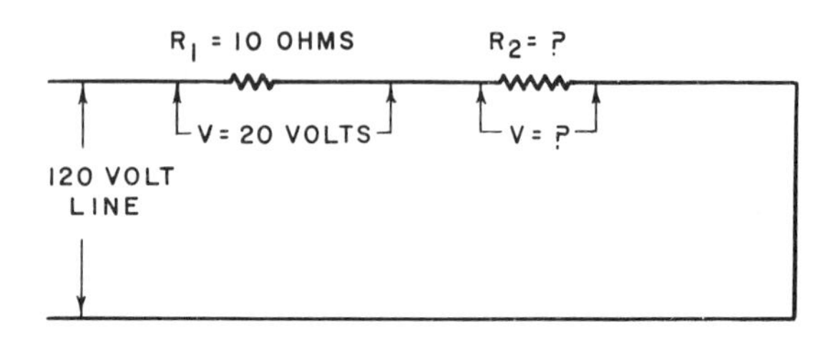

(A) To find current in R_2, one might first try Ohm's Law, but E and I are not yet known. Observe from the diagram that the current in R_2 must be the same as the current in R_1, which we can find from $I = E/R$, using volts and ohms for the single resistor:

$I = 20v/10\ ohm = 2\ amp$, (for all parts of the circuit.)

(B) To find volts across R_2, again we try Ohm's Law, $E = IR$, but we still lack the value of R_2 in ohms. Recall that individual voltages must add to equal the applied line voltage, 120. The voltage across R_2 must therefore be 100 volts, to add with the 20 volts on R_1 to make the 120-volt total. Now that we have the current in R_2, 2 amp, and the voltage on R_2, 100 volts, we can also find the ohms for R_2: $R = 100/2 = 50$ ohms.

VOLTAGE DROP ON A LINE

"Why do the lights in a house dim when a motor starts?" is answered by Ohm's Law and the use of the series-circuit principle, "sum of individual voltages equals total applied voltage."

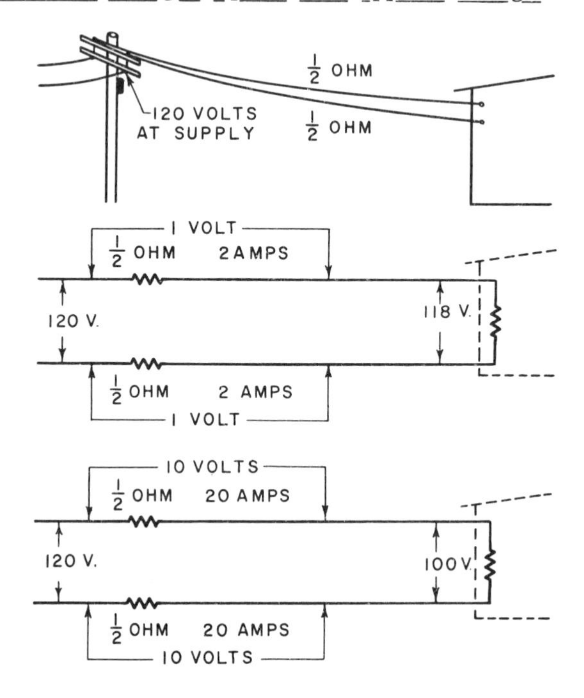

Assume that each wire leading to the house has 1/2-ohm resistance, and lamps in the house cause a 2-amp current in the line. We have then a series circuit, and we can calculate the voltage at the house.

Each line wire is, in effect, a 1/2-ohm resistor with 2 amps in it.

$E = IR = 2 \times 1/2 = 1$ volt which is potential energy used to maintain the 2-amp current in the 1/2-ohm of wire. 1 volt is used on each wire, so that leaves, from the 120, 118 volts potential difference between wires at the house.

If a motor is turned on, so that the current in the line becomes 20 amps instead of 2 amps, more volts will be used up on the line leading to the house.

$E = IR = 20 \times 1/2 = 10$ volts for one wire, and another 10 volts for the other. Subtracting this 20 volts from 120 volts, leaves 100 volts delivered at the house.

With 2 amps in the line, voltage at the house was 118 v. With 20 amps in the line, voltage at the house is 100 v. Lights are dimmer on 100 volts than they are on 118 volts, because with less voltage, there is less current in the lamps. This 2-volt or 20-volt loss is called "voltage drop on the line", and, by Ohm's Law, depends on the resistance of the line and current in the line.

Example of Use of a Line-Voltage Drop Calculation

A certain electric motor requires at least 12 amps at 110 volts to operate properly. It is to be used 500 feet from a 120-volt power line. What size of copper wire must be used for the 500 ft. extension?

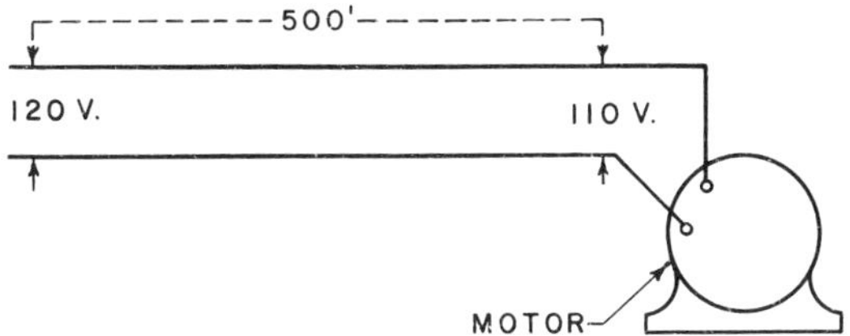

Solution: 120 volts is available at the start. 110 volts must be delivered to the motor, so we can allow 10 volts to be used on the wires when current is 12 amps.

Knowing the 10 v and 12 amp, we can find resistance of the wires of the extension: R = E/I = 0.83 ohm. (These wires are a resistance in series with the motor. In Ohm's Law, we used the 10 volts to find the resistance of the wire that is responsible for the 10-volt potential difference.)

Wire size can now be found from the tables: The 500-ft. extension uses 1000 ft. of wire, with not more than .83-ohms resistance. Using the "Ohms per 1000 ft." column, we find the closest wire size is No. 9. (And if No. 9 copper is not available, the line should be made of No. 8.)

VOLTAGE AT AN OPEN ELEMENT IN A SERIES CIRCUIT

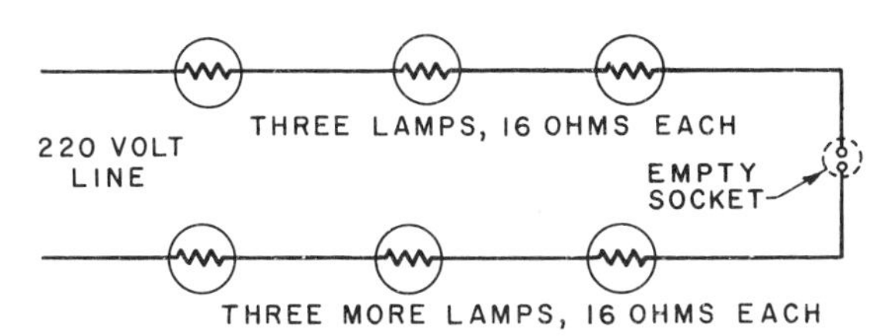

There were once seven lamps in this series circuit, but one has been removed. How much voltage, if any, exists across the open socket? (If you say "none" for a quick answer, maybe you should put your thumb in the socket to prove you are right.)

One way of arriving at a right answer is to consider how much of the 220 volts is being used on each of the six remaining lamps, using E = IR. The current in each lamp is zero; therefore, zero volts is being used up on each lamp, so the entire 220-volt potential appears at the open socket.

The same reasoning applies to voltage at an open switch. The pressure is there, even though it may not be causing any current.

POINTS TO REMEMBER

- There is only one current in a series circuit. Each device has the same current as the other devices.
- Current depends on applied voltage and total resistance. Total resistance is the sum of individual resistances.
- The sum of the individual voltages is equal to the total applied voltage. Individual voltages are found from E = IR, used for individual resistances.

REVIEW QUESTIONS

1. Name examples of useful series circuits. Would it be reasonable to connect the two headlamps of an automobile in series?

2. In a circuit like Fig. 5-1, if the current is 5 amps entering the first resistor, how much current is there leaving the last resistor? And how much current at a point half-way around the circuit?

3. What is "used up" in an electric circuit – electrons, current, or what?

4. Resistors of 500, 5000, and 4500 ohms are connected in series to a 100-volt source. Calculate the current in each, and find the potential difference (volts) across each.

5. Two wires lead from a pole to a house. The resistance of each wire is 0.4 ohm, the current is 10 amps, and the voltage between wires at the pole is 122 volts. Calculate:

   (a) Voltage drop in the line (both wires combined).

   (b) Voltage between wires at the house.

6. If the current is 25 amps in the same line described in Question 5, how much is the voltage drop in the line, and voltage at the house?

7. A certain motor needs at least 8 amps at 209 volts to operate properly. It is to be used 600 feet from a 225-volt source. How much resistance can the line have? (Suggestion: find voltage drop first.)

8. A 10-ohm resistor is connected in series with another resistor (of unknown resistance) to a 120-volt source. The voltage measured across the 10-ohm resistor is 48 volts. Find (a) current in each resistor; (b) resistance of the second resistor.

9. A simple amplifier is to be built, using tubes 35Z5, 12SQ7, and 50L6. The tube manual shows that each of these tubes operates with 0.15 amp through the filament, and the individual voltages are, respectively, 35, 12, and 50. Calculate how to operate these tubes from a 120-volt line.

10. In a series string of eight Christmas-tree lamps, used on a 120-volt line, how much is the voltage across each single lamp? If two more lamps are connected in the string, making a series of ten lamps, how much voltage across each? What effect will this have on the current in the lamps? And what effect on life of the bulbs?

Unit 6 PARALLEL CIRCUITS

When two or more devices are connected to a source of energy in such a way that the total current splits up, with electrons flowing through each device in a separate path, the devices are said to be connected "in parallel."

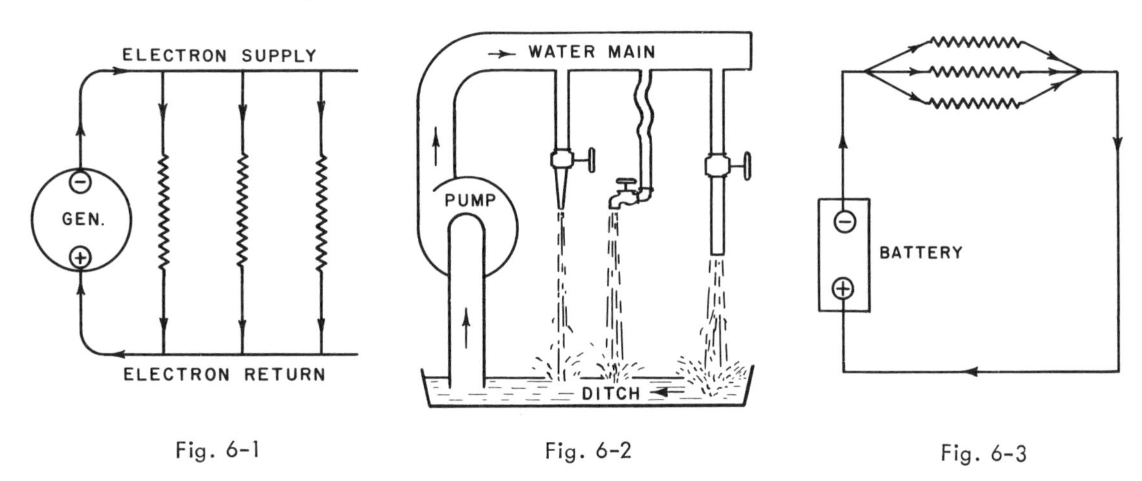

Fig. 6-1 Fig. 6-2 Fig. 6-3

Everybody uses parallel circuits. Various lamps and appliances in a house are connected in parallel, so that each one can be operated independently. A series circuit is an "all or none" circuit, in which either everything operates or nothing operates. If devices are to be turned on and off separately, without affecting other devices, they are wired in parallel.

Trace through the circuits above, noticing how the current divides and re-combines. Compare the electron circuit of Fig. 6-1 with the water circuit, 6-2. (Fig. 6-3 is equivalent to Fig. 6-1 — it is just another way of picturing a parallel circuit.)

ELECTRONS	WATER
● The wires are full of electrons, whether there is current or not.	● The water main and ditch are full of water, whether there is current or not.
● There is a potential difference (volts) between the "electron supply" and the "electron return." This potential difference drives electrons through each device; each operates at the same voltage.	● There is a potential difference (pressure difference) between the "water main" and the ditch. This potential difference drives water through each device; each operates at the same pressure.
● Branches A, B, and C can have separate currents. A could have 2 amps, B, 3 amps, and C, 4 amps, with a total of 9 amps through the generator.	● Branches A, B, and C can have separate currents. A can have 2 gals/sec, B, 3, and C, 4 gals/sec, with a total of 9 gals/sec through the pump.

AMPERES, VOLTS, AND OHMS IN PARALLEL CIRCUITS

Calculating Currents in a Parallel Circuit

Notice that each switch controls only one device. If all switches are open, there is no current, but the 120-volt potential difference exists between the two line wires.

In a simple parallel circuit, all devices operate on the same line voltage.

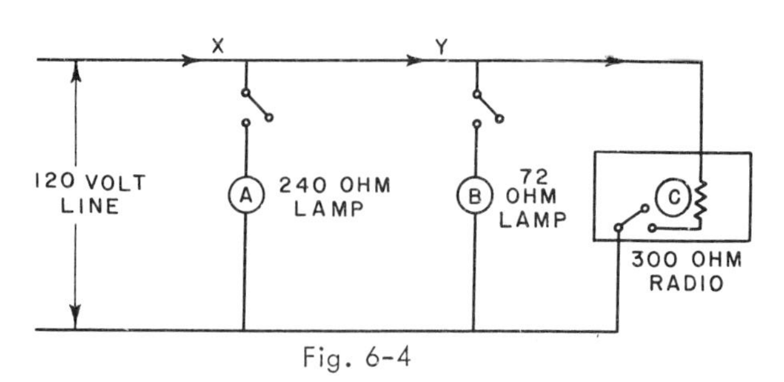

Fig. 6-4

Assuming switches are closed, the current in each device is found by Ohm's Law, $I = \frac{E}{R}$:

For A: $\frac{120}{240} = 0.5$ amp   For B: $\frac{120}{72} = 1.67$ amp   For C: $\frac{120}{300} = 0.4$ amp

To find the current in the line at X: All electrons pass point X, that is, the current at X is 0.5 + 1.67 + 0.4 = 2.57 amps.

The total current in a parallel circuit is the sum of the individual currents.

How much current is there at point Y? The diagram shows that electrons must pass point Y on their way to B and C, so the current at Y is 1.67 + 0.4 = 2.07 amp.

Another example, using the above principles: R can be found by Ohm's Law, if we can first find the current in R.

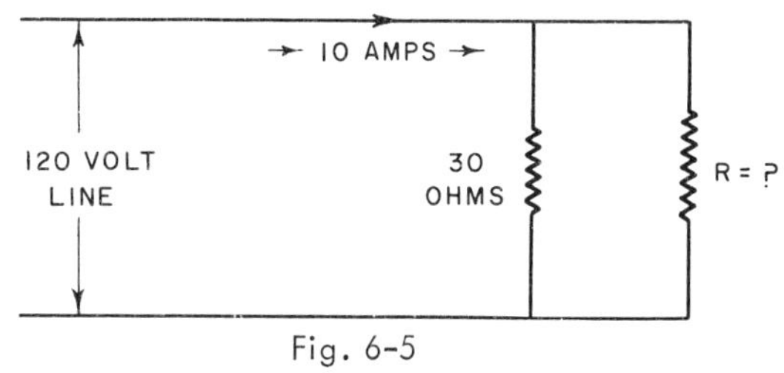

Fig. 6-5

The 30-ohm resistor on 120 volts can have how much current? I = 120/30 = 4 amps. If the total current is 10 amps, then the unknown resistance must have a current of 6 amps in it.

$$R = \frac{120}{6} = 20 \text{ ohms, Ans.}$$

The example just above, with 6 amps in a 20-ohm resistor, 4 amps in the 30-ohm resistor, and 10 amps total current, can serve to illustrate a few facts about parallel circuits:

(1) With both resistors in use, there is more total current than if only one is connected. Each resistor is another opportunity for electrons to move from one line wire to the other. This combination of two resistors allows a total current of 10 amps from a 120-volt source, so, in effect, it acts as a single 12-ohm resistor.

As more resistors are connected in parallel to a line, the total effective resistance of the combination is reduced, and line current increases.

(2) Why do people say "the current all takes the path of least resistance"? They say that because they do not know any better. There is more current in a low-resistance branch than in a high-resistance branch, but each has a current that is determined by I = E/R.

Finding the Total Resistance of a Combination of Parallel Resistors

Here are three ways of finding the combined resistance of a group of resistors in parallel. Which method should be used depends partly on the type of problem, and partly on personal preference. Method (2) is often recommended because it will solve most practical problems, without getting involved in too much arithmetic.

(1) If all of the resistors in the group have the same ohms-resistance, divide the resistance of one by the number of resistors in the group.

Three resistors, 60 ohms each, are in parallel. It is three times easier for electrons to go through the group than it is to go through only one; so the total effective resistance is 20 ohms.

Four resistors, each rated 12,000 ohms, are in parallel. Their total resistance is 12,000 ÷ 4 = 3,000 ohms.

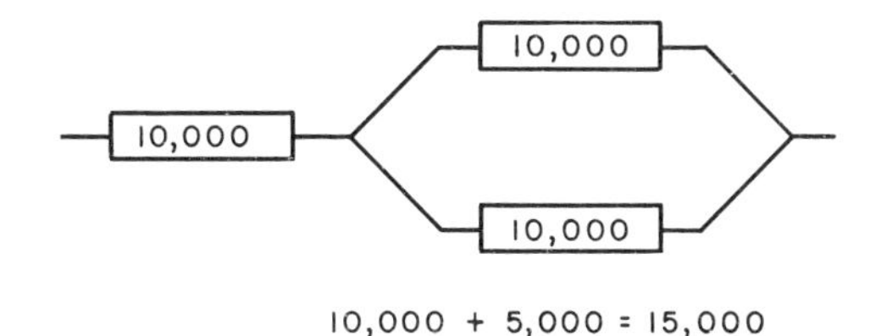

10,000 + 5,000 = 15,000

A repairman needs a 15,000-ohm resistor, but all he has is a drawerful of 10,000-ohm resistors. How can he combine them to make 15,000 ohms? One way: two 10,000-ohm resistors in parallel equal 5,000 ohms. Another 10,000, added in series to the parallel-pair, makes the 15,000.

(2) If the resistors are not alike, the "total" resistance of two resistors in parallel can be found by dividing their product by their sum.

A 30-ohm and a 20-ohm resistor are paralleled. Find their total resistance.

$$R = \frac{\text{product}}{\text{sum}} = \frac{30 \times 20}{30 + 20} = \frac{600}{50} = 12 \text{ ohms, Ans.}$$

This method can be used for only two resistors at a time. Given the problem of finding the total resistance of 30-ohm, 20-ohm, and 10-ohm in parallel, the 30 and 20 can be combined as before, giving 12 ohms. Then this 12-ohm can be combined with the 10-ohm:

$$R = \frac{12 \times 10}{12 + 10} = \frac{120}{22} = 5.45 \text{ ohms, Ans.}$$

(3) Another method, useful for unlike resistors, is the formula $\frac{1}{R} = \frac{1}{r_1} + \frac{1}{r_2} + \frac{1}{r_3} + \frac{1}{r_4}$ in which R is the total resistance and each small "r" is the resistance of one of the resistors in the group. The formula uses as many 1/r terms as there are single resistors.

Find the total resistance of resistors of 30, 20, and 10 ohms.

$$\frac{1}{R} = \frac{1}{30} + \frac{1}{20} + \frac{1}{10} \qquad \frac{1}{R} = \frac{2}{60} + \frac{3}{60} + \frac{6}{60}$$

$$\frac{1}{R} = \frac{11}{60}; \quad \frac{R}{1} = \frac{60}{11}; \qquad R = 5.45 \text{ ohms, Ans.}$$

In all cases, the total combined resistance of a group of resistors in parallel is less than the resistance of the smallest resistor in the group. "Adding" resistors to a parallel circuit is not a matter of increasing the opposition to current, but rather adding opportunities for electrons to flow from one line wire to the other.

CONDUCTANCE

The term "conductance" may be thought of as the opposite of resistance. A good conductor has high conductance and low resistance. A good resistor has low conductance. Numerically, conductance is the reciprocal of resistance:

$$\text{Conductance} = \frac{1}{\text{Resistance}}$$

(The "reciprocal" of a number is the result of dividing the number into 1. The reciprocal of 2 is 1/2, the reciprocal of .02 is 50.)

The unit of measure for conductance is the "mho"; reasonably enough, since that is "ohm" spelled backwards.

Referring to Fig. 6-2, opening more faucets increases the conductance of the circuit. Likewise, in Fig. 6-4, connecting more devices in parallel adds to the conductance of the circuit.

The third method given for combining parallel resistors, on the preceding page, is based on the idea of adding conductances. If resistors have values of 30, 20, and 10 ohms, then the numbers $\frac{1}{30}$, $\frac{1}{20}$, and $\frac{1}{10}$ are their conductances. Adding them gives the total conductance of the circuit, which is $\frac{11}{60}$ mhos.

THE CIRCUIT NOBODY LOVES: THE SHORT CIRCUIT!

A parallel path of very low resistance, often caused accidentally, is given the name "short circuit."

For example, frayed insulation on an appliance cord may permit the two wires to touch each other, forming a path of practically zero resistance. This permits an unreasonably large current in the wires leading to the place of contact.

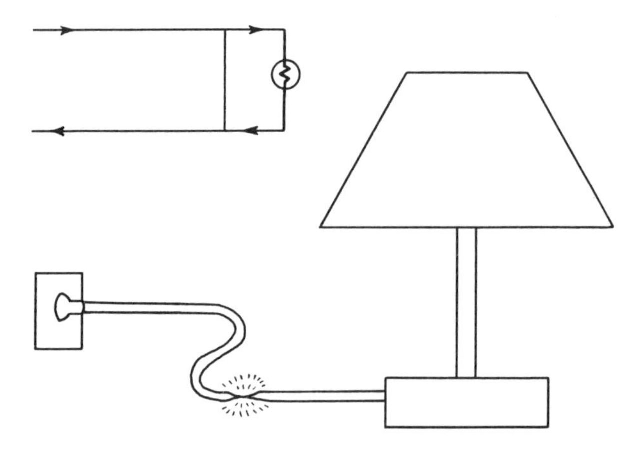

The wires would overheat, to the point of starting a fire. To prevent this sad result, fuses are used in series in each house circuit. Excessive current melts the fuse wire, thereby stopping the flow. The fuse "opens" the circuit.

The term "open circuit" is applied to a circuit containing an open switch, a burned-out fuse, or any separation of wires which prevents current. If an appliance fails to operate when connected, but does not blow fuses, an open circuit in the device may be sought as the cause of the trouble.

SERIES AND PARALLEL COMBINATIONS

Complicated-looking circuit problems may be solved by using the same basic principles that have been pointed out in Units 5 and 6. Briefly: In series, current is the same, voltages add. In parallel, voltage is the same, currents add.

There is no magic formula that solves the whole problem at one blow. Ohm's Law, applied first to one part of the circuit and then to another part, will lead from what we know to what we need to find.

1. The circuit at the right consists of two parallel branches, A-B and C-D. In order to find the current in each resistor, we may note first that since the branches are in parallel, the same voltage (120) is applied to each branch.

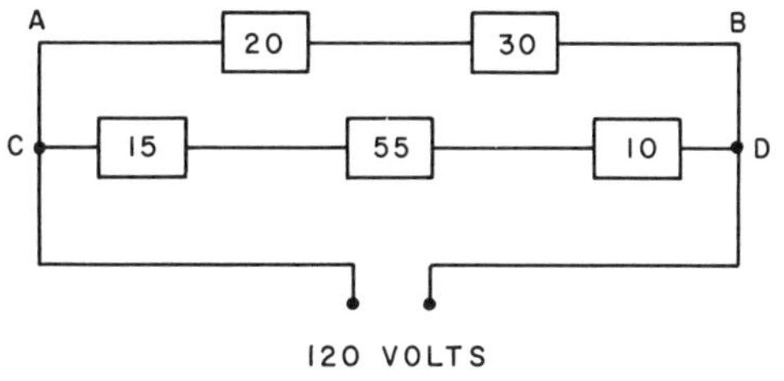

A B 20 30
C D 15 55 10
120 VOLTS

While finding the current in the top (A-B) row of resistors, we can disregard C-D entirely, and just give attention to the fact that A-B is two resistors in series, with 120 volts applied to them. The two resistances must be added, $20 + 30 = 50$ ohms; using $I = \frac{E}{R}$, $I = \frac{120}{50}$, we find the current in them is 2.4 amps.

This 2.4 amps is the current in the 20-ohm resistor; it is also the current in the 30-ohm resistor, since both currents are the same current.

The lower C-D branch is calculated by itself; it is independent of whatever is happening in the A-B branch. The total resistance of the C-D series is 80 ohms; the current in it is $120/80 = 1.5$ amps. This figure, 1.5 amps, is necessarily the same for each resistor in the C-D string.

If we need to know the total current in the 120-volt line, we add the currents in the two parallel branches. 3.9 amps enters on one wire, divides into two parts, 2.4 amps taking the A-B path and 1.5 amps the C-D path. These two currents then combine again, forming the 3.9-amp current in the out-going wire.

The voltage across any single resistor is found by applying Ohm's Law to that single resistor. If we need to know the voltage applied to the 55-ohm resistor, use $E = IR$. I is the already-found current, 1.5 amps. R is the resistance we are concerned with, 55 ohms. $1.5 \times 55 = 82.5$ volts, Ans. In similar fashion, we can find that the voltage across the 15-ohm resistor is 22.5 volts, and across the 10-ohm, 15 volts. $82.5 + 22.5 + 15$ necessarily equals the total applied voltage, 120.

Sometimes one may become needlessly concerned with the voltage that "goes through" a resistor. He should be reminded that what goes through the resistor is electrons, not voltage. Voltage is a potential energy difference between two points. In the above example, "find the voltage going through the 55-ohm resistor" is a meaningless question. The term "voltage across the resistor" reminds us that we connect the voltmeter across the resistor to read the voltage that is used in the resistor.

2. In the problem at the right, information is not immediately available to find the unknown E and R. From the fact that there is 10 volts across the 5-ohm resistor, the current in it is $10/5 = 2$ amps. This same 2 amps flows through the 7-ohm resistor in series. The voltage across the 7-ohm is $2 \times 7 = 14$ volts. Since these two resistors are in series, the total voltage across them is $10 + 14 = 24$ volts.

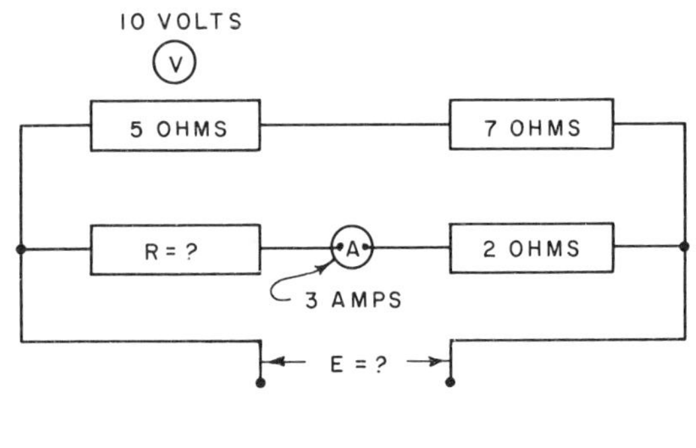

This 24 volts is the previously-unknown line voltage, E. Since there are 3 amps through the lower parallel branch, the total resistance of this branch must be $24/3 = 8$ ohms. A 2-ohm resistor is already shown in this branch, so the unknown resistance must be 6 ohms.

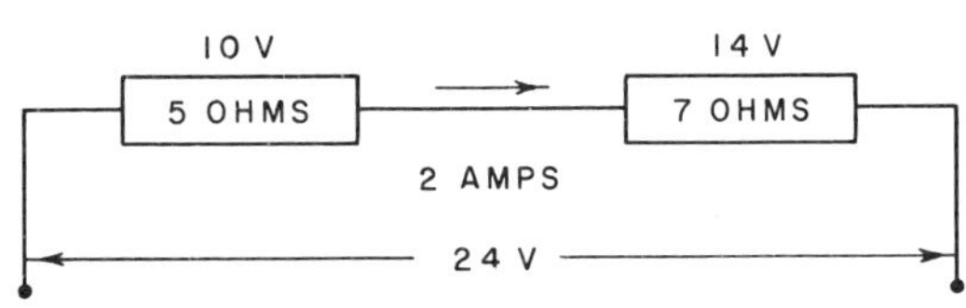

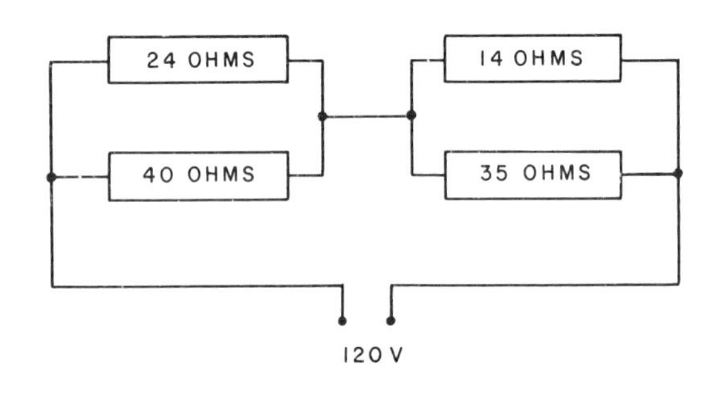

3. To find the individual currents and voltages in this next example, one must recognize that the two parallel-groups are in series with each other.

The first step is to combine the resistors in each parallel group, making the whole circuit appear more like a simple series circuit.

Using $\frac{\text{product}}{\text{sum}}$ on 24, 40 combination, the combined resistance is $\frac{24 \times 40}{64} = 15$ ohms.

The combination of 14 and 35 is equivalent to $\frac{14 \times 35}{49} = 10$ ohms.

The entire circuit is, in effect, 15 ohms and 10 ohms in series, which totals 25 ohms. 120 volts working on 25 ohms produces a total current of $\frac{120}{25} = 4.8$ amps.

4.8 amps through 15 ohms is responsible for a voltage $4.8 \times 15 = 72$ volts. The same 4.8 amps through 10 ohms tells us that the voltage across the 10-ohm is 48 volts. $(72 + 48 = 120)$

These voltages, 72 and 48, may now be applied to the individual resistors in the original parallel branches.

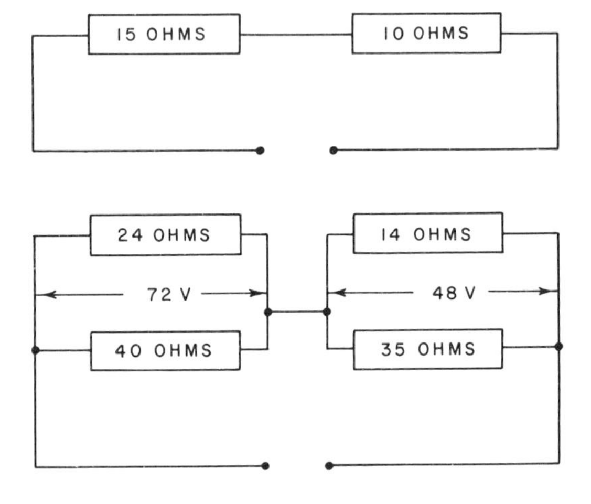

In the 24-ohm, 72 volts produces $72/24 = 3$ amps. In the 40-ohm, the same 72 volts produces $72/40 = 1.8$ amps. $(3 + 1.8 = 4.8$ amps$)$

In the 14-ohm, 48 volts produces $48/14 = 3.43$ amps. In the 35-ohm, the same 48 volts produces $48/35 = 1.37$ amps. $(3.43 + 1.37 = 4.8$ amps$)$

POINTS TO REMEMBER

For Parallel Circuits --

- Line current divides, so electrons pass through each separate device, independent of other devices.
- Total line current is the sum of the individual currents in the parallel paths.
- If several equal resistors are in parallel, their combined resistance equals

$$\frac{\text{Resistance of one}}{\text{Number of resistors}}$$

- The combined resistance of any two resistors in parallel is equal to

$$\frac{\text{Product}}{\text{Sum}}$$

- A short circuit is an accidental path of too-low resistance.

REVIEW QUESTIONS

1. What features distinguish a parallel circuit from a series circuit?

2. Three resistors, one 4-ohm, one 10-ohm, and one 6-ohm are connected in parallel to a 12-volt battery. Calculate the current in each resistor. Calculate the current in the battery.

3. Four resistors, 2200 ohms each, are connected in parallel. This group is connected to a 110-volt line. Find the current in each single resistor. Find the total current in the line leading to the group of resistors. Find the combined resistance of the group of resistors, by two different methods.

4. Three lamps, of resistances 48, 72, and 240 ohms are connected in parallel to a 120-volt line. Find the current in the line.

5. Three resistors are connected in parallel to a 120-volt line. Total current is 12 amps. One resistor is 20 ohm, one is 30 ohm. Calculate ohms for the third resistor.

6. A 50-ohm resistor, carrying 0.48 amp, is in parallel with a 60-ohm resistor. Find the current in the 60-ohm resistor.

7. Three resistors are in parallel: One is 200 ohm, one is 400 ohm, one is 100 ohm. The 200-ohm resistor has a current of 60 ma. Calculate the current in the other two resistors, and the total current in the line.

8. Three resistors, 15 ohms, 30 ohms, and 10 ohms, are connected in parallel across a 120-volt supply. Find: (a) The current in each of the three branches of the parallel circuit. (b) The total line current required by the entire parallel circuit. (c) The combined resistance of the parallel circuit.

9. A 4-ohm, 8-ohm, 12-ohm and 16-ohm resistor are connected in parallel. (a) Calculate the combined resistance of this parallel grouping of resistors. (b) When this group is connected across a 120-volt source, find the current in each resistor, the total current, and the combined parallel-circuit resistance by using Ohm's Law.

10. A line supplies current to twenty-four 300-watt, 120-volt lamps, each having a hot resistance of 48 ohms. This line also supplies sixty 60-watt, 120-volt lamps, each having a hot resistance of 240 ohms. Find the total current in the 120-volt line that feeds these 84 lamps.

11. A coil of 8.27 ohms, a 2.38-ohm lamp, and a 12.25-ohm heater are connected in series. The current is 6.5 amperes. Find the line voltage.

12. Three resistors are joined in series. R-1 is 300 ohms, R-2 is 240 ohms, R-3 is 112 ohms. The current through R-2 is 2.6 amps. Find (a) The voltage across R-1. (b) The voltage across R-3. (c) The voltage applied to the whole series circuit.

13. Three devices are connected in series across a 115-volt source of supply. They fail to operate. A voltmeter connected across each of two of these three devices reads zero, and when connected across the third device indicates 115 volts. What circuit fault is indicated?

14. A certain string of Christmas-tree lamps consists of eight lamps in series. Lamp #3 fails to light, but the other seven light brightly. When lamp #3 is removed from the socket, the other seven remain bright. Is there any fault in the circuit? If so, what?

Unit 7 THE RESISTANCE OF WIRES

Wherever a quantity of wire is used electrically, the selection of wire is originally based on someone's calculation of its resistance. Resistance of wire determines voltage drop (as shown in Unit 5.) Resistance also enters into production of heat: either useful heat in a device, or useless heat in wires leading to a device. In power-line wires, too small wire wastes energy; too large wire wastes copper.

EFFECTS OF LENGTH, KIND OF MATERIAL, AND CROSS-SECTION AREA

(1) Resistance is directly proportional to the length of the wire. For example, if 50 ft. of wire has one-ohm resistance, then 100 ft. of the same wire has 2-ohms resistance. (Think of the 100 ft. as two 50-ft. lengths in series; their resistances add.)

(2) Resistance is dependent upon the kind of material. (See Table of Resistance of Metals and Alloys, Appendix Page A-1.)

(3) Resistance is inversely proportional to cross-section area. This is a way of saying that the larger the wire the less its resistance, provided we are comparing wires that differ only in thickness. A thick wire lets a lot of electrons move through easily, just as a wide road can carry a lot of cars per hour, or a large pipe can easily let a lot of water flow through.

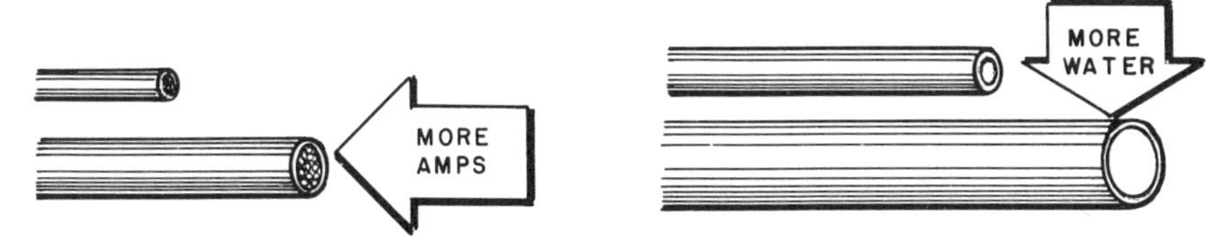

These three ideas can be combined into one useful formula, as soon as we decide how to represent length, cross-section area, and kind of material numerically.

Length: For ordinary use, feet is the convenient measurement.

Area: Because the use of square inches or square feet would require inconvenient calculations and inconveniently small numbers for ordinary sizes of wire, a more convenient small unit of area is used.

Let this circle represent the end of a wire that is one-thousandth of an inch thick. The distance, 0.001 inch, is often called "one mil."

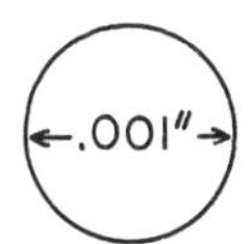

The area of this circle, one mil in diameter, we call one circular mil. A circular mil is a unit of area measurement. It is the same sort of thing as a square foot or an acre. Let's see why this unit is convenient to use.

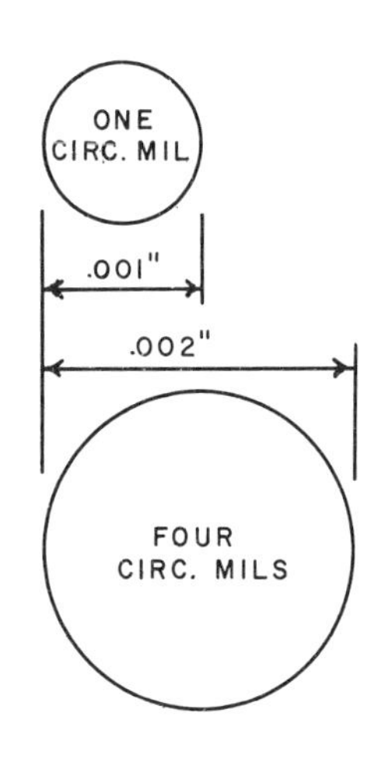

A circle of .001″ diameter has one circular mil area, by definition. A circle of .002″ diameter has how much area? (We could find it from $A = \pi r^2$ and get an answer in square inches . . . a lot of useless work.)

A circle .002″ in diameter has exactly 4 times as much area as a circle .001″ in diameter. Comparing the two circles, recall that doubling the dimensions of any flat surface multiplies its area by four. Or, using area of a circle $= \pi r^2$, when r is 5, r^2 is 25; when r is 10, r^2 is 100. Comparing the 25 and the 100, we see that the radius-10 circle is four times as large in area as the radius-5 circle. The areas of circles may be compared by comparing the squares of their radii, or the squares of their diameters.

"A .002″ diameter circle has how much area?" Four times as much as a one-mil circle, or 4 circular mils.

"A circle .003″ in diameter has how much area?" .003″ is 3 mils. 3^2 is 9. This circle is 9 times as large, in area, as a one-mil circle. Its area, therefore, is 9 circular mils. The convenience of the circular mil area unit is that, by its use, we reduce the job of finding the area of a circle to this:

> (1) Write the diameter of the circle in mils.
>
> (2) Square this number (multiply by itself) and the result is the area of the circle, in circular mils.

For example, the diameter of 12-gage wire is .081 inches, or 81 mils. 81 × 81 is 6561. The cross-section area of the wire is 6561 circular mils. (Even this calculation is not always necessary, for tables that tell the diameters of wires often also tell the circular mil cross-section area.)

Returning to our resistance calculation, in which we were to decide how to represent length, area, and kind of material numerically, length is in feet, cross-section area is to be expressed in circular mils. Next, how shall we express numerically the kind of wire?

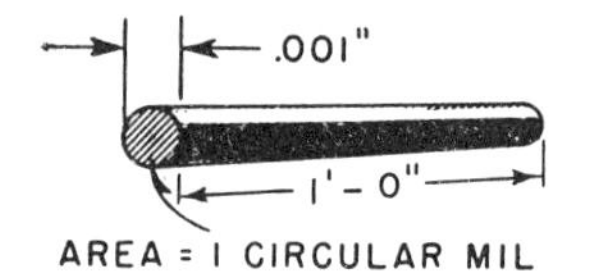

To make our proposed formula as simple as possible, the number used as a standard is the resistance of a piece of wire one foot long and one circular mil in cross-section area. (Such a shape of wire is called a mil-foot.)

For example: Find the resistance of a copper wire 20 feet long and 50 circular mils in end-area.

We know from previous measurements that the resistance of a mil-foot of copper is 10.4 ohms. (Table, next page.)

We multiply the 10.4 by 20 (because resistance increases with length) and then divide by 50 (because, the larger the area, the less the resistance.)

$$R = \frac{10.4 \times 20}{50} = \frac{208}{50} = 4.16 \text{ ohms}, \quad \text{Ans.}$$

OHMS RESISTANCE PER MIL-FOOT (at 70° F)	
Aluminum	17
Brass	42
Copper	10.4
German silver	200
Iron	60
Nichrome	600
Silver	9.6
Steel	75
Tungsten	33

Ohms/mil-ft. for other metals can be calculated from resistivity table, Page A-1, Appendix

The preceding calculation can be put in formula form:

$$R = \frac{K \times L}{C.M.}$$

in which K is the ohms resistance of one mil-foot of the kind of wire used, L is the length of the wire, in feet, and C.M. is the circular mils cross-section area of the wire.

The value of K for common wire materials is given in the list at the left.

The C.M. area for various wire sizes may be found from the wire table, Page A-2, Appendix.

Use of the Wire-Resistance Formula – $R = \frac{K \times L}{C.M.}$

(1) Find the resistance of 150 ft. of #20 aluminum wire. (From table above, K is 17. Wire table gives, for #20 wire, 1020 C.M. cross-section area.)

$$R = \frac{17 \times 150}{1020} = 2.5 \text{ ohms, Ans.}$$

(2) How long a piece of #20 nichrome will have 30 ohms resistance? (Using the same formula, put 30 for R, 600 for K, C.M. is 1020.)

$$30 = \frac{600\ L}{1020} \qquad 30600 = 600\ L \qquad 51 = L \qquad 51 \text{ ft., Ans.}$$

(3) A two-wire power line 1200 ft. long (that's 2400 ft. of wire) is to be erected. The resistance of the line should be not more than 1.5 ohms. What size of copper wire should be used?

$$1.5 = \frac{10.4 \times 2400}{(C.M.)} \qquad 1.5\ (C.M.) = 24960 \qquad C.M. = 16{,}640$$ which is close to #8 wire

In using this formula, as in most electrical calculations, it is sensible to round off figures. A good rule is to round off numbers after the first three figures. For example, if the arithmetic problem is 10.4 × 2317, multiply 10.4 × 2320 and call the answer 24100.

Our measuring instruments, ammeters and voltmeters, seldom can be read to more than 3-figure accuracy. And when a $10 voltmeter reads "118 volts", it means only that the voltage is somewhere between 116 and 120. According to the tables, #20 wire has 404 C.M. area, but wire-makers too are allowed a tolerance. A given sample of #20 wire might be 401 C.M. or 408 C.M.

Arithmetic processes deserve to be done with no more accuracy than the original measurements possess, or the final answer requires. In calculating a wire size, for example, whether the correct answer is 1483 C.M. or 1552 C.M. is of no concern, because #18 wire (1624 C.M.) will have to be used.

ADDITIONAL INFORMATION FROM THE WIRE TABLE

Notice that the tables give ohms per 1000 ft. for copper and aluminum. This information makes it easy to find resistances of given lengths by comparison.

Examples: Find the resistance of 3000 ft. of #6 copper.

Table gives .395 ohm/1000 ft.; three times as much wire will have 3 × .395 = 1.19 ohm, Ans.

Find the resistance of 200 ft. of #18 copper.

Table says that 1000 ft. has 6.39 ohms. 200 ft. is one-fifth of 1000, so we will take one-fifth of 6.39 ohms, = 1.28 ohms, Ans.

The American (B.& S.) wire gage was arranged so that the diameter of a given wire is 1.123 times as much as the next smaller diameter wire. This makes the area ratio between two adjacent wire sizes, 1.261. Sizes two gage numbers apart (like #12 and #14) have an area ratio about 1.6. Sizes three gage numbers apart (like #7 and #10) have an area ratio of practically two. That is, #7 wire is twice as large as #10, in cross-section. Sizes ten gage numbers apart have an area ratio of about ten.

Knowing that #10 wire is about 10,000 circular mils area enables one to estimate other wire sizes from the above ratios.

1000 ft. of #10 copper has 1 ohm resistance, from which resistance of others may be estimated.

Example: Find the resistance of 1000 ft. of #16 wire.

#10 is <u>one ohm</u>, #13 would be <u>two ohms</u> (3 numbers, area ratio is 2), #16 is <u>four ohms</u> per 1000 ft.

Conductors larger than 0000 (also written 4/0) exist. Stranded cables larger than 4/0 are rated directly in circular mils. For flexibility, stranded wire is available. No. 16 stranded has the same amount of copper, and the same current-carrying area, as No. 16 solid. Solid rectangular conductors (bus bars) are used for large currents. They are often easier to assemble and more economical of space than large round conductors, and the flat shape provides more surface-area from which heat can radiate.

Resistances of wires of various materials may be found by calculating information from the copper-wire table, then multiplying by factors given in the table at the right.

(See also, nichrome wire table, Unit 25, Page 301.)

RESISTANCES OF METALS COMPARED TO COPPER (Copper = 1.)	
Aluminum	1.59
Brass	4.40
Gold	1.38
Iron	6.67
Lead	12.76
Nichrome	60.
Nickel	7.73
Platinum	5.80
Silver	0.92
Steel	8.62
Tin	8.2
Tungsten	3.2
Zinc	3.62

STRANDED WIRE AND CABLE

Bunch Stranding: Bunch stranded wire is a collection of wires twisted together, with no particular geometrical arrangement. For example, #18 lamp cord contains sixteen #30 wires, loosely twisted together in the same direction.

Concentric Stranding: A center wire is surrounded by one or several definite layers of wires. Each layer contains six more wires than the layer immediately beneath it. When several layers are used, each layer has a twist opposite to that of the layer under it.

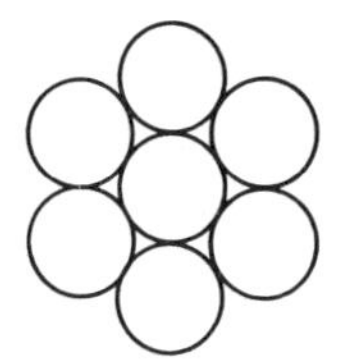

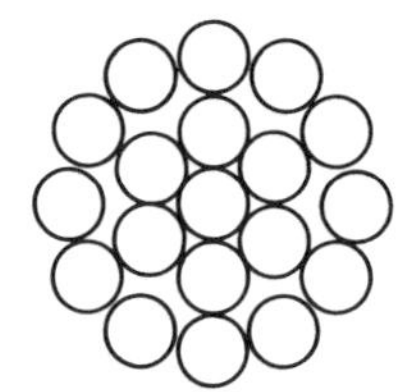

NUMBER OF WIRES OVER CENTER WIRE	1	2	3	4	5	6	7
TOTAL NUMBER OF WIRES IN CABLE	7	19	37	61	91	127	169

CONCENTRIC STRANDING

The size of wire strands used in making up the cable depends on the flexibility required. For example, #00 cable may be made up of seven strands of #7 wire, or 19 strands of #12, or 37 strands of #24, the last one being rated "extra flexible".

A rope-stranded cable is a concentric-stranded assembly made up of several concentric cables twisted together. The 7″ × 19″ rope-stranded cable shown at the right consists of seven 19-strand conductors twisted together.

Cables larger than #4/0 are rated in circular mils. Standard sizes range from 200,000 C.M. to 5 million C.M. These cables may be covered with any of a great variety of insulation materials.

ROPE STRANDING

Cables are made in other forms than circular. Flat braid of many shapes and sizes exists; one use is the battery grounding strap on an automobile.

CONVERSION OF C.M. AREA TO SQUARE MIL AREA

When problems are encountered involving rectangular busbars, it is sometimes necessary to find the square mil area of the conductor, rather than the circular mil area. We can find the circular mil area from wire tables or by the methods described on Page 54.

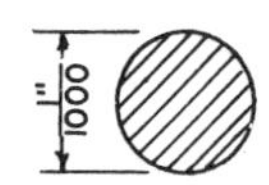

A CIRCULAR MIL

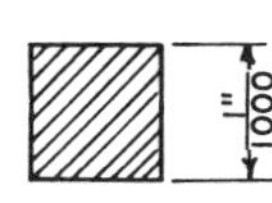

A SQUARE MIL

Since the area of a circle is equal to .7854 × diameter^2, and diameter^2 is equal to the circular mil area, it follows that the circular mil area × .7854 must equal the square mil area.

$$\text{C.M. Area} \times .7854 = \text{Square Mil Area}$$

If the square mil area is known and it becomes necessary to convert this to circular mils, we can transpose the formula as follows:

$$\text{C.M. Area} \times .7854 = \text{Square Mil Area}$$

$$\text{C.M. Area} = \frac{\text{Square Mil Area}}{.7854}$$

EFFECT OF TEMPERATURE ON RESISTANCE

Resistance depends not only on length, area, and kind of material, but also on the temperature of the material. The wire table in the back of this book gives two sets of values for resistance of copper, at different temperatures. (The higher-temperature values are used in calculation of motor and transformer windings, which are intended to operate warm.) These figures illustrate the fact that as temperature rises, the resistance of metals increases.

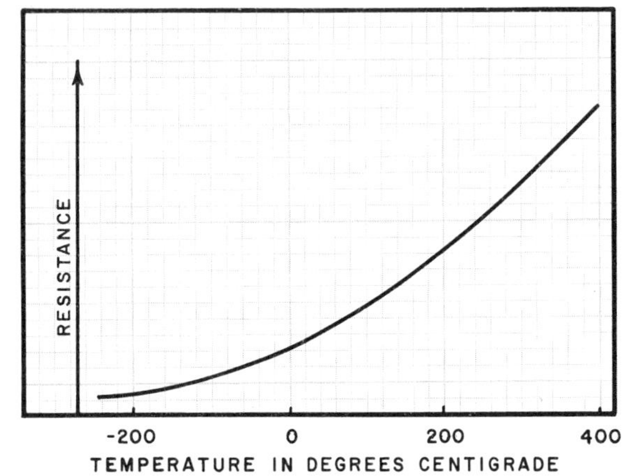

The graph at the left shows, in a general way, how the resistance of most metals increases as the temperature goes up. At higher temperatures, not only is the resistance higher, but also is increasing at a faster rate.

The resistance of carbon decreases slightly with rise in temperature, the resistance of conducting liquid solutions decreases rapidly with temperature rise, and the resistance of semi-conductors such as germanium and metal oxides decreases very rapidly as the temperature goes up.

Not all metals increase in resistance at the same rate; the rate at normal temperatures is given as the "temperature coefficient of resistance" in the table, Page A-1, in the Appendix.

Using Temperature Coefficient to Find Resistance at Higher Temperature

The resistance increase is the original resistance multiplied by the temperature coefficient, multiplied by the number of degrees rise in temperature:

$$\text{Resistance increase} = R \times \text{coefficient} \times \text{degree rise}$$

This amount of increase is added to the original resistance to give the resistance at the higher temperature.

Example: Find the resistance of 10 feet of #30 platinum wire, in an oven at 500° F.

Step 1 We can find the resistance of 10 ft. of #30 platinum at room temperature by comparison with copper:

Tables give 1000 ft. of #30 copper = 103 ohm; therefore,
10 ft. of #30 copper = 1.03 ohm.

Platinum has 5.80 times as much resistance as copper, so 10 ft. of platinum has 1.03 × 5.80 = 5.97, call it 6 ohms.

This 6 ohms is resistance at 68° F, the "original resistance" in our formula for finding the amount of increase.

Step 2 The temperature coefficient given in the table is .003. This coefficient applies for temperature rise measured in Centigrade degrees.

Step 3 We must find degrees rise of temperature, and express it in Centigrade degrees. From 68° F to 500° F is 432 Fahrenheit degrees. It takes 9 Fahrenheit degrees to equal 5 Centigrade degrees. 432 divided by 9 and multiplied by 5 gives 240 as the equivalent number of Centigrade degrees.

Step 4 We now have the three numbers needed to calculate amount of change in resistance. The amount of increase = 6 ohms × .003 × 240 = 4.3 ohms. Add this to the original resistance, 6 ohms, to get 10.3 ohms, the resistance of the 10 ft. of #30 platinum at 500° F.

The Resistance of Copper at Various Temperatures

The curve that graphically represents copper's change in resistance with temperature is practically a straight line in the region of temperatures of ordinary equipment. This straight line, extended to the left in the graph, meets the zero-axis at Temp. = -234.5° C.

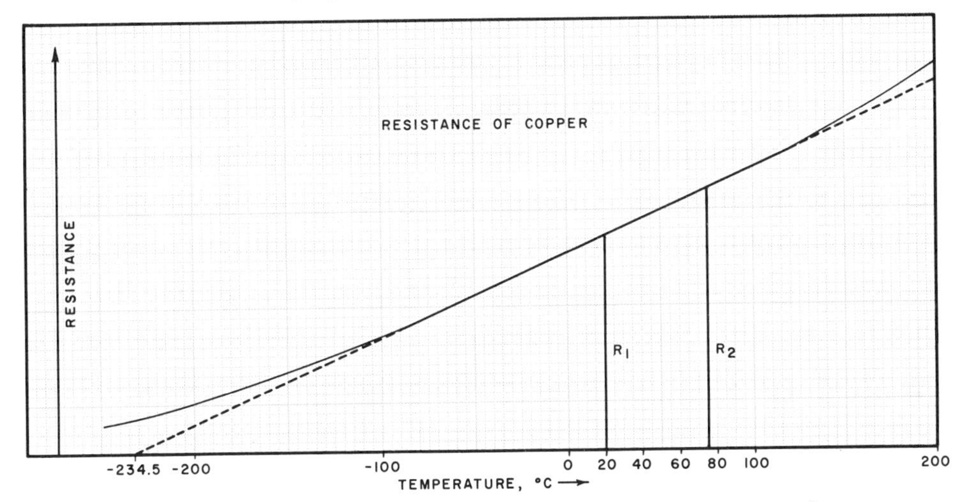

In the graph above, line R_1 represents the resistance of copper at 20° C. Line R_2 represents the resistance of the same piece of copper at 75° C. Note that in the diagram there are two similar triangles:

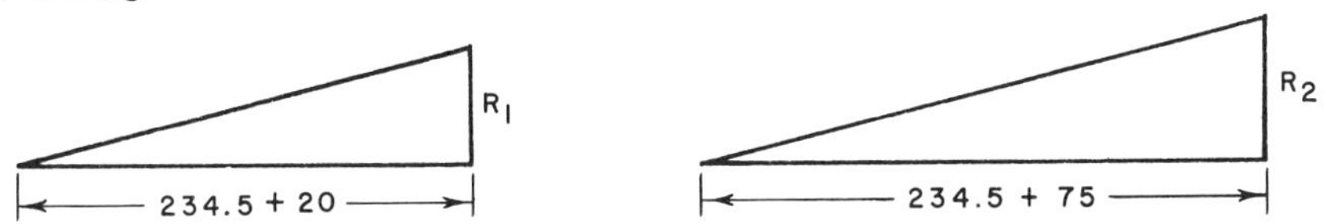

Using the fact that corresponding sides of similar triangles are proportional,

$$\frac{R_1}{234.5 + 20} = \frac{R_2}{234.5 + 75}$$

The temperatures 20 and 75 are used above merely as examples to show the numerical relationship. To make the above formula generally useful, instead of 20 and 75 we may have any two temperatures, call them T_1 and T_2, and the general formula becomes

$$\frac{R_1}{234.5 + T_1} = \frac{R_2}{234.5 + T_2}$$

To illustrate the use of this formula:

1. We have a magnet coil, resistance 240 ohms at 77° F (= 25° C). To find its resistance at a higher operating temperature, say 40° C (104° F):

$$\frac{240}{234.5 + 25} = \frac{R_2}{234.5 + 40}$$

$$R_2 = \frac{274.5 \times 240}{259.5} = 254 \text{ ohm}$$

2. When a copper-wound magnet coil was first connected in a circuit, it took a current of 1.25 amps at 219 volts. At that time, its temperature was 15.5° C. After two hours of steady operation, meter readings were: Line voltage 221, coil current 1.12 amp. Calculate the temperature of the magnet winding.

From Ohm's Law, $R_1 = \frac{219}{1.25} = 175$ ohms, $R_2 = \frac{221}{112} = 197$ ohms

$$\frac{175}{234.5 + 15.5} = \frac{197}{234.5 + T_2}$$

$$234.5 + T_2 = \frac{250 \times 197}{175} = 281.4$$

$$T_2 = 281.4 - 234.5 = 46.9, \text{ call it } 47° \text{ C.}$$

It should be understood that the 234.5 figure applies only to copper. A similar formula for aluminum wire uses 229.2 instead of 234.5.

POINTS TO REMEMBER

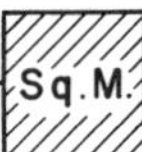

- $R = \frac{K \times L}{C.M.}$ Find K from table, Page 55, C.M. from wire table, Appendix Page A-2. Use formula to find resistance, length, or wire size.

- C.M. area = (diameter in mils)^2
  Square mil area = C.M. area × .7854

- Resistance is
  - more for a long wire than a short one,
  - more for a thin wire than a thick one,
  - more for a hot wire than a cold one,
  - more for iron than it is for copper.

- Change in resistance, due to temperature change, is original resistance × coefficient × degrees change.

- Resistance of copper compared with temperature:

$$\frac{R_1}{234.5 + T_1} = \frac{R_2}{234.5 + T_2}$$

REVIEW QUESTIONS

1. In wire measure, what is a mil? What is a circular mil? What is a mil-foot?

2. How much is the cross-section area of a wire .012″ in diameter? Of a wire .0155″ in diameter?

3. Find the diameter of a wire that has 81 C.M. area.

4. Find the resistance of these wires, using $R = \frac{KL}{C.M.}$

   a. 100 ft. of #14 aluminum
   b. 25 ft. of #20 nichrome
   c. One mile of #8 iron
   d. 6 inches of #18 copper

5. A power line is to use 12,000 ft. of wire, the total resistance of which should not exceed 5 ohms.

   a. What size copper wire meets these requirements? What will it weigh?

   b. What is the smallest size of aluminum wire that meets the requirements? What will it weigh?

6. A connecting wire in an ammeter is found to require 0.0005 ohms resistance. What length of #10 copper will have .0005 ohms?

7. In Question 5, the specific resistances for copper and aluminum, 10.4 and 17, are true for 68° F (= 20° C). Find the resistance of the wire at 0° F (= -18° C) and at 104° F (= 40° C).

8. Calculate resistance of a strip of aluminum foil, .001″ thick, 1/8″ wide, and 2′ long.

9. A nichrome ribbon measures 1/8″ wide, .02″ thick. Find the nearest equivalent wire size.

10. The field-magnet winding of a 230-volt D.C. generator has a resistance of 54.5 ohms at 20° C. Find the resistance of the winding (copper) when the temperature rises to 50° C.

11. A coil of copper wire has 150-ohms resistance at 20° C. After several hours' operation, its resistance is 172 ohms. Find its temperature. Of what use is such a calculation?

Unit 8 ELECTRIC POWER AND ENERGY

Of all the electrons in the world around us, some are of especial interest and value because they can perform useful services for us. This ability to perform useful work is called energy. This useful ability appears in many forms, some of which will be discussed in some detail because they contribute to an understanding of electrical energy.

ENERGY

Energy can be defined as the ability to do work or the ability to accomplish physical changes. The type of work or change referred to is one that involves force and motion. For example, these changes all require energy: Producing mechanical movement, producing heat or light, producing sound, changing one chemical compound into another, or producing radio waves. The amount of energy required for changes of these types, although it is nonmaterial and invisible, is readily measured. In common conversation, the words "work" and "energy" have a broader usage. The physical work or energy that we are concerned with here does not include such things as the work done by a sitter counting cars passing a corner, the work done in getting someone to change his mind, or the energy with which one tackles an arithmetic problem.

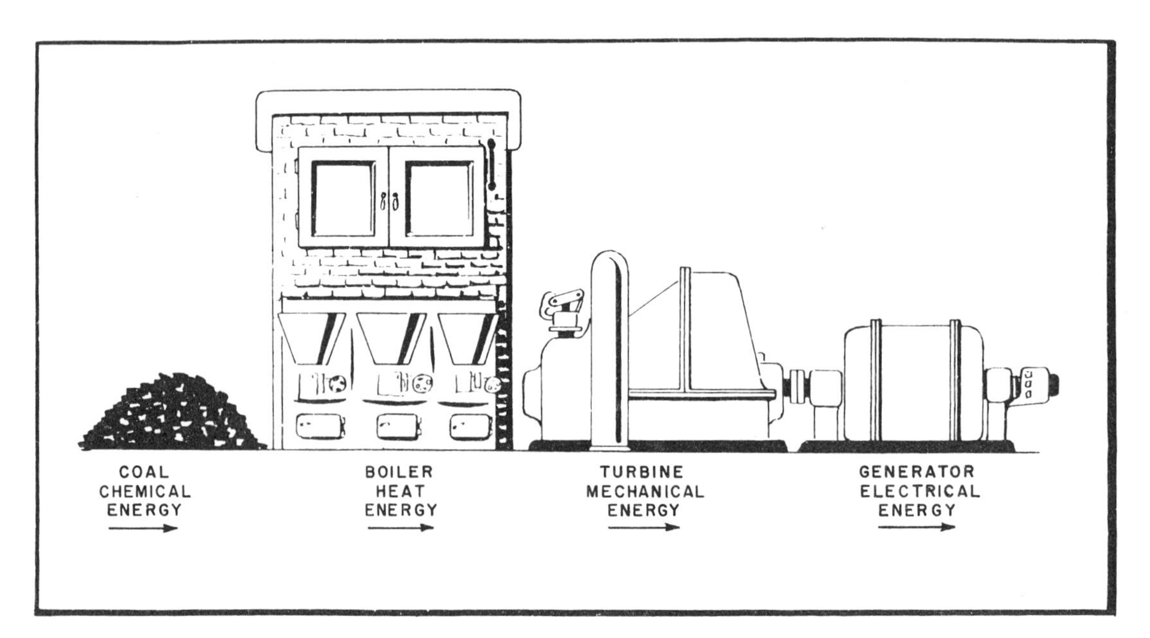

Fig. 8-1 Conversion of Energy

Most of our daily activities involve the conversion and control of energy. One of the main functions of a house is to control heat (which is the energy of motion of molecules.) The main function of an automobile is to convert the energy of gasoline into the energy of mechanical movement. Gasoline and other fuels are useful only because of the energy they possess. The energy of the sun can be used to change water, dirt and air into sugar, vitamins, and other useful chemical compounds; the technicians who run this process are called farmers.

The energy of the sun also produces most of our electrical energy. Last year, the sun's heat evaporated water from the oceans, which fell as rain and snow. This water, stored behind dams, supplies the energy to run some of our electrical generators this year. A hundred million years ago some sun-energy was stored in the dehydrated vegetation that we call coal; this year we will burn some of that coal in boilers, releasing that heat to form steam to run turbine-generators.

Mechanical Energy

The lifting of a weight will illustrate the meaning of one of our units for measurement of energy. To lift a one-pound weight one foot is said to require one foot-pound of energy, or one foot-pound of work. (Work and energy are the same thing, so far as measurement goes.)

We can define a foot-pound as the energy used when a one-pound force moves something a distance of one foot, with the one-foot movement being in the same direction as the force.

How much work is done in lifting a 20-pound weight five feet vertically?

Work = Force × Distance

A 20-pound force traveling one foot accomplishes 20 foot-pounds of work; if it must travel five feet, that's 100 foot-pounds of work.

Foot-pounds = Feet × Pounds

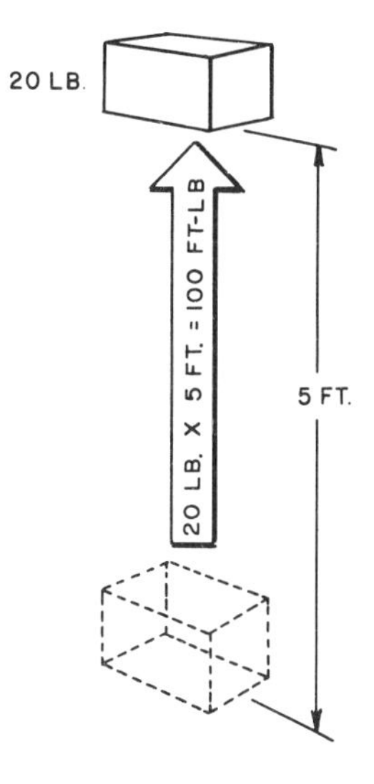

Fig. 8-2

Potential Energy

What becomes of this 100 ft.-lb. of energy? It is saved up; the lifted 20-pound weight has 100 extra foot-pounds of energy that it did not have when it was on the ground. This saved energy is called "potential energy." When the weight is let fall back to earth, it will deliver 100 foot-pounds of energy to whatever it hits.

How much work is done in dragging a 200-pound box horizontally along the floor a distance of 6 ft.? Stated this way, this question cannot be answered. The 200 pounds is a vertical force, not in the same direction as the motion. Suppose we find, with a spring-scale, the additional information that the horizontal force is 50 pounds. Now we can find how much work is done,

$$50 \times 6 = 300 \text{ ft.-lb.}$$

What becomes of this 300 ft.-lb. of energy? It is wasted, converted into heat by the process of friction against the floor. The box has not gained potential energy. The energy has not vanished; it has uselessly warmed the floor and the bottom of the box.

Kinetic Energy

How much work is done when a 3/4-pound ball is thrown, if a force of 8 pounds is applied through a distance of 6 feet?

Work = Force × Distance = 48 foot-pounds

What becomes of this energy? It exists as energy of motion of the ball, which is called "kinetic energy." The ball in flight has 48 ft.-lb. of energy, which it will deliver to whatever it hits.

Turning back to the example of potential energy, when the 20-lb. weight which rests 5 feet above the floor is allowed to fall, its potential energy of 100 ft./lb. becomes kinetic energy, energy of motion.

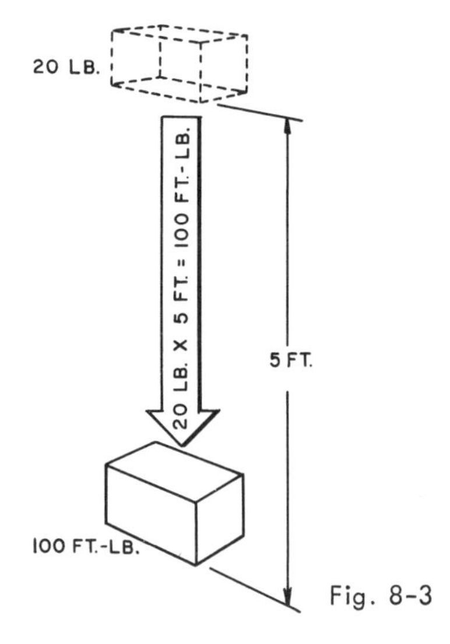

Fig. 8-3

The purpose of these mechanical examples has been to illustrate the meaning of such terms as work, energy, potential energy and kinetic energy. They often enter into electrical discussions, but may be easier to visualize with a mechanical example.

The discussion of "Potential Energy of Electrons" in Unit 3 deserves re-reading at this point.

Units of Energy

The foot-pound is the common energy unit used in British system measurements. There is one metric-system unit of energy that deserves mention, because some common electrical units are based on it: The metric unit of energy called a joule is the work done when a force of one newton is exerted through a distance of one meter. (A newton is 100,000 dynes, which is about 3 1/2 ounces; a meter is about 39 inches.) One joule is 0.738 ft.-lb.; one ft.-lb. is 1.35 joules.

Two units of measurement that are used particularly for heat energy should become familiar. The British unit for heat, called a B.t.u. (British Thermal Unit), is the amount of heat needed to raise the temperature of a pound of water one Fahrenheit degree.

How much heat would be needed to warm 10 pounds of water from 50° F to 65° F? 10 pounds, times a 15 degree rise, requires 150 B.t.u.

The metric system unit of heat, called a calorie, or gram-calorie, is the energy needed to raise the temperature of one gram of water one centigrade degree. (The calorie used in food-energy calculations is a kilogram-calorie, which raises 1000 grams of water one degree.)

Fig. 8-4

1 B.t.u. = 778 ft.-lb.; 1 B.t.u. = 252 cal.

POWER

In everyday language, people use the word "power" to mean a variety of things. In the accurate language that engineers have to use, power means how fast work is done, or how fast energy is transferred.

"Power is the rate of doing work" and "Power is the rate of energy conversion" are two useful definitions of the term.

The fact that power is a rate deserves attention. Accurately, we do not buy or sell "power"; the commodity that we buy or sell is energy. "Power" tells how fast energy is used or produced.

> For a mechanical example: If an elevator lifts 3500 pounds a distance of 40 feet, and it takes 25 seconds to do it, $40 \times 3500 = 140{,}000$ foot-pounds of work is done in 25 seconds. The rate of doing work can be stated in foot-pounds per second: The rate is
>
> $$\frac{140{,}000 \text{ ft.-lb.}}{25 \text{ sec.}} = 5600 \text{ ft.-lb./sec.}$$
>
> (The division sign / is read as "per"; ft.-lb./sec. reads as foot-pounds per second.)

Power can as well be expressed in foot-pounds per minute. If a pump needs 10 minutes to lift 5000 pounds of water 60 feet, it is doing 300,000 ft.-lb. of work in 10 minutes, which is a rate of 30,000 ft.-lb./min.

Horsepower

When James Watt started selling steam engines, he had to rate his engines in comparison with the horses they were to replace. He found that an average horse, working at a steady rate, could do 550 foot-pounds of work per second. This rate is the definition of one horsepower.

1 h.p. = 550 ft.-lb./sec.

The elevator referred to above, doing work at the rate of 5600 ft.-lb./sec., is doing work at the rate of a little over 10 h.p.

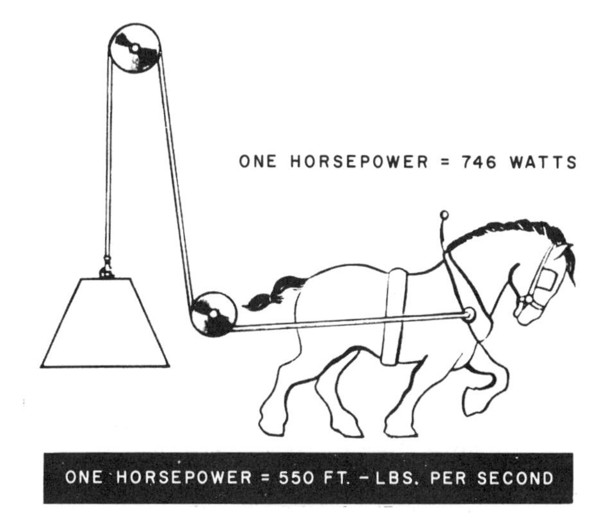

Fig. 8-5

In the previous discussion of energy, a metric-system unit called a joule was mentioned. In metric units, power can be measured in joules per second, which corresponds to foot-pounds per second in British units. Joules per second is used so often that the one word, watt, is used to replace the three words, joules per second.

A watt is a measurement of power. One watt is a rate of one joule per second.

Heading Rates

Rate of using or producing heat energy can be measured in B.t.u./sec., or calories/sec., or calories/min. Household heating equipment is rated in B.t.u. per hour.

For comparison of power units:

1 h.p.	= 746 watts
1 watt	= 3.42 B.t.u./hour
1 B.t.u./sec.	= 1055 watts
1 cal./sec.	= 4.19 watts
1 ft.-lb./sec.	= 1.36 watts

Two More Energy Units

The statement "Power is rate of using energy" can be written briefly in algebraic form:

$$\text{Power} = \frac{\text{Energy}}{\text{Time}}$$

(If we had needed a formula, we could have used this one to find ft.-lb./sec. when we knew the foot-pounds and the time in seconds.)

This formula can be re-arranged to say: Energy = Power × Time. This formula seems hardly necessary, because one could do this problem without it:

"How much work (energy) is done by a 1-h.p. engine in 20 seconds?"

1 h.p. is 550 ft.-lb./sec. and we would multiply that by
20 seconds to find the work done.

The purpose of that formula, here and now, is to introduce two common energy units. By multiplying a power unit by a time unit, we can get an energy measurement. If a 1-h.p. engine works for 1 hour, we can call the work done, 1 horsepower-hour.

Using the metric-system units that are used for electrical quantities, if a device uses electrical energy at the rate of one watt, and it uses energy at this rate for one hour, we will call the energy used = one watt-hour.

$$\underset{\text{(energy)}}{\text{Watt-hours}} = \underset{\text{(power)}}{\text{Watts}} \times \underset{\text{(time)}}{\text{Hours}}$$

Watt-hours are generally lumped together and sold by the thousand. (The prefix kilo- means thousand.)

One kilowatt-hour (KWH) is 1000 watt-hours.

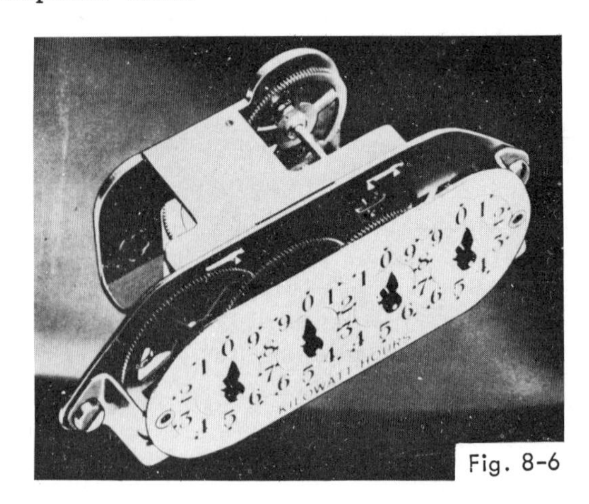

Fig. 8-6

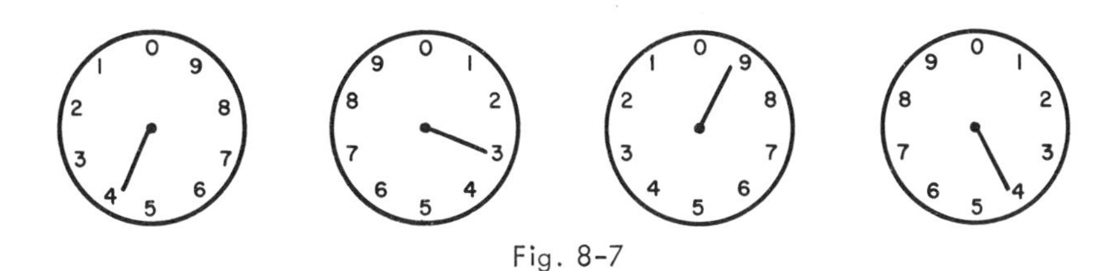

Fig. 8-7

The illustration above represents the register of a kilowatthour meter with four dials. The dials reading from right to left represent units, tens, hundreds and thousands. In reading the meter, starting with the left-hand dial, we simply write down the last number which the pointer has passed and we get a registration of 4294 KWH.

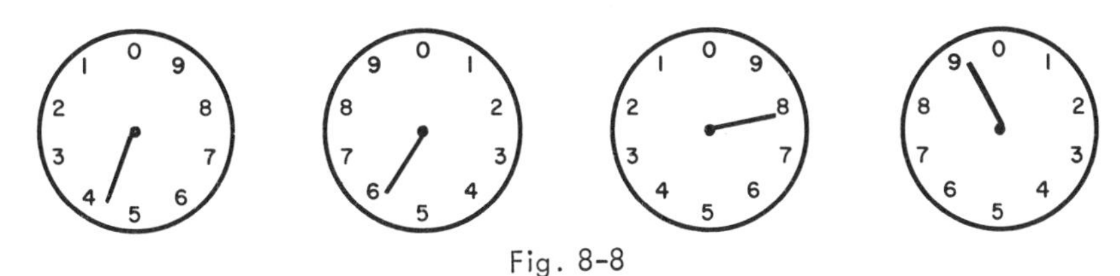

Fig. 8-8

If we read the meter a month later (see illustration above) and find the dials register 4579 KWH, then by subtracting the 4294 from 4579 we know we have used 285 KWH during the month.

The reason for using KWH for measuring energy is that it is a unit of convenient size. If we calculated our ordinary energy requirements in foot-pounds or in joules, the numbers would be inconveniently large. 1 KWH = 2,655,000 ft.-lb. or 3,600,000 joules or 3413 B.t.u.

THE ENERGY OF ELECTRONS

Electrical energy and power measurements are based on the metric unit of energy, the joule. Our more familiar units are derived from it.

What Do We Buy From the Power Company?

Electrons? No. We buy the electrons when we buy the lamp bulb. We pay the power company to move the electrons.

Power? No. Power is a rate. Ever hear of anyone buying 10 horsepower? Or 40 miles per hour?

Current? No, that's a rate, too.

Energy? Why, sure. Electrons do useful work, or produce useful heat, by giving up energy.

How to Calculate Power

There are two useful formulas for calculating watts of power:

Watts = Volts × Amps (or Power = EI) and Watts = I^2R (I is amps, R is ohms)

Why Should Volts × Amps Give Power?

Recall (from Unit 3) that the volts tell the energy carried by each coulomb of electrons. Amps tell how many coulombs pass by each second. If the voltage is 120, that means that each coulomb will deliver 120 units of energy. If the current is 5 amps, that means that five coulombs are delivering energy each second. Five per second, each delivering 120 energy units, means that 600 energy units (joules) are delivered each second. 120 volts × 5 amps gives 600 joules each second, but we call joules/sec., "watts."

Using W = EI (Watts = Volts × Amps)

1. How many watts can we have on a house circuit if it is a 120-volt circuit, protected by a 15-amp fuse?

   Watts = 120 × 15 = 1800 watts. This 1800 watts is the maximum total of all appliances in use on the one circuit.

2. How much current (amps) in the line when four 60-watt lamps are in use? Four lamps, 60 w. each, that's 240 watts. If it is a 120-volt line:

   $$W = V \times A$$

   $$240 = 120 \times X$$

   $$2 = X$$ Ans. is 2 amps

3. A 220-volt DC motor takes 10 amps. How many watts is that?

   220 × 10 = 2200 watts, or call it 2.2 kilowatts (KW)

Using Watts = I^2R

This formula can be derived from W = EI, or W = IE. If we substitute for E, a quantity that is the same as E, IR, (E = IR), the formula becomes $W = I \times (I \times R)$, which can be rewritten I^2R.

1. A flatiron of 11 ohms resistance is intended to operate on 10 amps. What is its rating in watts?

   $$\text{Watts} = I^2R$$

   $$\text{Watts} = 10^2 \times 11 = 100 \times 11 = 1100 \text{ watts}$$, Ans.

2. A 10,000-ohm resistor in a radio has a current of 15 milliamps in it. Find watts.

   15 milliamps = .015 amps

   $$\text{Watts} = (.015)^2 \times 10{,}000 = .000225 \times 10{,}000 = 2.25 \text{ watts}$$

Which formula is better to use, Watts = EI or Watts = I^2R? It makes no difference, both give right answers. If E and I are known at the start, use EI. If I and R are known, use I^2R. If E and R are known, but not I, find I from Ohm's Law (I = E/R); then use either formula.

RELATIONSHIPS OF WATTS, AMPS, OHMS AND VOLTS

Most problems can be solved conveniently enough with the knowledge that Watts = Volts × Amps (or I^2R) plus use of Ohm's Law. Several rearrangements of these formulas are possible, each of which can be useful in some specific problem.

To show how these formulas are obtained:

Starting with W = E I,

dividing by I gives $\frac{W}{I} = E$, or $E = \frac{W}{I}$

Or, dividing by E, $\frac{W}{E} = I$, or $I = \frac{W}{E}$

Since $I = \frac{E}{R}$, we can insert $\frac{E}{R}$ in place of I in the formula $W = E \times I$,

which becomes $W = E \times \frac{E}{R} = \frac{E^2}{R}$

This last statement can be rearranged, multiplying by R, to

$$WR = E^2$$

from which $R = \frac{E^2}{W}$

and also, $E = \sqrt{WR}$

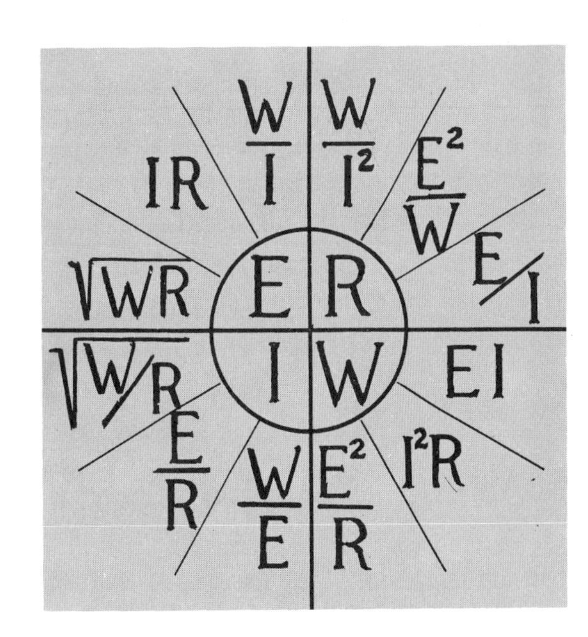

From $W = I^2R$, dividing by R gives $\frac{W}{R} = I^2$, from which, $I = \sqrt{\frac{W}{R}}$

These formulas are summarized in the circular chart above. Each quantity in the center can be found by three methods. Examples:

1. A resistor is rated 1500 ohms, 2 watts. Find the greatest potential difference (E) that should be applied to it.

   Since W and R are given, we can use $E = \sqrt{WR}$

   $E = \sqrt{2 \times 1500} = \sqrt{3000} = 54.8$ volts, Ans.

2. A lamp is rated 300 watts, 120 volts. Find its resistance, when operating.

   $R = \frac{E^2}{W} = \frac{120^2}{300} = 48$ ohms, Ans.

   (Or, as an alternate method, amps could be found from watts and volts, then R can be obtained by the use of Ohm's Law.)

3. Find the greatest current allowable in a 1500-ohm, 2-watt resistor, that will not exceed its power rating.

   $I = \sqrt{\frac{W}{R}} = \sqrt{\frac{2}{1500}} = \sqrt{.00133} = .0365$ amp $= 36.5$ ma. Ans.

HOW TO CALCULATE ENERGY AND COST

Electrical energy is normally calculated in kilowatt-hours. Watts × hours gives watt-hours. The answer is expressed in KWH by dividing watt-hours by 1000.

1. A 500-watt heater is operated for 10 hours. How many KWH of energy are used?

   500 × 10 = 5 thousand watt-hours, which is 5 kilowatt-hours.
   If kilowatt-hours of energy cost 3 cents each, the cost of this operation is 15 cents.

2. A 120-volt, 10-amp iron is operated for 3 hrs. Find the cost at 2.5¢/KWH.

   120 volts, 10 amps = 1200 watts

   1200 watts × 3 hrs. = 3600 watt-hours = 3.6 KWH

   3.6 KWH × 2.5¢ per KWH = 9¢

3. What does it cost to leave two 60-watt lamps on all night (8 hrs.)?

   120 watts × 8 hrs. = 960 watt-hours (call it about one KWH)
   How much does one KWH cost you?

Household energy rates are based only on energy used per month. Industrial energy rates are based on energy used, plus a charge based on maximum power required.

CONVERSION OF ENERGY OR POWER

"Energy is never created from nothing, and energy never vanishes" is one way of stating a principle long known as the "Law of Conservation of Energy." Each KWH we use in lamps or motors comes from the burning of some coal or the release of some stored water. If we light our lamps from batteries, the energy of coal is still responsible, for coal was oxidized to release the zinc or lead of the battery from other elements when the metal was refined. The electrical energy that we ordinarily use daily is soon converted to heat, by one process or another, lost to the air, and radiated out into space. Electric-energy users store some energy when they charge batteries, or pump water into a storage tank, but such examples of energy-storage are few. Usually we convert energy from one form to another so that we can see at night, or saw wood, or hear music. The efficiency of this energy conversion is a way of measuring how well the energy-converting device accomplishes its task.

$$\text{Efficiency} = \frac{\text{Useful energy obtained}}{\text{Total energy used}} \quad \text{or} \quad \text{Efficiency} = \frac{\text{Power output}}{\text{Power input}}$$

Take, for example, a D.C. motor that takes 4.2 amps on a 120-volt line, and is producing one-half horsepower. What is its efficiency?

The power output is 0.5 h.p., or 373 watts. (Because 1 h.p. = 746 w.)

The power input is 120 v. and 4.2 amp = 504 watts.

The efficiency of the motor is 343 ÷ 504 = .68, or 68%

The efficiency of any device can be no more than 100%, which is a way of saying that the device cannot give out more energy than it takes in. The efficiency of all electrical heating devices is 100%; electrical production of heat is easy. Heating devices may vary, however, in how effectively they deliver heat from the coils in which it is produced to the place where it is to be used.

Referring back to the motor with 68% efficiency, the other 32% of the energy used appears as heat. If the motor is stalled, so it can produce no mechanical power, it becomes a 100%-efficient heating device.

Another example: Find the efficiency of an electrical generator, requiring 10 h.p. input, and producing 50 amps at 100 volts.

Power output: 50 amps $\times$ 100 v. is 5000 watts

Power input: 10 h.p. is 7460 watts

$$\text{Efficiency is } \frac{5000}{7460} = .67$$

An often-proposed scheme is, "How would it work to drive an electrical generator with an electric motor, and let the generated current run the motor?" The answer is, "It would not work very good" and the reason may be apparent from the preceding discussion. Both the motor and the generator waste some of the energy applied, so one is not going to produce enough energy to run the other.

POINTS TO REMEMBER

- Work = Force $\times$ Distance
- Energy is ability to do work.
- Power is rate of using energy.
- Power $\times$ Time = Energy
- Watts = Volts $\times$ Amps
- Watts = $I^2 R$
- Watts and kilowatts measure power, which is a rate.
- Watt-hours and kilowatt-hours measure energy.
- Efficiency = Output $\div$ Input

REVIEW QUESTIONS

1. What is a foot-pound?

2. A crane lifted a 25-ton freight car a distance of 6 feet. How much work did it do? How much energy is needed to throw a 6-pound projectile 50,000 feet into the air?

3. If 300,000 foot-pounds of work has to be done in 5 seconds, how much is the horsepower required?

4. If 300,000 ft./lb. of work is to be done in 5 minutes, how much h.p. is required?

5. One pound of coal releases 12,000 B.t.u. when it is burned. This is equal to how many foot-pounds?

6. If the energy of a pound of coal is converted into electrical energy (KWH) by means of equipment that has an overall efficiency of 30%, how many KWH are obtained from a pound of coal?

7. Assuming that 50,000 B.t.u./hr. is required to heat a house in cold weather, how many watts of electrical heating would be needed to produce heat at this rate? (Electrical heating is 100% efficient.)

8. Calculate watts for each of these devices:

   a. A 60-volt 10-amp arc lamp.
   b. A 100-ohm resistor carrying 1/2-amp.
   c. A 12-amp, 110-volt heater.
   d. A 2-ohm resistor on a 6-volt line.

9. Calculate resistance of a 60-watt, 120-volt lamp when operating.

10. Find operating current for an 800-watt, 115-volt toaster.

11. A 20,000-ohm resistor is rated 5 watts. What is the maximum current it can carry without exceeding its 5-watt rating?

12. Find the cost of operating the toaster of Question 10 for 5 hours per month, if energy costs 3 cents per KWH.

13. A 6-volt battery is charged at a 5-amp rate for 24 hours. How many KWH of energy is put into the battery?

14. A certain 1/4-h.p. D.C. motor is 70% efficient. How many amps does it take, on a 120-volt line, when delivering 1/4 h.p.?

15. A D.C. motor, taking 5 amps on a 110-volt line, is 60% efficient. Find the h.p. output. Find the heating rate, in watts.

16. Calculate watts that must be supplied to a 40-gallon electric water heater so that it can raise the temperature of a tank full of water from 50° F to 150° F in two hours. Assume no heat is wasted. 1 gallon = 8 1/3 lb. Calculate the cost of this heat, at 2 cents per KWH.

17. Calculate time required for a 1600-watt heating element to warm 30 gallons of water from 50° F to 150° F.

18. Find the time required to heat 1900 grams of water (about 2 qts.) from 10° C to boiling (100° C) on a 660-watt hotplate.

19. Find the time required for the above heating operation if the process is 90% efficient, that is, only 90% of the heat input is effectively delivered to the water.

Unit 9 MAGNETISM

One of the most familiar and most used effects of electric current is the ability to produce the force we call magnetism. This magnetic force is responsible for the operation of motors, generators, electrical measuring instruments, communication equipment, transformers, and a great variety of electrical control devices.

All magnetism is electromagnetism, an effect of the energy of motion of electrons. A great deal was learned about magnets before this basic fact was discovered: Currents traveling in the same direction attract each other; currents traveling in opposite directions repel each other. But first we shall take up some of the earliest-known facts of magnetism, and then see how they are explained by action of electrons.

To start with, it must be understood that magnetism is a different force than the attraction and repulsion forces due to static electric charges. Both kinds of force have been recognized, separately, for centuries. The first hint that magnetism was in some way connected with electrical behavior was given in 1819, when Hans Oersted, a physics professor in Denmark, noticed that a magnetic compass needle was affected by a wire that he had connected to a battery.

If a wire is punched through this black spot on the page (Fig. 9-1), connected to a battery, and held perpendicular to the paper so that electrons come from below the page toward you, compasses placed on the paper near the wire will point in the directions shown in the diagram. The North ends of the compasses are pushed in the direction shown by the clockwise arrows around the wire. Some already known facts about magnets are used as a help in picturing the reason for this compass-affecting force, facts that must now be reviewed.

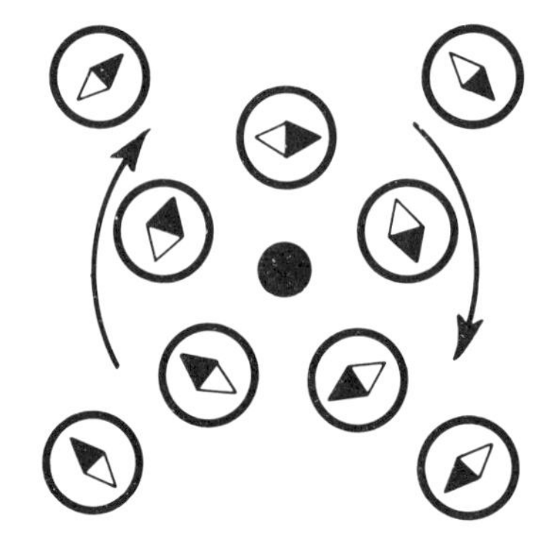

BLACK END OF COMPASS IS NORTH
WHITE IS SOUTH

Fig. 9-1

SIMPLE MAGNETS

A magnet is a piece of material that attracts iron and steel, and a few other materials, such as nickel, cobalt, and a few minerals and alloys.

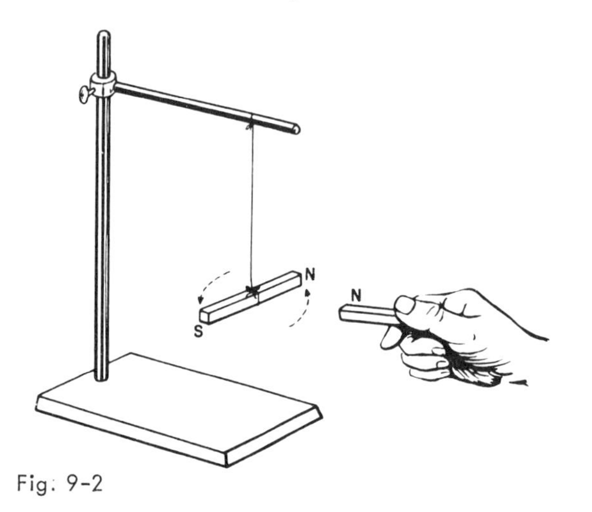

Fig. 9-2

Magnets do not attract copper, aluminum, wood, paper; in fact, they do not attract most substances. This is quite unlike electrical attraction, which works on everything.

The force of the magnet is strongest at two spots on the magnet, called "poles." It was found that, if a magnet is supported by a string or on a pivot, one of these poles turns toward the north, the other toward the south. The end of the magnet toward the north is called, logically enough, its North end, or North pole; the other, the South pole. A compass needle is merely a pivoted lightweight strip of magnetized steel.

It was soon discovered, by bringing compasses near each other, that the North end of a compass (or any magnet) repels the North end of another magnet, and attracts the South. The South pole of a magnet repels the South pole of another magnet, and attracts the North. This is summarized in the magnetic attraction and repulsion law: Like poles repel, unlike poles attract. (Even though this sounds like the electrical attraction and repulsion law, remember that magnets are one thing, electrical charges are another.)

The term "poles" means "opposite parts", as used in "positive and negative poles of a battery" or "north and south geographic poles" of the earth. It might have been better if magnet poles had been named, instead of North and South, some other harmless pair of names, such as black and white, or right and left, or Hank and Emma. One must realize that the geographic poles of the earth are the ends of the axis on which the earth turns, and they are not spots of magnetic attraction. The earth does have magnetic poles. There is a place in northern Canada that has the same kind of magnetic force as the South pole of a steel magnet. There is a place in the Antarctic that has the same kind of magnetic force as the North pole of a steel magnet.

THE MAGNETIC FIELD

The force in the space around a magnet can be pictured by examining the pattern made by iron filings, sprinkled on a card placed over the magnet. Each little splinter of iron acts like a compass needle, attracting other filings at its ends and repelling those lying parallel to it. These chains of filings led to the assumption that the region ("field") around a magnet contains invisible "lines of force."

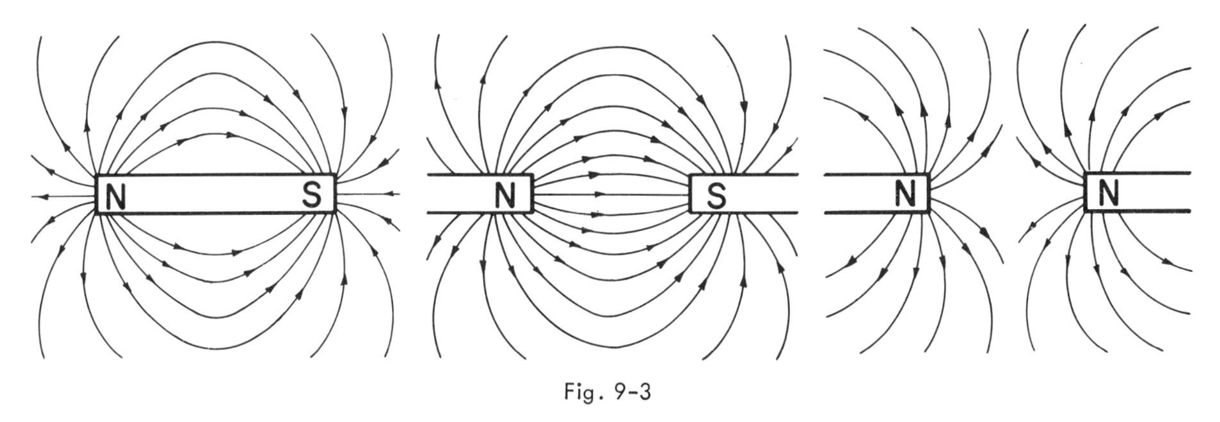

Fig. 9-3

Michael Faraday (English, 1840) suggested that the behavior of magnets could be explained by the interaction of these lines of force: The lines act like stretched rubber bands in attempting to contract lengthwise, thus pulling N and S together, and also push against each other sidewise as they try to contract. They are apparently closed curves that could be continued through the inside of the magnet.

Lines of force are defined as lines showing the direction that the North pole of a compass is forced to point, at any particular spot. The density, or concentration, of the lines represents the amount of force. The lines cannot cross, by definition, because the compass does not point two ways at once.

Like electric lines of force, these magnetic imaginary lines represent a very real force.

MAGNETIC MATERIALS AND THE MAGNETIZING PROCESS

Iron, nickel, and some oxides and alloys are called magnetic materials because they can be magnetized. A magnet is a piece of magnetic material that has magnetic poles developed on it. The magnetizing, or pole-forming, process is accomplished either by putting the material inside a coil of wire that has current in it, or by placing the material near another magnet.

Long ago, it was found that heating or hammering a magnet would cause it to lose some of its strength. Both heating and hammering tend to shake and stir up the atoms of the metal. Furthermore, it was found that if an ordinary steel bar magnet (or any magnet) with only two poles were cut into fragments, each fragment had two poles, N and S. Theoretically, this cutting process could go on until we came to the smallest possible fragment of iron, which is an atom. Thus arose the idea that all atoms of magnetic materials are themselves permanent magnets.

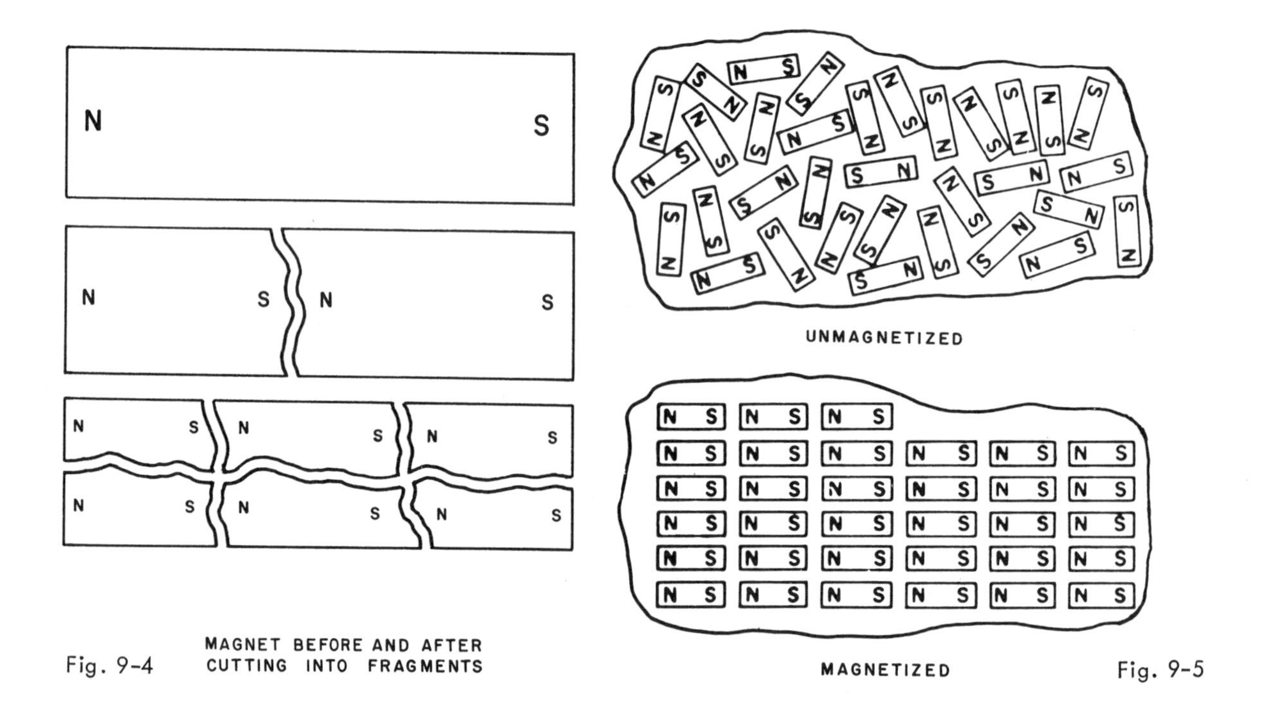

Fig. 9-4 MAGNET BEFORE AND AFTER CUTTING INTO FRAGMENTS

Fig. 9-5

In an unmagnetized piece of iron, the atoms of iron are arranged in a haphazard fashion, with the atomic N- and S-poles pointing every-which-way. The magnetizing process rotates these atoms so that the N-pole sides of atoms are facing in the same direction.

When a magnet is cut, without disturbing the atom arrangement, the atomic S-poles are exposed on one side of the break, and a group of N-poles on the other. Before the cutting, these poles exerted their attraction force on each other, so that there was no force reaching out into space around them.

Recently the above ideas have been changed slightly by the discovery of a little order in the magnetic disorder of an unmagnetized piece of iron. Within a crystal grain of iron, a few thousand atoms form a group called a magnetic "domain." Within one domain, the atoms are lined up with N-poles all facing in one direction. This group of atoms acts like a little permanent magnet.

MAGNETIC SATURATION

The strength of a given permanent magnet is limited. When all of the atoms are perfectly in order, all facing in the same direction, the magnet is at its maximum strength, called "saturation." The explanation uncovers a new question: Why are atoms of iron, magnets?

The answer to this question has been arrived at by a mass of complex experimental and theoretical investigations of electrons in atoms. All electrons themselves are apparently in a perpetual dizzy spin on their own little axes. This spin is the reason given for the fact that each electron is a tiny permanent magnet. In most atoms, electrons pair up, spinning in opposite directions, that is, their N- and S-poles are as close together as possible, and their magnetic effects cancel out, so far as having any distant effect is concerned. (Compare two permanent bar magnets, placed together with N against S.)

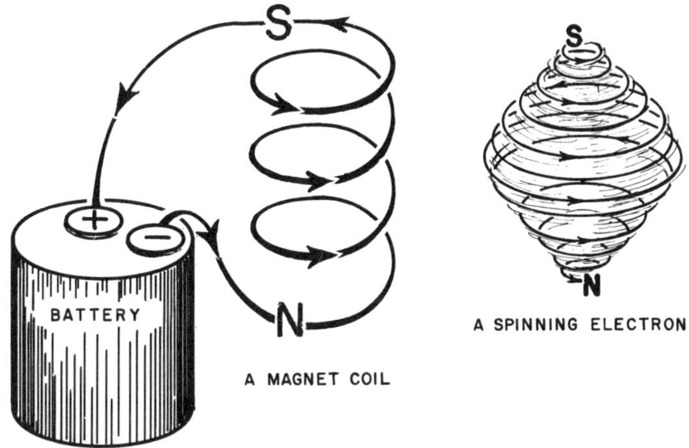

Fig. 9-6 Fig. 9-7

An atom of iron contains 26 electrons. Of the 26, 22 are paired up, spinning in opposite directions, canceling each other's outside magnetic effect. In the next-to-the-outermost ring of electrons, four are uncanceled, all four spinning in the same direction and being responsible for the magnetic character of the atoms of iron.

There is still a lot more to find out about electrons in atoms. Electron spin-directions in an atom are affected by temperature and by the presence of other atoms. At 1420° F., iron loses its magnetism, due to an electron-spin rearrangement. Strongly magnetic alloys and compounds have been made from elements that in the uncombined form are either weakly magnetic or not magnetic at all.

TYPES OF MAGNETIC MATERIALS

For a rough classification, magnets may be divided into two groups: permanent or temporary. A permanent magnet is intended to keep its atomic arrangement steady after the magnetizing force is removed. Permanent magnets are used in telephone receivers, door latches, small D.C. motors, electrical measuring instruments, magnetos, speedometers, and a great variety of gadgets. For years, high-carbon tool steel, and a few alloy steels (cobalt, molybdenum, chrome-tungsten) were the only useful permanent magnet materials. Later, various alloys were developed, two of which deserve mention: Heusler's alloy, little-used, is of interest for its composition of manganese, copper, and aluminum, metals that alone are not magnetic. Alnico is a widely used permanent magnet alloy (aluminum, nickel, cobalt, iron) of high magnetic strength.

Recent developments include manganese bismuthide (MnBi), a permanent magnet material of excellent prospects; a ceramic, barium ferrite, ($BaO \cdot 6Fe_2O_3$); and "elongated single domain" iron-cobalt mixes, in which specially-shaped particles of metal are compressed to form the alloy by the powder-metallurgy process. A 77% platinum, 23% cobalt alloy is used as the permanent magnet in the driving motor of Hamilton's 1957 electric wrist watch.

Temporary-magnet materials, which are easily and strongly magnetized but lose most of their strength when the magnetizing force is removed, are of more importance than permanent-magnet materials, both in total amount in use and in variety of applications. The first-used material for temporary magnets was plain iron, as pure as could be obtained, softened by annealing (slow cooling). A soft metal is one in which atoms slide around readily, permitting atoms to be magnetically disarranged easily. The most-used material is silicon iron (2-4% Si), a soft alloy used in transformers, most motors and generators, relays and other magnetic equipment built in large quantities. The continuous attempt to produce better magnetic materials has followed these patterns:

(1) Improvement of existing materials, by specialized heat treatment, mechanical treatment, and investigation of effects of impurities.

(2) Development of new alloys:

Permalloy (78% nickel, 21% iron)

4-79 Permalloy (4% molybdenum, 79% nickel, 21% iron)

Mumetal (75% nickel, 2% chromium, 5% copper, 18% iron)

Supermalloy (79% nickel, 5% molybdenum, 15% iron)

1040 Alloy (72% nickel, 14% copper, 3% molybdenum, 11% iron)

These have all been in use 15 years or more. They have properties superior to iron or silicon-iron. These properties, called permeability, residual magnetism, and coercive force, are described later in this Unit.

(3) Powder metallurgy, the process of forming alloys by mixing powdered metals and subjecting them to high pressure, has been used to produce alloys useful for temporary as well as permanent magnets. Two of the dozens of recent mixes are:

Supermendur (2% vanadium, 49% iron, 49% cobalt) which has the lowest coercive force of the iron-cobalt alloys.

Sendust (85% iron, 9.5% silicon, 5.5% aluminum) developed by Japanese metallurgists.

(4) Ferrites are mixtures of iron oxide with other oxides, pressed and kiln-fired, first developed in Holland. Iron oxide mixed with oxides of manganese, cobalt, nickel, copper, or zinc produce temporary-magnet materials. Their combination of high permeability and high electrical resistance has its advantages in electronic equipment. Recently, synthetic garnet-like crystals have been made by melting iron oxide together with oxides of various rare metals: These garnets are expected to be valuable in microwave amplifiers.

These improvements in magnetic materials are one part of a research effort to find out more about the behavior of atoms and electrons in solids.

THE RELATION OF MAGNETIC FIELD TO CURRENT DIRECTION

A. FOR A SINGLE WIRE

Information similar to that shown in Fig. 9-1 can also be obtained with the help of iron filings, which make the circular pattern of the magnetic field evident.

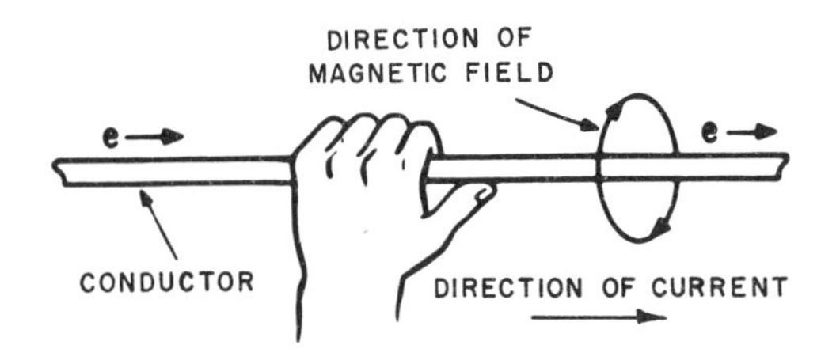

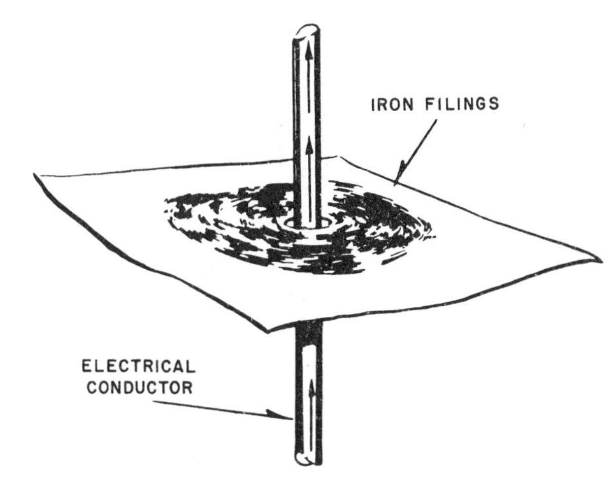

Fig. 9-8 Left-Hand Rule for Magnetic Field Around a Wire

If the direction of electron flow is known, the direction of the magnetic field may be found as shown in Fig. 9-8: Imagine grasping the wire with the left hand, with the thumb pointing in the direction of the electron current; then the fingers encircle the wire in the same direction as the magnetic lines of force. (Direction of the field means the direction in which the N-pole of the compass points.)

If the direction of the current is sought, the field direction may be found with a compass. Then, grasping the wire so that the fingers point around the wire in the same direction that the N-pole of the compass takes, the thumb gives the direction of the electron flow.

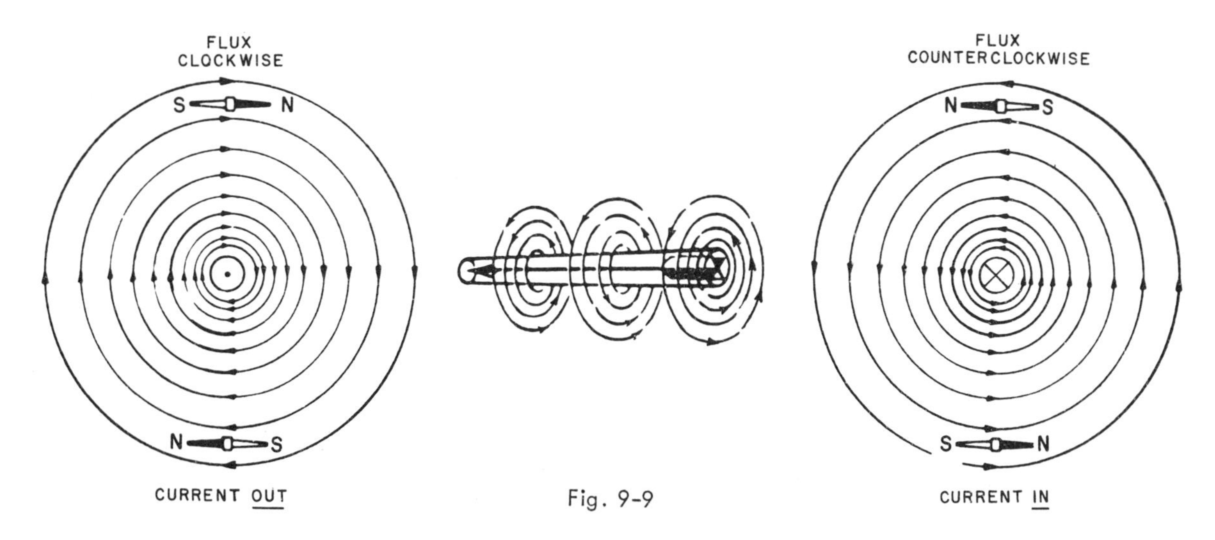

Fig. 9-9

The pattern of the magnetic field may also be shown by the diagram above. The dot in the center of the left-hand wire indicates the point of the current-direction arrow coming toward the observer; the X at the right represents the tail of the current arrow pointing away from the observer.

B. FOR A COIL

When wire is wound into a coil, as in Fig. 9-10, each turn of wire is surrounded by its own circular magnetic field. These little whirls of force combine to make the one large field shown surrounding the entire coil.

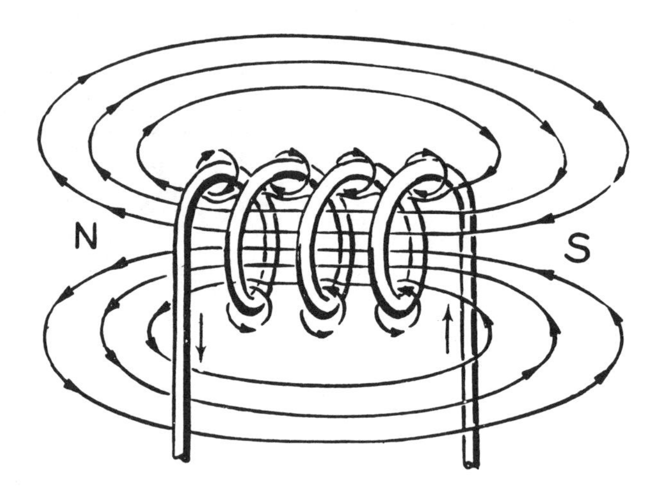

Fig. 9-10 Magnetic Polarity of a Coil

A magnetic coil of this shape is termed a solenoid. Fig. 9-11 shows a way of remembering the relation between current direction and field direction for a coil.

The ends of the coil are, in effect, magnetic poles, whether there is any iron core in the coil or not.

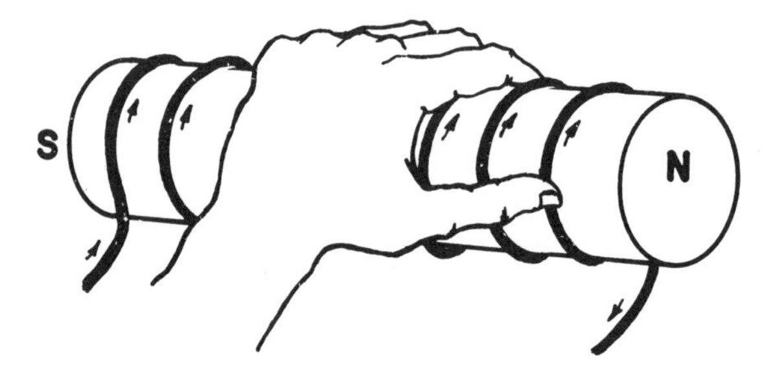

Fig. 9-11 Left-hand Rule For a Coil

If the coil is grasped with the left hand so that the fingers point in the same direction as the electron current in the wires, the thumb lies at the North end of the coil.

If the current direction is unknown, but the field of the coil is known or can be found with a compass, then the current direction can be found by use of this rule.

FORCES BETWEEN PARALLEL CURRENTS

Early in this Unit, it was pointed out that all magnetism is an effect of electron motion, and the basic fact is that currents in the same direction attract each other; currents traveling in opposite directions repel each other.

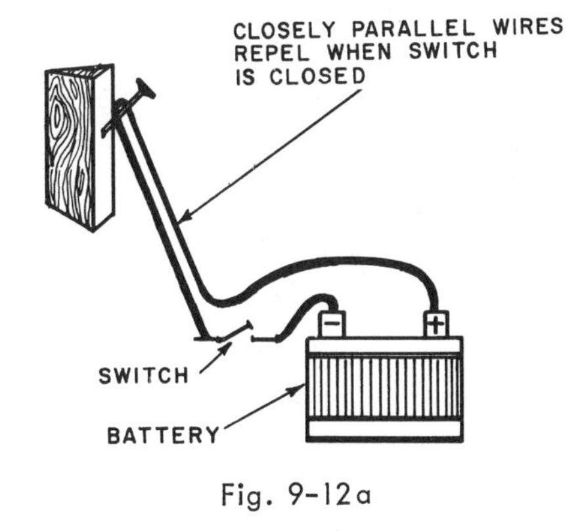

Fig. 9-12a

This fact is nothing new. Andre Ampere reported in 1822: "I observed that when I passed a current of electricity in both of these wires at once they attracted each other when the two currents were in the same direction and repelled each other when they were in opposite directions. . . . . . . the attractions and repulsions . . . are facts given by an experiment which is easy to repeat . . . We now turn to the examination of this action and of the action of two magnets on each other and we shall see that they both come under the law of the mutual action of two electric currents . . ." Ampere's idea that there are currents inside of a permanent magnet had to wait more than 100 years to be finally justified by the discovery that atoms contain spinning electrons.

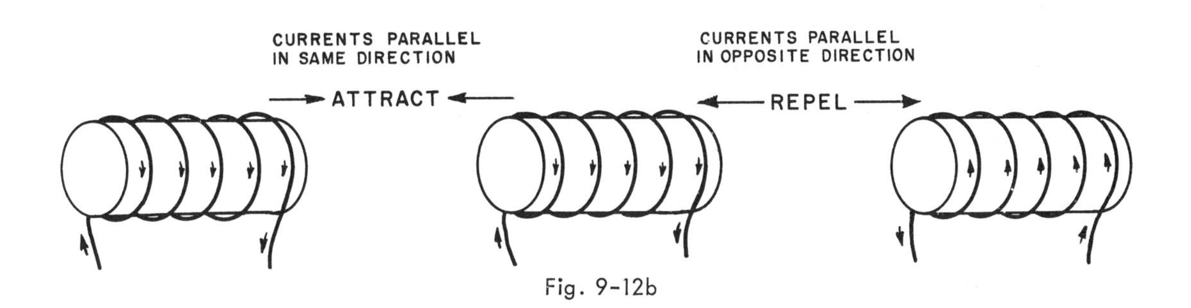

Fig. 9-12b

If the attraction and repulsion shown in Fig. 9-12 (B) is not immediately reasonable, one might apply the hand-rule for magnet poles, and locate N and S on each coil.

THE MAGNETIC CORE IN THE COIL

The "magnetizing ability" of a coil may be described and measured conveniently in either of two ways:

(1) A system of formulas has been set up so that a certain magnetizing ability, or magnetic strength, can be represented by a certain number of lines of force in each square inch of sectional area of the coil. The number of lines of force per square inch is called the "flux density." "Flux" means the total number of lines.

(2) The magnetizing ability can also be represented by the "ampere-turns" of the coil. Ampere-turns is the result of multiplying the number of turns of wire by the current (amps) in the coil. Two amps in 20 turns has the same magnetic effect as 4 amps in ten turns, or 1/2 amp in 80 turns. 2 amps in a 100-turn coil has five times as much magnetizing force as 2 amps in a 20-turn coil.

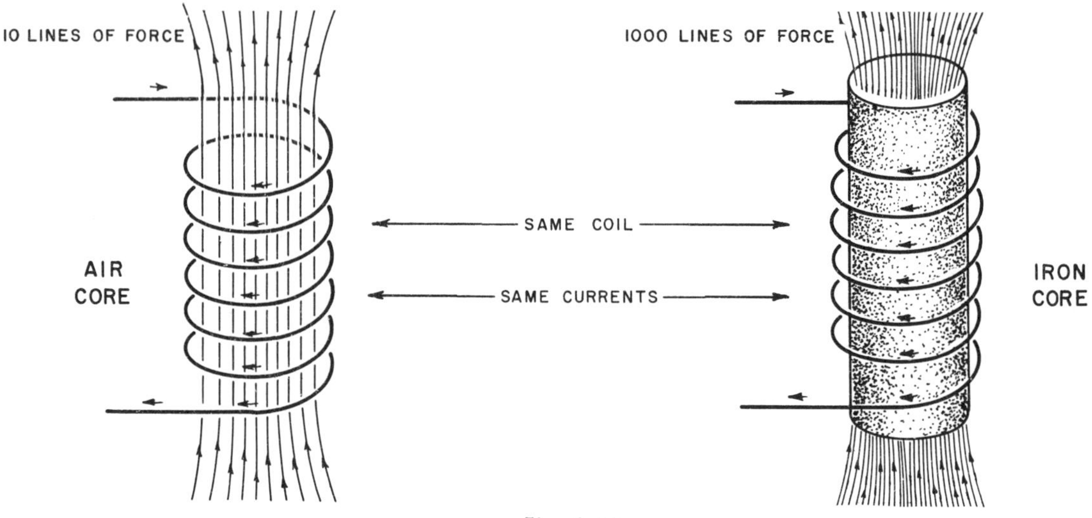

Fig. 9-13

The presence of nonmagnetic materials in the D.C. magnet coil has no appreciable effect on the coil magnetism. Insertion of any magnetic material results in a great increase in the total number of lines of force. Assume we have a long coil of wire (Fig. 9-13) with enough current in it to produce a magnetic field whose strength we shall indicate by drawing 10 lines of force. When we insert a bar of magnetic material into the coil, we may find that, due to the magnetization of the material, that there are now 1000 lines of force instead of 10. Inserting the bar of material has increased the magnetic field 100 times.

The ability of a magnetic material to increase field strength in this way is called permeability. Permeability is a measure of the material's willingness to become magnetized. More accurately, it is the number of times that the flux density is increased by adding the material. In the example above, the permeability of the iron core is 100.

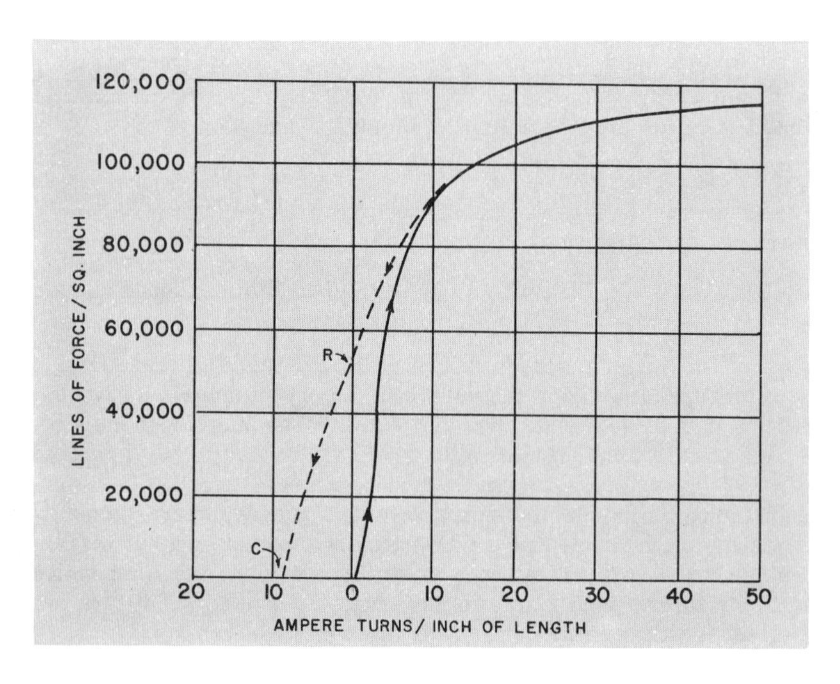

Fig. 9-14

A manufacturer of magnetic devices needs to know also just how the magnetic flux density builds up when the current in the coil increases. This is best shown by a graph, such as Fig. 9-14. The makers of magnetic alloys can provide such charts for their materials. The expression "ampere-turns per inch of length" on the graph means the amp-turns of the coil divided by the total inches length of the path of the lines of force.

Two other properties of special interest can also be indicated on the graph, (see Fig. 9-14). The dotted line shows the magnetic behavior of the material as the current in the magnetizing coil is reduced. The height of the point R above the zero level represents Residual Magnetism, which is the amount of magnetism remaining in the core after the magnetizing force (current in coil) is removed.

The residual magnetism should be high in permanent magnets — 50,000 or more. In good temporary-magnet materials, the residual magnetism is very low.

The distance on the ampere-turns scale from zero to the point C is a measure of Coercive Force. The measurement to the left on the scale indicates current in the reverse direction that has to be put through the coil in order to remove the residual magnetism, bringing the magnetization of the core down to zero level. If the coercive force is a large amount, that means that the magnet is difficult to de-magnetize, which is a desirable property for permanent magnets. The best temporary-magnet materials have a coercive force that is very close to zero.

ENERGY IN THE MAGNETIC FIELD

When a battery circuit is closed and a current starts, electrons are set in motion by potential energy stored in the battery. This potential energy becomes a sort of kinetic energy, but the moving electrons, unlike flying baseballs, have neither enough weight or speed to account for the energy that the current possesses. This energy of the current lies in the magnetic field around it. The calculation of this energy is of value in the design of induction coils and magnetos, in which the energy of a magnetic field is delivered usefully to a circuit when a current is suddenly stopped, (Unit 19).

Around a coil carrying a constant D.C., the magnetic field does not have to be continually supplied with more energy to maintain itself. Once the current is established, and the field set up, all of the energy of the current is used to produce heat, overcoming the resistance of the coil of wire (I^2R).

INTERACTION OF MAGNETIC AND ELECTRIC FIELDS

The connection of electric and magnetic forces is sometimes summarized this way: "A magnetic field is produced by a moving electric field; and an electric field is produced by a moving magnetic field." In other words, a magnetic field is produced by electric charges in motion; and the motion of the magnets can produce electric force. The last part of this statement, the production of an electron-moving-force from the motion of magnets, is the subject for discussion later, in connection with generators.

DERIVATION OF MAGNETIC QUANTITIES

Electrical and magnetic quantities are ordinarily measured in metric-system units. In the metric system, force can be measured in "dynes." One dyne is a rather small force; one ounce is equal to about 27,800 dynes.

Imagine two long thin magnets with their N poles one centimeter (cm.) apart, and the magnets so weak that the repelling force between them is only one dyne.

N N
← 1 cm →

These poles illustrate "unit magnetic poles", meaning their strength is to be called, numerically, 1. A unit magnetic pole is therefore defined as one that repels a similar unit pole, one cm. away, with a force of one dyne. (It would also attract an opposite unit pole, one cm. away, with a force of one dyne.)

Both theory and experiments show that the force (attraction or repulsion) between two magnet poles in air depends on distance and pole strengths in this manner:

$$\text{Dynes force} = \frac{M_1 \times M_2}{D^2}$$

M_1 is the strength of one magnet pole, measured in "unit magnetic poles"; M_2 is the strength of the other magnet pole. D is the distance between the poles, in centimeters.

Example: To find the attraction force between an N-pole of strength 10 units and an S-pole of strength 20 units, placed 3 cm. apart:

10, N 3 cm 20, S

$$\text{Force} = \frac{10 \times 20}{3^2} = \frac{200}{9} = 22.2 \text{ dynes, Ans.}$$

MAGNETIC FIELD STRENGTH

The region around a magnet is called its "field." The number of dynes of force exerted on one unit magnetic pole placed in the field is called "magnetic field strength."

Example: How strong is the magnetic field at a point 5 cm. away from a magnetic pole whose pole-strength is 5000 units?

5000 5 cm 1

Imagine a pole of strength one unit, placed 5 cm. away from the 5000-unit pole. The force on the one-unit pole will be

$$\frac{5000 \times 1}{5^2} = \frac{5000}{25} = 200 \text{ dynes per unit pole, Ans.}$$

Another example: How much is the magnetic field strength at a point halfway between these two poles?

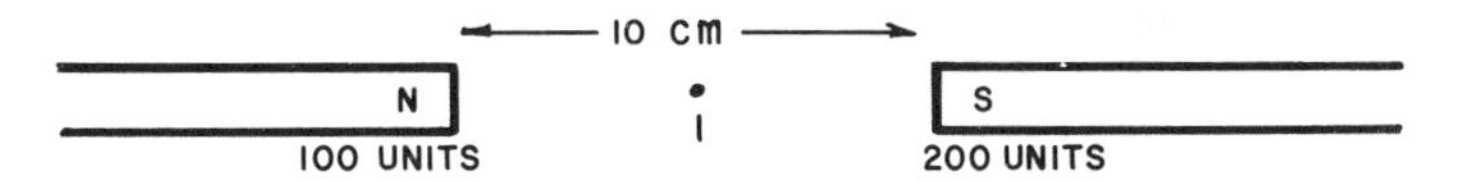

Put a unit N-pole at the halfway point; it will be affected both by the N-pole and the S-pole. It has a force on it, due to the large N-pole, of

$\frac{100 \times 1}{5^2}$ = 4 dynes; and also a force due to the S-pole, $\frac{200 \times 1}{5^2}$ = 8 dynes.

These two forces add together, because the test unit N-pole is pushed to the right by the N-pole and also pulled to the right by the S-pole, so the total force is 12 dynes on the unit pole.

Magnetic field strength is pictured graphically by the concentration of magnetic lines. To represent a force of 12 dynes per unit pole, we draw, or think of, 12 lines of force per square centimeter in the space where the field strength is 12.

The sketch below illustrates this idea: Think of a one-centimeter square piece of paper held crosswise to the magnetic lines, halfway between the poles.

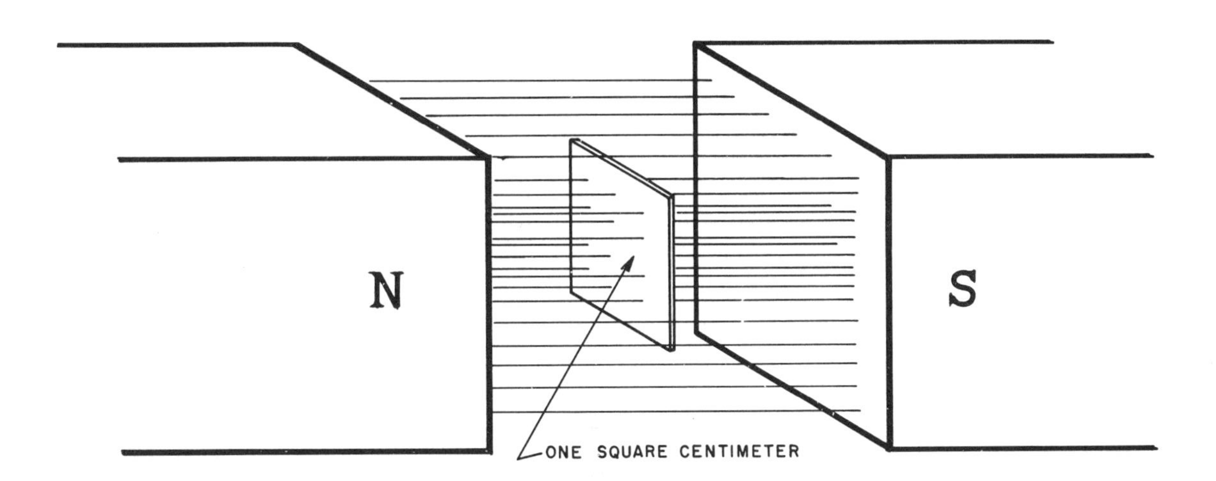

We draw 12 lines passing through this square to represent the field strength of 12 dynes per unit pole. In metric system magnetic discussion, the term "gauss" is equivalent to "lines per sq. cm." and the term "oersted" is used to mean "dynes per unit pole."

Magnetic field strength may also be pictured as the number of lines per square inch. A square inch is bigger than a sq. cm. (1 sq. in. = 6.45 sq. cm.) so in a region where the density of lines is 12 per sq. cm., there would be 12 × 6.45 or about 77 lines per square inch. These quantities, lines per sq. cm. or lines per square inch, are also called "flux density." Flux means the total number of lines of force. "A region of high flux density" is just another way of saying "a region of high magnetic field strength."

MAGNETIC FIELDS DUE TO CURRENTS

By using mathematical methods described in more advanced electrical books, it can be proven that the magnetic field strength, in dynes/unit pole, at the center of a circular turn of wire is

$$\frac{2 \pi I}{10 R}$$

in which I means the current (amperes) in the wire, and R is the radius of the circular turn, in centimeters.

If there are several turns of wire, wound so closely together that they act like one wire, the strength of the field is multiplied: it becomes

$$\frac{2 \pi I N}{10 R},$$

in which N is the number of turns of wire. $I \times N$, which is amperes $\times$ turns, can be called ampere-turns.

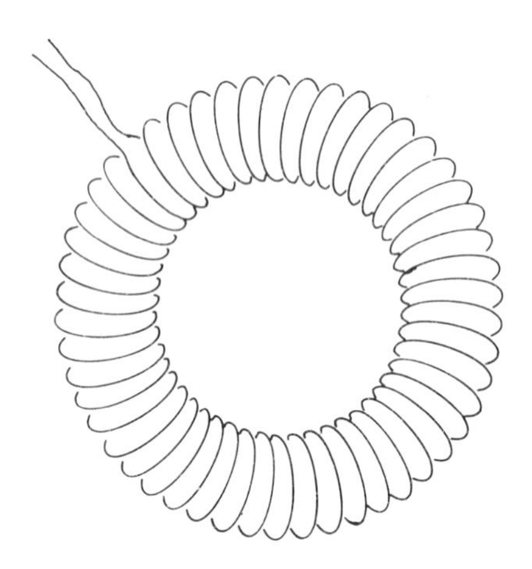

To find the field strength, or flux density, at a point inside a long coil of many turns, another formula was developed, which is more accurate for a doughnut-shaped coil, but is also usable for a long straight coil. This formula summarizes the total effect of all of the separate turns of the coil:

$$\text{Field strength} = \frac{4 \pi I N}{10 L}$$

$I \times N$ is ampere-turns, and L is the cm. length of the magnetic lines inside the coil. If L is measured in inches, the formula becomes

$$\frac{4 \pi I N}{3.94 L} \quad \text{(because 10 cm. = 3.94 inches)}$$

And since $\frac{4\pi}{3.94} = 3.19$, we can simplify this flux density formula to: $\frac{3.19 I N}{L}$.

To put the formula in words, the flux density inside an air-core coil is 3.19 times the ampere turns divided by the inches length, or 3.19 times the ampere turns per inch.

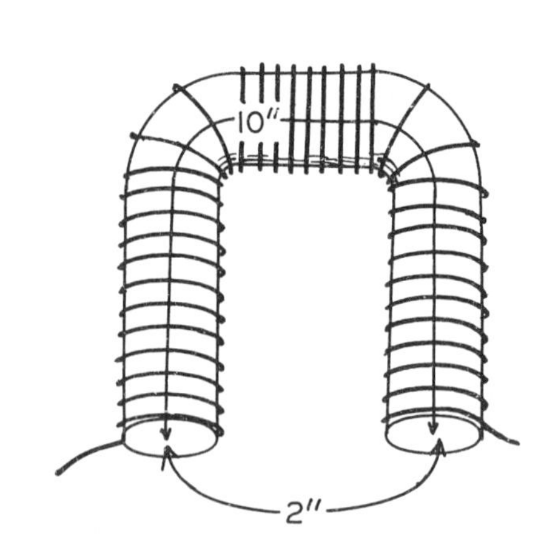

It must be noted that "per inch" refers to the inches length of the lines of force. For example, if the coil at the right is 10 inches long, and the lines of force through the coil also pass through 2 inches of space which is not surrounded by wire, the "magnetic path" is 12 inches long. If this coil has 600 ampere-turns, then the ampere turns per inch is $600 \div 12 = 50$ ampere-turns per inch.

This quantity, ampere-turns per inch, is sometimes given the elegant title "Magnetomotive Force", or "Magnetic Gradient."

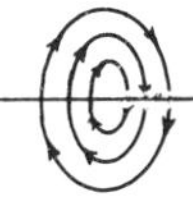 POINTS TO REMEMBER 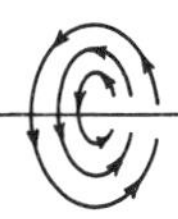

- All magnetism is due to electron motion — either the movement of electrons around and around as they pass through a coil, or the spinning-like-a-top motion of electrons in atoms.
- Like poles repel, unlike poles attract.
- The strength of a magnetic field is represented by the density of lines of force. Direction of the field means the direction in which the N-pole of a compass points.
- Most materials are nonmagnetic. The internal electron spins in atoms of iron, nickel, and some alloys and oxides make them magnetic.
- Atoms of iron are little permanent magnets. The magnetizing of a piece of iron is a matter of arranging these atoms so that like poles face in the same direction.
- A left-hand rule for a single wire: Thumb in direction of electron flow, fingers in direction of field.
- A left-hand rule for a coil: Thumb at N-pole, fingers in direction of electron current.
- Parallel currents in the same direction attract; in the opposite direction, repel.
- Magnetic strength of a coil can be measured in ampere-turns (amps × turns).
- Permeability is the ability of a material to become magnetized. Residual magnetism is flux density that it retains after the magnetizing force is removed. Coercive force is oppositely-directed magnetizing force applied to make the material lose its magnetism.
- A magnetic field contains useful energy.
- Moving electrons exert force on magnets; moving magnets exert force on electrons.

REVIEW QUESTIONS

1. A negative-charged rod is first brought near the North pole of a magnetized strip of steel suspended on a string, then it is brought near the South pole of the magnetized strip. What happens at each trial — attraction, repulsion, or nothing? Why?

2. A permanent magnet hung on a post is given the job of holding up ten pounds of iron for six months. Does this weaken the magnet?

3. A certain air-core coil has a flux density of 60 lines per square inch. The insertion of an iron core raises the flux density to 60,000 lines per square inch. Calculate the permeability of the iron.

4. What is saturation of a magnet?

5. What made the old-timers think that atoms of iron are magnets all the time?

6. Define coercive force, residual magnetism, and permeability.

7. Do the nearby turns of wire on a current-carrying coil attract, repel, or pay no attention to each other?

8. All of these questions are unfair in one way or another. Watch out.
   a. Which is the N-pole of a magnet coil — the end where the current enters or the end where it leaves?
   b. Why do N and S poles attract each other?
   c. Why do parallel currents in the same direction attract?
   d. Might a small sliver of iron not be attracted by a magnet if it happened to lie between lines of force?
   e. A popular writer a few years ago published the explanation that flying saucers obtain their terrific energy by using the energy obtained when lines of force cross each other. Reasonable?

9. Could a magnet have three poles?

Unit 10 MAGNETIC DEVICES

A listing of all of the applications of magnetism would be long enough to become tiresome. Measuring instruments, motors, and generators are important enough to merit special discussion - in Units 12, 17, 18, 20, 21, 22. The few devices described in this section are chosen not only for their own importance, but also to illustrate principles that are used in many devices.

PERMANENT MAGNETS

Commonly used permanent magnets are often of the horseshoe shape, Fig. 10-1. Bringing poles close together in this manner creates a much stronger magnetic field than would be obtained from the same amount of steel in a straight bar.

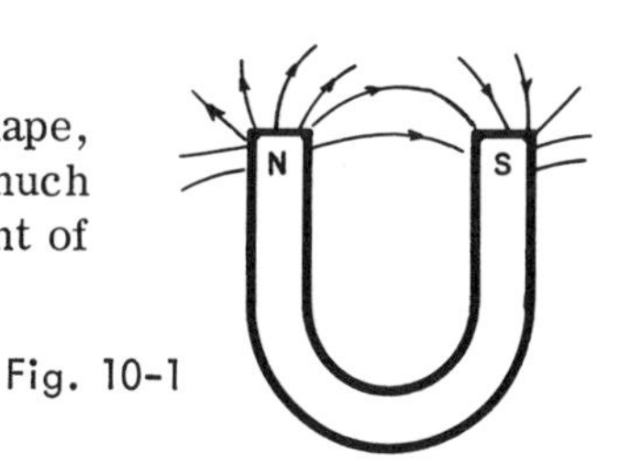

Fig. 10-1

LIKE POLES OF ATOMS AT THE POLE-FACE OF A MAGNET REPEL EACH OTHER

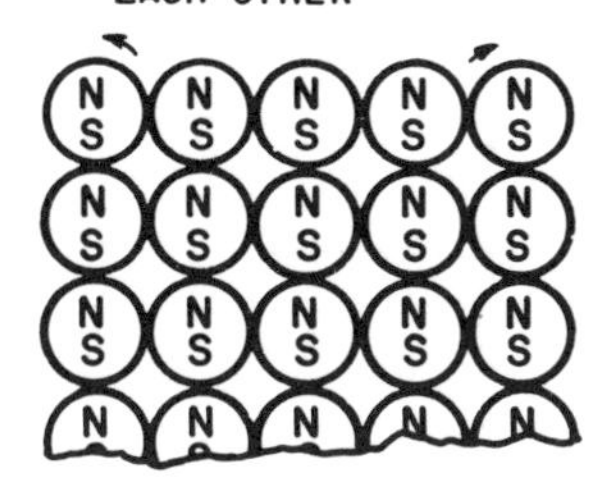

AND SOON SCATTER THEMSELVES INTO THIS SORT OF AN ARRANGEMENT:

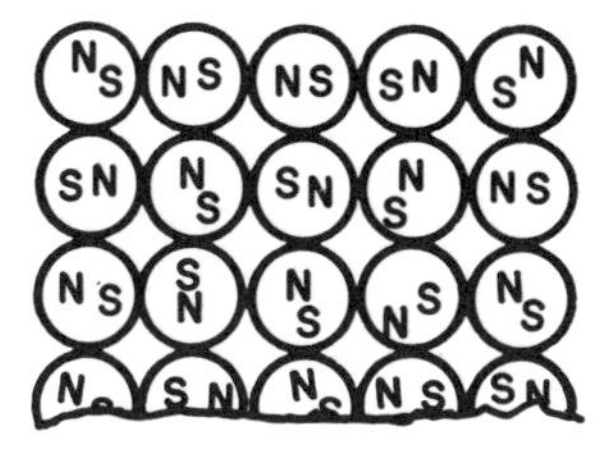

A SOFT IRON "KEEPER" BECOMES MAGNETIZED AND ITS POLES HOLD THE ATOMS OF THE PERMANENT MAGNET IN ALIGNMENT.

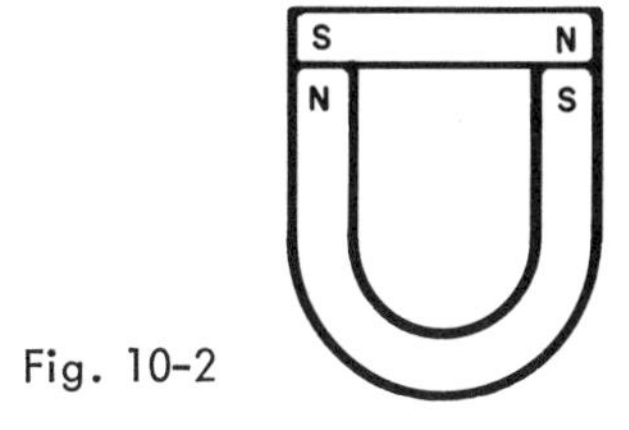

Fig. 10-2

If a permanent magnet is to keep its strength for a long period of time:

1. It should be made of a properly hardened alloy of high coercive force. (Alnico is preferable to steel.)

2. Excessive heat, mechanical shock, and nearness to the magnetic field of A.C. machinery should be avoided.

3. The presence of other iron on or between the magnet poles is desirable, in that it tends to prevent self-demagnetizing, Fig. 10-2.

Fig. 10-3

A small permanent magnet may be remagnetized by placing its poles against the poles of an electromagnet, Fig. 10-3, or against a strong large permanent magnet. While in this position, a strong applied field will remagnetize the permanent magnet quickly. If the poles of the permanent magnet are to be kept the same as originally, the N-pole of one magnet must be placed in contact with the S-pole of the other.

Lifting Magnets

Lifting magnets were one of the first applications of magnetic force developed by electric current. As now constructed, the coil is nearly surrounded by iron, with one pole formed on the core inside of the coil, the other on the shell that surrounds the coil. This "circular horseshoe" is a way of producing a concentrated strong magnetic field.

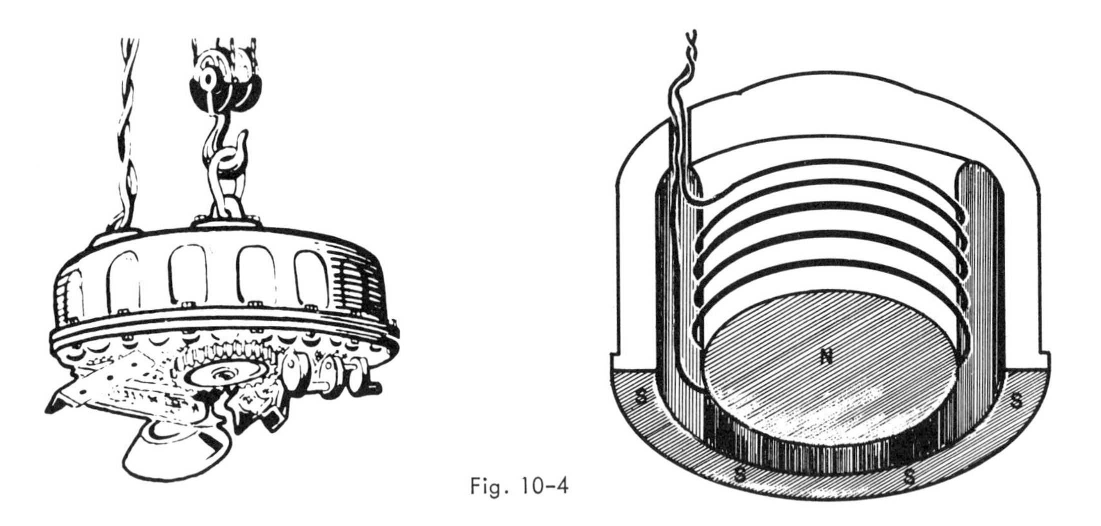

Fig. 10-4

Magnetic Separators

Hundreds of industries use various magnetic separation devices, to sort magnetic ore from nonmagnetic rock, scrap iron from coal, scrap iron from other metals, iron particles from sand and ceramic clays, and unpalatable nails and baling wire from cattle feed, to name a few examples. In the arrangement shown, magnetic materials are attracted to the pulley and carried around until they fall into hopper No. 2 as the belt finally separates them from the pulley.

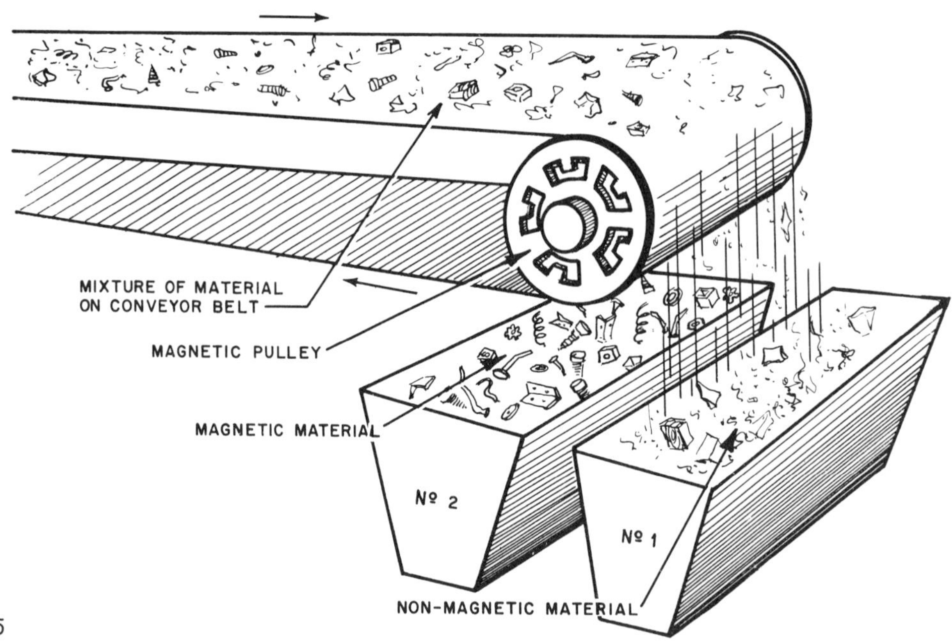

Fig. 10-5

Magnetic Control at a Distance

In 1826, young Joseph Henry was hired to teach physics and math at the Academy in Albany, New York. Interested in magnetism, he found out how to build stronger lifting magnets than had been made before. He then found by using a high-voltage battery to force a small current through poorly conducting wire then available, and by using a magnet with a large number of turns, that he could get a magnet to work at a long distance from the battery and switch. He published a full description of his magnetic signalling device in a little periodical, a copy of which came into the hands of one Samuel F. B. Morse, a portrait painter. Mr. Morse realized that a device of this sort was a good thing, and the use of it should not be limited to Joe Henry's telling his wife when to expect him for supper. So Morse secured a patent on the electromagnetic telegraph, got a subsidy from Congress, and started stringing wire from Washington to Baltimore.

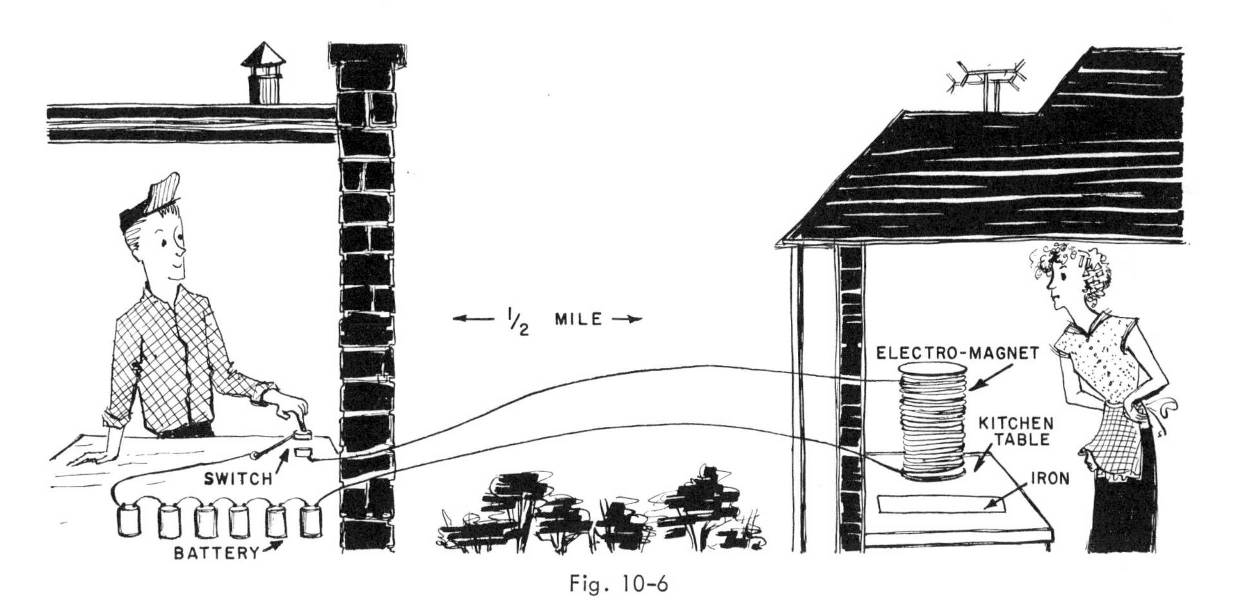

Fig. 10-6

The Electromagnet Pulls a Switch: The Relay

A relay is a switch which is closed and opened by the operation of an electromagnet. It was originally devised by Henry to solve a problem met in the early telegraph circuits. As first used, the "small current" at the left was the feeble current in a long telegraph line, too weak to operate a sounder or recording mechanism. This small current could cause the electromagnet, M, to tip the pivoted iron armature, A, over toward the magnet. C is a stationary contact. When A touches C, the circuit at the right is completed, and the voltage source can cause a large current in the nearby controlled device. As used in the first telegraph systems, the controlled device was the recording mechanism, which required a larger current to operate it than could be supplied from a far-distant battery.

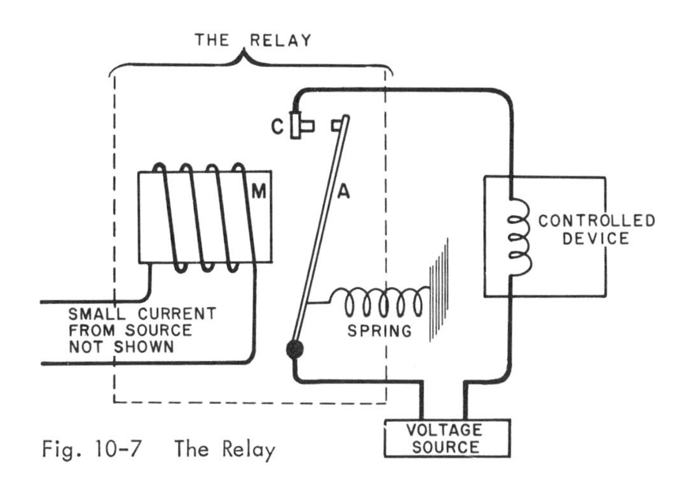

Fig. 10-7 The Relay

Relays are now used in hundreds of control devices. The "small current" is often the current in a vacuum-tube circuit, which is made to respond to some change in temperature, light, sound, or position of a machine part. The "voltage source" is the power line, and the "controlled device" may be a motor, a lighting circuit, or anything imaginable. Also, relays are used to control switches in remote locations, or locations that are inaccessible due to space, temperature, radiation or some high-voltage hazard.

Note from the circuit, Fig. 10-7, that the magnet current does not get into the controlled circuit. The magnet merely closes a switch in the controlled circuit. If the stationary contact C is placed to the right of A in the diagram, the magnet-pull will open the controlled circuit, rather than close it. Often, a relay may have multiple contacts on both sides of the movable armature so that several contacts are opened and several are closed by one movement of the iron armature.

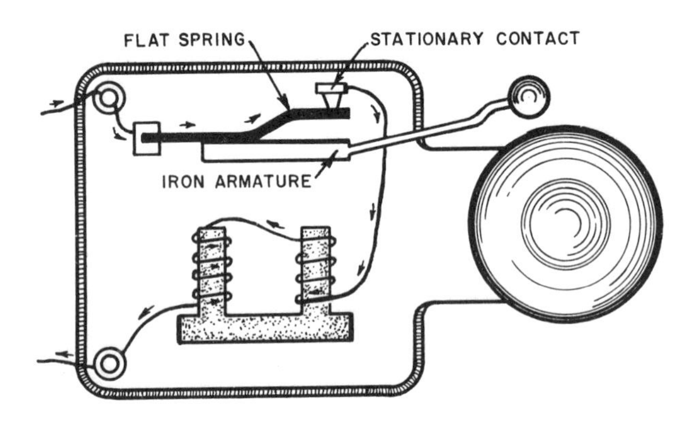

Fig. 10-8 The Electric Bell

Magnetic Vibrators – The Electric Bell or Buzzer

The flat spring and iron armature is a movable assembly, pivoted at the left end of the spring in Fig. 10-8, where the spring is held. When the bell is idle, the loose end of the spring touches the stationary contact. When an external switch (pushbutton) is closed connecting the bell to a battery, the current path is that shown in the diagram. When the iron horseshoe is magnetized, the armature is attracted, pulling the spring away from the stationary contact and breaking the circuit at this point. When the spring leaves the contact, current in the circuit stops so the magnet loses its magnetism, no longer holding the armature. With the magnet turned off, the elasticity of the spring brings armature and spring away from the magnet, the spring touches the contact again, and the whole process repeats. Removal of the gong converts the bell to a buzzer.

This arrangement is used to produce vibratory motion, or it may be used for the main purpose of turning the current on and off rapidly. There is a high-voltage-producing device called the induction coil (yes, Joseph Henry invented that, too) in which a direct current has to be started and stopped rapidly; this is accomplished by placing a buzzer in the circuit. The Model T Ford spark coil is an example of an induction coil with a buzzer.

The Solenoid-and-Plunger Magnet

This arrangement, no different in principle from the armature-type magnets shown previously, is used where a greater amount of distance of motion is desired. Magnetizing the core causes the plunger to be drawn into the coil. The magnet may be arranged so that the plunger falls out of the magnet due to its own weight, or it may be pulled out by a spring when the magnetic force is released. These solenoids are used for operating switches, opening or closing valves, operating magnetic brakes, operating circuit breakers, and so on.

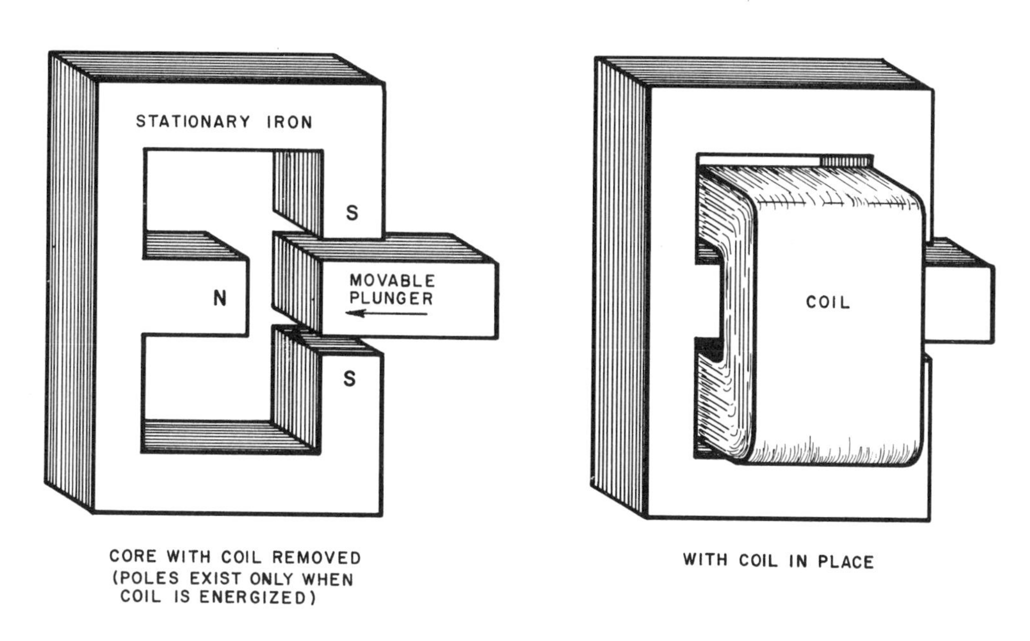

Fig. 10-9 Solenoid and Plunger

Magnetic Production of Sound

Mechanical vibration produces sound. Vibrations in the range from 20 to 18,000 vibrations per second can be heard by human ears. The higher the frequency of vibration, the higher the pitch. The greater the extent of the back-and-forth movement, the greater the loudness.

Fig. 10-10 represents a coil of wire wound on a paper sleeve and suspended so that it can move freely near the pole of a permanent magnet. If an alternating current is put through the coil, the coil is alternately attracted (A) and repelled (B), and vibrates at the same frequency as the frequency of the electron vibration of the alternating current.

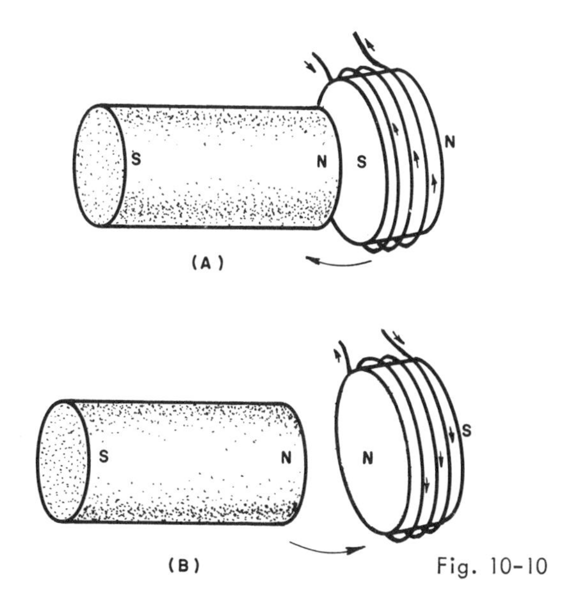

Fig. 10-10

Most radio loudspeakers are built similar to the one shown in Fig. 10-11. To obtain a uniform magnetic field in which the moving coil can vibrate, one pole is just inside the moving coil, and the other is brought around to surround the moving coil. The moving coil is attached to a paper-composition cone, vibration of which produces sound when alternating currents are fed into the movable "voice coil" from an amplifier.

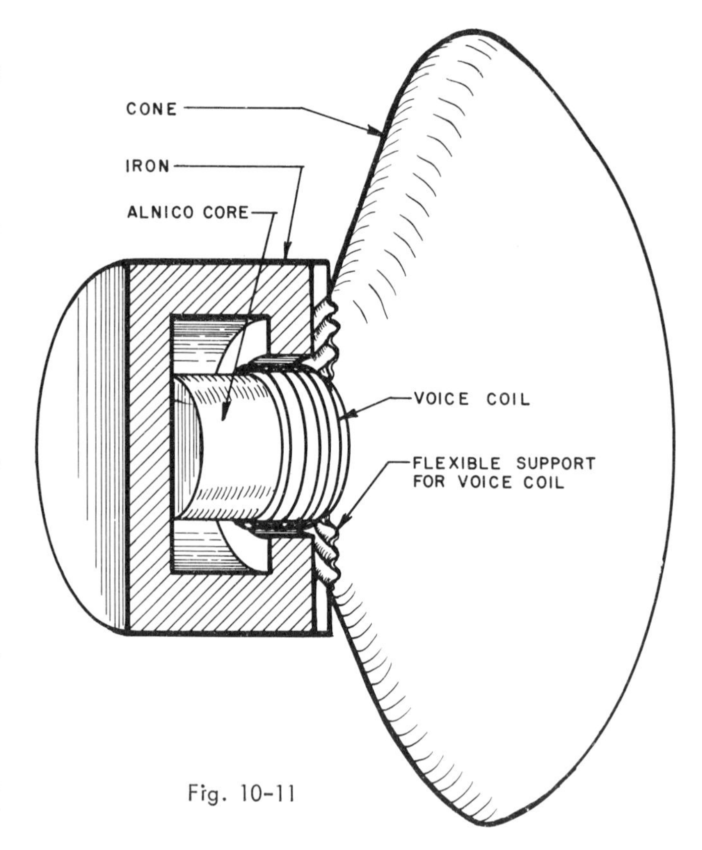

Fig. 10-11

Before Alnico was developed, most speakers used a D.C. electromagnet, instead of a permanent, to provide the field for the voice coil to work in.

The phone receiver shown in Fig. 10-12 uses a stationary coil of many turns of fine wire wrapped around the poles of a permanent horseshoe magnet. This receiver is intended to operate on a much smaller current than that which is needed to operate a loudspeaker; hence the large number of turns of wire. The alternating current in the coils alternately strengthens and weakens the pull of the magnet of a flexible iron disk (diaphragm) which is supported at its edges. This varying pull causes the disk to vibrate in accordance with the alternations of the incoming current.

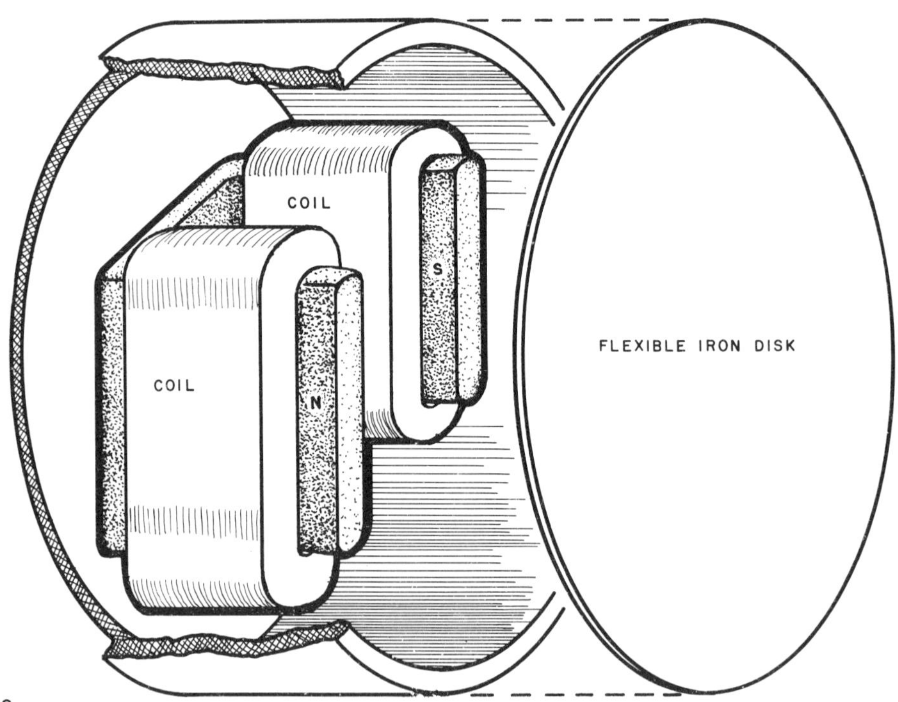

Fig. 10-12

Principles Common to All Magnets

A general law applies to electrical and mechanical processes, and to human endeavors, too: Accomplishment is directly proportional to effort, and inversely proportional to the hindrances. One example of this general statement is Ohm's Law, $I = \frac{E}{R}$, stating that the current produced is directly proportional to the Electromotive force and inversely proportional to the Resistance. In the attempt to produce magnetism, the accomplishment is the production of magnetic lines of force, or flux. The applied effort is the ampere-turns of the magnetizing coil, or, more accurately, the magnetomotive force is the ampere-turns per inch. The hindrances to magnetism are called reluctance. Air is a high-reluctance material; iron is a low-reluctance material. That is another way of saying that air is nonmagnetic and iron magnetizes easily. Reluctivity is the opposite of permeability.

The similarity of this relation, $\text{Flux} = \frac{\text{Magnetomotive force}}{\text{Reluctance}}$, to Ohm's Law, $\text{Current} = \frac{\text{Electric force}}{\text{Resistance}}$, leads to using the name "Magnetic circuit" for the path of the lines of force through a magnetic device, even though there is no motion along the lines of force. All magnetic devices have a magnetic circuit which can be traced by following the path of lines of force from any point, around through iron and air and back to the starting point.

Since it is easy to magnetize iron, but it is relatively difficult to produce lines of force through air, one aim in all magnetic devices is to make the path of the lines through air or non-magnetic solids as short as possible.

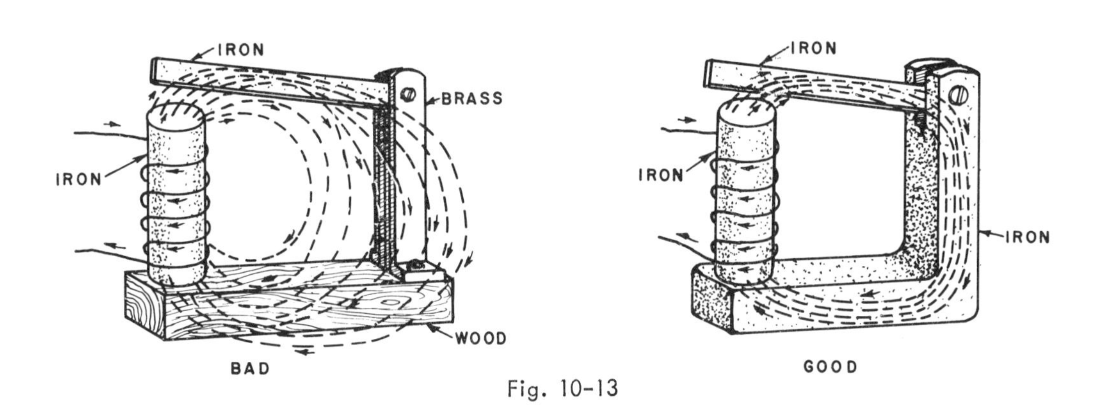

Fig. 10-13

The sketch above represents two arrangements in which a pivoted iron bar is to be attracted to an electromagnet. If the ampere-turns is the same in each coil, the pulling force in the first one will be only a small fraction of the pulling force in the second, because the reluctance is so large in the first magnetic circuit. Or, in order to achieve the same flux in each, a lot more ampere-turns would be required in the first coil.

In many D.C. electromagnets, the parts are assembled from solid bars or rods. In magnets of D.C. vibrators, motors and generators, and in A.C. equipment, the magnetic parts are an assembly of thin sheets of iron called laminations. In these last-named applications, magnetic fields are in motion; the lines of force are bouncing around as current is turned on or off, or reversed.

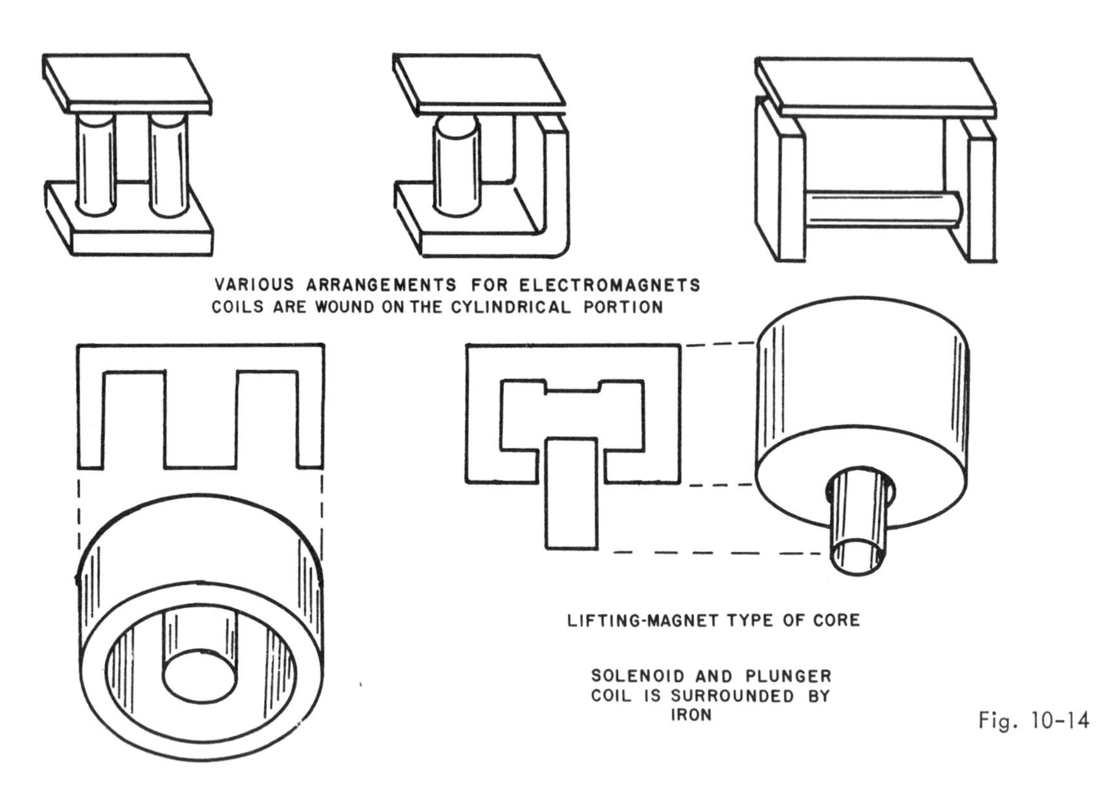

Fig. 10-14

Whenever lines of force sweep across a piece of any kind of metal, they tend to generate a current in the metal. In Fig. 10-15 (A), the dotted line is the direction of current that would be generated inside the iron core of the electromagnet any time that the current in the coil is changed in amount or direction. This current, called an "eddy current" is a useless nuisance, because it takes energy from the coil circuit and heats the iron core.

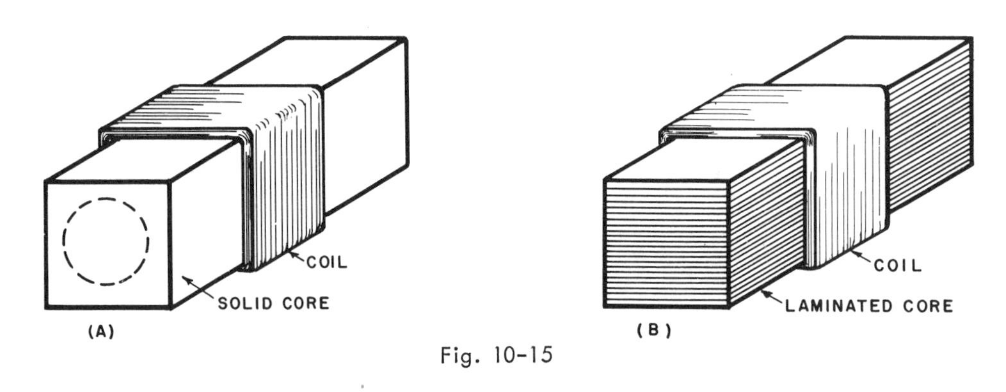

Fig. 10-15

In Fig. 10-15 (B) the core is a stack of laminations (thin sheets of iron). Not much current can circulate around in that pile of iron sheets because of poor electrical contact between the sheets. Lacquer and iron oxide on the sheets can make this contact still less.

By preventing the formation of an "eddy current", the loss of energy and production of heat is prevented. Iron containing a few percent of silicon has high permeability (that's good) and high electrical resistance - which is good, too. High electrical resistance in a core material hinders the setting-up of these unwanted eddy currents inside the core material.

Demagnetizing

The removal of magnetic poles on a piece of steel is accomplished by completely disarranging the atoms in the steel. The stator windings of a discarded 1/4-h.p. motor, connected to an A.C. power line through a current-limiting resistor, makes a convenient demagnetizer for small objects.

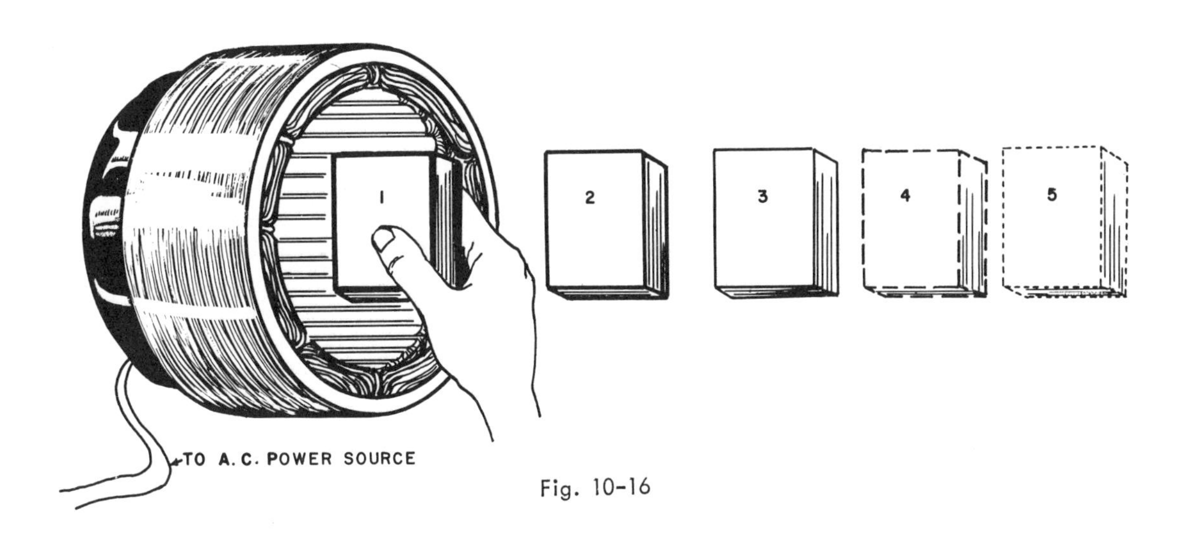

Fig. 10-16

A piece of steel in position (1), Fig. 10-16, will be magnetized, its upper end changing from N to S and back again 60 times per second on an ordinary A.C. line.

As it is removed from the coil, at position (2) it is still being magnetized and remagnetized 60 times/second, but not as strongly as at (1).

At (3) the same effect is still weaker.

At (4) the upper end is alternately very weak N or very weak S.

By the time it gets to (5) the directions that it has been receiving from the coil are so faint that the atoms are left in general disarrangement.

The steel hair spring of a watch, if magnetized by approach to magnets or D.C. machinery is put out of order because the coils of the spiral spring stick together when magnetized. A watch can be demagnetized in a few seconds by the above process. Most good watches use nonmagnetic springs, so there is no worry about magnetism.

Steel plates often need to be demagnetized before arc-welding is done on them. A magnetic field pushes the arc current sidewise, making it difficult to maintain the arc and do a smooth welding job. The steel plates are passed through large coils carrying alternating current to accomplish the demagnetizing.

Derivation of Magnet-Coil Formula

In Unit 7, we derived the formula $R = \frac{K\ L}{C.M.}$ in which R is the ohms resistance of a wire; L, the wire length in feet; C.M., circular mil area; and K, specific resistance which is 10.4 for cool copper, but about 12 for warm copper as in a magnetic winding.

In a magnet then, using 12 for K instead of 10.4, the formula becomes

$$R = \frac{12\ L}{C.M.}$$

Since L is length of wire in feet, 12 L is incidentally the same number as the length of the wire in inches. Instead of 12L, we can write L″, meaning length of the wire in inches. This is convenient since magnet coils are generally of such a size that measurement in inches is simpler than in fractions of a foot.

Using the expression, $R = \frac{L''}{C.M.}$ to replace the R in the Ohm's Law formula, E = IR, the Ohm's Law formula becomes

$$E = \frac{IL''}{C.M.}$$

Rearranging this algebraically, $E \times C.M. = IL''$

$$\text{and } C.M. = \frac{IL''}{E}$$

L″ is the length of the entire wire in inches which is equal to the length of the wire in one turn times the number of turns. Since turns close to the core are shorter than turns on the outside layers, we must specify that the average length of a turn (a turn in the middle layer) is to be taken as "length of wire in one turn."

$L'' = N \times L_t$ where N is number of turns and L_t is length of an average turn. Substituting $N \times L_t$ for L″ in the C.M. formula above,

$$C.M. = \frac{I \times N \times L_t}{E} \quad (I \times N \text{ is amps} \times \text{turns})$$

This last formula is the useful one for calculating wire size for a magnet winding. It may be put into words as,

$$\text{Circular mils} = \frac{\text{Ampere-turns} \times \text{average length of a turn}}{\text{Voltage used on the coil}}$$

The use of this formula is limited to copper wire, since K = 12 ohms per mil-foot for warm copper entered into the derivation.

POINTS TO REMEMBER

- Maintenance of strength of a permanent magnet depends on:
  (1) type of alloy
  (2) avoidance of excessive heat, shock, and A.C. magnetic fields
  (3) keeping iron between the poles.
- It is easy to remagnetize a permanent magnet.
- The magnetizing force of a coil is the number of ampere-turns per inch of the magnetic circuit. The ampere-turns may be produced by large current and few turns or small current and lots of turns.
- A relay is a switch operated by a magnet, so that one current can turn a larger current on or off.
- D.C. turns itself repeatedly on and off in a bell or vibrator.
- Sounds are produced in speakers and phones by using the changing magnetic field of an alternating current to produce vibration of mechanical parts.
- The complete path of lines of force through a magnet, air, and the iron that the magnet pulls on, is called the "magnetic circuit".
- A material's unwillingness to be magnetized is called "reluctance".
- $$\text{Total number of lines of force} = \frac{\text{Magnetizing force in amp-turns/inch}}{\text{reluctance of the magnetic circuit}}$$
- The use of laminated cores prevents energy loss in eddy currents.
- Silicon steel is preferable to ordinary steel, due to improved permeability and less eddy-current energy loss.

REVIEW QUESTIONS

1. If alternating current is bad for a permanent magnet, why aren't the magnets in phones and speakers demagnetized by the A.C. field?

2. In diagrams, arrows are often drawn from the N-pole to the S-pole of a magnet. What travels out of the north pole and into the south?

3. What is a solenoid?

4. What are eddy currents?

5. A piece of steel is placed in a coil such as Fig. 10-16, the current (A.C.) turned on for a while, and then the switch is opened. Would that demagnetize the steel?

6. What is a magnetic circuit?

7. What is meant by "reluctance"?

8. What is meant by "magnetizing force"?

9. A certain coil has 3 amps in 160 turns of wire. The lines of force have a path 8 inches long, 6 inches of which is iron and 2 inches is air. How much is the magnetomotive force (magnetizing force)?

10. In the equipment of Question 9, a 1-inch block of iron is placed so that the magnetic circuit now consists of 7 inches of iron and 1 inch of air. Is there any change in magnetizing force? Any change in flux?

Unit 11 CALCULATING MAGNET-COIL WINDINGS

Normally, a magnet-builder starts with some knowledge of the general shape and dimensions of the device to be built, and knows what voltage (preferably D.C.) will be available to operate it. With this information available, calculations can follow this sequence:

- Find magnetic flux density, from pounds-pull that is needed.
- Assume dimensions and arrangement of materials.
- Calculate ampere-turns required.
- Calculate wire size and heat produced.

Before outlining a sample calculation, the above four items deserve some discussion.

1. Find Magnetic Flux Density

Starting from the basic definitions of a "unit magnetic pole" and "field strength", it is possible to prove that

$$\text{Pounds-pull} = \frac{B^2 \times A}{72{,}000{,}000}$$

"B" means lines of force per square inch.

"A" is the area through which the pull is accomplished, usually the area of the ends of the magnet poles, (Fig. 11-1).

We use the formula to find out how much flux density (B) the magnet must have in order to produce the pounds-pull needed in the device.

If the magnet in Fig. 11-1 has to exert 3 pounds force,

$$3 = \frac{B^2 \times 4}{72{,}000{,}000}$$

$$B^2 \times 4 = 216{,}000{,}000$$

$$B^2 = 54{,}000{,}000$$

$$B = 7400 \text{ lines per square inch}$$

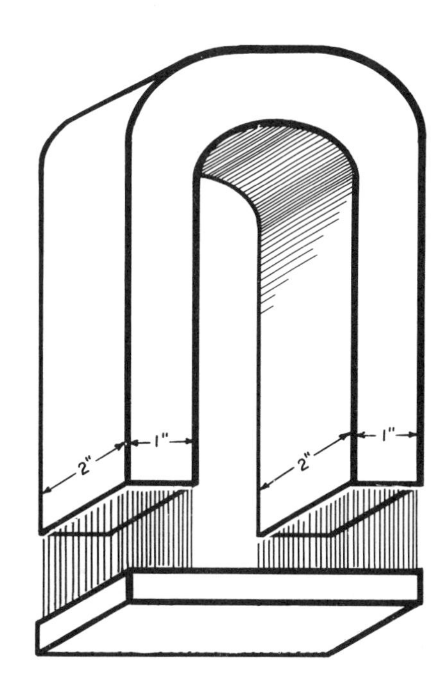

Fig. 11-1

2. Assume Dimensions and Arrangement of Materials

As pointed out in Unit 10, the magnetic path should be arranged so that lines of force pass mainly through iron. The path of magnetic lines through nonmagnetic material should be as short as possible.

3. Calculate Ampere-Turns Required

Calculation of ampere-turns is done in two steps:

a. Find ampere-turns needed to produce the required flux density in the iron of the magnet.

b. Find ampere-turns needed to produce the required flux density in the air gap, the path of the lines through the air.

These two figures will be added to find how many ampere-turns are needed for the magnet.

The ampere-turns needed to magnetize the iron can be found from charts which are available to describe the magnetic properties of all magnetic materials. (See Fig. 11-3, Page 105.)

The ampere-turns needed to produce a magnetic field in air are found by using the fact that the flux density in air is 3.19 times the ampere-turns per inch of air, (derived in Unit 9, Page 86).

To produce 1000 lines of force/sq. in., $1000 \div 3.19 = 313$ ampere-turns needed per inch of air. To produce one line of force, 0.313 ampere-turns per inch are required.

When the flux density (lines per sq. in.) is already known, and the distance that the lines of force must travel through the air is known, this formula finds ampere-turns:

$$\text{Ampere-turns} = \text{Flux density} \times 0.313 \times \text{length of air path in inches}$$

4. Calculate Wire Size

Wire size is found from this formula (see Page 98):

$$\text{Circular Mils} = \frac{\text{ampere-turns} \times \text{average length of one turn}}{\text{volts}}$$

The importance of wire size (circular mils) may be seen from some considerations of the above formula. If the diameter of a coil is not changed, and the applied voltage is not changed, ampere-turns then depend only on changes in wire size. In practice, dimensions are often limited, and only one voltage may be available, so that the ampere-turns magnetizing force is controlled by choice of wire size.

This same idea can be arrived at by using Ohm's Law and a little arithmetic:

> Suppose we have a coil that consists of 100 ft. of #25 copper wire, made up into 300 turns, averaging 4 inches each. (Circumference of middle layer of wire is 4 inches.) 100 ft. of #25 wire has about 4 ohms resistance, from wire table. A 12-volt battery will put 3 amps through 4 ohms. The number of ampere-turns is 3 × 300 = 900 ampere-turns.

Let's calculate the effect of putting on an additional 300 turns, making 200 ft. of wire in the coil. Will the magnet be stronger?

> 200 ft. of wire has 8 ohms resistance, so the current is 12 ÷ 8 = 1.5 amps. 1.5 amps × 600 turns is still 900 ampere-turns; the strength has not been increased by adding more wire. As we add more turns of the same size wire, the resistance increases, and the amps become less, so that the product, amps × turns, is not increased.

The way to strengthen the magnet, without changing voltage or dimensions, is to use larger wire, even though there are less turns of it.

> Continuing the above comparison, we might replace the 100 ft. of #25 wire by 50 ft. of #22 copper, which can make about 150 turns. #22 has twice the cross-section area of #25; its resistance per foot is half as much, about 2 ohms per 100 ft., or one ohm for 50 ft. Using one ohm (50 ft., 150 turns) of #22 on a 12-volt battery, the current is 12/1 = 12 amps. Ampere-turns are 12 × 150 = 1800. Or, using 2 ohms (100 ft., 300 turns) of #22 copper on the 12-volt battery, the current is 6 amps. Ampere-turns are 6 × 300 = 1800 again.

By summarizing these examples in a table, we may see more clearly that if we want twice as many ampere-turns, the way to get it is to use wire that is twice as big. (#25 is 320 C.M., and #22 is 640 C.M.)

Wire Gage No.	Length	Resistance	Number of Turns	Current	Ampere-Turns
25	100 ft.	4 ohms	300	3 amps	900
25	200 ft.	8 ohms	600	1.5 amp	900
22	50 ft.	1 ohm	150	12 amps	1800
22	100 ft.	2 ohms	300	6 amps	1800

Increasing the turns decreases the current, so that Ohm's Law is responsible for making ampere-turns dependent only on wire size, provided voltage and coil diameter are not changed.

HEAT PRODUCTION

The values given in the above table were made on the assumption that a 12-volt battery was in use. The rate of heat production in each coil can be calculated from watts = volts × amps.

The power used is 36 watts in the first coil, 18 watts in the second, 144 watts in the third, 72 watts in the last. The third coil might be unpleasant to operate, not so much on account of the cost of electrical energy as on account of the smell of burning insulation.

The permissible rate of heat production (watts) in a coil depends on many factors:

1. Length of time coil operates. A large rate can be allowed for short intervals, separated by longer cooling-off periods.

2. Ease of heat loss by conduction, convection, and radiation. A well-ventilated coil, with a lot of iron and other heat-conducting metal near-by can dissipate heat faster than a coil enclosed in nonmetallic material.

3. The type of wire insulation determines the maximum temperature that can be allowed.

4. Heat-insulating properties of the coil itself. Enough heat can accumulate in the interior of a multi-layer coil of cotton-covered wire to produce damage before any evidence shows up outside the coil.

For these calculations, we will assume that a small magnet coil, in steady use, can dissipate heat at the rate of one watt per square inch of exposed surface without damage due to overheating. In view of all of the above factors, it should be understood that actual coils may vary widely above and below this suggested rating.

Sample Calculation of a Magnet Winding

Assume that we bend a 9-inch long, half-inch diameter iron bar into a U-shaped magnet of dimensions shown in Fig. 11-2. In use, it is intended to exert a pull of 8 ounces (1/2 lb.) on a 1/8″ × 3/4″ × 3″ strip of iron, when the strip is at a distance of 1/8 inch from the magnet poles. The magnet coil will operate on 12 volts D.C.

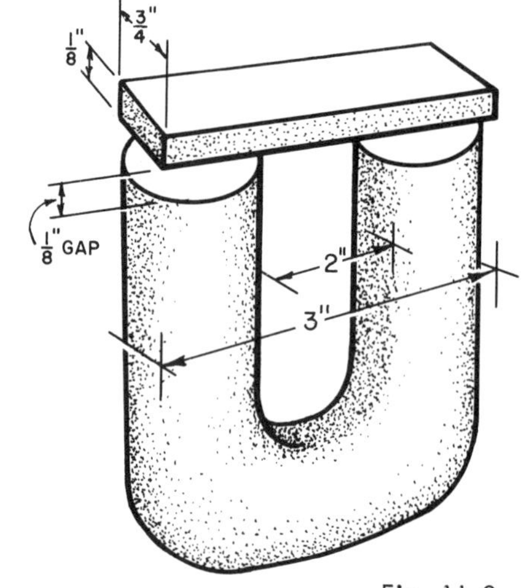

Fig. 11-2

1. To find the required flux density, we use the formula,

$$\text{Pounds-pull} = \frac{B^2 \times A}{72{,}000{,}000}$$

Pounds is 1/2, A is the area of both pole faces added together. Each pole-face is a 1/2″ diameter circle.

Using $A = \pi R^2$, the area of one circle is: $3.14 \times (1/4)^2 = 0.197$, call it 0.2 sq. in.

The two pole faces through which the lines of force pass = 0.4 sq. in.

$$1/2 = \frac{B^2 \times 0.4}{72{,}000{,}000}$$

Cross-multiplying:

$$0.8 \times B^2 = 72{,}000{,}000$$

$$B^2 = 90{,}000{,}000$$

$$B = 9500 \text{ lines per sq. in.}$$

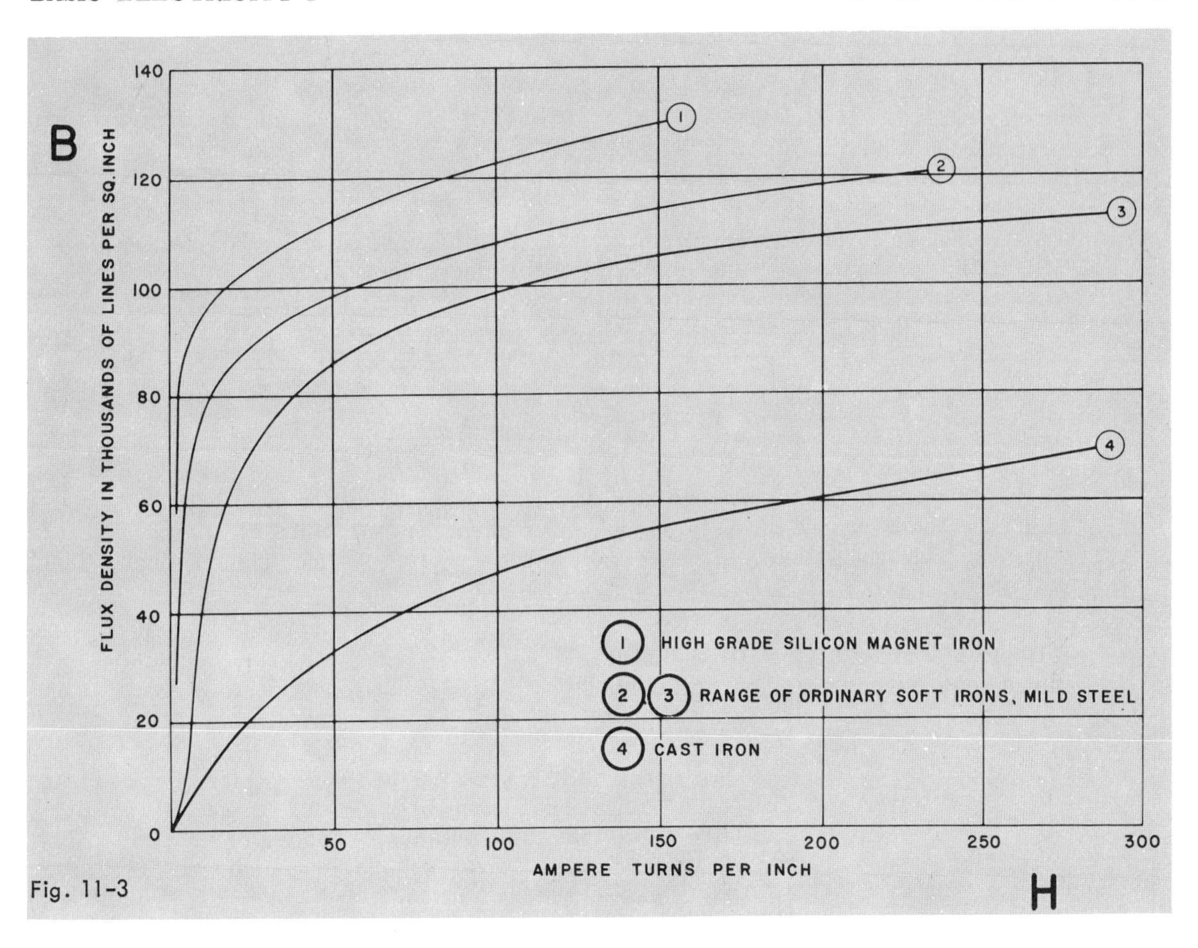

Fig. 11-3

2. To find ampere-turns needed to produce 9500/lines/sq. in. in iron and in air:

   For iron, the required information is found from a graph. Assuming we use an iron whose magnetic properties are shown by curve No. 3, B = 9,500 is found about half-way between 0 and 20, and the corresponding point on curve 3 is about at 5 ampere-turns per inch. (We will find later that the difficulty of reading the graph accurately at this low flux density need not concern us.)

   In the magnet (Fig. 11-2) the flux path is about 12 inches long in iron; 5 ampere-turns per inch × 12 inches = 60 ampere-turns required to magnetize the iron.

   The ampere-turns needed for the air gap are found from:

   $$\text{ampere-turns} = \text{flux density} \times 0.313 \times \text{length of air gap}$$

   The total air gap is two 1/8 inch gaps, 1/4 inch altogether.

   $$\begin{aligned}\text{ampere-turns} &= 9500 \times 0.313 \times 0.25 \\ &= 745 \text{ ampere-turns.}\end{aligned}$$

   The total ampere-turns needed for the coil is 745 (air) plus 60 (iron):

   $$= 805 \text{ ampere-turns}$$

   Notice that in a magnetic circuit with an air gap, the ampere-turns needed to magnetize the iron is relatively small compared with that for the air.

3. To find the wire size required:

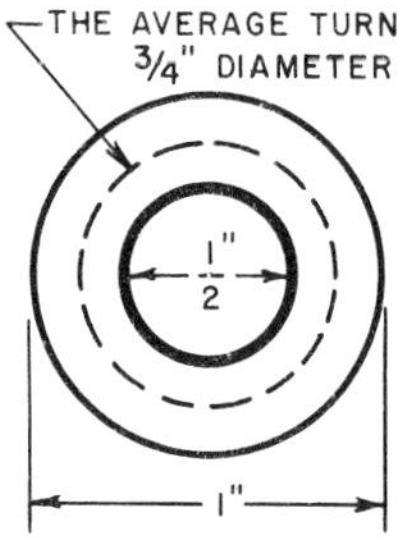

$$\text{Use C.M.} = \frac{\text{ampere-turns} \times \text{length of average turn}}{\text{volts}}$$

To determine the average length of turn, we must decide one more dimension: the diameter of the coil. Suppose we wind wire on the 1/2" bar until the outside diameter of the coil is one inch. The average turn, 3/4" in diameter, has a length $C = \pi D = 3.14 \times .75 = 2.35$ inches.

THE AVERAGE TURN 3/4" DIAMETER

Fig. 11-4

$$\text{C.M.} = \frac{805 \times 2.35}{12} = 157 \text{ C.M.}$$

Now we find from the wire table (Appendix, Page A-2) the gage number to use - 157 C.M. falls between #28 and #29. The larger wire size is chosen (#28, 160 C.M.) because it will make the magnet slightly stronger, rather than weaker, than the original specifications.

How much of the #28 wire is to be used is a matter of convenience, limited only by dimensions already assumed, and the desired rate of heat production.

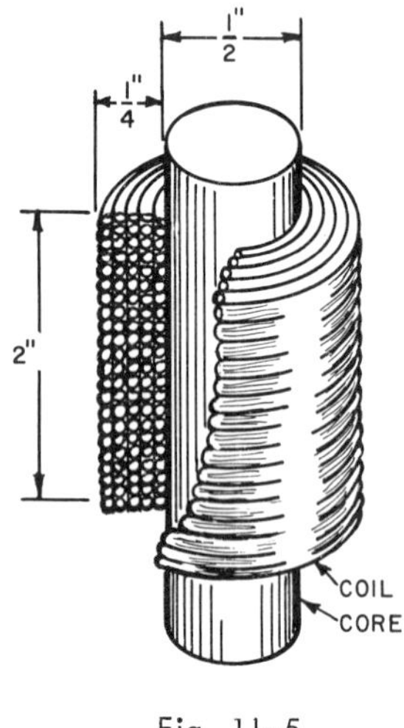

Fig. 11-5

As a possibility, say we decide to use a coil two inches long. The 1/4" thickness has already been decided (1" outside diameter.) The wire table gives the number of wires per square inch for various types of magnet wire. #28 plain enameled wire (P.E.) has 4670 wires per square inch, meaning that a one-inch square bunch of this wire, tightly packed, would consist of 4670 wires. The assumed dimensions of our magnet-coil give a bunch of wires 1/4" × 2" which is 1/2 sq. in.; 1/2 of 4670 is 2335 turns.

2335 turns, averaging 2.35 inches each, is 457 ft. of wire.

The table states that #28 copper has about 75 ohms per 1000 feet when warm. The resistance of this magnet coil is

$$75 \times \frac{457}{1000} = 34.3 \text{ ohms}$$

At 12 volts, the current is $\frac{12}{34.3} = .35$ amps

The watts is 12 v. × .35 amps = 4.2 watts, which is a small enough rate of heat production to cause no overheating.

The weight of copper in the coil is sometimes of interest; it can be found from the wire table. #28 weighs about 1/2 lb. per 1000 ft., so this coil will have slightly less than 1/4 lb. of copper.

A few modifications in the preceding magnet are worth taking up to gain a better understanding of a few magnetic principles.

Would More Than One Coil Be Desirable?

The calculation assumed only one coil. Two coils, one around each pole, are better. With only one coil in use like A in Fig. 11-6, the lines of force are scattered rather than concentrated at the second pole-face. The total flux in A may be the same as that in B, yet A is a weaker magnet. The reason is that the pull depends on the square of the flux density (B^2 in the pounds-pull formula).

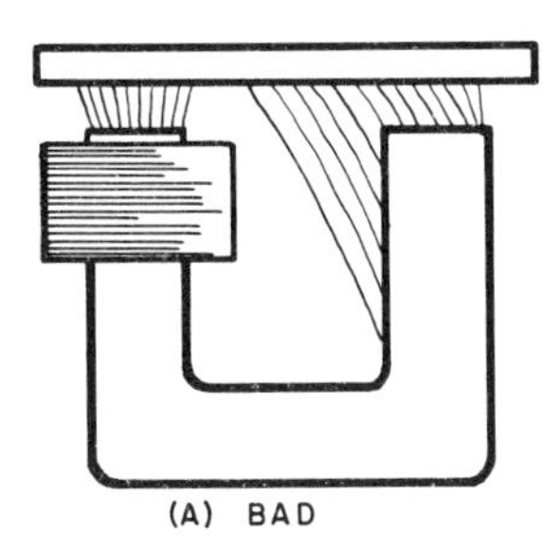

(A) BAD Fig. 11-6 (B) GOOD

When 1000 lines pull on one square inch of surface, B is 1000, A is 1, and B^2A is 1,000,000. If the 1000 lines are scattered over 2 sq. in., B is 500, A is 2, and B^2A is 500,000, which is only half of the previous amount. Scattering the lines over twice as much area has cut the pulling force in half.

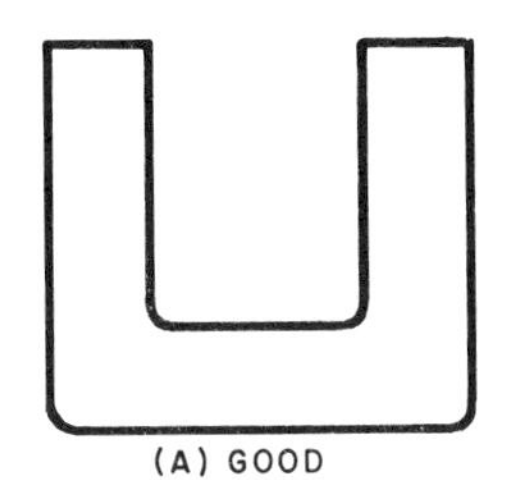

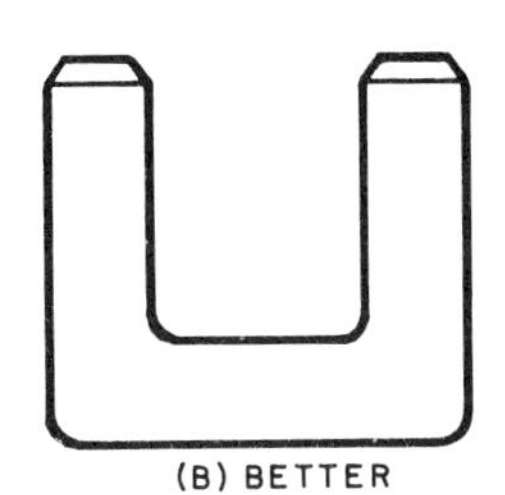

(A) GOOD Fig. 11-7 (B) BETTER

Permanent magnets, and electromagnets operating with the iron nearly saturated, often have the pole ends chamfered as in B, Fig. 11-7. The purpose is to concentrate the field, making the flux density a little more at the pole, and therefore increasing the pulling force.

When Two Coils Are Used, How Should They be Connected — Series or Parallel?

We calculated one coil as having 34 ohms, 2335 turns, and .35 amps on 12 volts. If the coils are in series, we have 68 ohms, 4670 turns, and .175 amps. Ampere-turns are not affected, so the strength of the magnet is the same. The reduction in current means that only half as much heat is produced.

If the coils are placed in parallel, each coil still has .35 amps. The total turns is 4670, so the ampere-turns have been doubled, increasing the strength of the magnet over the original specifications. The rate of heat production has been doubled also, each coil is still producing 4.2 watts, or 8.4 watts for both.

Planning the two coils in series results in simpler calculations.

Would it be Better to Use a Larger Diameter Core?

For the magnet that we have been working on, no. It would be worthwhile to re-calculate the previous magnet, using a 3/4″ diameter bar, with other dimensions the same as far as possible. The necessary flux density will be less, the ampere-turns less, the length of an average turn more, and the necessary wire size about the same, only slightly less. The resulting magnet will be twice as heavy. A larger core should be chosen only if the first calculation shows the iron saturated (at 80,000 lines/sq. in. or more) and an unreasonably large number of ampere-turns required to magnetize the iron. Continuing with our original example, a reasonable modification would be to try a core that is a little smaller, both in length and diameter, to produce a less bulky magnet that still pulls with the 1/2-pound force.

How Hard Can the 1/2-Inch Magnet Pull?

That depends on several factors. If we have a #28-wire coil and a 12-volt battery, it pulls with 1/2-pound force on iron 1/8 inch away, as calculated. If we used, instead of 12 volts, a 24-volt supply, the ampere-turns become twice as much, the flux density becomes nearly twice as much, and the pulling force becomes nearly four times as much, with four times as much heat.

Returning to the 12-volt battery: Some important changes take place while the magnet pulls the loose iron armature up to the magnet poles. The air gap is reduced, so there is less reluctance for the magnetizing force to overcome, and the flux density increases greatly.

If the pole faces and armature are ground to a tight fit, so that the air gap is practically zero when they are in contact, the entire 805 ampere-turns are used to magnetize 12 inches of iron. 805 ÷ 12 = 67 ampere-turns per inch. According to the magnet-iron chart (Fig. 11-3), 67 ampere-turns per inch produce about 95,000 lines per square inch in the iron. (Curve #3) The pulling force has now become

$$\frac{B^2 A}{72{,}000{,}000} = \frac{95{,}000 \times 95{,}000 \times 0.4}{72{,}000{,}000} = 50 \text{ lb.}$$

The amount that the magnet can hold is 50 lb. How much it can lift or draw toward itself is much less, and depends on distance.

Which is Better — A Long, Thin Coil or a Short, Stubby One?

We had a coil of #28 wire, consisting of 2335 turns, and having 805 ampere-turns on 12 volts. Its dimensions are shown in Fig. 11-8. If we used a coil 2″ thick and 1/2″ high, it would still have the 2335 turns, but would require a lot more wire because the length of an average turn now is 7.85 inches. The ampere-turns have been reduced to about 245, which is a distinct disadvantage.

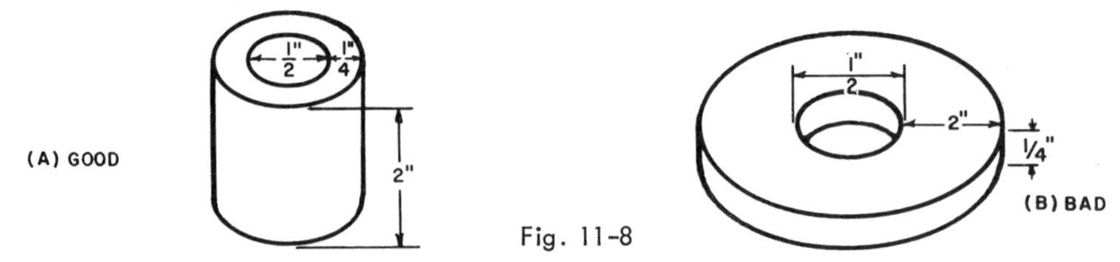

Fig. 11-8

The effective ampere-turns actually are still less, for a reason that the formulas do not show; the reason is that wires a long way out from the core are not as effective as those close in, because some of the magnetic field of far-out wires never reaches the core. This effect is called "magnetic leakage". Leakage is a general name for flux that does not follow the hoped-for path through the iron.

POINTS TO REMEMBER

- To Calculate Magnet-Coil Windings:

  1. Find magnetic flux density using formula, $\frac{B^2 \times A}{72,000,000}$

  2. Assume dimensions and arrangement of material. Keep magnetic path mainly through iron; keep path through non-magnetic material as short as possible.)

  3. Calculate ampere-turns needed to produce required flux density by adding:

     a. Required flux density in iron of magnet. (Given in charts such as shown on Page 105)

     b. Required flux density in air gap. (amp-turns = flux density × .313 × length of air path)

  4. Calculate wire size by using the formula:

     $$\text{circular mils} = \frac{\text{amp-turns} \times \text{average length of one turn}}{\text{volts}}$$

- To increase ampere-turns, increase the wire size.

- To increase pulling power of magnet, (a) concentrate the magnetic field by chamfering the magnet-pole ends, (b) use two coils instead of one. (When two coils are used, it is preferable to put them in series rather than in parallel.)

- Magnetic leakage is flux that does not follow the planned path through the iron. Keeping wires as close as possible to the magnet core minimizes leakage.

REVIEW QUESTIONS

1. By trial with a spring balance, it is found that a force of 25 pounds is needed to pull a 1/2″ × 1″ piece of iron away from the pole-face of a magnet. Calculate the flux density.

2. a. Are gage numbers and wire sizes the same for copper and aluminum?

   b. Does the formula circular mils = ampere-turns × length÷ volts work for aluminum wire?

3. How many ampere-turns are needed to produce a flux density equal to 8500 lines per square inch in the air gap of this magnet core (see A below). (Calculate ampere-turns for air, disregarding iron.)

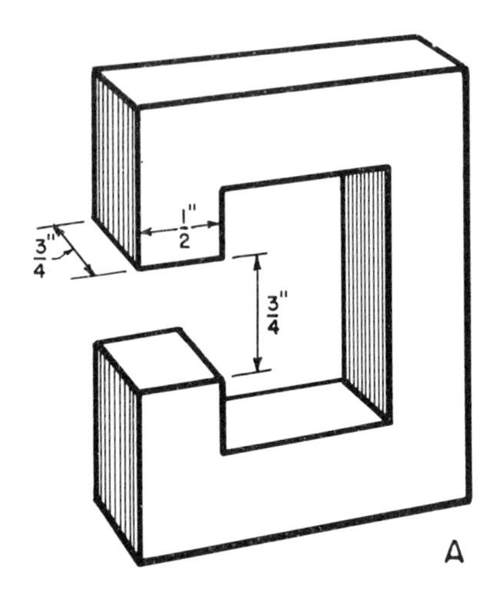

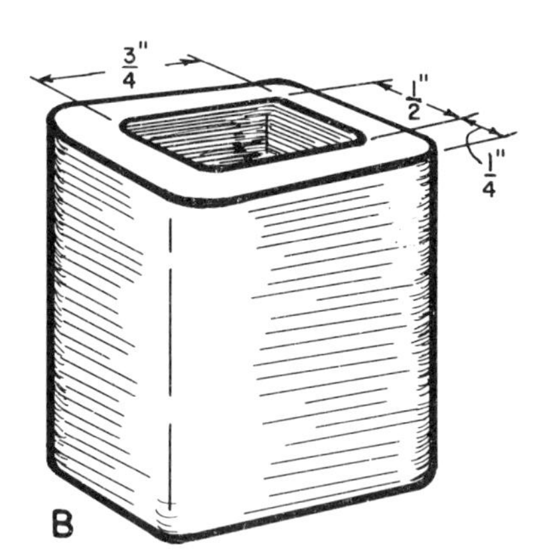

4. A coil of wire 1/4″ thick, 2″ long, is wound to fit over a 1/2″ × 3/4″ core. The coil is to have 2000 ampere-turns.

   a. Find the length of average turn.

   b. Find wire size to use, if coil is supplied with 6 volts.

   c. Find wire size to use, if coil is supplied with 12 volts.

   d. Find number of turns in coil if No. 19 P.E. wire is used. (712 wires per square inch)

   e. Find number of turns if #22 P.E. wire is used.

   f. Find resistance of each coil at 167° F (table) (d. and e. above).

   g. Calculate current in coil (d) at 6 volts; current in coil (e) at 12 volts.

   h. Calculate watts for each coil.

5. A coil of #20 formvar copper magnet wire, 3″ long, 1″ inside diameter, is operated at 12 volts. Find:

   a. length of average turn.

   b. number of turns.

   c. ampere-turns, from circular mils.

   d. amperes, from turns and ampere-turns.

   e. resistance of coil at 167° F from number of turns, length, tables.

   f. amperes, by Ohm's Law.

   g. Why don't answers (d) and (f) agree? Is the disagreement serious?

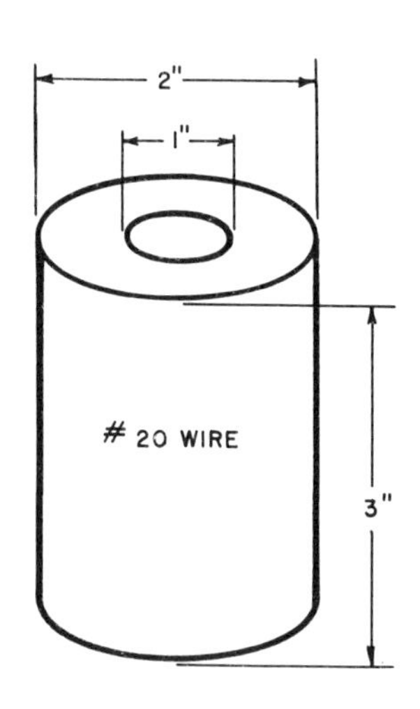

Unit 12 MEASURING INSTRUMENTS

Previous discussion of current, potential difference, resistance, and power indicates the need of measuring these quantities so that one knows what is going on in an electrical circuit. Such measurements need to be made to repair equipment, to locate troubles and to find whether portions of a circuit are functioning properly or not.

The most commonly used instruments are ammeters, voltmeters, and ohmmeters. All of these are similar in construction, being modifications of a simple basic instrument called a "galvanometer". Like most measuring instruments, the galvanometer action depends on the magnetic effect of a small current.

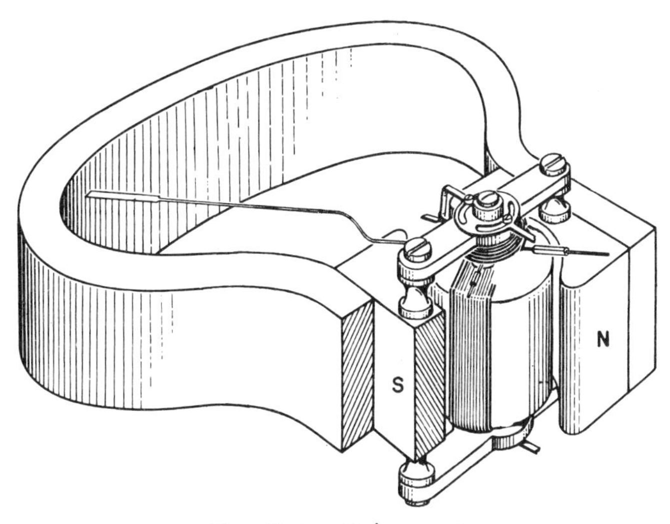

Fig. 12-1 Galvanometer

The essential parts of a D.C. galvanometer are shown in Fig. 12-1. N and S are the poles of a permanent magnet. The stationary cylindrical iron core between the poles makes an evenly distributed, uniformly strong magnetic field in the space where the moving coil operates. This uniform magnetic field makes it possible to have uniformly spaced numbers on the scale of the meter. The movable coil is generally supported by jewelled pivots, similar to those that support the balance wheel of a watch.

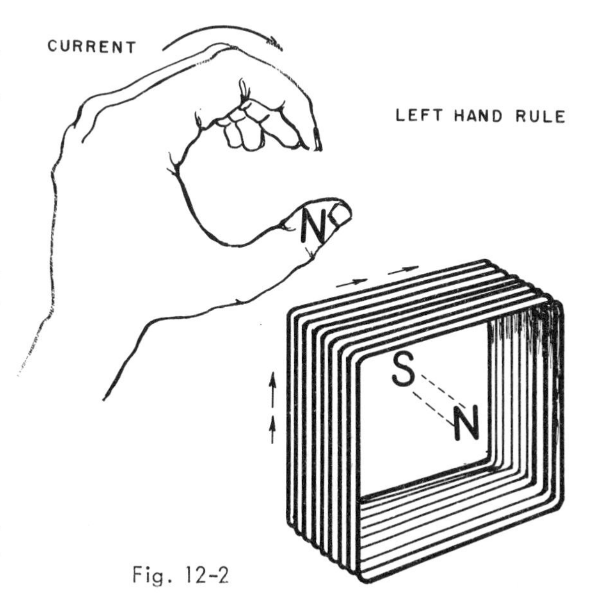

Fig. 12-2

What makes the pointer move? The coil, to which the pointer is fastened, becomes an electromagnet when there is a current in it. In the diagram right, if there is a current in a clockwise direction as we look at the coil, then the coil acts as a magnet, with its N-pole near us, and its S-pole on the farther side of the coil.

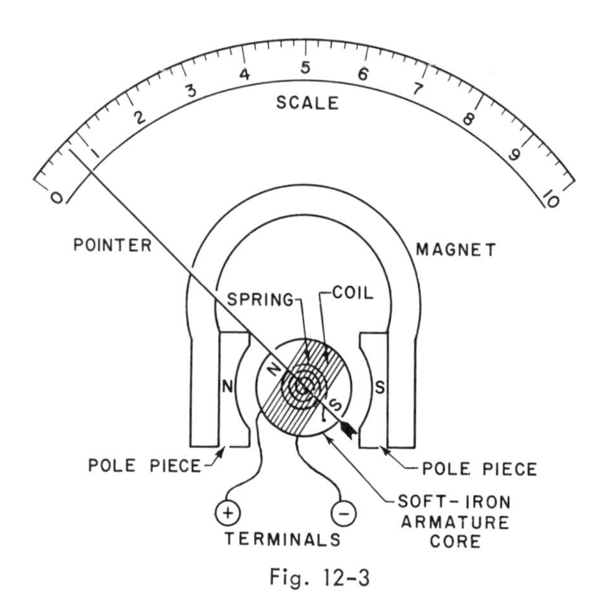

Fig. 12-3

Due to magnetic attraction and repulsion forces, the coil will try to turn so that unlike poles will be as close together as possible. The amount of turning force will depend on the strength of the permanent magnet, and on the ampere-turns of the movable coil. The motion of the coil is mechanically resisted by hairsprings. If the current in the moving coil is increased, the magnetic effect of the coil is stronger, so the coil turns farther, thus indicating the increased current on the scale. When the current is stopped, the spring returns the moving coil and pointer to the zero mark. Since one end of the hairspring is fastened to the moving coil and the other end of the spring is stationary, it is convenient to let these springs also serve as conductors to connect the movable coil to the stationary wiring in the meter.

This type of meter, and other meters based on this construction, operate only on direct current. If an alternating current is put through this meter, the magnet poles of the coil reverse rapidly. The coil is too large to swing back and forth 60 times per second (that's a common A.C. frequency); therefore, it does not turn at all. A meter intended for one ampere D.C. would not be damaged by one ampere A.C., but the meter would read "zero" on the A.C.

The ordinary simple galvanometer, by itself, is of very limited use. As a current indicator, only a very small current can be allowed in the fine wire of the moving coil. And, since this coil has a low resistance, only a very small voltage can be applied to the moving coil. The most useful galvanometers are scaled as milliammeters or microammeters, telling how many thousandths or millionths of an ampere pass through the meter.

D.C. AMMETERS

To make it possible to measure large currents with the galvanometer, a known large fraction of the large current is bypassed through a parallel low resistance called a "shunt". Only a small fraction of the total current passes through the moving coil. The scale is marked to tell the total current through the entire ammeter (galvanometer plus shunt combined).

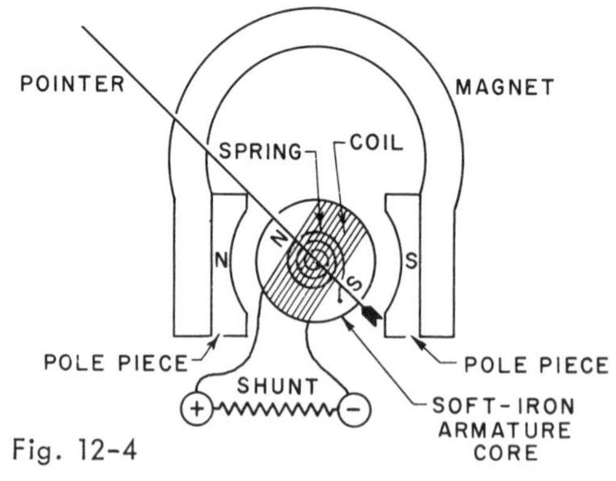

Fig. 12-4

Calculation of Shunt for an Ammeter

Assume we have a one-milliampere meter movement (that's a galvanometer in which one ma. in the moving coil is enough to move the pointer from the zero to the end of the scale). We are also told that this meter has 50-ohms resistance, which is a commonly used meter movement.

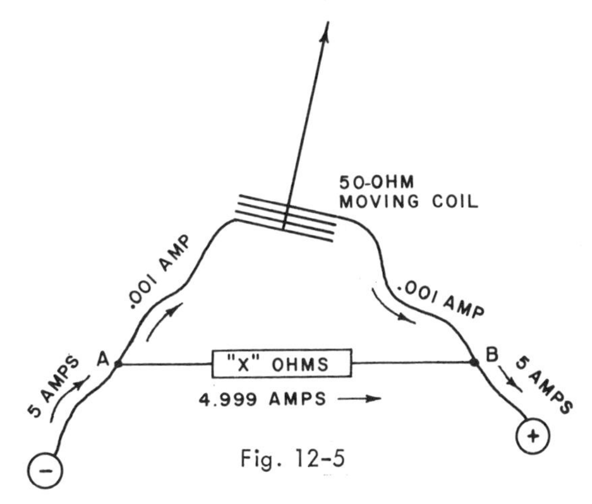

Fig. 12-5

Problem: Convert this milliammeter to a 5-amp ammeter; that is, arrange a shunt circuit so that a current of 5 amps through the entire meter will cause a full-scale movement of the pointer. The scale will be renumbered to indicate 5 amps.

Notice that the shunt is a parallel resistance. When there is a 5-amp current through the meter, only 0.001 amp can pass through the moving coil, and the rest, 4.999 amp, must go through the shunt. Looking at this as an Ohm's Law problem, we could find the "X" ohms if we knew the potential difference between A and B. This voltage between A and B can be found by using the fact that there is a current of .001 amp in the 50-ohm coil. $E = IR = .001 \times 50 = 0.050$ volt. This voltage is the same for the two parallel parts of the circuit, so we can use the 0.050 volt for the shunt-resistance problem. $E = IR$, $.050 = 4.999\,X$, $X = .01$ ohm.

So, by combining a resistance of .01 ohms in parallel with the one-milliamp meter, the combination becomes a 5-amp ammeter.

An experimenter planning to make this meter conversion need not look for a 0.01 resistor in his supply catalog. He can make a shunt of copper wire. This shunt would be soldered or firmly attached in place to avoid introducing resistance due to poor contact. The procedure is:

1. Decide on a reasonable length of wire (3 inches, for example).
2. Find the resistance of 1000 feet of this wire (3 inches is .01 ohms, one foot is .04 ohms, 1000 feet is 40 ohms).
3. Look in the wire table to see what size copper wire has about the same ohms per 1000 feet as has just been calculated. (No. 26 is close to 40 ohms per 1000 feet.)
4. Use the nearest available wire size, and calculate required length, either reversing the above order of calculations, or using methods shown in Unit 7.

In manufacturing practice, meter shunts are made of manganin (a copper-nickel-manganese alloy) rather than copper. Its advantage is that its resistance does not change appreciably with temperature changes. Furthermore, since its resistivity is greater than that of copper, a short strip of the alloy makes possible a sturdy assembly in a small space.

AMMETER: A LOW-RESISTANCE METER

In order to measure a current correctly, the meter should not interfere with the current being measured. The ammeter has a low-enough resistance so that we may assume that putting the meter into the circuit will not reduce the current.

Using an Ammeter

The purpose of an ammeter is finding out how much current there is in some piece of electrical equipment. The current through the equipment must also pass through the meter, hence the ammeter must be in series with the equipment that is being tested.

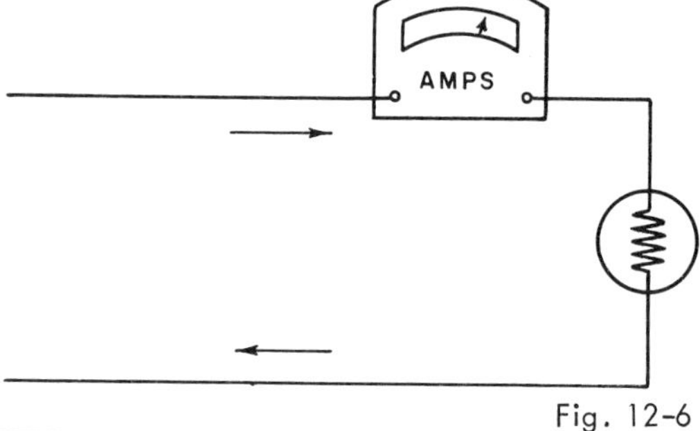

Fig. 12-6

To measure current, connect ammeter in SERIES with the device.

Occasionally, someone will use an ammeter to find out how much current he can get from a power line or from a car battery. What he finds out is that he gets enough current to burn out the ammeter. The ammeter, being of very low resistance, needs something in series with it to limit the current to a safe value. An ammeter connected directly to a current source, or in parallel with a device, acts as a short circuit.

However, an ammeter of sufficient range may be used as a short-circuit test of small dry cells. The internal resistance of the dry cell limits the current; contact is made only momentarily, otherwise the cell is damaged.

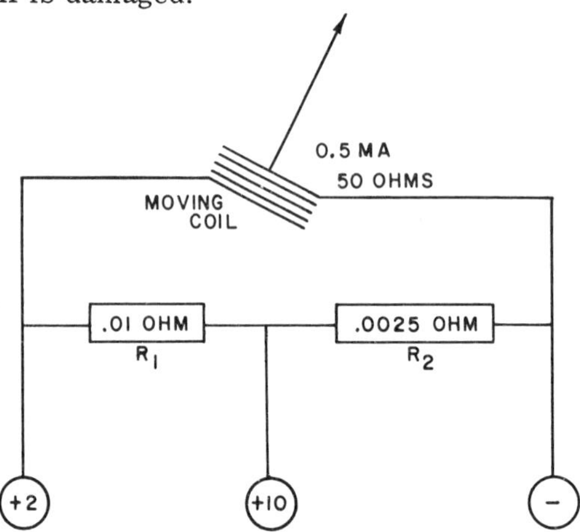

Fig. 12-7

MULTI-RANGE AMMETERS

The diagram above represents a preferred arrangement of shunts for an ammeter with two scales. The circles marked 2 and 10 can represent either binding posts, or selector switch contacts. A possible set of values of resistance is shown.

When the 2-amp contact is used, the shunt consists of R_1 and R_2 in series.

When the 10-amp contact is used, R_2 acts as the shunt; R_1 is in series with the moving coil.

This type of arrangement is called an Ayrton shunt. A three-scale ammeter contains a three-section shunt.

VOLTMETERS

To make a voltmeter, a high resistance is connected in series with the galvanometer movement. Unlike an ammeter, a voltmeter is intended to be connected directly across the source of energy, that is, in parallel with any other device to which the measured voltage is supplied.

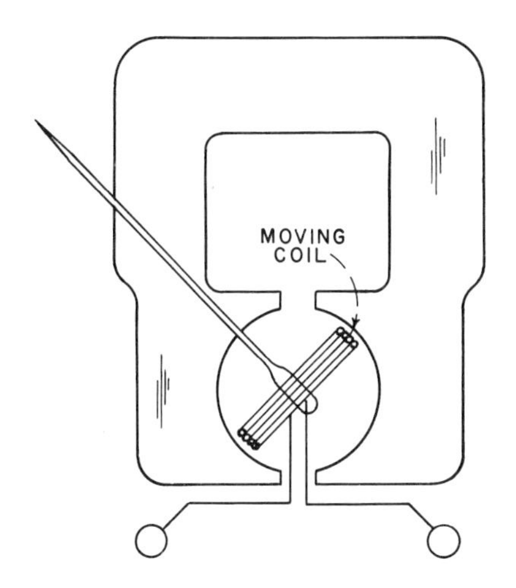

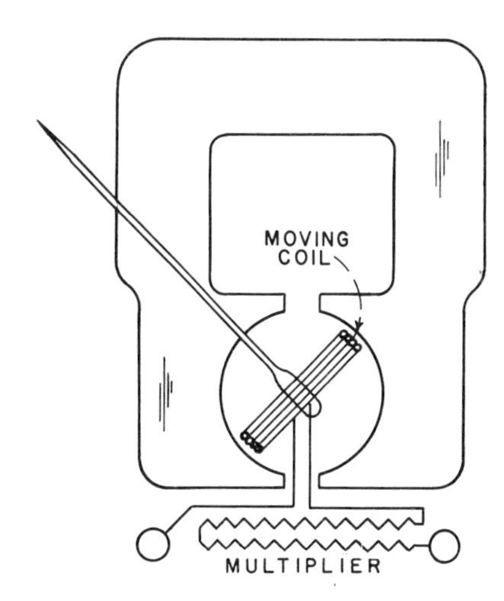

Fig. 12-8 A Resistor Converts the Galvanometer to a Voltmeter

The complete voltmeter must be a high-resistance instrument, for two reasons:

- Only a tiny current can be permitted through the moving coil, and
- The insertion of the voltmeter in the circuit should not cause a drain on the source which would reduce the electrical pressure being measured.

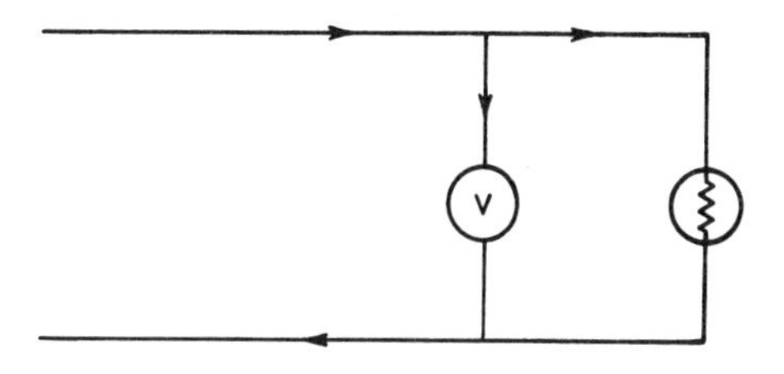

The conversion of a galvanometer (milliammeter or microammeter) to a voltmeter is easy, both in calculation and construction. We need only to calculate the series resistor which will limit the current to the full-scale galvanometer amount when the intended full-scale voltage is applied. (Ohm's Law again.)

For example, we may have a meter scaled 0 to 200 microamperes (200 microamps = 200 millionths = 0.0002 amp). Assume we want a voltmeter reading up to 200 volts. The completed voltmeter must have a resistance found from:

$$R = \frac{E}{I} = \frac{200}{.0002} = 1{,}000{,}000 \text{ ohms}$$

This value is the total resistance of the voltmeter, the moving coil plus the series resistor. Ordinarily, resistance of the moving coil is so small (50-100 ohms) that this last figure is disregarded. In this case, a one megohm resistor connected in series with the galvanometer coil makes the assembly a 200-volt voltmeter.

Anyone concerned about the inaccuracy introduced by disregarding 100 ohms coil resistance should consider these questions: If someone offered you a 999,900-ohm resistor, how would you tell whether it was 999,900 ohms or 1,000,000 ohms? How accurate is the microammeter movement that we started with? How accurately can you read a voltmeter? To answer one of these questions: $10 to $15 meters usually are accurate to 2%, $60 meters to 1%.

Multi-range voltmeters have several resistors. Which one is in use is determined by choice of binding posts, or selector switch setting.

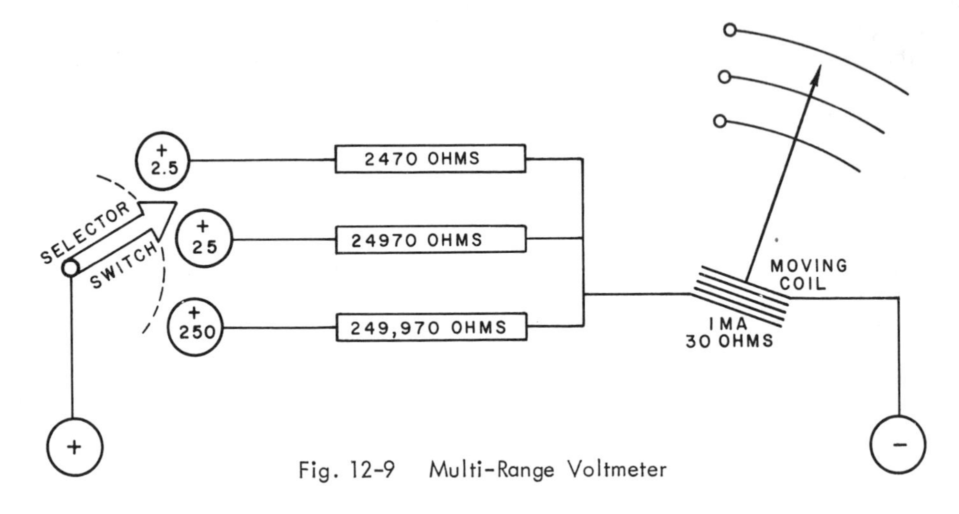

Fig. 12-9 Multi-Range Voltmeter

Fig. 12-9 shows theoretical values for the resistors. Actual values can vary 1% or 2%.

Using the 2.5-volt connection, $R = \frac{2.5}{.001} = 2500$ ohms total. (30 in meter plus 2470 in series resistor.)

On 25 volts, $R = \frac{25}{.001} = 25{,}000$ ohms

For 250 volts, $R = 250{,}000$ ohms

Sensitivity of Voltmeters

The "sensitivity" of voltmeters is stated in ohms per volt. In the first example, the 200-volt meter had 1,000,000 ohms resistance.

$$\frac{1{,}000{,}000}{200} = 5000 \text{ ohms per volt}$$

The multi-range voltmeter shown in Fig. 12-9 has a sensitivity of 1000 ohms per volt, on all scales. A large number of ohms per volt is desirable, for a high-resistance voltmeter takes a very small current to operate the meter movement. A meter rated 1000-ohms/volt takes 1 milliamp for a full-scale reading; a 20,000-ohm/voltmeter operates on 50 microamps at full scale. For checking electron-tube circuits the 1000-ohm/voltmeter would be undesirable, because at some points in the circuit there is not enough current available to operate the meter.

OHMMETER

An ohmmeter contains a battery, series resistors, and a galvanometer (microammeter) movement. Batteries used may range from 1.5 to 45 volts. The moving coil assembly of this meter is the same type that we have been using in all of the meters discussed so far. Increasing the current in the meter moves the pointer to the right. The meter is scaled, however, so that it indicates the amount of ohms-resistance placed between the tips of the external test leads.

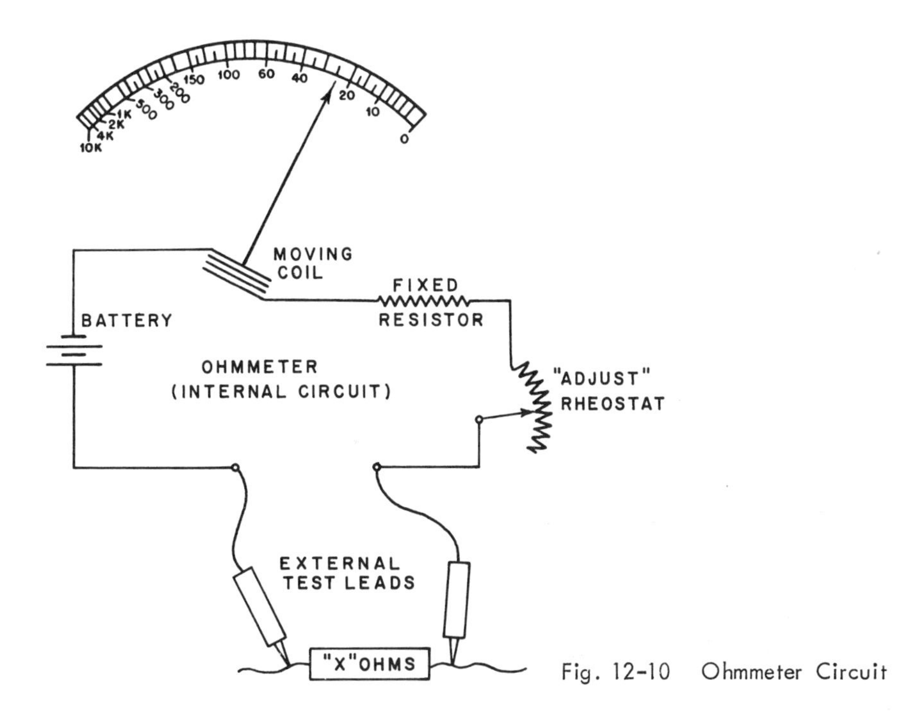

Fig. 12-10 Ohmmeter Circuit

To use this instrument, the tips of the test leads are first held together (short-circuited) and the rheostat adjusted so that the pointer of the meter moves over to the right-hand end of the scale, where the "zero ohms" mark is placed. The meter now indicates something we know already, that there is zero resistance between the test leads. The purpose of the adjustment is to compensate for changes in the resistance of the battery as it ages.

When the test leads are separated, there is no current in the circuit, and the pointer drops back to the left end of the scale, where the "infinity ohms" mark is placed. (Note that when there are several inches of air between the test leads, there is a lot of ohms resistance between them.)

When the test leads are touched to the ends of a resistor of unknown value, the resistance is read directly from the "ohms" scale. Normally, an ohmmeter has several ranges, with different combinations of series resistance and battery voltage used in each range.

The ohmmeter diagrammed in Fig. 12-10 is called a series ohmmeter, and is usually installed in a case containing multiple-contact switches, voltmeter resistors, and ammeter shunts, forming the "multi-meter" or "volt-ohmmeter" that is widely used in testing electronic equipment.

For measuring very low resistances, a shunt-type ohmmeter is used. The scale reads from left to right because high resistance permits more current through the meter. Zero resistance in the test-lead circuit permits most of the current to bypass the meter.

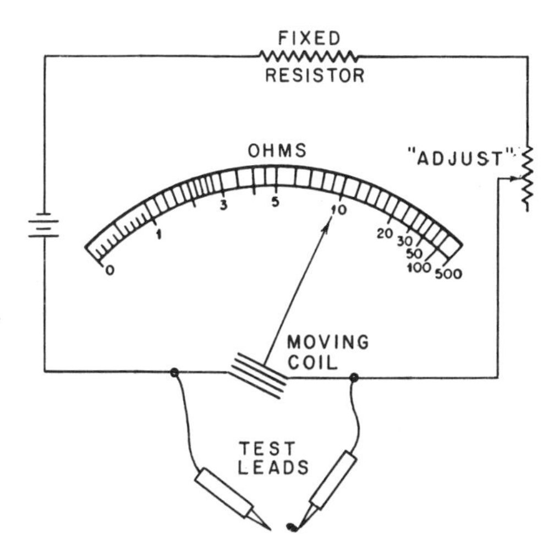

Fig. 12-11 Shunt-Type Ohmmeter

MEGOHMMETER

For insulation testing, and similar high-resistance tests, a type of ohmmeter called a "megger" is often used. It contains a high-voltage hand-cranked generator which produces current through series resistors, the unknown resistance, and a special two-coil mechanism which operates the pointer.

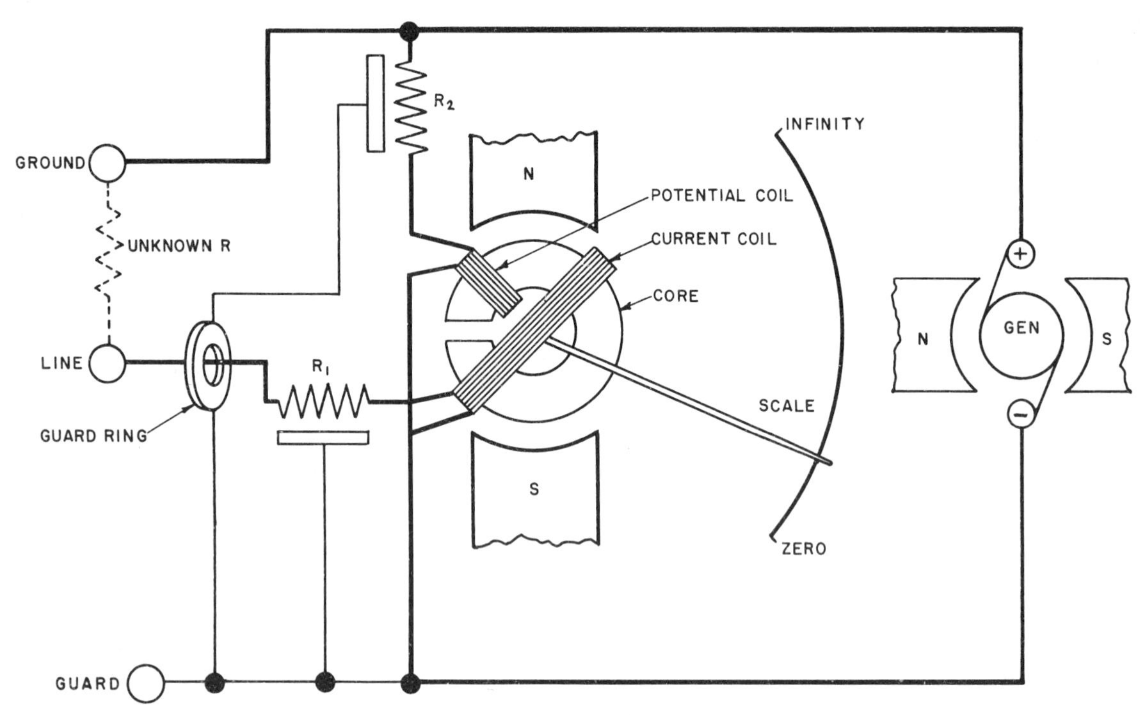

Fig. 12-12 Megohmmeter

Permanent magnets supply the field for the D.C. generator and the field for the moving-coil assembly. The "potential coil" is in series with R_2 across the generator output. The "current coil", being in series with the unknown resistance, will have a current that depends on the value of the unknown resistance. These two coils are fastened together, and can rotate only as a single assembly.

There is no spring, so the coils and pointer can take any position when the meter is not in use. With no external connection across the "ground"-"line" terminals, if the generator is operated the current in the potential coil causes a magnetic force that rotates the coil assembly counterclockwise and moves the pointer to the infinity-ohms (open-circuit) mark. If the "ground"-"line" terminals are shorted (unknown R = O ohms) there is practically no current in the potential coil, and the strong field of the current coil rotates the assembly clockwise, moving the pointer to the "zero-ohms" mark.

With a reasonable unknown R, currents in the two coils produce opposing torques, and the assembly comes to rest at a position where these torques balance each other. Low external resistance permits the current coil to turn the assembly nearer the zero, pushing the potential coil far enough into the N-pole field to repel further turning. With a high external resistance, the current coil has less effect, permitting the potential coil to move the pointer nearer to the infinity end of the scale. The scale is marked to show external resistance in megohms.

WATTMETER

It has been pointed out (Unit 8) that, in D.C. circuits, watts = volts × amps. To measure watts, a meter must have two coils, one affected by voltage and one affected by amps. The voltage coil is the moving coil, connected across the line so that the magnetic strength of this coil is proportional to the line voltage. Note that this coil with its series resistor is like the voltmeter previously described. But, instead of a permanent magnet to provide the magnetic field for the moving coil to work with, there are "current coils" to provide magnetic field, The magnetic strength of these coils is proportional to the current in them, which is the current taken by the device being tested.

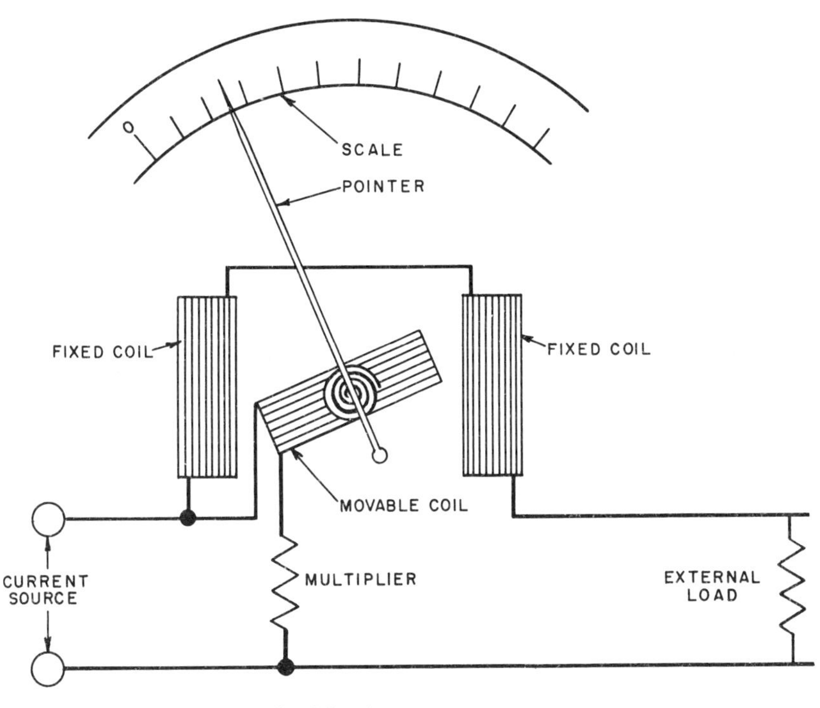

Fig. 12-13 Wattmeter

The amount of movement of the moving coil and pointer depends on the strength of both coils. If there is voltage but no current, then the current coils provide no magnetic field to turn the moving coil so the pointer reads "O". Increasing the magnetic strength of either coil increases the turning force, that is, the turning force depends on the product of the magnetic strengths of the two coils, just as the force between any two magnets depends on the product of their magnetic strengths, (Unit 9).

This coil arrangement thus gives us a pointer reading that depends on the product of volts on one coil times amps in the other coil, so we scale the meter in watts. These coils are air-core coils, no iron. A wattmeter operates on A.C. as well as D.C., since when the current reverses, the magnetic polarity of both coils reverses and the turning force is still in the same direction.

Wattmeters are more necessary in A.C. measurements than in D.C. With D.C., watts always equal volts × amps, and we could get along without a wattmeter. In A.C. circuits, there are occasions in which watts do not equal volts × amps, but the wattmeter still tells the power consumption in the circuit.

CONNECTING METERS IN A CIRCUIT: POLARITY

The ⊖ terminal of the voltmeter or ammeter is connected to the ⊖ of the supply source. See Fig. 12-14.

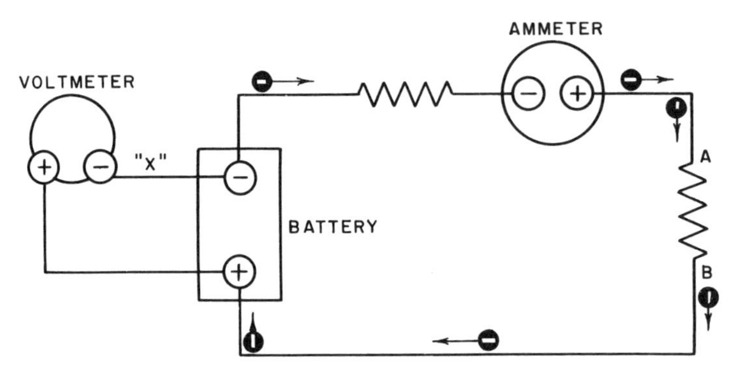

Fig. 12-14

Electrons run through the meter from the ⊖ terminal to the ⊕ terminal of the meter.

Locate the wire marked X above. Which way do electrons move in it? Toward the meter? Yes, because the battery provides the driving force. The ⊖ on the meter has meaning only as compared to the ⊕ of the meter; the ⊖ on the battery is to be compared with the ⊕ of the battery; the ⊖ signs on each end of wire X are meaningless if compared with each other.

If a voltmeter is to be connected across resistor AB, above, where do the ⊕ and ⊖ of the meter go? Electrons run from A to B; therefore, A is more negative than B, so connect the ⊖ of the meter to A, ⊕ to B.

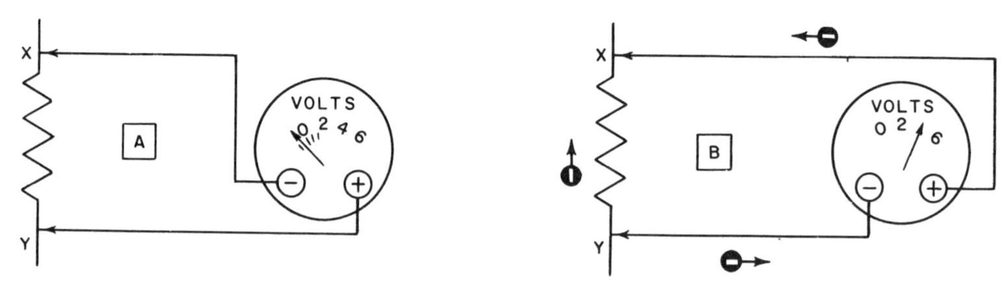

Fig. 12-15

Here's a resistor in a circuit, (Fig. 12-15) and we do not know the current direction, but wish to find out. Assume we connect a voltmeter as shown in [A], and the meter tries to read backwards, the pointer moving to the left.

Since the meter is connected wrong, reverse the meter connections [B] so it reads correctly. Now we see that point Y is more negative than X; therefore, electrons flow from Y to X.

PRECISION INSTRUMENTS AND STANDARDS

By this time, one might reasonably have inquired, "How did anybody know how much an ampere or volt is, in the first place? And who decides how much resistance is one ohm?"

In the past, scientists have set up several systems of electrical units: electromagnetic units, electrostatic units, and so on. Many men contributed to this work in the years 1840-1890. Our practical units, amperes, volts and ohms, are based on measurements of magnetic effects.

Convenient sizes were chosen for units of current, potential difference, and resistance, in order to avoid the continual use of extremely large or extremely small numbers in calculations. Furthermore, the units were established of such a size that the formula, "E = IR" rather than "E = I × R × some inconvenient number" would express the relation between current, potential difference and resistance.

The Ampere

Back in Unit 2, one ampere was stated to be a flow rate of one coulomb per second, and that is true. But historically, the ampere was established first. The fundamental definition of an ampere is given by formulas that tell the magnetic force developed by coils of wire with current in them. The most accurate instrument for measuring current is a type of balance that measures the force between two carefully built coils that have the same current in them. Such an instrument at the National Bureau of Standards can measure current with an accuracy of about one part in a million. This highly-sensitive instrument, time-consuming and requiring special skill in its use, is not used for ordinary standardizing of instruments, but is used only occasionally in checking other primary standards of resistance and voltage.

A simpler method for standardizing an ammeter involves using a special electroplating device, in which a steady current is allowed to deposit silver from a plating bath, and the silver deposited during a given time is weighed. It was found that one ampere will deposit 0.001118 grams of silver each second. This statement was adopted in 1893 as the definition of the "international ampere" and is now the legal standard.

The Standard Ohm

One highly accurate method for establishing the ohms-resistance of a resistor involves equalizing a potential difference across the resistor with the voltage generated by a disk spinning in a magnetic field. The formulas are not too complex, and only the area of the disk, the number of turns of wire in the coil, and the r.p.m. of the disk have to be measured accurately.

This device, like the "current balance" described above, is used only for establishing the resistance of certain standard coils. These standard resistances, accurate to a few parts in a million, are usable in routine comparison work. Legally, the "international ohm" (London, 1908) was defined as the resistance of a uniform column of mercury, at 0°C, 106.3 cm. long and weighing 14.4521 grams. But, more convenient and more accurate than this mercury standard, there are ten one-ohm coils of wire at the Bureau of Standards which are our real standards of resistance.

For ordinary everyday checking of electrical instruments, their reading is compared with that of similar instruments. Sending a ten-dollar ammeter to the Bureau of Standards for calibration is even less reasonable than taking your old lawnmower in for a wheel-balancing and alignment job. Electrical laboratories, college or commercial, can readily check instruments of 0.1% using standard resistances and voltage sources accurate to one part in 1000, which is precision enough.

The Standard Volt

The standard volt is legally defined by Ohm's Law. One volt is what produces one ampere in one ohm. Theoretically, the volt is set up as the e.m.f. generated when a wire cuts 100,000,000 lines of force per second, but no highly-accurate instrument has been devised to measure voltage from this principle.

As a real standard of voltage, there is a type of battery called a "Weston standard cell". (More details on cells in Unit 15). A standard cell is used only in a voltage-comparison circuit, in which it is permitted to produce not more than a few microamperes for a short time. The Weston standard cell is essentially a mercury-cadmium cell with cadmium sulfate solution as the electrolyte. At 20° C, its e.m.f. is a constant 1.0183 volts.

CIRCUITS USED IN ACCURATE MEASUREMENTS

(1) The Wheatstone Bridge

The Wheatstone Bridge is a frequently-used arrangement for accurate measurement of resistance. The information it gives is considerably more precise than an ohmmeter reading. To introduce the idea of the circuit, we should do a few Ohm's Law problems, (see Fig. 12-16).

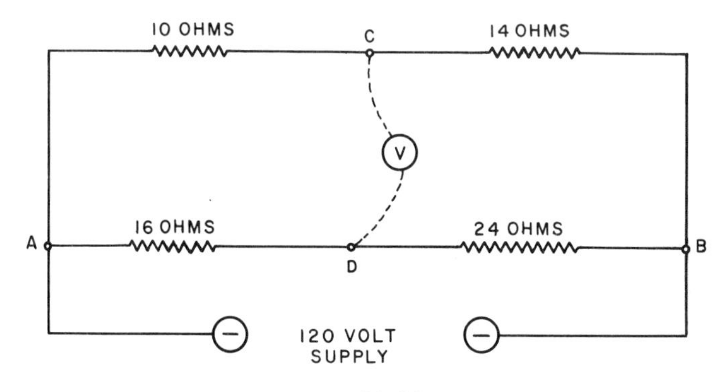

Fig. 12-16

(a) Calculate the voltage across each resistor.

The 10- and 14-ohm resistors are connected in series to the 120-v supply.
$120 \div 24 = 5$ amps in the 10- and 14-ohm resistors.
$5 \times 10 = 50$ volts across the 10-ohm; $5 \times 14 = 70$ volts across the 14-ohm.

The 16- and 24-ohm resistors are also in series on 120 volts.
$120 \div 40 = 3$ amps in the 16- and 24- ohm resistors.
$3 \times 16 = 48$ volts across the 16-ohm; $3 \times 24 = 72$ volts across the 24-ohm.

48 volts + 72 volts = 120 volts

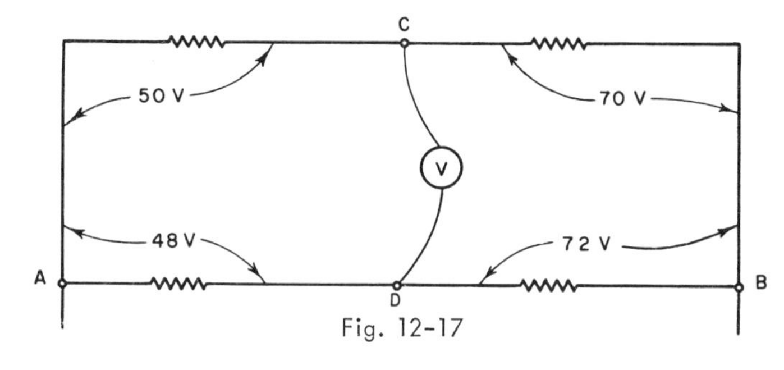

Fig. 12-17

(b) How much would a voltmeter read between C and D?

Electrons going from A to C lose 50 volts; those going from A to D lose 48 volts, so electrons at D must have 2 volts more energy than those at C. So voltmeter between C and D reads 2 volts. (The same answer can be obtained using the 70 volts and 72 volts.)

Say we arrange a similar but slightly different circuit, in which the voltmeter between C and D reads zero: that is, there is no potential difference between C and D, or C and D are at the same potential.

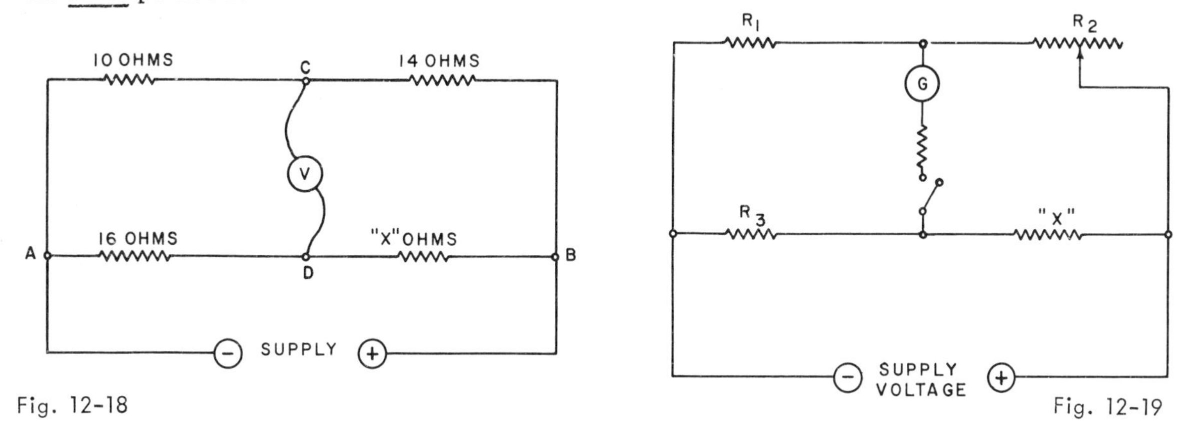

Fig. 12-18

Fig. 12-19

Problem: To find ohms resistance of "X", Fig. 12-18.

Call the current in the 10-ohm and 14-ohm resistors, I_1, and the current in the 16-ohm and X-ohm resistors, I_2.

Since C and D are at the same potential, the voltage across the 10-ohm equals the voltage across the 16-ohm, or $I_1 \times 10 = I_2 \times 16$.

Likewise, the voltage across the 14-ohm (C to B) equals the voltage across the X-ohm (D to B) because C and D are the same in potential, or $I_1 \times 14 = I_2 \times X$.

Divide equals by equals: $\dfrac{I_1 \times 10 = I_2 \times 16}{I_1 \times 14 = I_2 \times X}$ The I's cancel, leaving: $\dfrac{10}{14} = \dfrac{16}{X}$

$10X = 14 \times 16, \quad X = 22.4$ ohms, Ans.

So what's the point of all this? A circuit like Fig. 12-19 can be used to determine, accurately, an unknown resistance, provided R_1, R_2, and R_3 are accurately known resistances and at least one of them is adjustable, permitting the circuit to be adjusted so that the zero-center voltmeter reads zero.

In practice, the standard resistors R_1, R_2, R_3 may be assembled in one unit, with external connections for the meter, battery, and unknown resistance. The battery and meter can be included in the unit also. The process of adjusting the resistors so that the meter reads zero is called "balancing". When an approximate balance is reached, the series resistor of the voltmeter is shorted out, so that the sensitive galvanometer movement alone can be used to get a more accurate balance.

Just as we arrived at $\frac{10}{14} = \frac{16}{X}$, above, for the Fig. 12-18 circuit, so we can arrive at $\frac{R_1}{R_2} = \frac{R_3}{X}$ for the Fig. 12-19 circuit. With R_1, R_2, and R_3 known, X can be calculated.

The equation is just as correct if written $\frac{R_1}{R_3} = \frac{R_2}{X}$ and may be easier to remember in this form, with the R's in the formula in the same relative position as in circuit diagram, (Fig. 12-19).

(2) The Potentiometer Circuit for Accurate Comparison of Voltages

The potentiometer circuit is based on a simple "voltage-divider" circuit, which should be understood at this point.

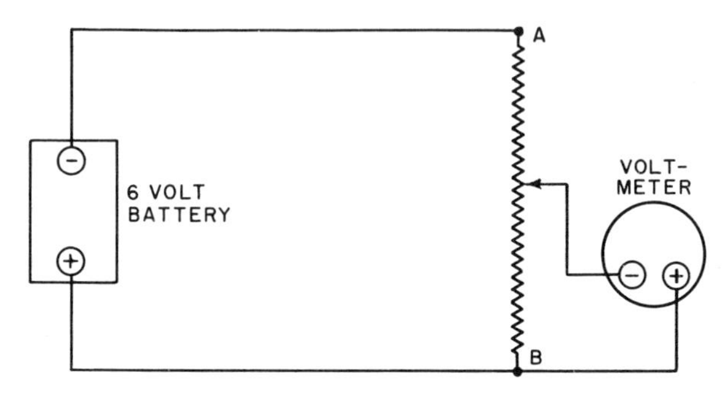

Fig. 12-20 Voltage Divider

Assume a 6-volt battery is connected to the ends of a resistor (rheostat A . . B) that has a sliding contact. What will the voltmeter read as the contact is moved up or down? With the slider at A, the voltmeter is directly connected to the battery, and reads 6 volts. With the slider at B, the voltmeter reads zero because both its terminals are connected to the same point. At points between A and B, the voltmeter will read between 6 and 0, depending on the amount of resistance between B and the slider (V = IR).

This voltage-divider circuit is useful in itself as a way of obtaining variable voltages from a fixed-voltage source.

Suppose we locate a point on the rheostat above where the voltmeter reads 4.5 volts. (Call this point C.) Leaving the slider at this point, suppose we insert in the circuit a 4.5-volt battery, as in Fig. 12-21.

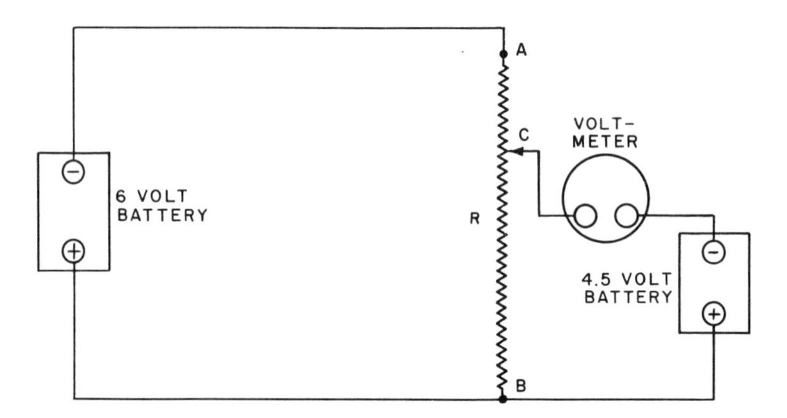

Fig. 12-21 Balanced Voltages

Will there be any tendency for any current through the meter?

Looking at the voltage drop on R, point C is 4.5-volts more negative than point B, according to previous use of the voltmeter. The minus terminal of the 4.5-volt battery is also 4.5 volts more negative than point B. Therefore, point C is at the same potential as the ⊖ terminal of the 4.5 battery, thus there is no tendency for electrons to flow through the meter.

This voltage-balancing idea is used in the complete potentiometer circuit. Between points A and B, which correspond to A and B in the simpler circuits earlier, is a series of standard resistors, both fixed and variable, arranged with movable contacts, so that the amount of resistance between contacts can be read off precisely.

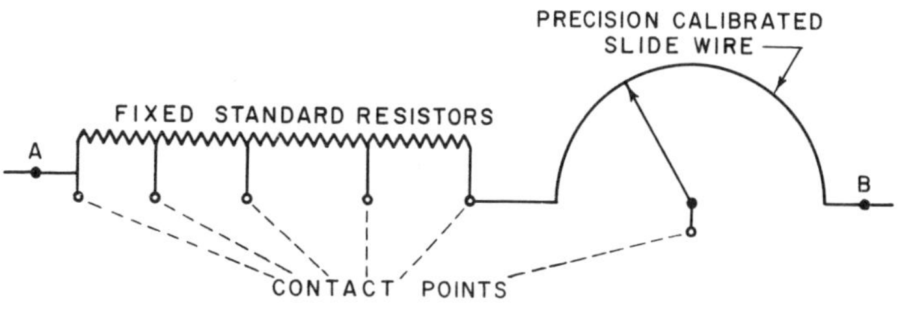

Fig. 12-22

This series of resistors is shown, for simplicity, as a single long resistor in Fig. 12-23. The storage battery maintains a constant current through this resistor. In use, the double-throw switch is connected to the standard cell momentarily, and contacts C and D are adjusted so that there is no current in the galvanometer. (Same idea as in Fig. 12-21.) As this "balance" point is approached, the resistance R_g in series with the galvanometer is reduced. With this balance attained, the voltage drop between C and D is just equal to the voltage of the standard cell. There is no current in the cell because the cell voltage opposes the voltage across C . . . D. At this time, the resistance between C and D is read accurately from dials. (Call this resistance R_s, the resistance in use when standard cell is in the circuit.)

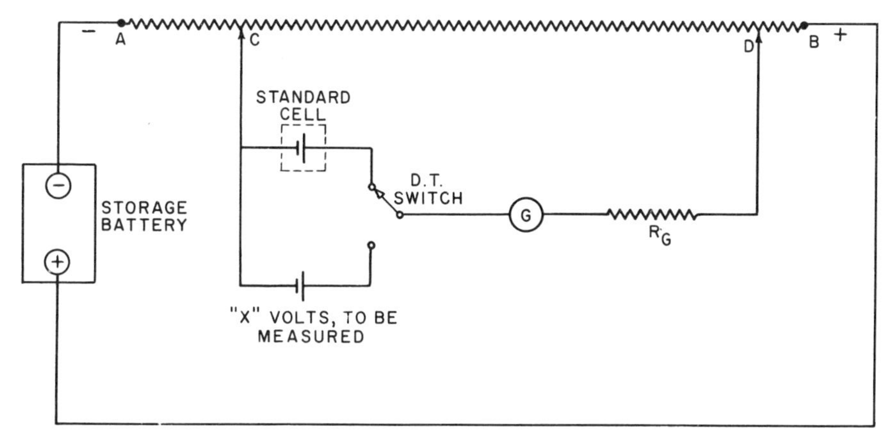

Fig. 12-23 Potentiometer

Then the double-throw switch is connected to the "X" volts to be measured, and the balancing process repeated. Both variable contacts C and D may be at new locations when this new balance is obtained. If "X" volts is more than the standard-cell voltage, there will have to be more resistance between C and D. Again, this new resistance between C and D is read from dials. (Call this resistance R_x, meaning the resistance in use when X is in the circuit.)

What good is all this? It enables us to calculate, with precision, the unknown voltage, X. Calling the current through the series of standard resistors, I —

The standard cell voltage, $E_s = I \times R_s$

The unknown voltage, $X = I \times R_x$

Dividing these equations, $\frac{E_s}{X} = \frac{\not{I} R_s}{\not{I} R_x}$

The I's cancel, leaving as a useful equation, $\frac{E_s}{X} = \frac{R_s}{R_x}$

This is useful because with E_s, R_s, and R_x, all known quantities, X can be calculated.

The advantage of determining voltage by the potentiometer circuit is accuracy, limited only by (1) reliability of the standard cell, (2) tolerance of standard resistors, and (3) the operator's ability to tell whether a galvanometer needle moves or not.

In some applications the fact that the potentiometer does not draw current from the X-voltage source is a great advantage. A potentiometer is used in calibrating voltmeters and ammeters, measuring the e.m.f. produced by a thermocouple (Unit 16), measuring voltage changes that occur during chemical reactions, and so on. In Fig. 12-23, the "X" voltage was indicated as being a cell, but actually any type of voltage can be inserted at X, including the voltage drop across a resistor in another circuit.

This Unit 12 may seem to be a long section, yet no description has been given of common A.C. meters, and many types of specialized meters have been omitted.

- A D.C. galvanometer consists of a small coil of wire, moved by magnetic action in the field of a permanent magnet, with spiral hairsprings to bring the pointer back to zero.
- Ammeter: A low-resistance meter, consisting of a galvanometer and shunt (parallel low resistance).
- Ammeter is to be connected in series with the device in which current is to be measured.
- Voltmeter: A high-resistance meter, consisting of a galvanometer plus a series resistor.
- Voltmeter can be connected directly to a voltage source . . and must be across (in parallel with) the device on which voltage is to be measured.
- Ohmmeter: A galvanometer, dry cells, and series resistors. Measures resistance between test leads to instrument. Must be used on "dead" circuit, NOT on resistors that have current in them from some other source.
- Wattmeter contains a voltage coil across the line, and a current coil in series with the line. Reads true watts, A.C. or D.C.
- There are more electrons on the negative terminal of a device (meter, resistor, battery, etc.) than there are on its positive terminal. (Use this idea to determine either polarity or electron current direction.)
- Electrical measurements are based on the accuracy of mathematical formulas and the reliability of high-precision instruments.

REVIEW QUESTIONS

1. State the purpose of hairsprings in a galvanometer, shunt in an ammeter, series resistor in a voltmeter.

2. Under what conditions would one use a Wheatstone bridge? A megger? A potentiometer? A Weston standard cell?

3. Diagram the internal circuit of a voltmeter, an ammeter, an ohmmeter, a wattmeter.

4. The user of an ohmmeter finds that when the test-prods are shorted, the adjustment will not make the pointer move over to the zero mark, as it should. Pointer stops at about R = 5. What's wrong?

5. Calculate the resistance of a shunt, to convert a 100-microamp meter with 40-ohm moving coil, to a 10-milliamp meter.

6. Calculate series resistor to convert the above 100-microamp meter to a voltmeter, scaled 100 millivolts full-scale.

7. Calculate series resistor to convert the same 100-microamp meter to a voltmeter scaled to 100 volts.

8. A pair of #28 copper wires in a telephone cable are accidentally short-circuited. On connecting a Wheatstone bridge to the accessible ends of the wires, the bridge gives $R_1 = 100$, $R_2 = 327.8$, $R_3 = 100$. Calculate distance from the accessible end of the cable to the point where the pair of wires are shorted (Temp. 70°F).

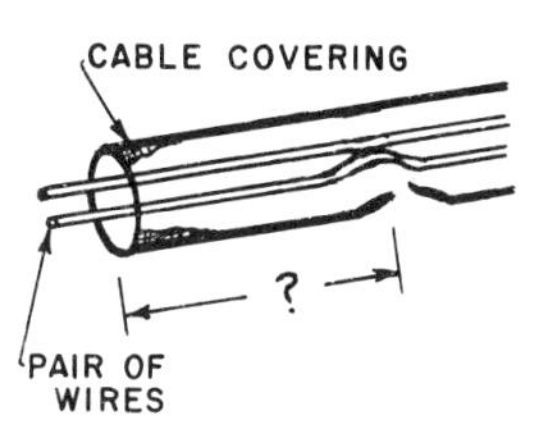

9. a. Using data from Fig. 12-7 (Page 114), calculate the voltage across the moving coil, and the voltage across the shunt, when 2 amps pass through the meter, using terminals (2) and (-) .

   b. When 10 amps pass through the meter, using the (10) and (-) terminals, find voltage across moving coil, and voltage across shunt.

10. Two resistors, A and B, are connected in parallel and this combination is placed in series with a third resistor, C. This entire group is connected across a 120-volt, D.C. supply. The current in C is 5 amps and the current in B is 3 amps. The resistance of A is 20 ohms.

    a. Determine the voltage across A, the resistance of B, and the resistance of C.

    b. If resistor A is accidentally open-circuited, find the new voltages across resistor A and resistor C.

11. A 0-150 volt voltmeter has a resistance of 2000 ohms per volt. It is desired to change this voltmeter to a 0-600 volt instrument by the addition of an external multiplier. What would be the resistance in ohms of this external multiplier?

12. A 0-150 volt D.C. voltmeter has a resistance of 100 ohms per volt.

    a. What is the instrument resistance?

    b. What is the instrument full-scale current?

    c. It is desired to extend the range of the voltmeter to 750 volts by adding an external multiplier. What must be the resistance of this external multiplier?

    d. What would be the power dissipation of the external multiplier when the voltmeter is used to measure 750 volts?

13. A D'Arsonval movement has a full-scale deflection at 25 milliamperes and the coil has a resistance of 2 ohms.

    a. What would be the resistance of a multiplier to make this instrument into a voltmeter with a full-scale deflection at 300 volts?

    b. What would be the resistance of a shunt to make this instrument into an ammeter with a full-scale deflection at 25 amperes?

14. The power to a 25-watt lamp is being measured with a voltmeter and an ammeter. The voltmeter, the resistance of which is 14,160 ohms, is connected directly across the lamp terminals. When the ammeter reads 0.206 ampere, the voltmeter reads 119 volts.

    a. What is the true power taken by the lamp?

    b. What percentage of error is introduced if the instrument power is neglected?

15. a. A D.C. instrument that has a resistance of 2.5 ohms gives full-scale deflection when carrying 20 milliamperes. What must be the resistance of a shunt so that the instrument will give full-scale deflection when the current is 10 amperes?

    b. What resistance must be connected in series with the above instrument movement so that full-scale deflection will occur when the instrument is connected across 150 volts?

16. The resistance of a 0-50 millivoltmeter is 10 ohms. It is connected with the external shunt in a circuit in which the current is 100 amperes.

    a. Draw a diagram showing the method of connecting the instrument and the shunt in the circuit.

    b. What instrument current will cause full-scale deflection?

    c. Determine the resistance of the shunt that should be used in conjunction with the instrument to cause full-scale deflection.

Unit 13 CONDUCTION IN LIQUIDS

Common liquids, such as gasoline, oils, pure water, alcohols, dry-cleaning solvents, etc., are classed as insulators, rather than as conductors. However, water dissolves a good many materials which give the solution the ability to conduct. In general, the other liquids do not become conducting when substances are dissolved in them. It is the purpose of this unit to explain the behavior of these water-dissolved materials, understanding of which is essential to explanation of electroplating processes, corrosion of metals, operation of batteries, and other chemical processes making use of electric current through water solutions.

ATOMS, MOLECULES, AND IONS

Unit 1 pointed out that atoms of all materials contain negative electrons and positive protons, equal in number in atoms of the pure element. Atoms of metals have a few loose electrons in the outermost ring of the atoms; the drift of these loose electrons is the electrical conduction process in pure metals and alloys. Atoms of nonmetals have several (5, 6, or 7) tightly-held electrons in their outermost rings; the difficulty of moving these electrons makes them nonconductors.

An outer ring of eight electrons gives an atom a condition of low potential energy, and all atoms have more or less tendency to get into this condition of low potential energy. All objects, whether large or small, have a tendency to lose energy and get into a state of low potential energy: water runs downhill, wound-up clock springs tend to unwind, bricks and bottles fall down instead of up. Electrons follow this same pattern of behavior. The loose electrons (1, 2 or 3) of the outer ring of a metal atom can fall off the atom, provided there is some other nearby atom that has spaces that these loose electrons can fall into. Atoms of nonmetals have such spaces that electrons can fall into.

For example, when a strip of magnesium metal is heated and surrounded by chlorine gas, the magnesium atoms lose their two outer electrons. These electrons fall into empty spaces in the outer ring of chlorine atoms. Important: As a result of this electron transfer, the magnesium atom has lost two electrons, and is now positively charged. Each chlorine atom has gained one electron, and is now negatively charged.

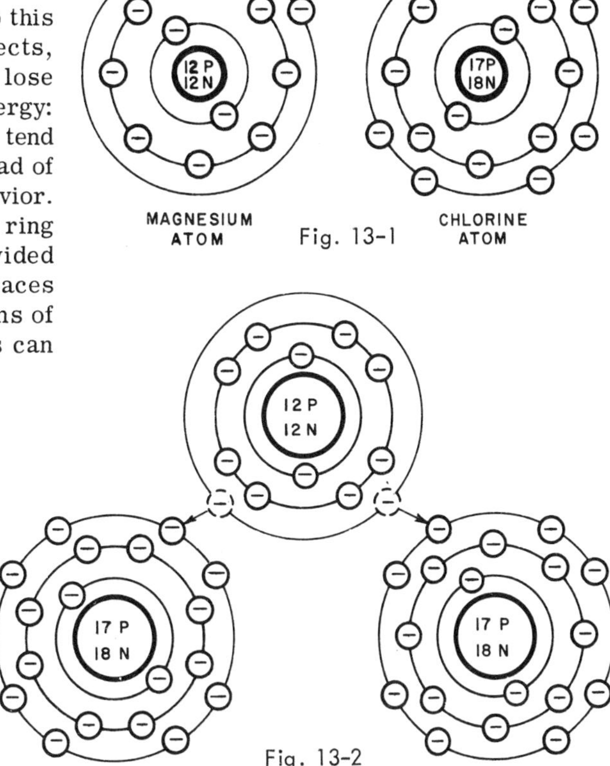

Fig. 13-1

Fig. 13-2

These atoms have been changed so terrifically by this electron transfer that they are no longer called atoms: they have a new name, ions. After an originally neutral atom has become electrically charged, it is called an ion. Note that each ion has 8 electrons for its outer ring.

The fact that these atoms have been changed greatly is evident from seeing magnesium and chlorine combine. Magnesium looks like aluminum. Chlorine is a miserable-smelling poisonous greenish gas. The process of electron transfer from magnesium to chlorine is a vigorous combustion. The end result of this process is one material, small lumps of a harmless salty-tasting white solid called "magnesium chloride". Magnesium chloride consists of magnesium ions and chlorine ions. These charged ions arrange themselves in a definite pattern.

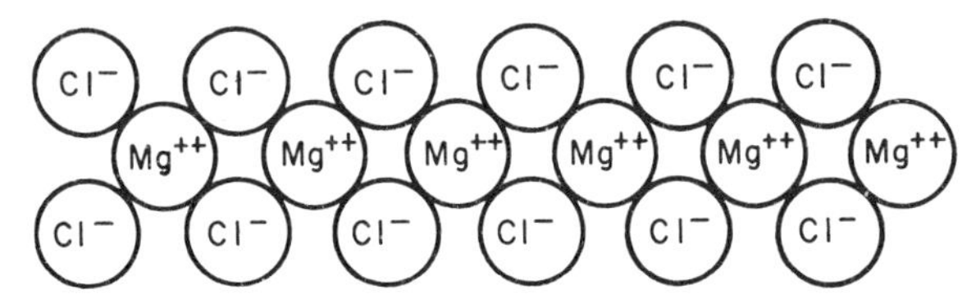

Fig. 13-3

Cl^- is the chemist's symbol for the negative-charged chlorine ion. Mg^{++} represents the positive-charged magnesium ion. (The two + signs indicate the loss of two electrons). Magnesium chloride is called a compound, meaning a definite combination of elements to form a new and different material. Chemists write $MgCl_2$ for the formula of a molecule of magnesium chloride, indicating that one atom of magnesium and two atoms of chlorine are necessary to form the smallest possible amount of the new compound, magnesium chloride.

From the above diagram, one may get the correct notion that each Mg^{++} ion is surrounded by Cl^- ions, and each Cl^- ion is surrounded by Mg^{++} ions in the three-dimensional crystal structure of a solid chunk of magnesium chloride. In fact, the electrical attraction between the oppositely charged ions is what holds them together in the solid state. (When carbon atoms join up with chlorine atoms, their electron-rings get tangled up, without any complete handing over of electrons from one atom to another. The resulting material, called carbon tetrachloride, is an easy-evaporating liquid, rather than a solid, because no electrical charges are developed that would help hold one molecule to another molecule.)

Magnesium chloride is in many ways similar to ordinary salt, which is a compound of a rather unusual metal, sodium, with the nonmetal, chlorine. The chemical name for ordinary table salt, sodium chloride, indicates the elements that compose it.

The conducting ability of salt in water can be quickly demonstrated with the equipment shown in Fig. 13-4. The glass might first be filled with kerosene, and the circuit connected to the 120-volt line. Nothing happens. Put some table salt or magnesium chloride in the kerosene. The neutral molecules of kerosene have no attraction for the charged ions of the salt, which is not dissolved, so there is no current.

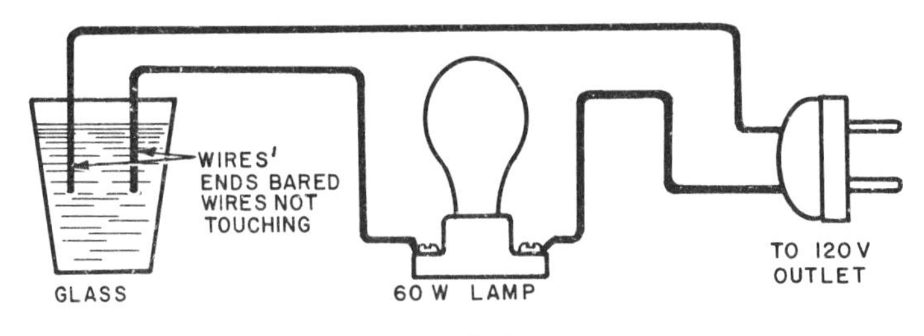

Fig. 13-4

Try another glass with pure distilled water, if it is available. Apparently nothing happens. Or, if faucet water is used, the lamp may light very dimly. When salt is added, it dissolves with stirring, and the lamp brightens. To explain this increased conductivity we need first to know what happens when magnesium chloride or sodium chloride dissolves in water.

Water molecules are rather unusual things. Like all molecules, they are, overall, electrically neutral. The unusual item is that water molecules are positive-charged on one end and negative-charged on the other. Pure water does not consist of ions: there is no transfer of electrons when hydrogen and oxygen combine. But the electrons in the molecule are not uniformly arranged, more of them seem to be clustered around the oxygen side of the molecule.

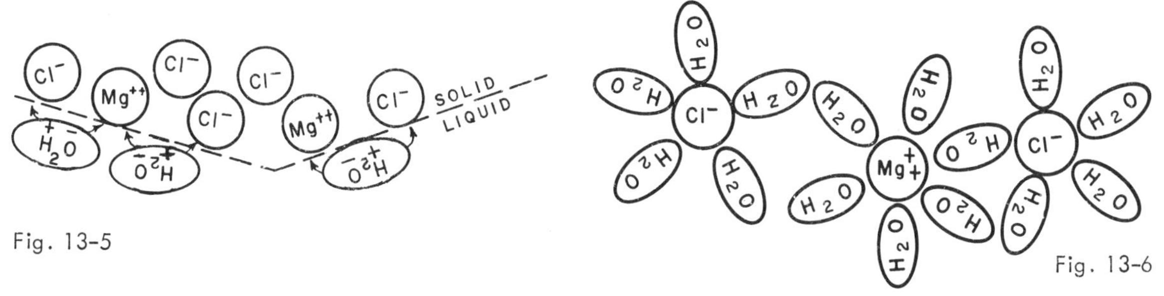

Fig. 13-5

Fig. 13-6

When water molecules are in contact with an ionic crystal, like a piece of magnesium chloride, the positive ions of the solid attract the negative (oxygen) ends of water molecules, and the negative ions of the solid attract the positive (H) ends of water molecules.

As a result of this attraction, the ions of the solid become surrounded by water molecules, but as soon as that happens, the ions of the solid are in no position to strongly attract one another, and they have become as movable as the water molecules are.

It is worth noticing that water molecules are not too movable: the positive end of one molecule attracts the negative end of a nearby molecule, and this attraction is enough to keep water in the liquid state at ordinary temperatures. If the electrons in water molecules were uniformly arranged, water molecules would have no electrical attraction for one another. Water would exist as vapor instead of liquid at low temperatures, so people like us wouldn't exist at all.

So how does the liquid conduct? The water molecules do not move toward charged wires, because they are pulled in opposite directions by each wire. There are no loose electrons, as in a metal, to drift from the negative terminal toward the positive. Metal ions are not metal: their loose electrons have been lost, and are tied down in negative ions. The charged ions are movable, and their motion through the liquid is the electric current. When magnesium chloride, or any ionic compound, dissolves in water, the ions attain a freedom of motion that they did not have when they were rigidly fixed in the solid. This loosening up, called "dissociation", happens whether there are any wires in the water or not. As soon as electrically charged wires are put into the solution, the positive ions drift toward the negative wire; the negative ions head for the positive wire. This two-way movement is the current. Just what happens to the ions when they bump into the wire depends on the kind of ions and the kind of wire used; some special applications will soon be described.

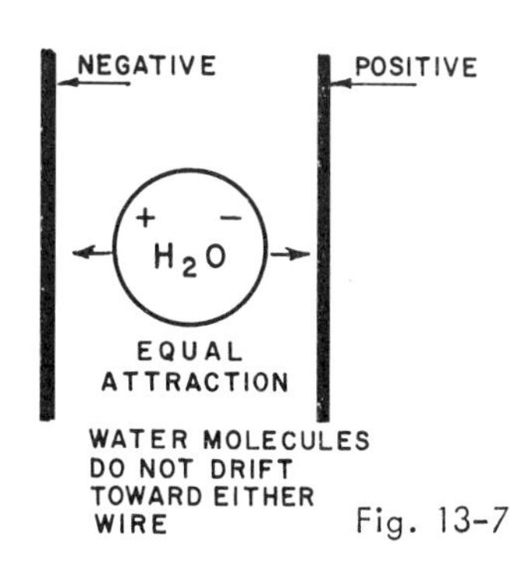

Fig. 13-7

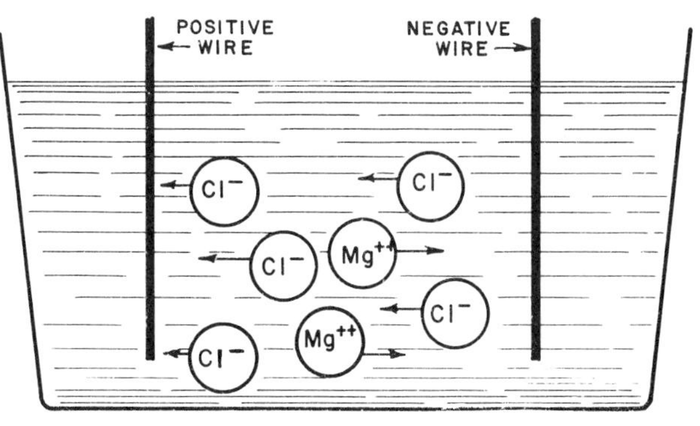

Fig 13-8

To summarize what has been discussed so far:

- Metals and nonmetals unite to form compounds, transferring electrons from the metal atoms to the nonmetal atoms.
- As a result of this transfer, the compound consists of positive-charged metal ions and negative-charged nonmetallic ions.
- Some of these compounds can dissolve in water. If they dissolve, they dissociate, the ions becoming separated and free-moving. Ions are much larger and heavier than electrons.
- Conduction in metals consists of movement of loose negative electrons.
- Conduction in solutions consists of movement of loose positive and negative ions, moving in opposite directions.

The ions we have discussed are formed by the electrical charging (positive or negative) of a single atom. There are also more complicated ions, consisting of charged groups of atoms. Here are four compounds, useful in electrical processes, that consist in part of these larger ions:

1. Sulfuric acid, the electrolyte in a car battery, has for its chemical formula, H_2SO_4. This states that one molecule of the acid contains two atoms of hydrogen, one of sulfur, and four atoms of oxygen. When mixed with water, each molecule can separate into these ions:

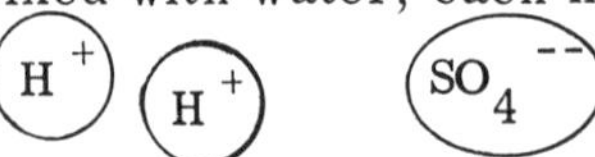

The + sign on the H symbolizes a hydrogen atom that has lost its one electron, called a hydrogen ion. (So a hydrogen ion is just one proton.) The SO_4^{--} is called a sulfate ion. It consists of one sulfur and 4 oxygen atoms, along with two extra electrons. The SO_4 group can not hold together without those two electrons. They are needed to fit into an electron-sharing arrangement that keeps the electron rings of the sulfur and four oxygens tied together.

2. The electrolyte solution in a dry cell contains ammonium chloride dissolved in water. Pure ammonium chloride is a white solid, like sodium chloride and magnesium chloride. The formula for ammonium chloride is NH_4Cl. Ammonium chloride separates into two ions when it dissolves: NH_4^+ and Cl^-. The symbol NH_4^+ means one nitrogen atom and four hydrogen atoms grouped together, with one electron having been lost. In this compound the electron lost by the NH_4 group is taken by the chlorine atom, forming a negative-charged chlorine ion, just like the chlorine ion of ordinary salt. The NH_4^+ group is called an ammonium ion.

3. In commercial electroplating of copper onto iron, a poisonous solid called "cuprous cyanide" is used to make the plating solution. Its formula is CuCN, the compound separates into Cu^+ and CN^-. Cu is the symbol for copper. Cu^+ represents a copper atom that has lost its outermost electron, now called a "cuprous ion". CN^- is one atom of carbon and one atom of nitrogen, held together with the help of the one electron taken from the copper atom. CN^- is named the cyanide ion.

4. Some copper plating processes use another copper compound, copper sulfate, $CuSO_4$, a blue crystal. When it dissolves in water it forms Cu^{++} and SO_4^{--} ions. Under some conditions a copper atom can lose two of its electrons, forming an ion called a cupric ion, written Cu^{++}. SO_4^{--} is the same sulfate ion described in connection with sulfuric acid.

An ion is an atom or group of atoms, electrically charged.

USEFUL PROCESSES DEPENDING ON CONDUCTION IN LIQUIDS

1. Electroplating. The plating of copper from a cyanide solution will serve to illustrate the electrical process that goes on in plating of metals. The object to be plated, which must be an electrical conductor, is connected to the negative terminal of a battery or D.C. generator and immersed in the cuprous cyanide solution. The positive terminal of the supply is connected to a copper bar in the solution. When the circuit is complete, positive-charged copper ions in the liquid move toward the object to be plated. When these copper ions touch the negative-charged object, they pick up electrons and become neutral atoms of ordinary copper. As ions become atoms at the surface of the negative-charged object, copper atoms pile up there and form a copper coating over the object. The generator pushes electrons onto the object to be plated, maintaining its negative charge.

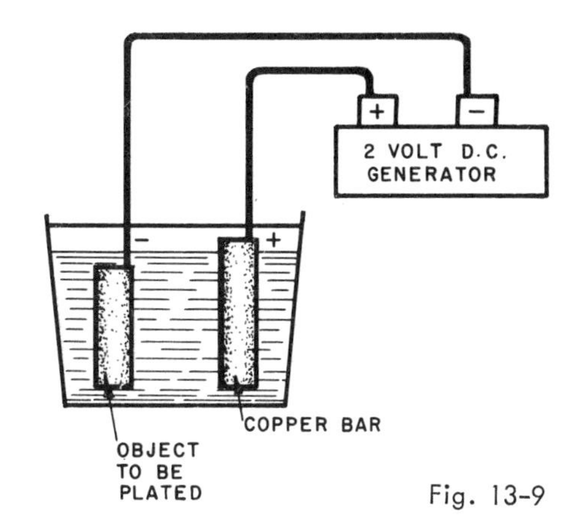

Fig. 13-9

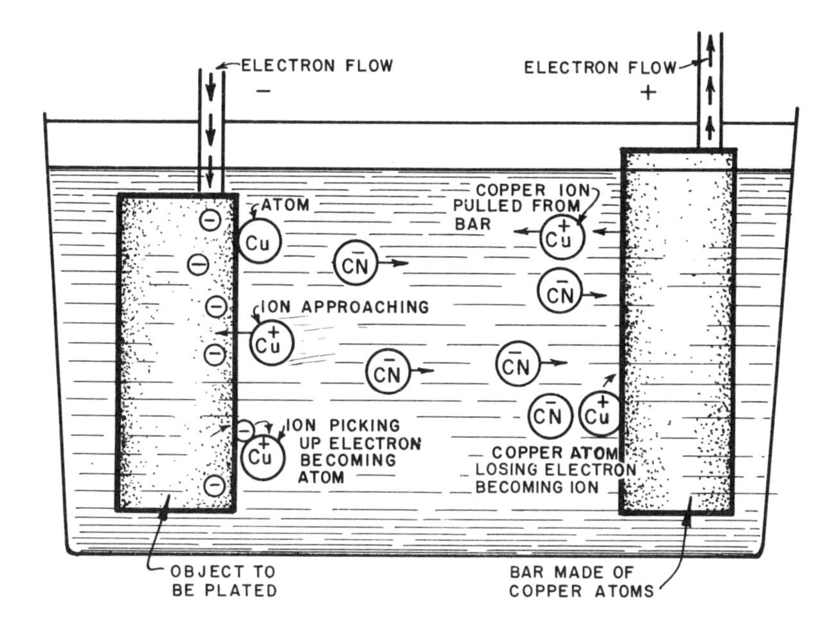

Fig. 13-10

When the cyanide ions bump into the positive copper bar at the right, copper atoms on the surface lose electrons and become ions. The negative CN ion pushes an electron off a copper atom, after which loss the copper is a positive ion, attracted into the solution by the negative ions. The electrons lost by the copper atoms drift toward the generator. Just as many copper ions dissolve from the copper bar as are plated on to the object to be plated, so the solution stays at constant strength.

In any electroplating process, copper, silver, nickel, etc., the solution must contain ions of the metal that is to form the coating. Metal ions are all positive, so the object to be plated is connected to the negative wire. The positive terminal normally is made of the same metal that is to form the coating. Plating processes are devised and controlled by chemists rather than by electricians. Plating solutions contain other ingredients than the dissolved metal compound, to prevent corrosion of the work to be plated, prevent poisonous fumes, and to aid in forming a smooth coating.

2. Purification of metals can be accomplished by performing a large-scale plating process. Practically all commercial copper is plated through copper-sulfate solution. Pure copper is built up on the negative plate. Impurities from the crude copper on the positive terminal either stay in the solution or never dissolve at all. Impure copper is high-resistance copper; the copper-wire industry has made electrolytically purified copper necessary. Zinc and other metals are purified in similar fashion.

3. The commercial production of metals and of nonmetallic elements is often a matter of separating the element from others with which it is chemically combined. In 1885, aluminum was a rare and precious metal, although aluminum oxide was not scarce. Aluminum metal became cheap when men found out how to take electrons from oxygen ions and put them back on to aluminum ions, forming aluminum atoms. Aluminum making is an electrical process similar to electroplating. Magnesium metal is made by electrically separating magnesium ions from chlorine ions (the magnesium chloride is obtained from sea water).

The term "electrolysis" means the separating of elements by using electrical energy. The electrolysis of water containing sulfuric acid deserves discussion because of its application in batteries. Hydrogen and oxygen are produced, but, for commercial use, these gases can be produced in large amount more cheaply by other processes.

ELECTROLYSIS OF SULFURIC ACID IN WATER

(On this diagram are two new words: "Cathode" means the terminal or electrode where electrons enter the cell. "Anode" is the electrode that carries electrons away from the cell.)

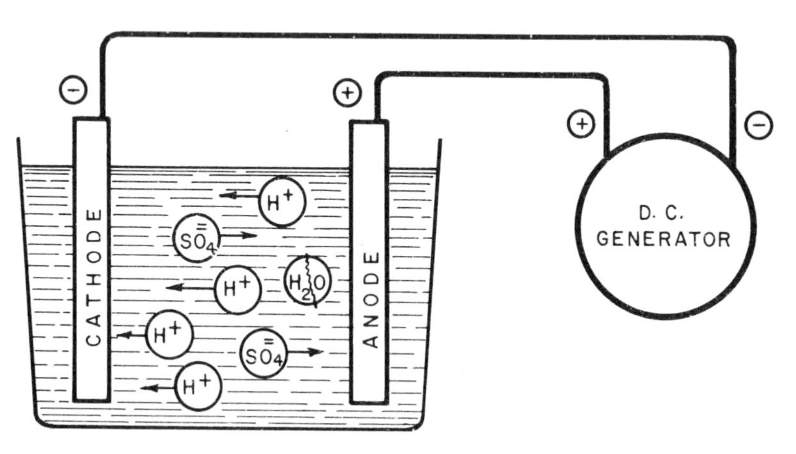

Fig. 13-11

Assume that the cathode and anode, Fig. 13-11, are made of materials that will not be affected by the acid, nor by the hydrogen or oxygen. When hydrogen ions touch the cathode, they pick up electrons from it, and become neutral atoms. Neutral atoms of hydrogen form ordinary hydrogen gas, which escapes as bubbles. When the sulfate ions approach the anode, in contact with water (H_2O) molecules, they force the breakup of the H_2O molecules. The positive anode will take electrons from something, and the SO_4^{--} ion does not part with its electrons as readily as a water molecule does. The removal of two electrons from the H_2O molecule leaves two H^+ ions and one oxygen atom. The oxygen atoms bubble away, and the H^+ ions stay in the solution. For each pair of hydrogen ions formed at the anode, a pair of hydrogen ions is discharged at the cathode. The amount of acid in the solution is constant; it is the H_2O that is broken up.

If this process is performed with lead plates for the cathode and anode, the oxygen does not all bubble away. A large share of it combines with the lead anode, forming lead dioxide. The hydrogen does not affect the cathode, which remains as pure lead. Plates of lead and lead dioxide in a solution of sulfuric acid are especially useful and are taken up further in Unit 15.

ELECTROLYTIC CORROSION

Corrosion is the rusting or chemical damaging or dissolving of a metal. Sometimes the process is desirable. For example, in copper plating, the copper anode dissolves and in that way maintains the needed dissolved copper in the plating solution. A similar but undesirable process goes on when there is an electrical current through the earth, which may follow buried water pipes for part of its path. At points where the buried metal is positive (anodic) compared to the earth, the attack on the pipe by negative ions converts useful metal atoms into useless metal ions, or more specifically converts iron pipe into iron rust. In the past, electrical railway systems have been accused, sometimes correctly, of such damage to nearby pipe.

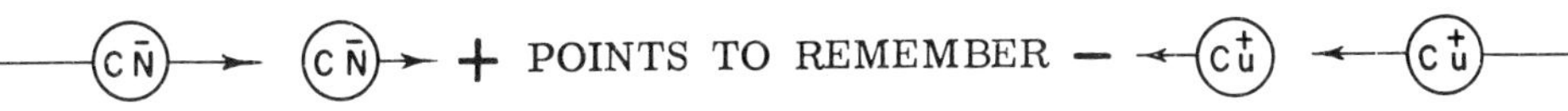

- Electrical conduction in liquids is the movement of both positive and negative ions. There are no individually loose electrons as in metal.

- Positive and negative ions are formed by a type of chemical combination in which one metallic element, (or group) transfers electrons to a nonmetallic element, (or group).

- If the above compound can dissolve in water, these charged ions become freely movable in the solution.

- In electroplating processes, the solution contains ions of the plating metal. The article to be plated is connected to the negative terminal of the current source. A bar of the plating metal is connected to the positive terminal.

- Metal taken from the plating solution to form the plate is replaced in the solution by metal dissolved from the positive bar.

- Liquid conduction moves positive ions one way, negative the other, resulting in a permanent separation of the parts of the compound. This decomposition is called electrolysis.

REVIEW QUESTIONS

1. How do metals differ from nonmetallic elements in the structure of their atoms?

2. What are ions?

3. Is dry salt a conductor?

4. Can a piece of wood be electroplated?

5. What would happen if the wires leading to the generator in Fig. 13-9 were reversed?

6. One of life's small disappointments: When disconnecting a car battery from the charging line by pulling the clip off the battery post, occasionally the top is blown off the battery. What's the cause and how can it be avoided?

7. Water is listed among the insulators in a table in the Appendix. If water is an insulator, how does it happen that electrocution is possible by contact between a power line and wet earth?

Unit 14 CONDUCTION IN GASES AND VACUUM

The development of induction coils for producing high voltages, the development of improved vacuum pumps, and the chemists' expanding knowledge of materials, made possible an entirely new field of study for the experimenters of 100 years ago. The conduction of current through gases captured the interest of scientists, for it provided a host of new observations to try to explain. Incidental to working out these explanations, and working out new experiments that the old ones suggested, we have been given these useful by-products: Electric arcs for lighting and welding, mercury vapor lamps to light the shop, sodium vapor lamps to light the highway, fluorescent lamps to light the kitchen, and neon lights to advertise all of them. From this same course of experimental work came vacuum tubes and the electronic industry, for investigation of the strange "cathode rays" found in some experiments led directly to the discovery and identification of a particle called an "electron".

Gases Are Normally Insulators

At atmospheric pressure, air and other gases are about as close to being ideal insulators as any material we have. With air, or other gases, as the insulator between two charged plates, Fig. 14-1, the current is practically zero as long as a moderate voltage is applied. At sufficiently high voltage, the gas suddenly becomes a conductor, with the amount of current limited only by the rest of the circuit.

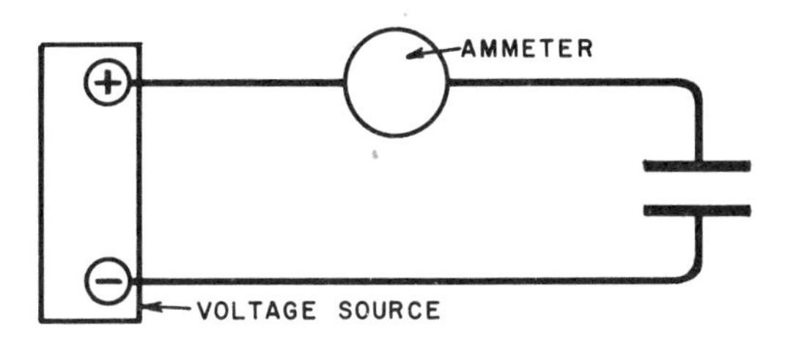

Fig. 14-1

At pressures lower than atmospheric, this breakdown in insulating ability occurs at lower voltage. If the pressure is increased, as in compressed air, the applied voltage necessary to start conduction has to be increased proportionally. For example, a higher voltage is required to fire a spark plug under compression in an engine than is required to create the spark in the open air.

Sparks and Arcs

A spark is a noisy, irregular discharge; successive sparks follow separate paths. (This statement refers to sparks that are electron paths. The sparks seen when a wire is brushed across the terminals of a car battery, spraying in all directions, are more like sparks from a grinding wheel, being tiny fragments of hot metal.)

An arc is a quieter and continuous discharge. An arc in air consists of a conducting path of highly heated gas or metallic vapor. The resistance of the air is broken down completely, and some sort of external resistance must be in the circuit to limit the current. The potential drop across the arc itself is moderately low, (15-50 v.). Most of the high intensity light of an arc comes from the vapor, but some comes from the hot cathode. Cathode temperature of a carbon arc can be 9000° F.

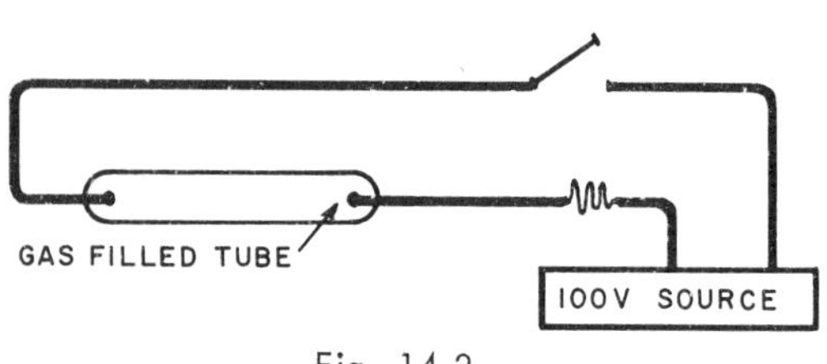

Fig. 14-2

How Is Conduction In a Gas Started?

If the gas is inside a glass tube at low pressure, with wires sealed into the tube, the application of just moderately high voltage (generally 50 volts or more) is enough to start conduction. In the air, a useful arc is started by touching, then separating, a pair of conducting contacts: example, welding arc or carbon arc.

But just how does the gas conduct? What goes on in the gas so that it becomes a conductor? IONIZATION. Electrons are torn away from gas atoms, causing the gas atoms to become positively charged ions. The loosened electrons are highly movable, and conduction in the gas is due mainly to electron flow (as in metals). Movable positive ions do exist (as in liquids). Even so, the nature of conduction in a gas differs greatly from conduction in a solid or a liquid.

How Ionization Occurs

(1) The most important process involved in ionization is electron impact. The process may start by an electron torn free from the negative wire, or more likely an electron set free from an atom by processes described under (2) or (3) which follow. Once an electron is set free, it picks up speed as it is repelled by the - wire and attracted toward the + wire. If it bumps into an atom while it is still moving slowly, it merely bounces off and again starts toward the positive terminal. When it gets moving fast enough, it will collide with an atom violently enough to knock one or more electrons loose from the atom.

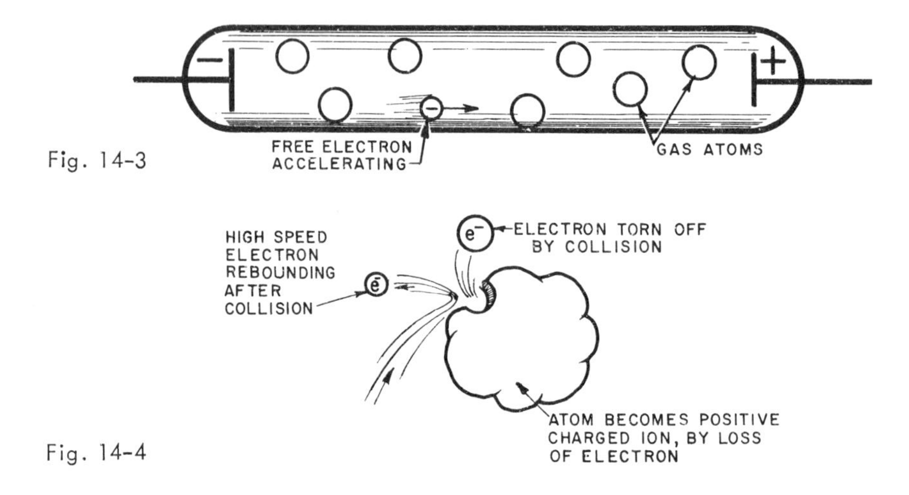

Fig. 14-3

Fig. 14-4

The minimum amount of energy that an electron must possess to cause this ionization is called "ionization potential" and depends on the kind of atom that is being hit. The ionization potential for sodium vapor is about 5 volts. For most gases it is between 10 and 25 volts (mercury vapor 10.4, neon 21.5, helium 24.5). That is, to ionize neon, an electron must have fallen through a potential difference of 21.5 volts.

Returning to the ionization process, Fig. 14-4, the original colliding electron has set another free. So now there are two loose electrons that start accelerating toward the positive wire. They collide with atoms. Each jars another loose. Now there are four. Their collisions loosen more electrons, and in a thousandth of a second a million electrons may have been released by these collisions.

As a comparison, picture what would happen in an apple tree, heavily loaded with apples, in which an apple will be jarred loose if hit by another apple that has fallen 6 inches. Accidentally one apple is jarred loose near the top of the tree . . . and the chain reaction causes a bushel of apples to hit the ground.

Gaseous conduction produces light as a result of collisions that are not violent enough to tear electrons loose. A moderately fast-moving electron, by collision, may give some of its energy to the electrons of the atom, producing a so-called "excited state" in the atom. This energy-loaded excited atom usually gets rid of its energy by emitting light. The color of the light is characteristic of the energy state of the atom.

(2) A second process that ionizes gas is radiation. Cosmic rays ionize a few atoms, and this is often the source of the first electron to initiate the collision process. After conduction has started, electron disturbances in atoms produce not only visible light, but also a lot of higher-frequency radiation (ultra-violet) which is absorbed by other atoms, giving them enough energy to cause electrons to separate.

(3) Another ionizing process is heat. A hot gas conducts better and starts conducting easier than a cold gas. Heat is movement of atoms and molecules. At higher temperature, collisions of atoms may become violent enough to dislodge electrons. Many of the individual atoms are at higher temperature than the average, and these temporary speed demons cause ionizing collisions. An ordinary flame contains many ions, hence is a poor insulator, as may be shown by bringing a match flame near a charged electroscope.

(4) There are other sources of electrons. For example, positive ions still have electrons and collision of positive ions can release more electrons, leaving the ions more strongly positive. Also, "excited" gas atoms, by colliding with other kinds of atoms, can cause a release of electrons from the other atoms they hit. For example, conduction is maintained better in neon gas if it contains a trace of nitrogen. Excited neon atoms, colliding with nitrogen, give enough energy to the nitrogen atoms to cause the nitrogen to release electrons.

Why Should a Low-Pressure Gas Conduct Better Then a High-Pressure Compressed Gas?

In gas at atmospheric pressure, a free electron collides with gas atoms so frequently that it has no chance for enough unhindered travel to pick up enough speed to ionize an atom by collision.

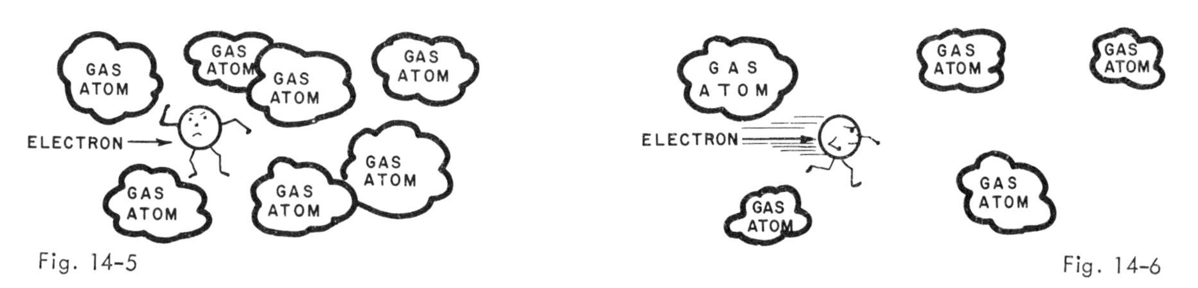

Fig. 14-5

Fig. 14-6

At lower pressures, gas molecules are farther apart, giving room and opportunity for an electron to gain enough kinetic energy for an ionizing collision.

Gas tube designers are, therefore, concerned with calculating the "mean free path" of electrons, meaning the average distance traveled by a particle between collisions.

What Becomes of All Those Electrons and Ions That Are Set Free?

The useful conduction is accomplished by those electrons that reach the positive terminal. In a glass tube, many of the free-moving electrons collect on the walls of the tube. Positive ions that bump into the walls are neutralized by the negative charge collected there.

In an ordinary gas-conduction tube, about 1 atom out of every thousand is ionized, on the average. The main part of the glowing discharge in the tube, filled with a swarm of positive ions, electrons, and neutral atoms, is called the "plasma". The voltage drop in this region is not large; most of the voltage drop occurs near the electrodes. We are likely to hear more about plasmas, because scientists are not through with their investigations of what can be accomplished in gas induction tubes. Presently, experiments are going on in which terrifically-high amperage bursts of current in hydrogen at low pressure produce plasmas that are contained by their own magnetic field. The purpose is to attain particle speeds that correspond to temperatures in the millions of degrees, at which temperature hydrogen nuclei can fuse into helium. This hydrogen fusion has been going on continually in the sun for a few million years. It happens suddenly when an H-bomb explodes. For hundreds of years, men have sought a cheap source of energy; maybe a tame little continuous H-bomb in a bottle will be the answer.

Conduction and Ions in Nature

The frequently visible Northern Lights (aurora borealis) is believed due to conduction in the very thin upper part of the atmosphere. This display seems to be caused by electrons given off by disturbances on the sun, traveling in toward the earth.

High-speed protons coming toward the earth from outer space strike air molecules and produce intense radiation that ionizes various layers of the atmosphere. These conducting layers have the ability of reflecting radio signals, which reflections are often useful.

Lightning is a high-voltage spark. Sometimes, conditions not violent enough to produce lightning cause a continuous discharge from steeple tops or ships' masts. A strong electric field ionizes the air at sharp-pointed electrodes; the discharge is visible if other illumination does not interfere. This type of discharge, called corona, occurs in all sorts of high-voltage equipment, and can be a serious source of power loss in high-voltage transmission lines.

Conduction in Vacuum

If gas is pumped from a glass tube until the pressure in the tube is reduced to about that of 0.0001 mm. of mercury (760 mm. of mercury = atmospheric pressure) the brilliant glowing of the conducting gas is no longer seen. Gas molecules are so far apart that few ions are formed, and conduction consists practically entirely of electron flow. The glass tubing itself may glow due to electrons striking the glass.

If the gas pressure is reduced much more, the discharge may stop entirely, in a cold cathode tube. If the cathode wire is arranged so that it can be heated by another current, conduction through the vacuum continues by means of electrons that escape from the hot cathode.

Eighty years ago, the many men experimenting with conduction in gases and vacuum had no idea of the existence of electrons. They gave the name "cathode rays" to whatever it was that was coming from the cathode in their tubes. In 1869 Hittorf, a German, described the glowing of glass struck by these rays, and showed by experiments that the rays traveled in straight lines. Crookes, an Englishman, found that the ray-paths could be bent by a magnet, they could be focused, they heat the objects they strike, and their speed depended on the applied voltage. Crookes suggested, in 1879, that these rays might be "an ultra-gaseous state of matter". Perrin, a Frenchman, in 1895, showed that the rays carried a negative charge and that positive ions were also formed. By 1897, J. J. Thomson, an Englishman, completed a series of experiments in which he was able to measure the ratio of weight to electric charge of the negative particles. From this work, Thomson is credited with clinching the discovery of tiny, lightweight, negative-charged particles, present in all materials, to which the name "electrons" is given.

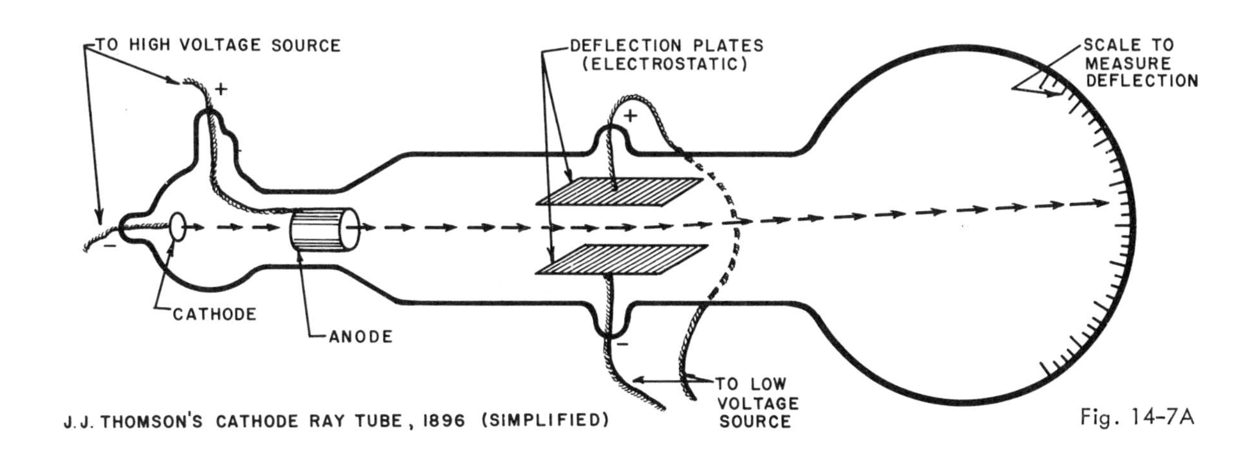

J.J. THOMSON'S CATHODE RAY TUBE, 1896 (SIMPLIFIED)

Fig. 14-7A

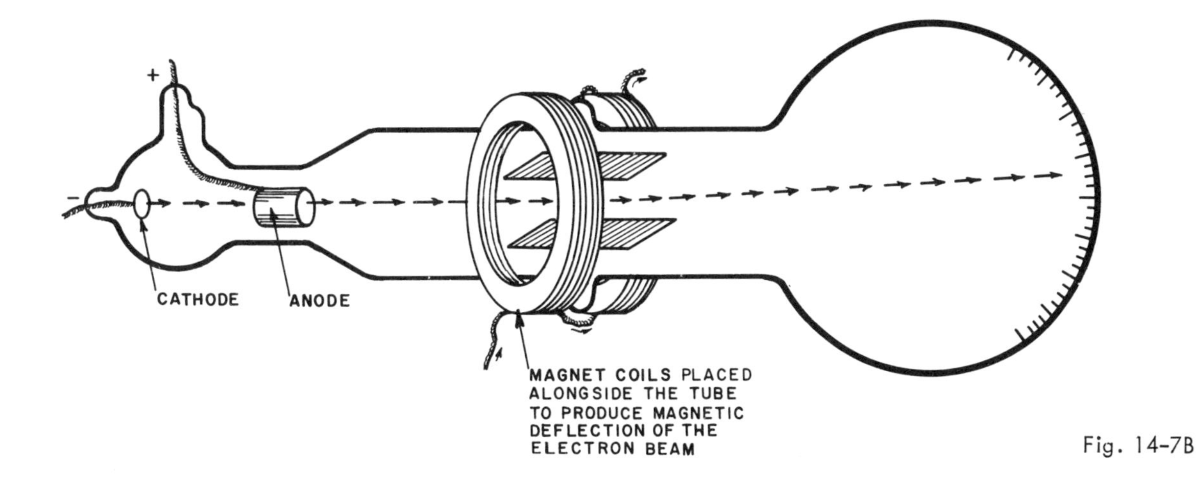

Fig. 14-7B

It was in 1895 that Wilhelm Roentgen, experimenting with cathode-ray tubes, found that when the cathode rays struck metal or glass a new kind of radiation was produced. These new invisible rays passed through air, paper, and wood very well, through thin metal better than thick, through flesh better than through bone, through aluminum better than through lead. The rays caused fluorescence in minerals, affected photographic plates, and were not bent by a magnet. Roentgen called them X-rays. Within a few months, physicians were using them as an aid in setting broken bones.

It should be noted that present day cathode ray tubes, used in oscilloscopes and TV picture tubes, use the same principles of electron-ray deflection that Thomson used in his experiments.

In oscilloscopes, the electron beam accelerated from the cathode is deflected horizontally at a known rate, and the voltage whose trace is to be observed is used to deflect the beam vertically at the same time, thus producing a time graph of the observed voltage, (Fig. 14-8).

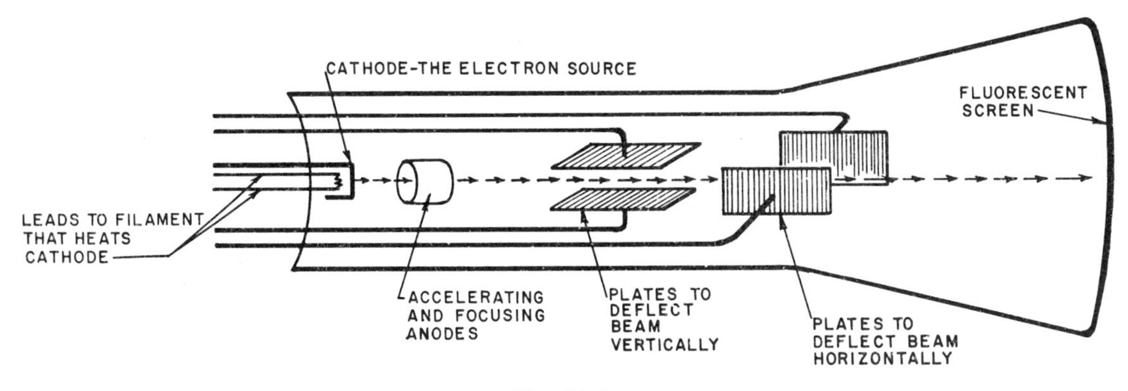

Fig. 14-8

In TV picture tubes, magnet coils are used to sweep the beam horizontally and vertically, while the intensity of the beam is changed to produce lights and darks in the picture.

There has been some concern as to the possibility of harmful X-rays being produced by the 20,000-volt electrons that strike the face of the TV picture tube. This voltage is not high enough to cause highly energetic and penetrating X-rays. Recent experiments have shown that, if there are any X-rays produced, they are all absorbed in the glass and in the first inch of air in front of the tube, so there is no cause for concern.

Edison had a chance to discover electrons, but missed it. As the story goes, one of his assistants accidentally connected a meter to a dead end wire sealed into one of Edison's experimental electric lamps, and found a small current, (Fig. 14-9).

The heated lamp filament was certainly emitting electrons, but nobody knew that at the time (1883). Those loose electrons, attracted to the positive wire through the meter, caused the current. This event was reported, but not used until 20 years later, when Fleming constructed a two-element valve to use as a rectifier. (The two "elements" are the filament, which emits electrons, and the plate, which catches them when the plate is positive. "Valve" is the British term for vacuum tube.) In later years, when Edison was asked why the third wire was sealed into his lamp bulb, he is reported to have said, "I have forgotten."

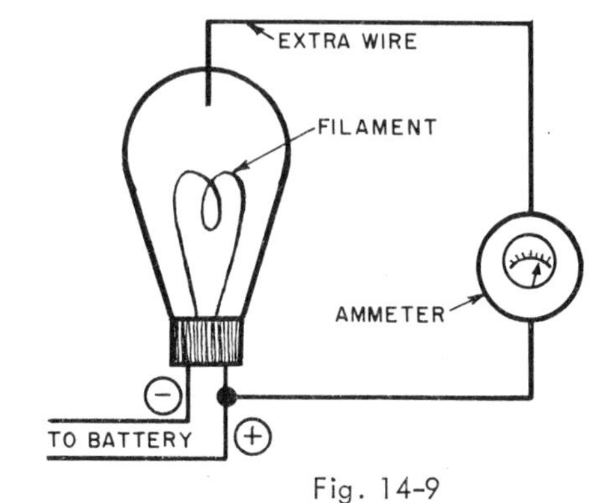

Fig. 14-9

The subject of electron conduction in vacuum tubes is not to be pursued further in this Unit. The applications of vacuum tubes and gas-conduction tubes in communication and control devices make up the field of Electronics.

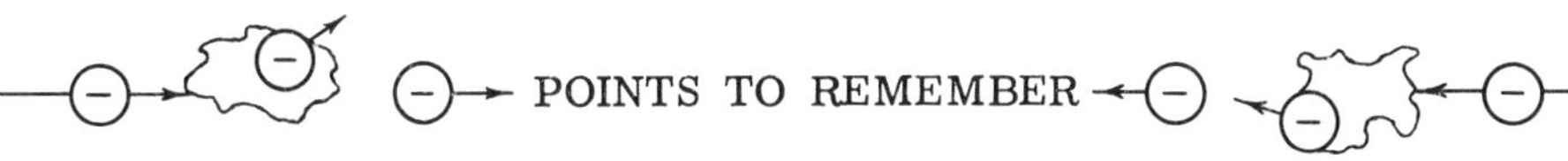

- The unfinished study of conduction in gases and vacuum has been especially rewarding to scientists, for the new knowledge obtained resulted in a great array of practical discoveries.

- Gases are good insulators - up to a point. When sufficient voltage is applied, sudden ionization changes them to conductors.

- Ionization of a gas is the loosening of electrons from gas molecules. The positive-charged gas atoms (or molecules) are the positive ions. The electrons are the movable negative particles.

- Conduction in a gas consists mainly of electron movement. As electrons collide with gas atoms, a continual new supply of electrons are shaken free from the atoms.

- Gases at low pressure become conducting more readily than gases at high pressure.

- At low near-vacuum pressures, electrons from the cathode travel out in straight paths, originally called cathode rays. The discovery of electrons consisted of measurement of their properties in cathode ray tubes.

REVIEW QUESTIONS

1. Special problems in insulation have had to be solved in development of electrical control systems for high-altitude missiles. Why should any special problems exist?

2. Who discovered electrons?

3. What's the difference between "cathode rays" and "electrons"?

4. Name some useful examples of gaseous conduction.

5. Is it true that practically all of the useful discoveries in this field have already been made?

As a reminder, e.m.f. abbreviates Electromotive Force, or electron-moving force. Like potential difference, we measure it in volts. By custom, rather than necessity, we often use the term e.m.f. for the voltage produced inside a current source such as a battery or generator.

And what is chemical energy? It is potential energy possessed by a material, or combination of materials, due to some particular arrangement of electrons or atoms. The combinations of materials that form batteries are some of the same combinations discussed in Unit 13: metals, nonmetallic elements, and ions of the salt-like materials formed when the metals and nonmetals combine.

A combination of materials that possess chemical energy was shown in Fig. 13-2, Page 129, magnesium and chlorine. The loose electrons of magnesium's outer ring tend to fall into the empty spaces in the outer rings of chlorine atoms. If we could make those electrons travel through a wire to get from the magnesium to the chlorine, this energy could be used to light a lamp or run a motor.

It was noted in Unit 13 that magnesium's outer electrons have so much tendency to drop into chlorine atoms that if we put a piece of hot magnesium into chlorine, a combustion results. This process makes magnesium chloride and a lot of heat.

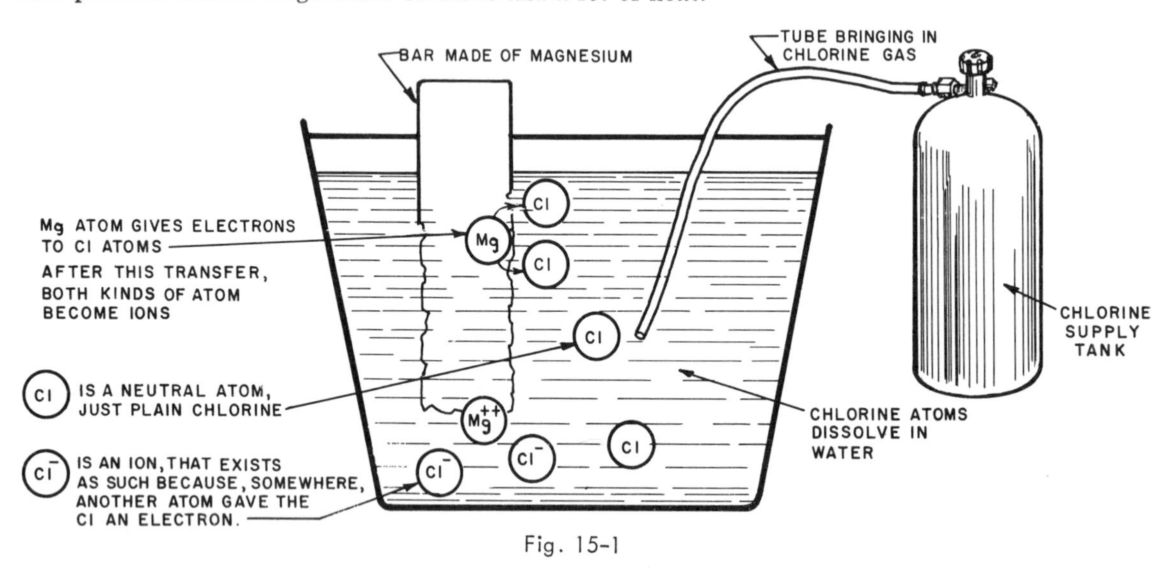

Fig. 15-1

The process could be slowed down by performing the getting-together of Mg atoms and Cl atoms in a dish of water, as in Fig. 15-1.

The magnesium bar will now dissolve gradually, corroding away under the action of the chlorine. Chlorine gas atoms that touch the magnesium bar convert themselves, with the Mg, into magnesium chloride.

But our original purpose, remember, was to produce electrical current. In the Fig. 15-1 equipment, the electrons jump directly from Mg atoms to Cl atoms, without doing any useful work on the way. Let's make them take a longer trip.

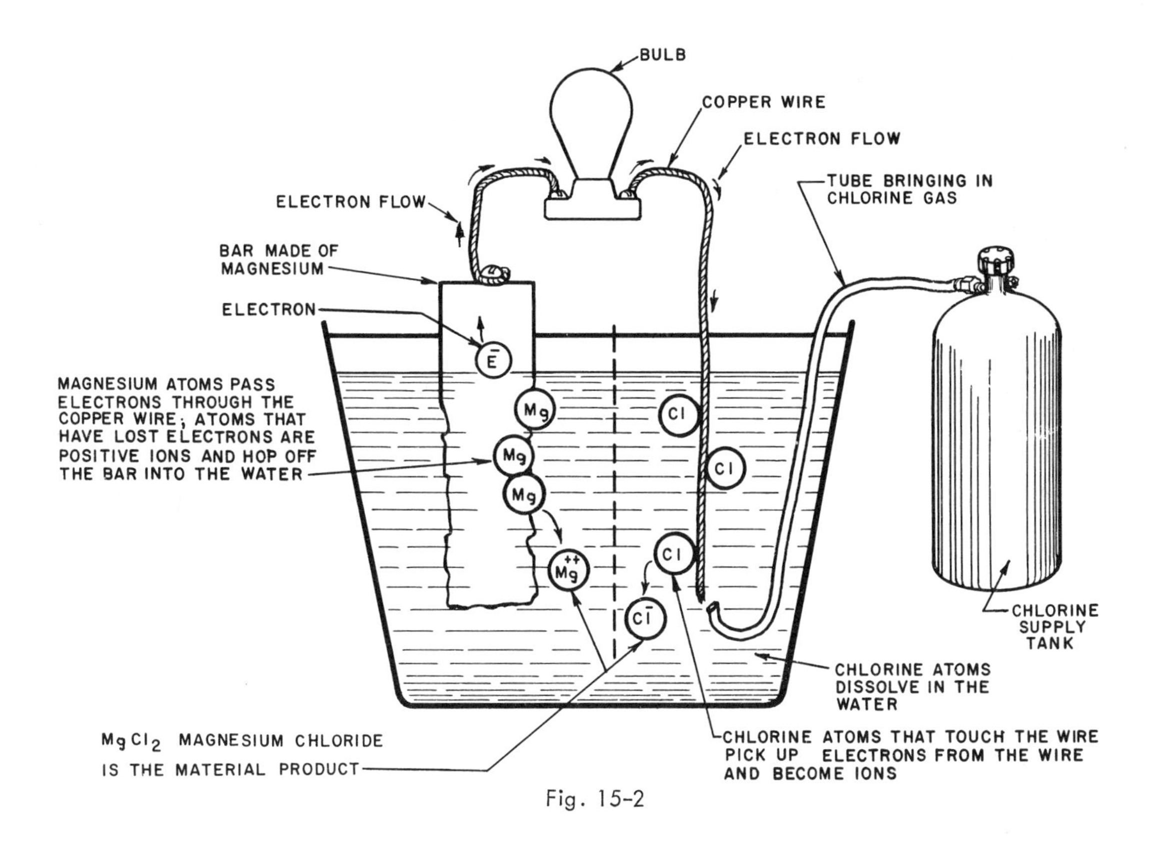

Fig. 15-2

In Fig. 15-2, we have added a copper wire and a lamp bulb. Let the dotted vertical line down the center represent some cotton in the water, just to prevent mixing of the water, keeping the Cl atoms from getting in contact with the magnesium directly. The copper wire, and bulb, is now an electron carrier from Mg to Cl, and electrons will have to take that path if they are going to get from the Mg to the Cl. Mg and Cl are the source of the potential energy difference (or e.m.f.) that moves electrons through the wire and lamp. There is no intention of suggesting that this is a practical cell. It is a fairly simple example of electron transfer, arranged to illustrate the idea that cells and batteries produce current just because loose electrons of metals travel to some other material that will accept them.

With Fig. 15-2 in view, some conclusions can be noted that apply to all cells and batteries: First, how shall we label the positive and negative terminals of this cell? Notice that electrons move through the lamp, from the magnesium to the copper wire in the liquid. Therefore, the magnesium bar will be labeled negative and the part of the copper that is in the liquid is the positive terminal.

Secondly - will this process ever stop? Yes, because the electrons that form the useful current come from the atoms of metal that make up the negative electrode. As long as current is produced, the negative electrode is being dissolved. When it is all dissolved, the process stops; the electron source is used up.

Third - does it make any difference what kinds of metals are used? Yes, the amount of voltage depends on what kinds of metals are used as well as on what kinds of atoms and ions are in solution. For example, if, instead of magnesium, a metal that has more tendency to lose electrons is substituted, more voltage (e.m.f.) is produced. Or, if a metal whose electrons have less tendency to escape is substituted, voltage is less.

Also, the positive electrode has an effect on the e.m.f. available. If the positive electrode hands electrons off into the solution easily, e.m.f. is higher than if there is some sort of energy-barrier at the surface of the electrode that makes it difficult for electrons to slide off the positive electrode into the ions in the solution.

ELECTROMOTIVE SERIES OF ELEMENTS
Sodium
Calcium
Magnesium
Aluminum
Zinc
Chromium
Cadmium
Iron
Cobalt
Nickel
Tin
Lead
Hydrogen
Copper
Mercury
Silver
Platinum
Gold

The term "loose electrons" of a metal has been used considerably. It is time to notice that ease of conduction in the metal is one thing and ease of escape from the metal is another. The column at the right lists metals in order of ease of escape of electrons into water solution. This is entirely different from a list arranged according to conductivity.

Metals at the top of the list lose electrons very readily. Elements at the bottom of the list have less tendency to lose them.

Although many combinations of materials are theoretically possible for making batteries, only a few combinations are really practical. With many combinations, undesirable chemical reactions take place that either cause the active metal to corrode away too fast, or interfere with useful current production by building up resistance.

The invention, or discovery, of cells and batteries was prompted by a few experiments performed on frogs' legs by Luigi Galvani, a professor of medicine at the University of Bologna, in 1791. Galvani noticed muscular contractions in frog legs when they formed what we would call an electrical circuit between a brass hook and an iron plate. His explanation was erroneous, but it was the first recorded note of the effect of a steady electric current, as opposed to the spark-like discharges of static electricity which were the only previously known form of electricity. For a while, this new form of electricity was called "galvanic" electricity, and devices for indicating it were called "galvanometers".

This investigation of Galvani's was taken up with useful results by a physics professor named Allessandro Volta. By 1800, Volta proved that the source of the electrical energy lay in the metals and liquid conductor, and the frogs' legs were unnecessary.

He showed how to make cells out of various combinations of metals with salt water, how to connect them in series to get increased e.m.f., and showed that their effects were similar to static discharges.

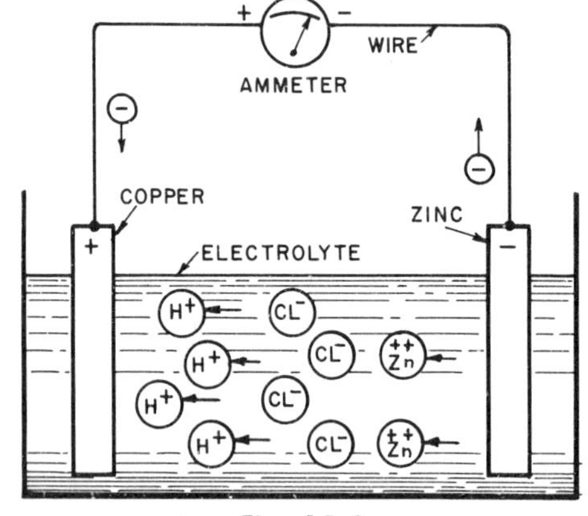

Fig. 15-3

Through the years, a great variety of cells have been manufactured, most of which are of interest only to museums. One type, although obsolete, deserves attention because it illustrates in a simple way a useful type of reaction.

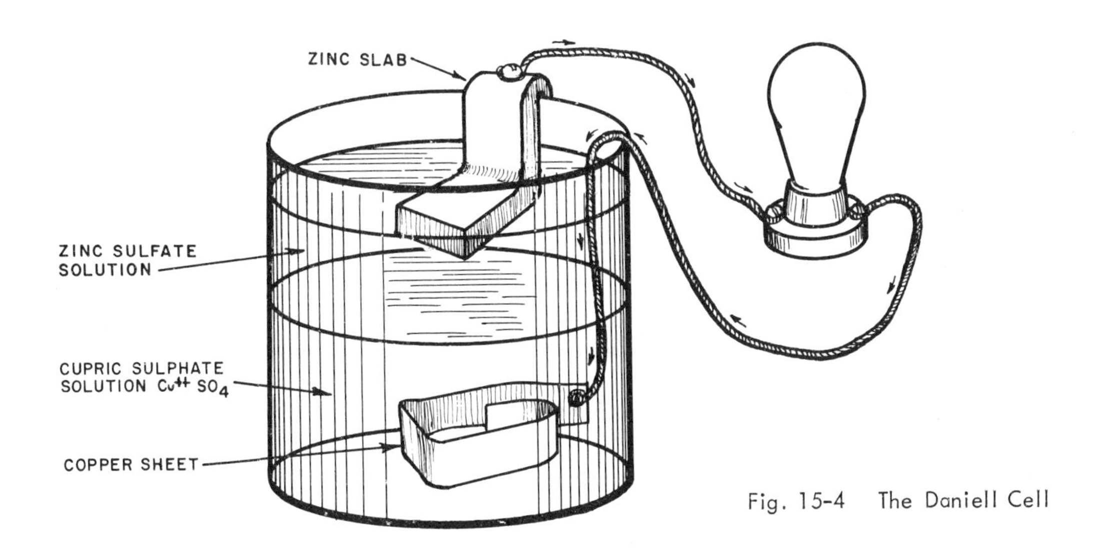

Fig. 15-4 The Daniell Cell

In the Daniell cell, the zinc slab at the top is the source of loose electrons. The cupric (copper) sulfate solution contains Cu^{++} ions and SO_4^{--} ions. The Cu^{++} ions take on the electrons that they attract from the zinc. Electrons given by the zinc travel through the wire, and jump off the copper sheet on to the positive Cu^{++} ions in the solution, changing them to plain copper, Cu.

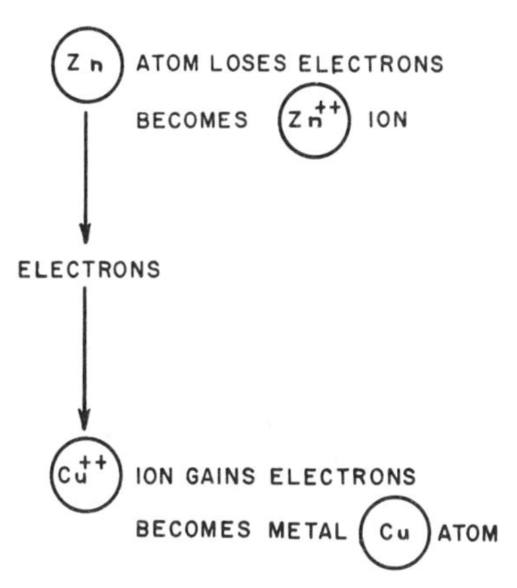

Loose electrons of the zinc, instead of being attracted by a nonmetal element as in a previous example, are attracted by a positive ion. This is just as good a combination of materials to produce e.m.f. from chemical energy.

What happens to the zinc slab? It gradually dissolves if continued current is permitted. It changes into Zn^{++} ions.

What happens to the copper sheet? Nothing happens to the original copper metal, but more copper metal collects on it because it is at the surface of this metal that copper ions pick up electrons and change to atoms.

Do these two solutions, zinc sulfate and cupric sulfate, mix? No, because $CuSO_4$ solution is heavier than $ZnSO_4$. No harm is caused if they do mix a little.

What happens to the SO_4^{--} ions? Not a thing. They float idly around in the solution, watching the number of Zn^{++} ions increase and the number of Cu^{++} ions decrease.

Why is this Daniell cell obsolete? Doesn't it work? It works, but it's inconvenient. It takes 110 of them in series to make 120 volts, they do not carry around easily, and purchasing zinc and copper sulfate is an expensive way of purchasing energy, even allowing for the trade-in value of the copper that is being made from the $CuSO_4$.

The Daniell is an example of a so-called Primary Cell, meaning one that uses up its active metal and cannot be recharged.

The most-used primary cell is the ordinary "dry cell". A new dry cell isn't dry inside, it's pasty. The source of electrons (negative terminal) is a piece of zinc that serves as the container for the cell. Electrons from the zinc are carried through the useful external circuit to a carbon rod in the center of the cell which conducts those electrons to positive NH_4^+ ions in the solution inside the cell. The solution in the cell is ammonium chloride (NH_4Cl) dissolved in water. The driving energy of the cell is the tendency of loose electrons to leave zinc atoms and go toward the NH_4^+ ions, very much like the action in the Daniell cell in some respects.

The above paragraph describes the production of the cell current. The following description is merely a few more chemical details, not essential to producing electron flow: When the NH_4^+ ion catches an electron, it splits into NH_3 which is ammonia gas and H which is hydrogen. The ammonia can either dissolve in moisture or combine with Zn^{++} ions, forming a complex $Zn(NH_3)_4^{++}$ ion. Hydrogen is oxidized, becoming H_2O when acted on by oxygen from yet another compound, manganese dioxide.

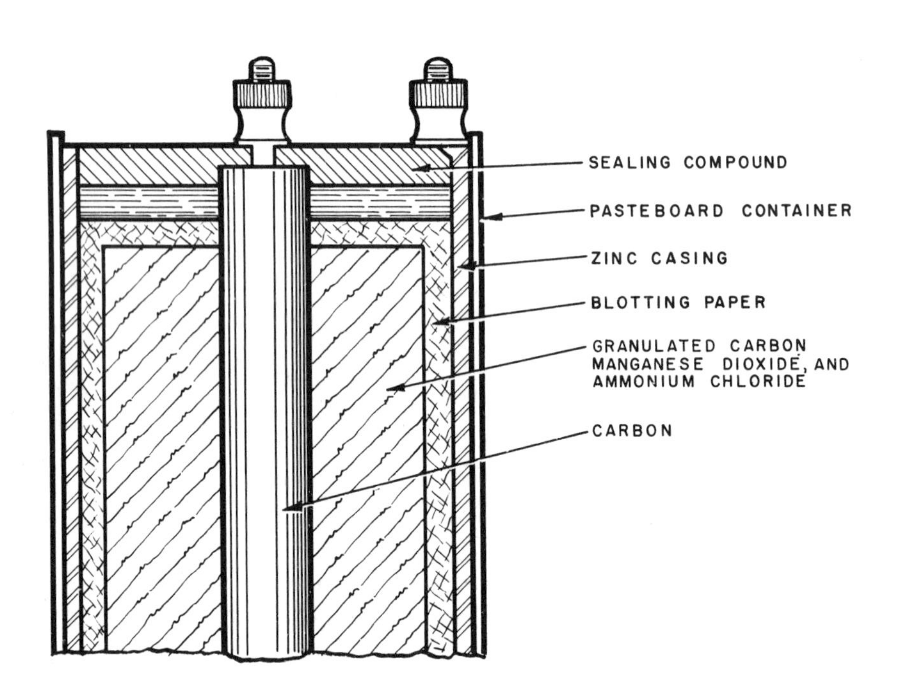

Fig. 15-5

As in other primary cells, when the zinc is dissolved, the "dry cell" is used up. Devices for recharging dry cells are occasionally sold to gullible people, reducing their purchasing power and probably preventing inflation.

To this point, e.m.f. of cells has been mentioned but what determines the current? In order to permit a large current (amperes) readily, a cell must have a large area of metal plate in contact with the electrolyte solution, on both the positive and negative terminals. This makes it easy for electron transfers to take place; in other words the resistance of the cell is low. A little pen-light dry cell has just as much e.m.f. as a large No. 6 dry cell, but it cannot produce as many amperes because the little cell has more internal resistance. (Ohm's Law is still working.)

COMPOSITION OF VARIOUS CELLS

Single-fluid Primary Cells

	Negative	Positive	Electrolyte	E.M.F.
Simple Voltaic Combinations	zinc	copper	dilute H_2SO_4	1.0
	zinc	silver	dilute H_2SO_4	1.2
	zinc	silver	salt (NaCl solution)	1.0
Leclanche (dry cell)	zinc	carbon	ammonium chloride	1.5
Edison-Lalande	zinc	copper	KOH solution	0.7
Silver Chloride	zinc	silver	NH_4Cl solution	1.0
R-M	zinc	HgO	KOH solution	1.3

Double-fluid Primary Cells

	Negative	Positive	E.M.F.
Daniell	zinc in 5% $ZnSO_4$	copper in $CuSO_4$ solution	1.08
Grove	zinc in H_2SO_4, $ZnSO_4$, or NaCl	platinum in nitric acid	1.7-1.9
Bunsen	zinc in dilute H_2SO_4	carbon in nitric acid	1.9
Bichromate	zinc in dilute H_2SO_4	carbon in potassium bichromate solution	2.0

Storage Cells

	Negative	Positive	Electrolyte	E.M.F.
Lead	lead	lead dioxide	dilute sulfuric acid	2.0
Edison	iron	nickel oxides	20% KOH solution	1.2
Main	zinc	lead dioxide	dilute sulfuric acid	2.5
Nickel-Cadmium	cadmium	nickel hydroxide	KOH	1.2
Regnier	copper	lead dioxide	$CuSO_4$, H_2SO_4	1.5

Standard Cell

	Negative	Positive	Electrolyte	E.M.F.
Weston	cadmium	mercury	cadmium sulfate solution	1.0183

The above tables include several obsolete cells of historical interest only, in order to illustrate the variety of possible cell materials.

A recent development is the RM (Ruben-Mallory) or mercury cell. It is light, compact, and maintains its voltage well up to the end of its useful life, when the voltage drops rapidly. A gradual falling off of voltage, as in ordinary dry cells, is undesirable, especially in hearing aids and portable radios. The negative terminal of the RM cell is the zinc button in the center. The positive terminal is the steel container that holds carbon and mercuric oxide. The mercury Hg^{++} ion of the mercury oxide takes electrons from the zinc.

THE LEAD STORAGE BATTERY

Each lead cell produces 2 volts. 6-volt automobile batteries have 3 cells in series; 12-volt batteries have 6 cells in series.

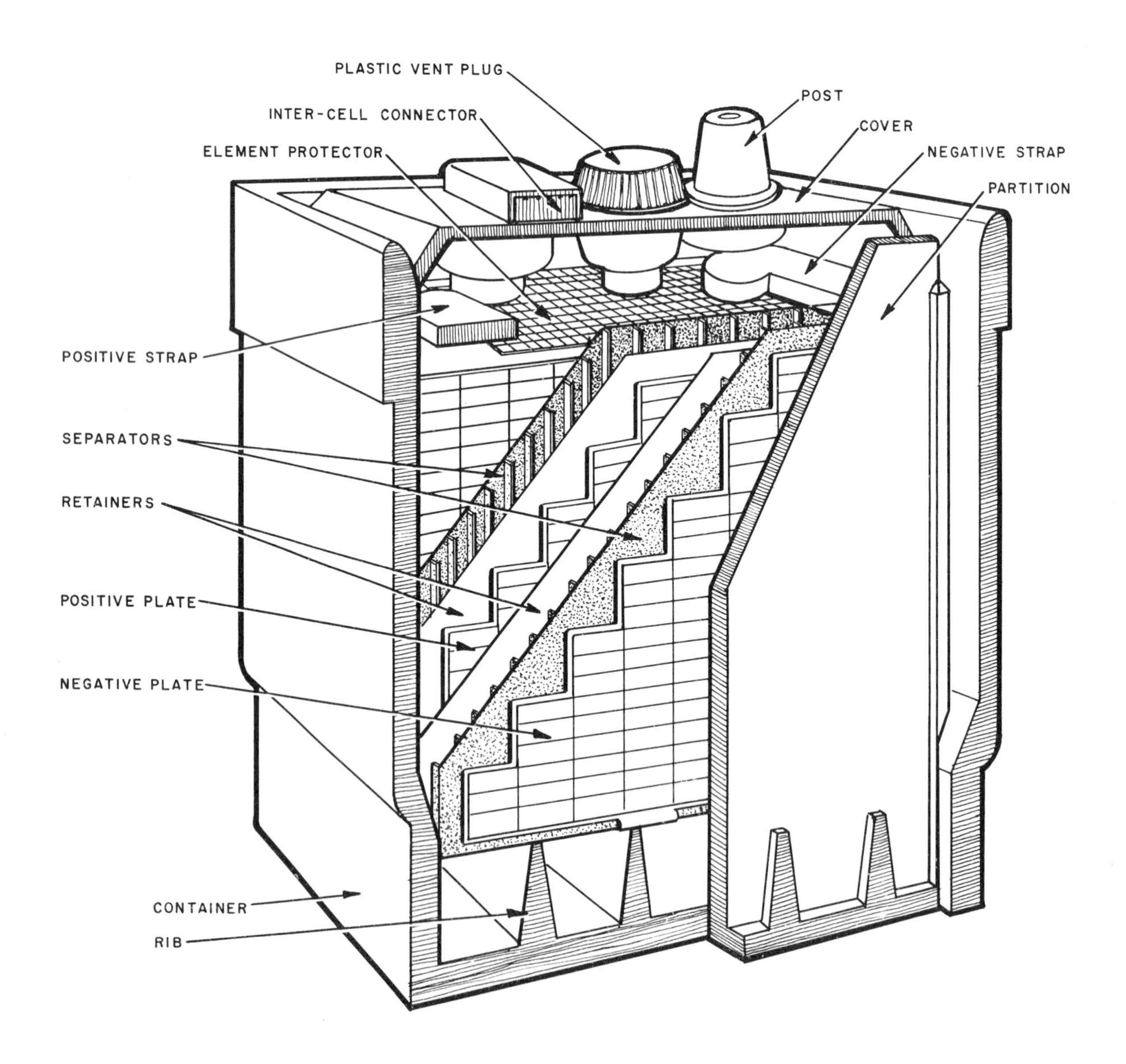

The Lead Storage Battery

The negative plate consists of metallic lead. When the cell is producing current, lead atoms on the surface of the plate lose two electrons each, becoming Pb^{++} ions. These Pb^{++} ions do not dissolve into the liquid, but remain on the plate and attract SO_4^{--} ions from the sulfuric acid solution, thus forming an invisibly-thin layer of $PbSO_4$ on the negative lead plate.

The positive plate consists of lead dioxide, PbO_2, in which each lead particle is lacking four electrons, which were given to the oxygen when the plate was formed. Each Pb^{++++} ion takes two electrons from the external circuit, becoming Pb^{++}.

The energy is obtained from the tendency of neutral lead atoms to give 2 electrons each to Pb^{++++} ions, both becoming Pb^{++} as a result of the transfer.

Incidentally, when the Pb^{++++} ions of the lead dioxide pick up the two electrons, they can no longer hold the oxygen, which goes into the acid solution and combines with hydrogen ions of the acid, forming water molecules. The Pb^{++} remains on the plate and picks up SO_4^{--} from the sulfuric acid solution, forming lead sulfate. These actions are shown on the diagram, Fig. 15-6.

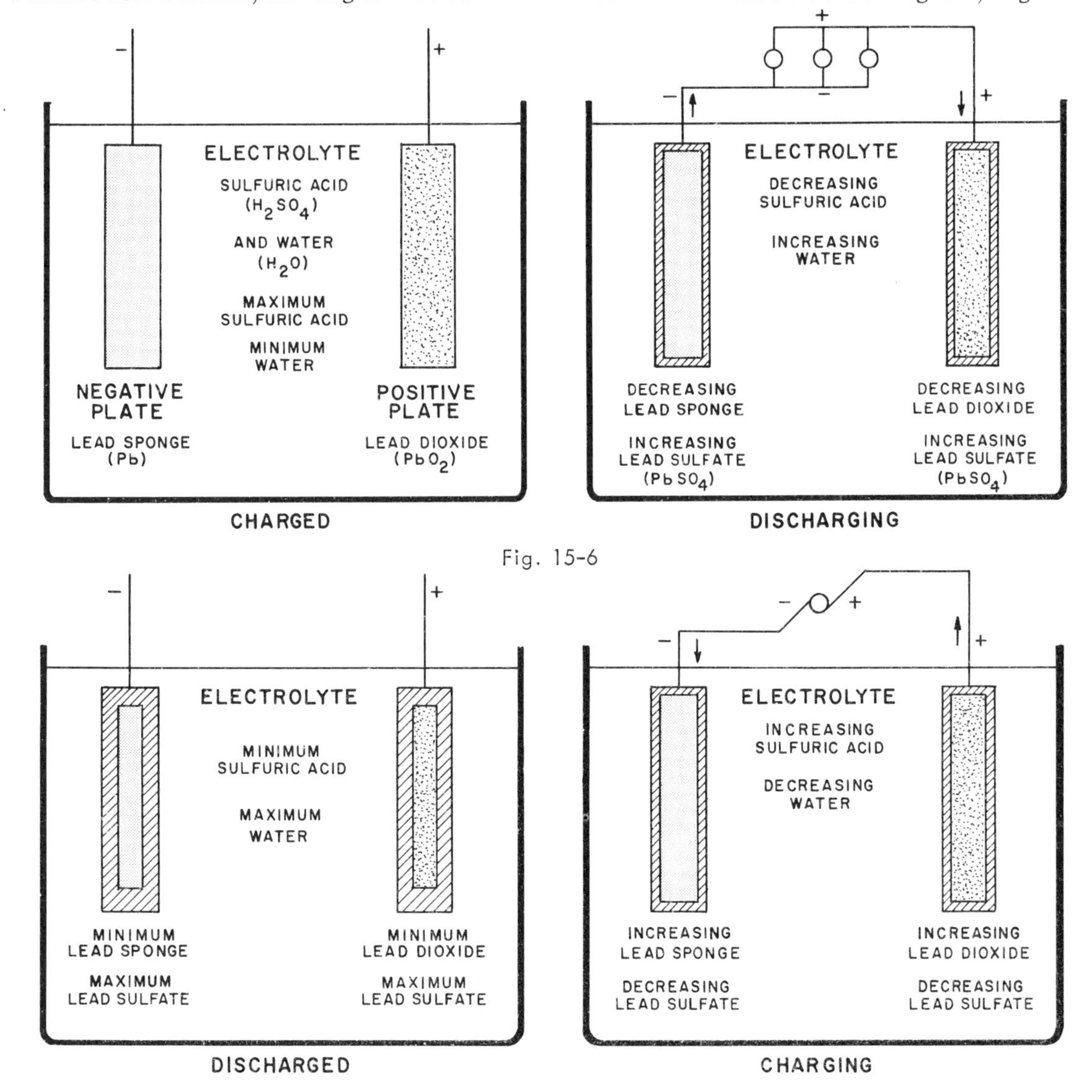

Fig. 15-6

This chemical action can go on only where the plates are in contact with the sulfuric acid solution. In order to produce a large current, the plates are made so that a lot of surface area is in contact with the solution. In a cell, the plates are arranged as shown in Fig. 15-7. The negative plate is made of lead sponge, and the positive lead dioxide plate is also a porous structure, permitting a large area of material to be wet by the electrolyte. Separators of wood, glass fibers or similar porous material keep the plates from touching each other. To provide mechanical strength, both plates consist of an open framework of a lead-antimony alloy, into which the active material is pressed. The electrolyte is dilute sulfuric acid of specific gravity 1.28.

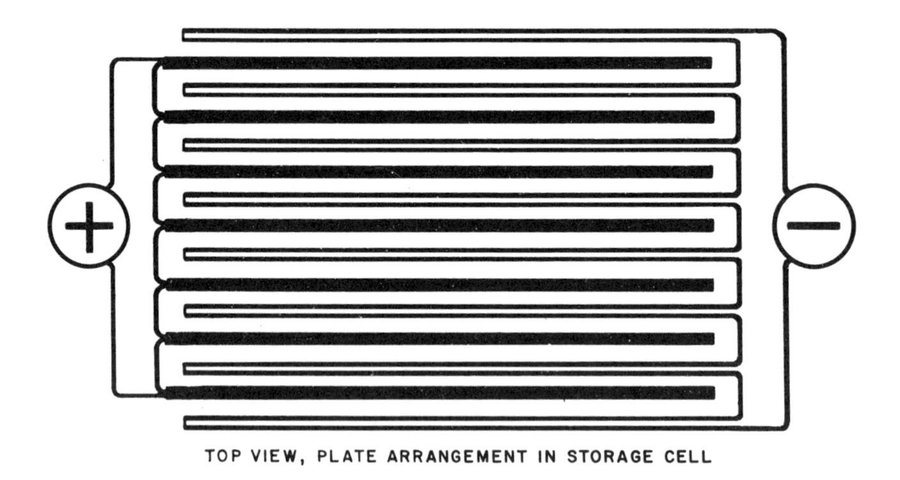

Fig. 15-7

Batteries may be shipped wet, filled with the electrolyte, or dry, with the electrolyte in a separate container. Relative packing and shipping costs determine which method is used.

The Ampere-Hour Rating

An ampere-hour is the amount of charge delivered by one ampere in one hour (1 amp-hr = 3600 coulombs). The ampere-hour rating of a battery is usually found from its ability to produce current for 20 hours, at 80° F. A battery that can produce 6 amperes steadily for 20 hours deserves a 120 ampere-hour rating. A 120 A.H. battery can produce more than 120 A.H. if its discharge rate is 1 or 2 amps instead of 6 amps. It cannot produce 120 amps for one hour; the actual A.H. production depends on the current.

Battery Charging

A rectifier or a D.C. generator is a necessity for battery charging. The battery is charged by forcing a current through it, opposite in direction to the current the battery normally produces. In the lead cell, this reversal of current reverses the chemical changes that took place in the cell when it was furnishing energy. (In so-called primary cells, this current-reversing process does not successfully reverse the chemical changes.)

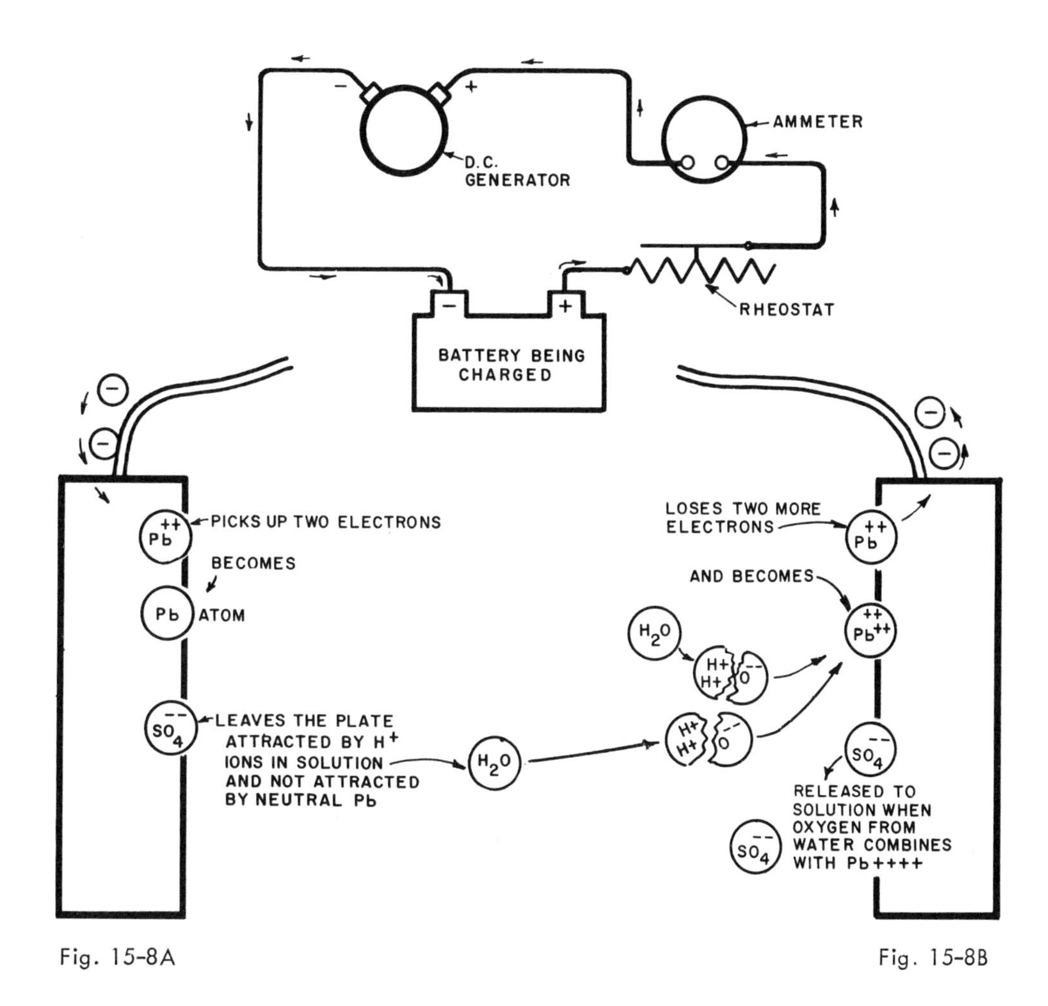

Fig. 15-8A Fig. 15-8B

To explain the charging process in the lead cell, we may recall that a current through a solution of sulfuric acid in water produces hydrogen at the negative plate, and oxygen at the positive plate, (Unit 13). If the plates are already covered with a thin layer of lead sulfate, the H^+ ions forced toward the negative plate combine with the SO_4^{--}, forming sulfuric acid again. The electrons forced on to the negative plate by the generator change the Pb^{++} ions back to plain lead, (Fig. 15-8a).

At the positive plate H_2O decomposes, the hydrogen combining with the SO_4^{--} on the plate to make more sulfuric acid, and the oxygen combining with the lead to form lead dioxide again. The Pb^{++} of the discharged positive plate is converted to Pb^{++++} as the generator pulls electrons away, (Fig. 15-8b).

By the use of chemical formulas, the above description can be summarized:

$$\underset{\text{(Negative)}}{Pb} + \underset{\text{(Positive)}}{PbO_2} + \underset{\text{(Liquid)}}{2\,H_2SO_4} \underset{\text{charging}}{\overset{\text{discharging}}{\rightleftarrows}} \underset{\text{(Negative)}}{PbSO_4} + \underset{\text{(Positive)}}{PbSO_4} + \underset{\text{(Liquid)}}{2\,H_2O}$$

Cells Connected in Series

As has been suggested already, cells are often connected in series in order to obtain higher voltages. The voltage produced by several cells in series is the total of the individual cell voltages. For example, three 2-volt lead-storage cells in series produce 6 volts; six such cells in series produce 12 volts; four 1.5-volt dry cells in series produce 6 volts. To produce 90 volts from dry cells, sixty of them in series are required.

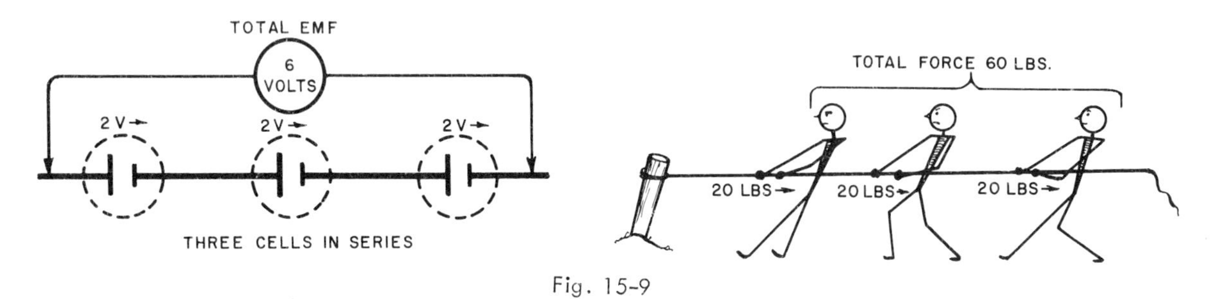

Fig. 15-9

Cells Connected in Parallel

When the negative terminals of several cells are connected together, (as in Fig. 15-10a) in effect one large negative plate is formed, and the connected positive plates act like one large positive plate. No increase in e.m.f. is obtained with this arrangement, but if the load resistor requires a total current of 15 amps, it can be provided by 5 amps through each cell.

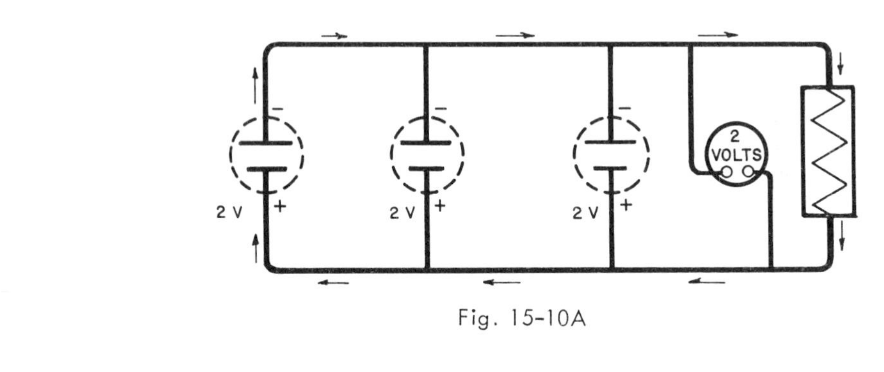

Fig. 15-10A

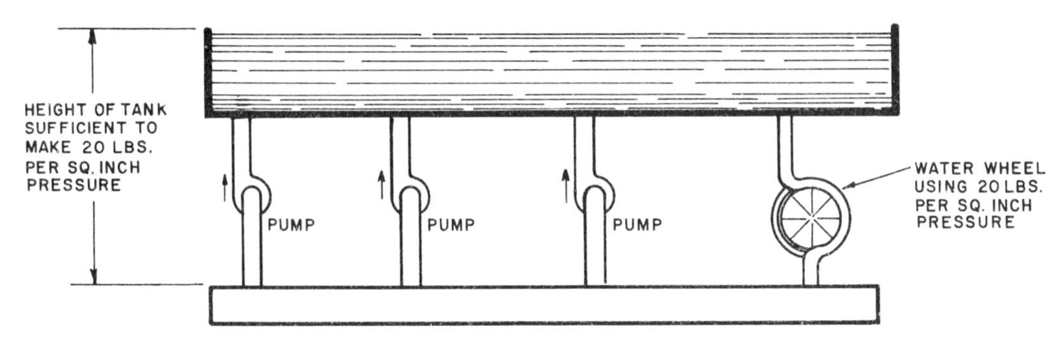

Fig. 15-10B

This may be illustrated by the water-pump comparison (10b). Three pumps in parallel pump more water into the open tank on top than one pump does; but, assuming the water level is kept steady, the pressure is the same as that produced by one pump. If each is pumping five gallons/second, then 15 gallons/second can run out through the waterwheel, which corresponds to the resistance load of the electrical circuit.

Ohm's Law in the Battery Charging Circuit

In a charging circuit such as Fig. 15-8, the generator voltage has two jobs to do: (1) it must equalize and overcome the battery e.m.f. and (2) it must also produce enough volts (= IR) to produce current through the resistance in the circuit.

For example, if the rheostat is set for 2 ohms resistance, and a 15-volt generator is charging a 6-volt battery, to find the current:

First, subtract the 6v from the 15v, which leaves 9 volts to produce current through the 2 ohms resistance in the circuit (assuming that the ohms resistance of the rest of the circuit is small enough to neglect).

$$I = \frac{9 \text{ v}}{2 \text{ ohm}} = 4.5 \text{ amps, Ans.}$$

A similar calculation would enable one to estimate the ohms resistance necessary in the circuit to limit the charging current to a reasonable rate: Assume a generator produces 24 volts, and the battery and wiring has 0.4 ohms resistance. A current of 6 amps is desired to charge a 6-volt battery. Calculate the necessary resistance to be added:

1. 24 - 6 = 18 volts to be used in the resistance of the circuit.
2. Total resistance of the circuit $= \frac{E}{I} = \frac{18}{6} = 3$ ohms.
3. Circuit has 0.4 ohms already; 3 - 0.4 = 2.6 more ohms must be added in series in the circuit.

A too-high charging rate can damage a battery by (1) overheating and (2) gas-bubble formation inside the spongy plate material which forces active material to break away from the plate structure. The safest charging procedure is a 10-amp rate, or less, requiring about 24 hours. A battery can be charged on a constant-voltage circuit in 6 or 8 hours, starting with a 30- or 40-ampere rate which tapers down as the battery charge builds up. With this method, however, the battery should be checked to see that it is not overheating. 110°F is the usually accepted limit.

Battery Testing

A hydrometer measures the specific gravity of the electrolyte in each cell. A charged battery has enough sulfuric acid in the electrolyte so that its specific gravity is 1.25 - 1.28, (water = 1.00). As the battery discharges, SO_4^{--} of the acid is tied up on the plates, and the electrolyte becomes more like plain water, its specific gravity approaching 1.1. Since occasionally a cell may not operate properly even when it has sufficient acid, a better method of battery testing measures the voltage of each cell when it is producing current. A good cell can produce 20 or 30 amps and maintain a 2-volt potential difference across the cell. A "dead" cell may read 2 volts when it does not have to produce current, but its voltage drops off as soon as a low resistance is placed across the cell.

Battery Care

Particular care should be taken to avoid getting dirt into a cell. When the cap is removed, it should be set in a clean place, if it has to be set down at all. Dirt, especially a few flakes of iron rust, can spoil a cell permanently. Probably a great many automobile batteries "go bad" because of the accidental entry of dirt into a cell.

A battery should not be allowed to remain in a discharged condition. If a battery is completely run down, it should be charged within a few hours, at a slow rate. If let stand discharged, the lead sulfate apparently hardens or crystallizes into some formation that is difficult to restore to lead and lead dioxide. The watery solution in a discharged battery can freeze in winter, breaking up the battery, another reason for keeping it charged.

The liquid should be maintained at a level that covers the plates. Distilled water is preferable, but faucet water is better than none at all. (Melted frost from the refrigerator is distilled water.) Water is lost from a battery mainly by evaporation, slightly from hydrogen and oxygen formed during charging. Acid is lost only by cracking the case or tipping it over, so acid seldom is needed.

There is no point in adding various amazing powders and liquids to a battery to improve its performance, life, and complexion. For many, many years it has been known that Epsom salt ($MgSO_4$) or sodium sulfate (Na_2SO_4) could be added to a lead storage cell electrolyte in small amounts, without damage to the battery, and with little likelihood of doing it any good, either. If acid has been lost from the cell, these materials provide ions that may be useful. But a teaspoonful of sulfuric acid (worth 2 cents, like the Epsom salt) would be more desirable in such a battery. When new and important discoveries relating to car batteries appear, more reliable announcements will be found in news articles and electrical engineering journals than in exclamatory and sensational advertising. Too many people have already paid too much for amazing new battery discoveries, consisting of misleading claims and a fancy wrapper on an ordinary battery, only to find that the manufacturer had ceased operations when it was time to fulfill his "guarantee".

Edison and Nickel-Cadmium Storage Cells

Two other types of storage battery are manufactured, besides the ordinary lead battery: The Edison battery (nickel-iron) and the nickel-cadmium battery. These are true long-life batteries.

The Edison is structurally stronger and lighter in weight than lead cells of the same current rating. The negative plates consist of a nickeled-steel grid containing powdered iron, with some FeO and $Fe(OH)_2$. The iron is the source of the electrons, which are attracted through the external circuit toward nickel ions, Ni^{++} and Ni^{+++} on the positive plate. The positive plates are nickel-plated tubes containing a mixture of nickel oxides and hydroxides, with flakes of pure nickel for increased conductivity. The electrolyte is a 21% solution of KOH (potassium hydroxide, caustic potash) which is chemically a base rather than an acid. The Edison and nickel-cadmium cells are often called alkaline cells, referring to the nature of the electrolyte.

The disadvantages of the Edison cell are (1) high initial cost, (2) high internal resistance that limits maximum current, especially so when the cell is cold. These disadvantages are enough to prevent its use in most situations. It is not damaged by remaining in a discharged condition. It is used in some portable lighting equipment and in a few marine installations, where it neither gets nor needs the attention that lead cells would.

The nickel-iron (Edison) cell was originally developed (1899) to serve as the motive power for electric motor-driven vehicles. Research was aimed at producing a battery having small weight and volume for a given ampere-hour rating, and especially one that could withstand repeated "cycling", which means frequent charging and complete discharging, every day or oftener for a long period.

The Edison battery is appropriate for running electrical traction equipment, such as mine locomotives and fork-lift trucks, but not appropriate for starting gasoline and Diesel engines, because its internal resistance limits the current too much.

The nickel-cadmium battery (Jungner & Berg, Sweden, 1898) followed a line of development that produced a battery not intended for frequent cycling, but rather a more general-purpose battery that enabled the user to draw as many amperes as possible from a battery of given amp-hour rating, without excessive falling-off of voltage. The starting of gasoline and Diesel engines, and the operation of signals, relays and controls are jobs for which the nickel-cadmium battery is suited. Although in chemical composition these two alkaline cells are similar, it may be noted from the Storage-Battery Comparison Chart that the nickel-cadmium is more similar in electrical characteristics to the lead cell, therefore more competitive with the lead cell.

Storage Battery Comparison Chart

	Lead	Edison (Nickel-Iron)	Nickel-Cadmium
Mechanical Properties (for similar amp-hour rating)			
Weight	Moderate	Light	Heavy
Volume	Varies	Small	Large
No. of plates per cell	Few	Few	Many
Mechanical strength	Poor	Good	Good
High temperature damage	Yes	No	No
Maintenance Factors			
Damage likely due to freezing	Yes	No	No
Rate of self-discharge	High	High	Low
Can be trickle-charged	Yes	No	Yes
Water consumption	Moderate	High	Low
Electrical Properties			
Internal resistance	Moderately high	High	Low
Voltage drop off on discharge	Slight	Yes	No
Voltage regulator control	Easy	Difficult	Easy
Gas production during charge	Yes	Yes	Slight
Ampere-hour production:			
reduced by over-charge	Yes	No	No
reduced by occasional over-discharge	No	No	No
reduced by frequent over-discharge	Yes	No	Yes

In making the nickel-cadmium battery, both sets of plates are mechanically alike, the active materials being held in finely-perforated thin flat steel pockets that are locked into a steel frame.

The active material put in the positive plate is nickel hydroxide mixed with graphite to improve conductivity; cadmium oxide is put into the negative plates. The electrolyte is potassium hydroxide (KOH) of about 1.2 sp. gr. When the cell is charged, the electrons forced onto the negative plate combine with Cd^{++} ions of the cadmium oxide (CdO) converting them to plain cadmium metal atoms. On the positive plate, electrons are removed from Ni^{++} ions of $Ni(OH)_2$, converting them into more-strongly positive charged Ni^{+++} ions. (The compound changes to $Ni(OH)_3$).

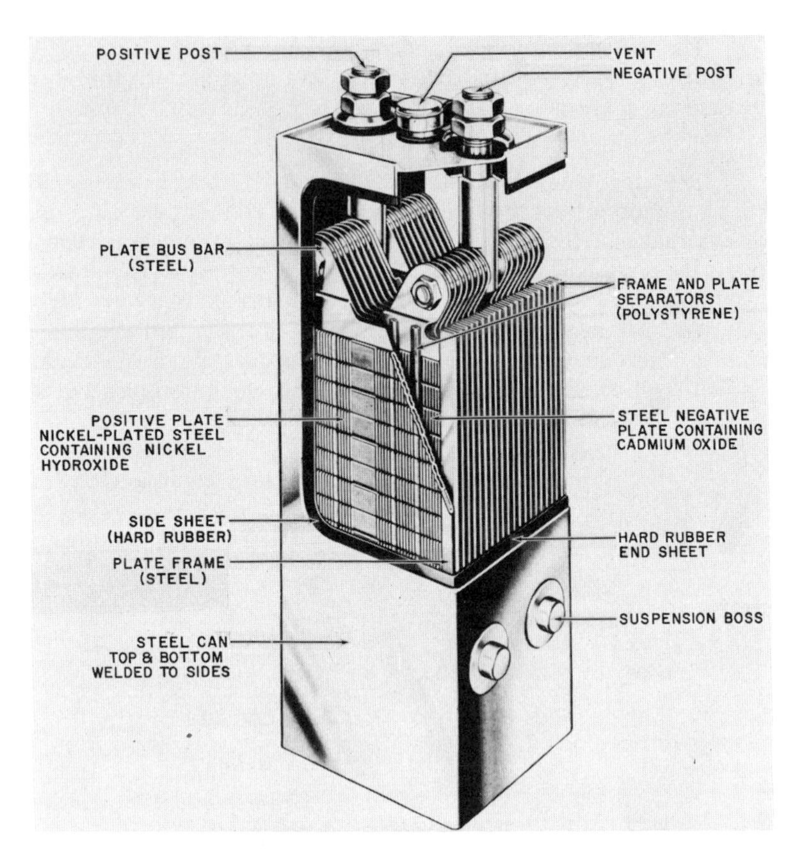

The active materials in the charged cell are, therefore,

On the Negative Plate	On the Positive Plate
Cadmium atoms which are the electron source	Ni^{+++} ions in nickel hydroxide which will take electrons

The chemical reaction may be written:

$$Cd + 2\,Ni(OH)_3 \underset{\text{charge}}{\overset{\text{discharge}}{\rightleftarrows}} CdO + 2\,Ni(OH)_2 + H_2O$$

The H_2O which is formed stays tied up in combination with the $Ni(OH)_2$ in solid form on the plate, and does not dilute the electrolyte. Therefore, the density of the electrolyte remains constant, and a hydrometer will not indicate the amount of charge.

Like the Edison, the nickel-cadmium battery is chiefly used in industrial service, where its ruggedness, long life and low maintenance cost outweigh the fact that the original cost of the nickel battery will average maybe four times as much as equivalent lead cells. Expensive manufacturing processes are required for nickel-cadmium cells, and the unprocessed metals, nickel and cadmium, are more costly than lead. Nickel-cadmium, in the U. S., is used in railroad signal systems, fire alarm systems, relay and switchgear operation, missile controls, and for starting aircraft engines, and Diesel engines in locomotives, buses, oil-well pumps, etc.

Ohm's Law and Batteries

Cells themselves have an internal resistance, which enters into a circuit calculation. In a circuit like Fig. 15-12, when electrons flow from the negative plate to the positive plate, there is a movement of ions in the electrolyte in the cell. This movement in the cell, like any current, does not go on with perfect ease; there is some resistance in the internal material of the cell.

A new large dry cell may have about .035 ohms internal resistance, and a high-resistance voltmeter will indicate its e.m.f. is 1.5 volts. Assume we connect it, as in Fig. 15-12 to an external resistance of 0.715 ohms. To calculate the current: The total resistance in the circuit is 0.715 + .035 = 0.75 ohms (both resistances must be added for they are effectively in series; there is only one current-path) and

$$I = \frac{E}{R} = \frac{1.5}{.75} = 2 \text{ amps}$$

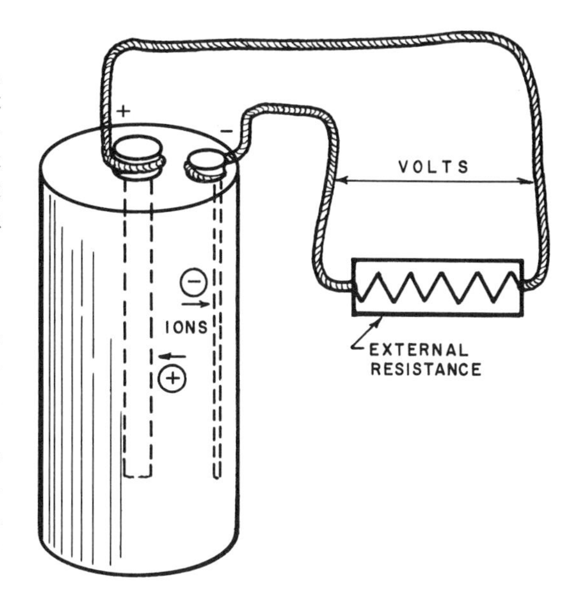

Fig. 15-12

Furthermore, how much would a voltmeter read if connected across the cell terminals while the 0.715-ohm resistor is there, too? There are two ways of calculating this voltage:

1. The voltmeter is connected across a .715-ohm resistor that has 2 amps through it. $E = IR = 2 \times .715 = 1.43$ volts.
2. The .035-ohm internal resistance of the cell has a 2-amp current in it. Of the 1.5-volt e.m.f. that the cell produces, some is used inside the cell, overcoming this internal resistance.

The voltage used inside the cell is $E = IR = 2 \times .035 = .07$ volt. This .07 volt, subtracted from the 1.5 volts, leaves 1.43 volts for the external circuit.

Will the cell always produce 1.43 volts instead of 1.5? No, that depends on both the internal and external resistances.

With the same cell as before, (1.5-volt e.m.f. and .035-ohm internal resistance) let's use an external load resistor of 0.115 ohm.

Calculating the total resistance of the circuit, .035 + .115 = 0.15 ohms.

Calculating the current in the circuit, $I = \frac{1.5}{.15} = 10$ amps.

And how much voltage exists at the terminals of the cell? Like calculation (1) above:

$$E = 10 \times .115 = 1.15 \text{ volts}$$

"This is supposed to be a 1.5-volt dry cell, and it puts out only 1.15 volts. Where does the rest of it go?" The rest of the voltage was used inside the cell; there is a voltage drop inside the cell. $IR = 10$ amps $\times$ .035 ohms = .35 volts.

$$1.50 \text{ v} - .35 \text{ v} = 1.15 \text{ volts}$$

The name Terminal Voltage is applied to this voltage at the terminals of the cell when it is in use, to distinguish it from the e.m.f., which is constant for a particular cell.

Maximum Current From a Cell

A cell produces its greatest current, uselessly, when it is short-circuited. Assume we connect a wire of practically zero-ohms resistance across the terminals of the 1.5-volt, .35-ohm cell.

The amount of current is limited only by the internal resistance of the cell:

$$I = 1.5 \div .035 = 42.8 \text{ amps}$$

The terminal voltage is now zero, because all of the cell e.m.f. is used inside the cell. If this condition exists for more than a few seconds, the cell overheats, gases form in it, the electrolyte starts boiling out the top of the cell, and the cell can soon be junked.

If a dry cell is used to produce a moderate current for 10 or 15 minutes, there may be a noticeable drop in terminal voltage and current by the end of this time. The reason for it is a temporary increase in internal resistance due to the formation of a very small amount of hydrogen around the positive plate. When the cell is let stand, on open circuit, this hydrogen is reconverted to H_2O, and the cell is restored to its original low internal resistance.

Dry cells generally fail because they really become dry, internally. An unused dry cell on a warm shelf for two years may lose its moisture by evaporation, despite the manufacturer's attempt to seal the top. A cell in use will lose its moisture when a hole is finally dissolved in the zinc. Drying out causes a great increase in internal resistance. A cell with one- or two-ohms internal resistance is of no value: it may produce enough current to make a voltmeter read 1.5 volts, but not enough current to half light a flashlight bulb.

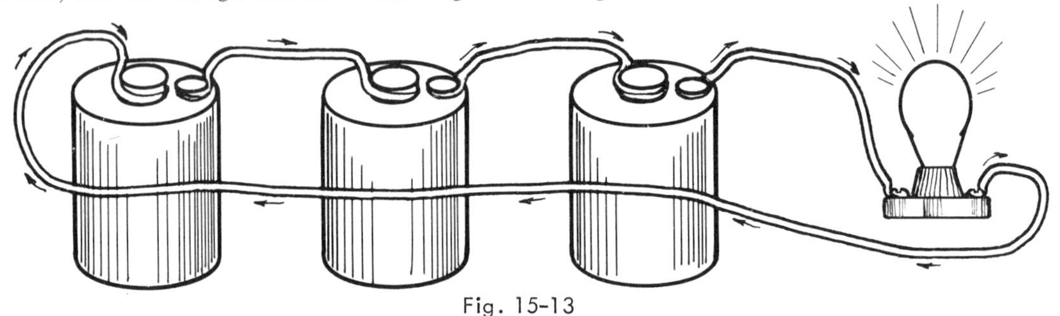

Fig. 15-13

Ohm's Law for Cells in Series

Three cells, 1.5-volt e.m.f. and .05-ohm internal resistance, each, are connected in series to a 2-ohm lamp, (Fig. 15-13).

Calculate current in lamp and voltage at the lamp:

The current will be found from the total e.m.f. and the total resistance. With three 1.5-volt cells in series, the e.m.f. is 4.5 volts. The total resistance in the circuit is .05 + .05 + .05 + 2 = 2.15 ohms.

$$I = 4.5 \div 2.15 = 2.09 \text{ amps}$$

The voltage across the lamp is: $2.09 \times 2 = 4.18$ volts.

Why Use Cells in Series?

The three cells above put 2.09 amps through the lamp; one cell would produce a current of only .73 amps (1.5 ÷ 2.05) in the lamp. Cells in series produce more voltage and more current.

Ohm's Law for Cells in Parallel

One might assume that three or four cells in parallel are no better than a single cell, because there is no increase in e.m.f. It is true that in many situations there is no advantage in placing several cells in parallel. When the load-resistance is rather small, there is an advantage, as shown in this example, (see Fig. 15-14):

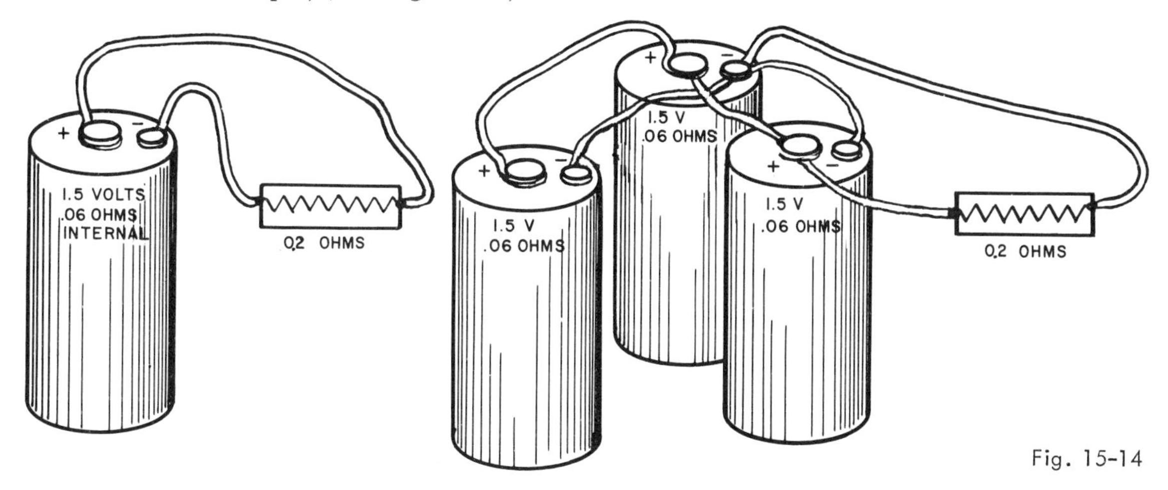

Fig. 15-14

When one cell is in use, the total resistance is 0.2 + .06 = .26 ohms, and the current is $\frac{1.5}{.26} = 5.77$ amps, which is a fairly large current for a single dry cell to produce for any length of time.

When three cells in parallel are used, the combined resistance of the three cells is .02 ohms (like three equal resistors in parallel, the combination has 1/3 the resistance of a single resistor) and the total resistance of the circuit is .02 internal plus 0.2 external = .22 ohms.

The current is $\frac{1.5}{.22} = 6.82$ amps, which is somewhat more than the 5.77, but more importantly, this current is divided among three cells, each one producing $\frac{6.82}{3} = 2.27$ amps.

Why Use Cells in Parallel?

This sharing of the current load among several cells delays the temporary increase of internal resistance. It also increases the life of each cell, which is an advantage in that it is more convenient to replace the group of 3 cells every 30 days than to replace one cell every 10 days. And since the internal resistance of the parallel group is less than that of a single cell, the terminal voltage will be closer to the cell e.m.f.

The Cost of Chemical Energy

The main advantages of batteries are that they are:

1. Portable: Submarines, automobiles, aircraft, and small boys with flashlights are four examples of devices that need to be independent of powerline operation.
2. Reliable and self-contained: Powerline service can be interrupted by storms. In such situations, batteries can provide emergency lighting and communication service.

The great disadvantage of batteries is that the energy they produce is expensive, so batteries are used only where the convenience outweighs the cost. For example, how much energy is there in an automobile battery? A 6-volt car battery may produce 6 amps for 20 hours (120 ampere-hours). Watt-hours of energy is volts × amps × hours, = 6 × 6 × 20 = 720 watt-hours, which is about three-fourths of one kilowatt-hour. Power corporations charge about three cents for one kilowatt-hour of energy.

An ordinary flashlight cell (size "D") contains a little over one-half ounce of zinc. According to the chemistry book, this amount of zinc is 1.5×10^{23} atoms. Each atom supplies 2 electrons, so if all of the zinc were dissolved usefully, 3×10^{23} electrons would be produced. One coulomb is 6×10^{18} electrons; 3×10^{23} electrons is equal to 50,000 coulombs.

$$\frac{3 \times 10^{23}}{6 \times 10^{18}} = \frac{3 \times 10^{5}}{6} = \frac{300,000}{6} = 50,000$$

It takes 3600 coulombs to equal an ampere-hour, so the flashlight cell, if 100% efficient, could produce 14 ampere-hours if <u>all</u> of the zinc could be dissolved. 14 amp-hours at 1.5 volts equals 21 watt-hours, so about fifty flashlight cells would be needed to produce one kilowatthour of energy.

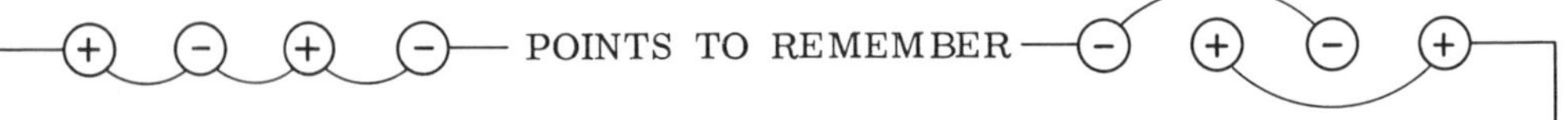

POINTS TO REMEMBER

- If electrons have a tendency to leave atoms of one material and combine with another material, the pair of materials are said to possess chemical energy.

- In an electromotive cell, materials are arranged so that electrons from a metal can flow usefully through an external circuit on their way to positive-charged ions in the cell.

- In series, cell voltages add. A parallel group has the same e.m.f. as one cell.

- Terminal voltage = e.m.f. minus voltage drop inside cell.

- Cell voltages: dry cell 1.5, lead storage cell 2.

- Keep dirt out of a car battery; keep it charged; add water when needed.

REVIEW QUESTIONS

1. A 6-volt car battery was discharged by producing 300 amperes to grind the starter for 5 minutes. How much energy was produced?

2. Fig. 15-7 shows a 13-plate lead storage cell. How are the plates connected -- series or parallel?

3. Name these chemical compounds: $MgCl_2$, H_2SO_4, $CuSO_4$, NH_4Cl, KOH, PbO_2, NaCl.

4. A suggestion has been made that an old dry cell could be restored by punching holes in the container and soaking it in salt water. Is it likely to work?

5. Name the active materials in a lead storage battery.

6. Could a lead storage battery be charged by adding more sulfuric acid?

7. What is an ampere-hour?

8. When a hard-rubber comb is negatively charged with static electricity, the electrons can be discharged quickly in a spark. Why don't the electrons all jump off the zinc plate of a dry cell just as fast?

9. How often should an ordinary car battery require charging?

10. Is a car battery damaged by being run down, as by leaving key or lights left on all night?

11. State items of main importance in care of a lead storage battery.

12. The chart Composition of Cells on Page 149 lists many types, some of which are obsolete. What is the fundamental similarity in electron behavior in all of them?

13. Since the electrolyte in a cell is a conductor, why can't electrons go from negative plate over to positive, right through the electrolyte?

14. Two 24-volt batteries, in series, are being charged by a 60-volt generator. Each battery has 0.02-ohms internal resistance. Calculate how much additional resistance is needed in the circuit to limit the current to 6 amps.

15. The sketches below (Fig. 15-15) represent various possible ways of connecting two dry cells and a lamp. The + and - are the terminals of the cells, shown in top view. The resistor represents the lamp. For each: State voltage at the lamp (0, 1.5, or 3 v). Classify circuits as good or poor.

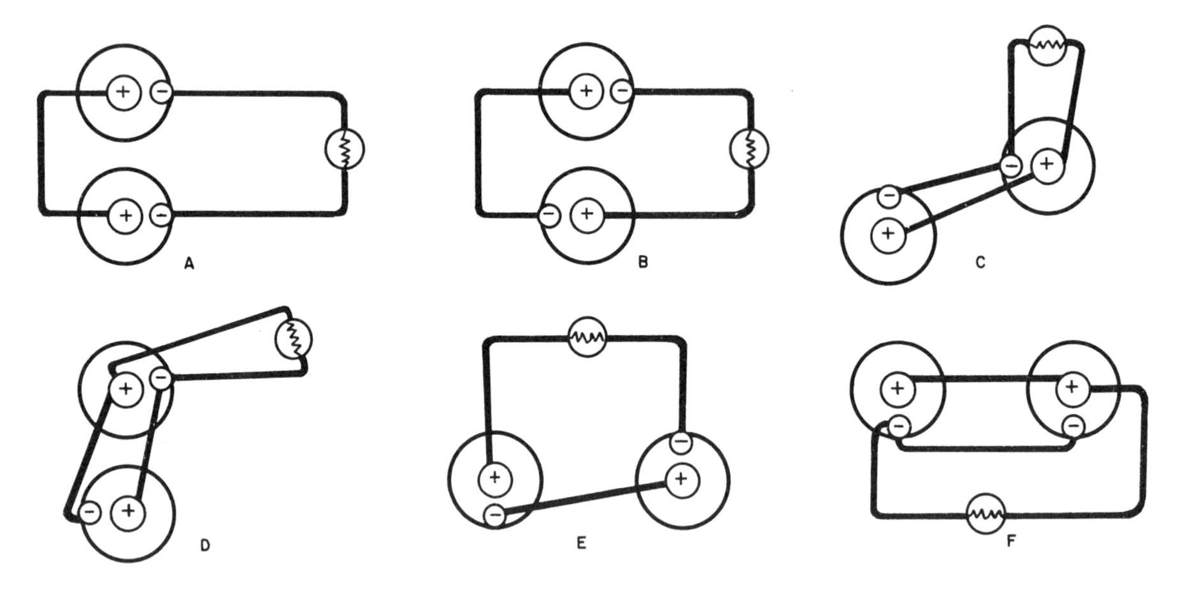

Fig. 15-15

16. Eight lead storage cells are arranged as in diagram. (Top view of cell connections.) The e.m.f. of this battery is how much?

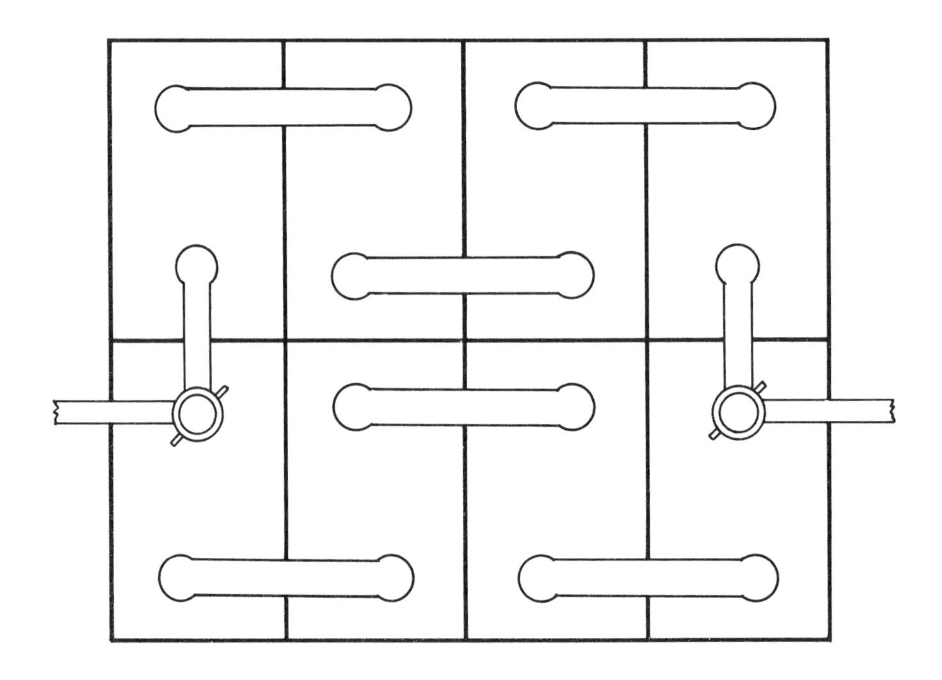

Unit 16 SMALL-SCALE SOURCES OF E.M.F. – THERMOCOUPLES, PIEZOELECTRIC MATERIALS, PHOTOCELLS

By far the greatest amount of industrial electrical energy is produced by rotating generators, turned by the mechanical energy of steam or water turbines. There are various methods for the direct conversion of heat, light, mechanical motion, and nuclear energy into electrical energy, without using water wheels or steam boilers and generators. So far, these methods are of no importance in the amount of energy they produce, yet are highly useful because the small voltages they produce are used to control the operation of other equipment. Thermocouples, photocells and pressure-sensitive (piezoelectric) materials are the sensing elements of the "electrical brains" that control furnaces, regulate speed of machines, play phonograph records, and perform a host of automatically controlled operations.

Furthermore, continuing investigation of these materials is producing new knowledge and suggesting new uses. There also is always the possibility that new methods of large-scale production of electrical energy may be developed.

THERMOCOUPLES: Direct Conversion of Heat to Electrical Energy

In Berlin, in 1822, T. J. Seebeck reported the discovery that a circuit like this one, Fig. 16-1, would produce a steady electric current, as long as the two junctions are at different temperatures. A and B are any two different metals. This direct production of an e.m.f. from heat is called the "Seebeck effect".

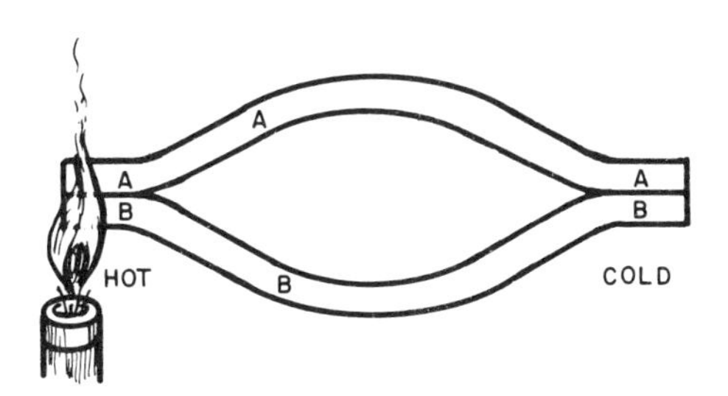

The Seebeck Effect
Fig. 16-1

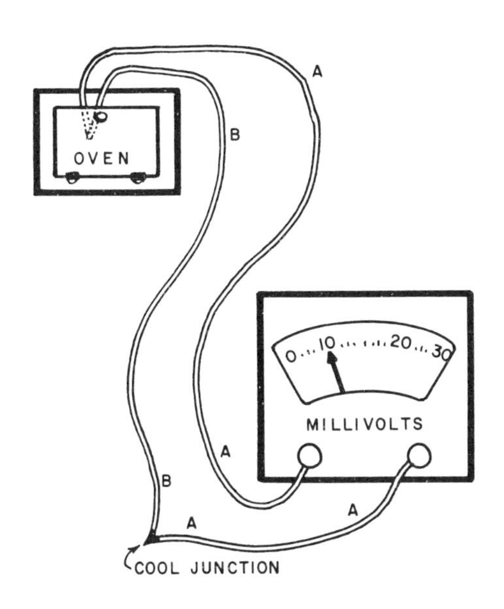

Fig. 16-2

This circuit is widely used for the measurement of temperatures, especially temperatures beyond the range of liquid-in-glass thermometers. Voltage measurements are made, rather than current measurements, because the e.m.f. depends only on materials and temperature, while current would be influenced by many factors that determine the resistance of the entire circuit.

For accurate work, the voltage is measured by a potentiometer, rather than by a millivoltmeter. A conveniently located potentiometer may be switched from one thermocouple circuit to another, permitting successive readings of temperatures at several different remote locations.

The explanation for the production of this e.m.f. is found by a study of electron-energies in the metals. When any two metals are in contact, there is a tendency for a slight excess of electrons to drift from one metal and accumulate on the other. This slight accumulation of electrons causes a so-called "contact potential difference" between the metals. It is a small voltage, very difficult to measure, and usually noticed only as a nuisance in delicate measurements.

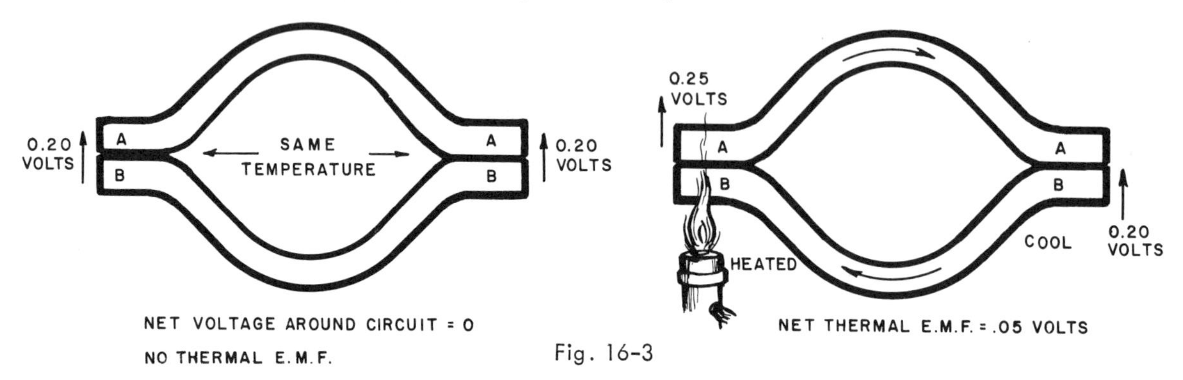

Fig. 16-3

Application of heat changes the contact voltage at the heated junction, producing the useful "Thermal e.m.f.". The materials most often used for thermocouple junctions are these:

- 300° F to 750° F: copper and constantan (60% copper, 40% nickel)
200° F to 2550° F: chromel and alumel
200° F to 3150° F: platinum and platinum-rhodium alloy

Increased voltage output can be accomplished by placing several thermocouples in series (Fig. 16-4). Such a device is called a thermopile.

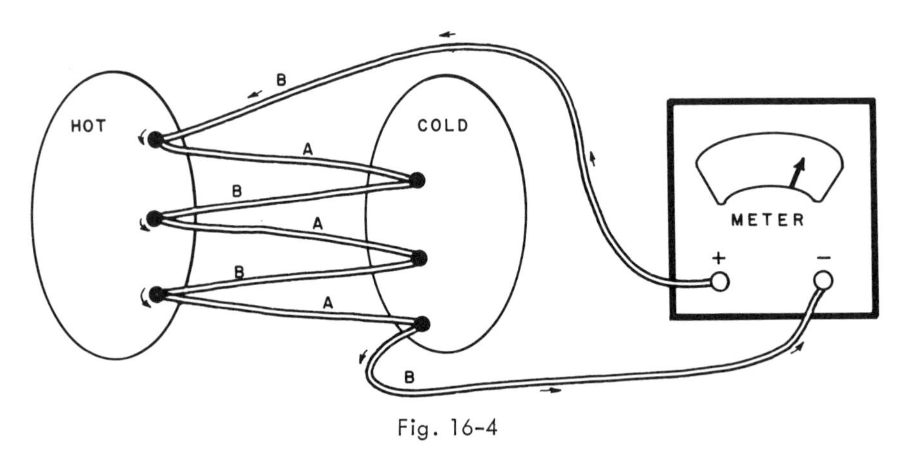

Fig. 16-4

Recent Thermocouple Developments

In the last few years, the thermoelectric properties of newly-developed semiconductor alloys have been investigated, in this country and in Russia, with promising results. In a piece of N-type (electron-rich) semiconductor, heated at one end, electrons are forced toward the cold end. In a P-type (electron-poor) semiconductor, electrons tend to accumulate at the hot end. If, in Fig. 16-3, A is an N-type semiconductor, and B is a P-type semiconductor, the thermal voltages add, both helping to drive electrons in the same direction around the circuit with a useful e.m.f. of a few tenths of a volt. A thermopile consisting of a few hundred such junctions can produce power in useful amounts. Small thermoelectric generators, powered by the heat of a kerosene lamp, produce about 15 watts for powering radio receivers in remote regions of the U.S.S.R.

Thermocouple voltages may be used to operate relays or electronic controls. A commonly-used circuit in gas-fired heating equipment is this one:

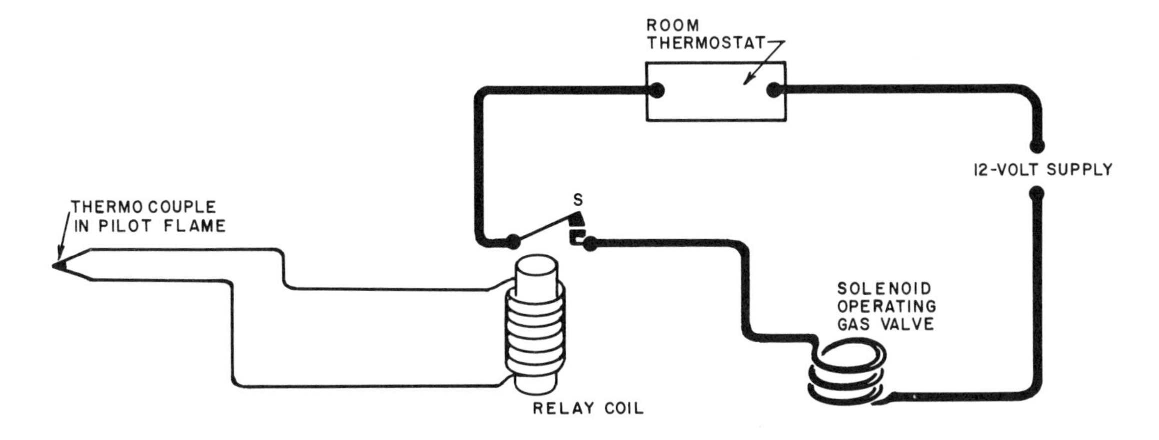

Fig. 16-5

Ordinarily the room thermostat acts as a switch, opening the gas valve to the furnace when the room cools. The gas coming into the furnace is ignited by a pilot light. The pilot light also heats a thermocouple, producing a voltage that operates the coil of a relay. This relay holds the switch S closed. If the pilot light goes out, switch S is opened, so that the main gas valve cannot be opened by the thermostat. This acts as a safety device, preventing an accumulation of unburned gas in the furnace, chimney, etc.

The ordinary thermostat is not a thermocouple; it is a switch, operated by the bending of a compound bar as the temperature changes. Invar is an iron-nickel alloy that does not change in size much when heated or cooled. Brass expands when heated, contracts when cooled. Strips of the two metals, brazed together, form the compound bar. Lengthening of the brass by heating forces the bar to bend as in Fig. 16-6; cooling bends it back again.

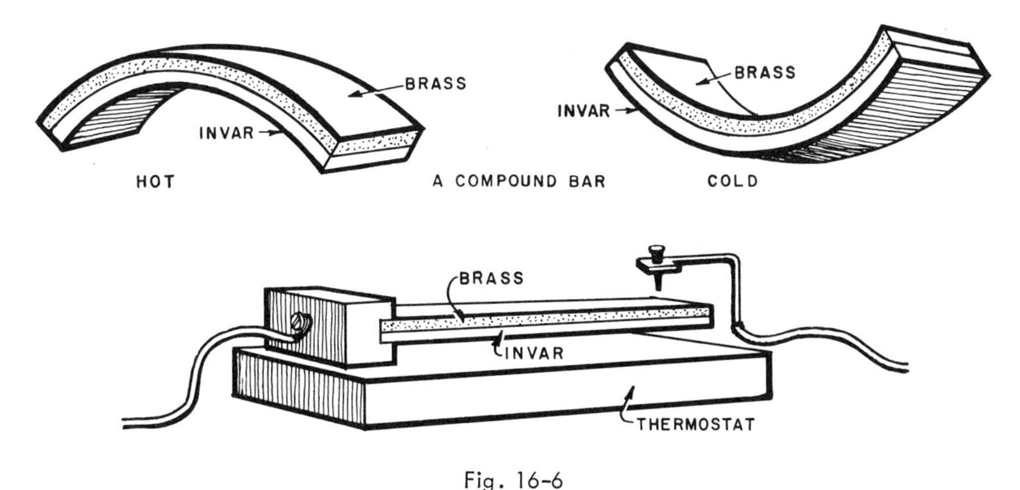

Fig. 16-6

In the thermostat pictured, the brass-invar strip acts as the moving part of a switch, bending as it cools, to meet the contact at the right. A contact could be placed below the bar, so that a circuit can be closed by a temperature rise. "Setting the temperature" on the thermostat is a matter of adjusting the relative position of the bar support and the contacts.

Energy Transfer in the Thermocouple

If a thermocouple circuit is allowed to produce current, heat is absorbed from the hot junction to produce the electrical energy. At the cool junction, that absorbed energy is reproduced as heat. The fact that this heat-to-electricity energy conversion can be reversed was discovered in 1834 by Peltier. If, in Fig. 16-3, we removed the heat source but inserted a battery in the circuit so it would maintain the same current, heat would still be absorbed at the left junction and be produced at the right. If we touch the junction at the left, heat is absorbed from our fingers and we find the junction feels cold.

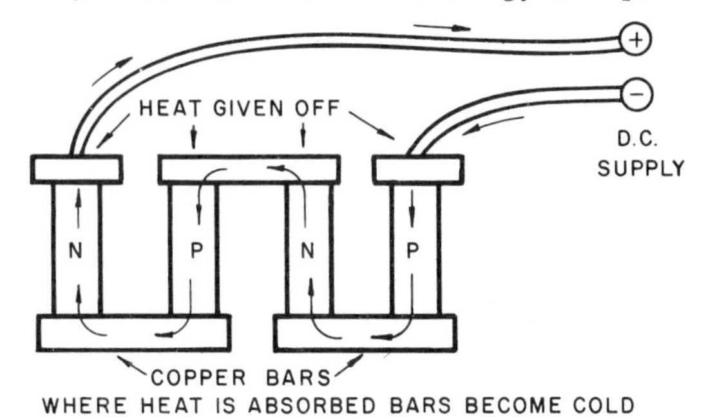

Fig. 16-7 Thermoelectric Refrigeration

If we use a temperature difference to produce electrical energy in the circuit, we call it a thermocouple; if we use the same materials so that electrical energy produces a temperature difference, we call it a Peltier circuit. The development of new semi-conducting materials has made the commercial manufacture of Peltier refrigerators practical. Lack of moving parts and noiseless operation are advantages. To date, they are not as efficient as mechanical refrigerators; hence they are more costly to operate.

PIEZOELECTRICITY: E.M.F. from Mechanical Pressure

The term "piezo" means pressure. Some materials, when compressed, twisted, bent or stretched, develop electric charges on opposite sides of the material. The most common application of this effect is the use of crystals of Rochelle salt (sodium potassium tartrate) in crystal microphones and in crystal pickups for record players. The voltage that is produced is used as the input signal voltage for an amplifier. Sidewise vibration of the needle twists the end of the crystal back and forth, producing alternating voltage on the sides of the crystal.

Many minerals show this piezoelectric effect; the best known such mineral is quartz. Like other pressure-sensitive materials, the slight bending of a properly cut slice of quartz develops opposite charges on its faces. This effect is reversible, that is, the application of a voltage (opposite charges) to the faces of the slice of quartz causes the crystalline quartz to bend slightly. By applying an alternating voltage, of a frequency close to the natural mechanical vibration frequency of the crystal, the crystal is caused to vibrate, bending rapidly back and forth. This mechanical oscillation in turn sustains the continued production of alternating charges on the face of the crystal. Since a given crystal will oscillate at only one definite frequency, the quartz crystal is used to control the frequency of rapidly alternating voltages used in radio transmitters.

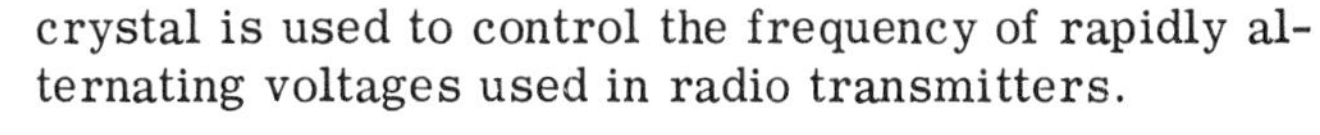

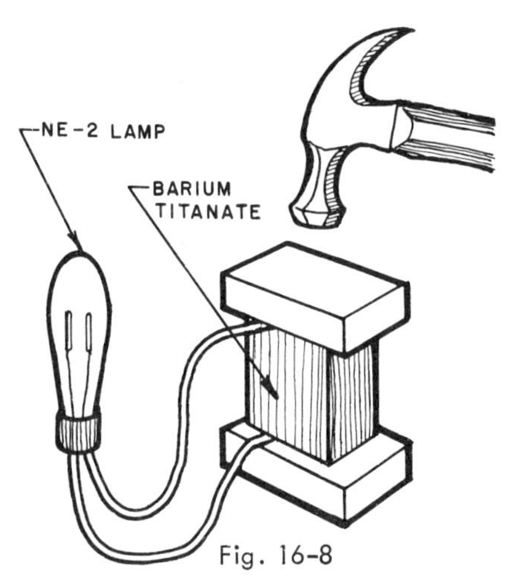

Fig. 16-8

Some ceramic materials, such as barium titanate, show this piezoelectric property and can be used in record-player pickups. A piece of barium titanate, tapped with a hammer, produces enough voltage to flash a small neon lamp, (NE-2, .04 watt). Wires from the lamp contact each end of the piezoelectric material, with a scrap of hard plastic as a cushion between hammer and the brittle barium titanate. Ultrasonic vibrations (50,000 cycles, more or less) are produced by applying alternating voltage of that frequency to properly shaped pieces of barium titanate. These materials also can be used in pressure indicators, and in indicators of mechanical vibration of machine parts.

PHOTOCELLS: E. M. F. From the Energy of Light

The term "photocell", as broadly used, includes three different types of light-sensitive devices:

1. The most-used photoelectric device is a phototube. Light striking the curved metal cathode gives some electrons enough energy to escape from the metal. The free electrons can travel through the vacuum or low-pressure gas to the anode-wire in the center, provided an external voltage is applied to make the anode more positive than the cathode. This photo-tube is not a voltage-producer; rather, it is a device that conducts when light falls on it. The so-called "electric eye" used in door-openers and counting or sorting operations is a phototube.

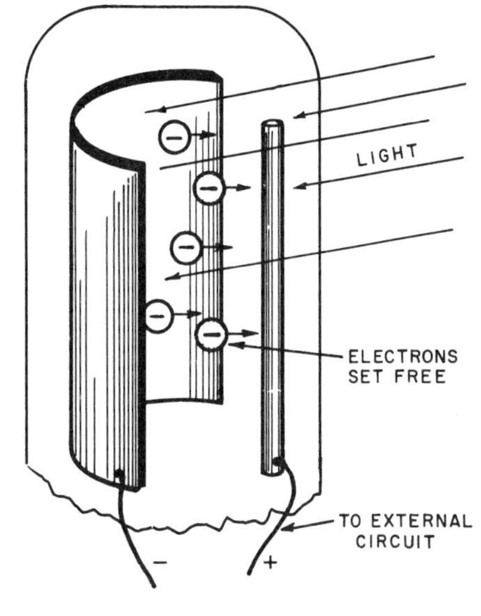

Fig. 16-9

2. Another photoconductive device consists of a thin layer of a semi-conductor (germanium, silicon, lead sulfide, cuprous oxide, for example) that can be used in a circuit. Light falling on these semi-conducting materials gives enough energy to some of the electrons in the solid to make them free-moving inside the solid, so that the solid semi-conductor is a better conductor when illuminated. These photoconductors do not produce voltage; still they are useful in control circuits that are energized by some other voltage source.

3. The term photocell, strictly should be applied to devices that produce e.m.f. when illuminated. This "photovoltaic effect" is produced when the junction or boundary-surface between a metal and a semi-conductor is illuminated. There are two ways of arranging the materials: (a) a very thin transparent metal film is deposited on a sheet of semi-conductor, or (b) a very thin transparent layer of semi-conductor is deposited on a metal. In both cases, the junction of metal and semi-conductor can be illuminated. The direction of electron-movement may be from metal to semi-conductor, or from semi-conductor to metal, depending on the nature of the impurities in the semi-conductor.

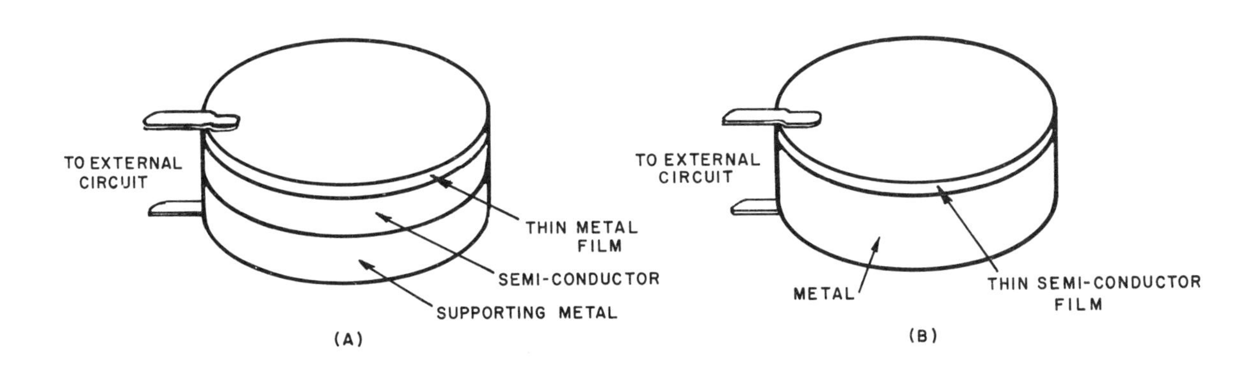

Fig. 16-10

ELECTRIC ENERGY FROM NUCLEAR ENERGY

Several commercial power plants now use nuclear energy from the break-up of uranium atoms as a source of heat. This heat is used to form steam, which drives an ordinary steam-turbine generator unit. The nuclear energy replaces coal as a source of heat. No new electrical principles are involved in the generator.

Still to be hoped for is the development of a new and entirely different method of efficiently directing nuclear energy so that it will immediately produce an electric current, without the necessity of going through the customary steam-driven generator process. In some experiments, charged particles that shoot out from a radioactive material are allowed to collect on a metal electrode. The tiny amount of charge produced does not seem to offer industrial possibilities.

Semi-conductor junctions, as in a germanium transistor, can produce a small voltage when radiated. This is the principle of the experimental RCA "Atomic Battery", sketched in Fig. 16-11.

"A" is the radioactive source; a mixture containing the isotope Strontium-90 has been used. "B" is the semi-conductor. Radiation from A releases electrons in the semi-conductor, and these freed electrons spill over into an electron-receptive alloy, C, in contact with the semi-conductor. Note the similarity of this process to that which takes place in a photovoltaic cell. The voltage produced is small.

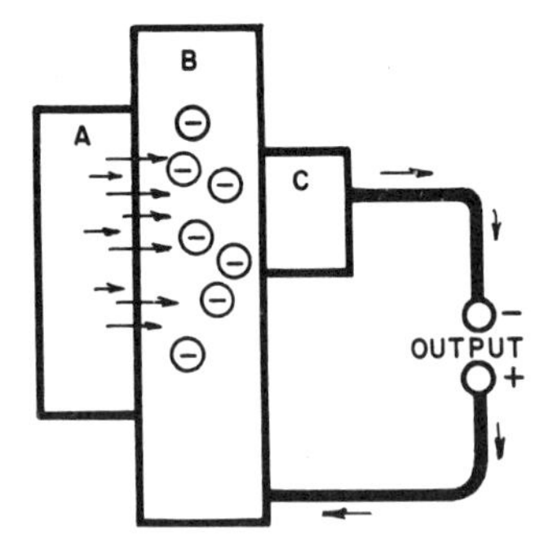

Fig. 16-11

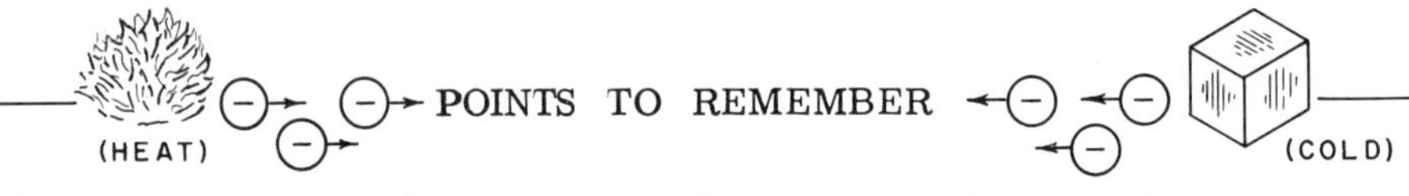

- Piezoelectricity (pressure-e.m.f.) is a voltage developed by mechanically distorting certain crystals and ceramics. This e.m.f. is used in pick-ups and control elements, not as a power producer.

- Heat applied to the junction of two metals will displace electrons from one metal to the other. This e.m.f. is used in thermocouples for high temperature measurement.

- The above energy conversions are reversible. Voltage applied to a piezoelectric material will change its shape; current through a pair of thermocouple junctions releases heat at one end and absorbs heat at the other.

- Light falling on the junction of a metal and a semi-conductor will displace electrons from one to the other. This e.m.f. is used in photocells.

- When radiation from a radioactive material releases electrons in a semi-conductor, an e.m.f. is produced. This is a direct conversion of nuclear radiation to electrical energy.

REVIEW QUESTIONS

1. What is the difference between a photocell and a phototube?

2. Could a piezoelectric material be used to produce sound in a headphone or loudspeaker?

3. Name several semi-conductors.

4. What is the difference between a thermocouple and a thermostat? Can one substitute for the other?

5. Name three piezoelectric materials.

The principal source of electric energy for all industry is the generator, a device for changing mechanical energy of motion into electrical energy. This energy conversion takes place by the action of magnetic forces; hence the name "electromagnetic."

An "induced voltage" or "induced current" is one that is produced by the action of magnetic forces, as contrasted with voltages produced by chemical action or other methods.

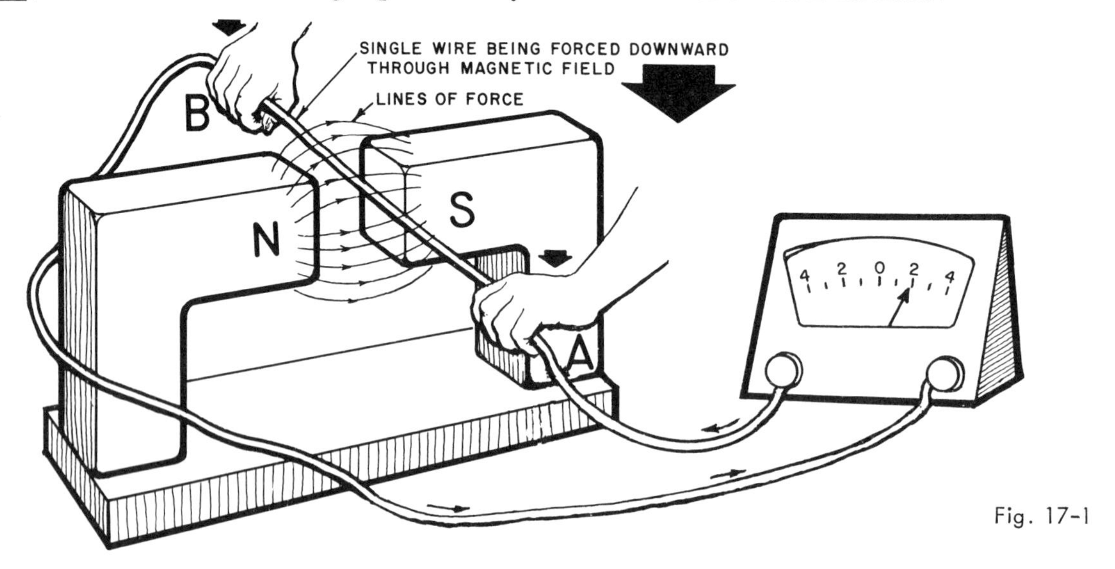

Fig. 17-1

A simple way of demonstrating this "induction" process is shown in Fig. 17-1. A piece of copper wire is connected to the terminals of a sensitive meter and moved downward through a magnetic field, the wire cutting across the lines of force. A strong horseshoe magnet (preferably Alnico) should be used. The meter may be either a milli-voltmeter, milli-ammeter, micro-ammeter, or galvanometer, preferably a zero-center type.

While the wire is moving, a voltage, or e.m.f., is produced, tending to drive electrons from A toward B, (Fig. 17-1). This e.m.f., "induced" by the movement of the wire across the field, causes a current if a complete circuit exists. If the magnet and wire are kept stationary, no e.m.f. is produced. Movement is necessary.

When the wire is moved upward through the magnetic field, Fig. 17-2, the meter needle is deflected in the direction opposite to its previous motion, showing that the induced e.m.f. and induced current has been reversed in direction.

When the wire is moved endwise through the field, as from A to B and back again, no e.m.f. is produced. If the wire is moved in a direction parallel to the lines of force, as from S toward N or from N toward S, no induced e.m.f. is generated. The wire has to move so that it cuts across the lines of magnetic force. This "cutting" is a quick way of describing the motion that must occur if any voltage is to be produced. (No one need be concerned about any damage to these imaginary lines during the cutting process. The cut ends must heal together quickly, for the field is just as strong after the wire has passed through as it was before!)

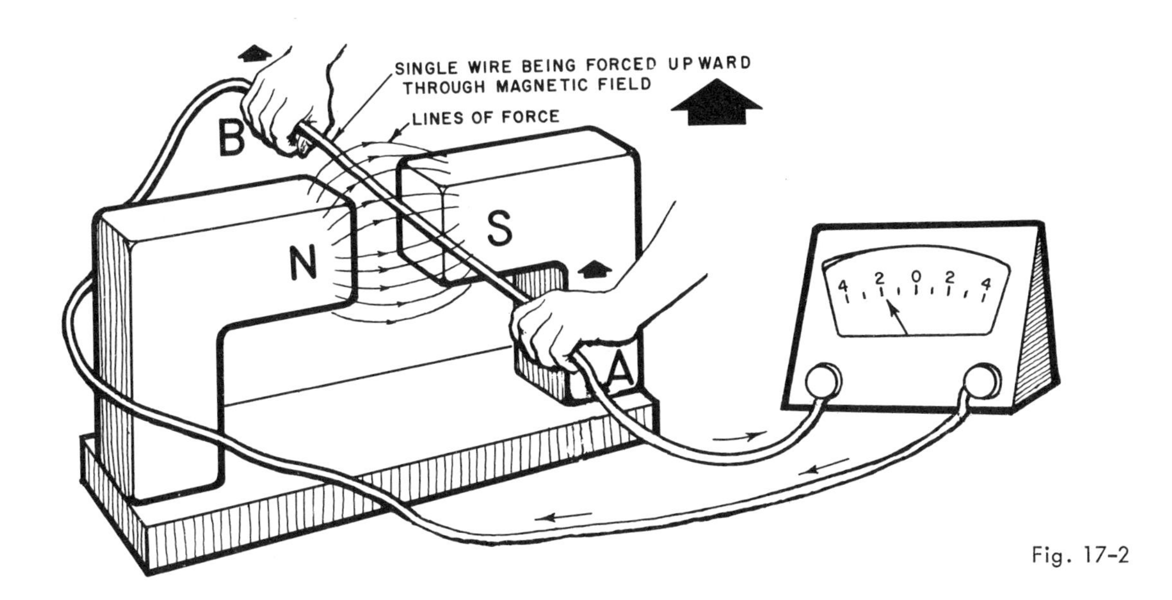

Fig. 17-2

Where does the electrical energy come from? In the demonstration shown in Fig. 17-1 and 17-2, the electrons are already in the wire, the energy to move them comes from the owner of the hands. The mechanical energy that is used to push the wire through the field is converted to electrical energy. Mechanical energy has to be put into the generating device at the same rate (watts) as electrical energy is produced.

This energy-conversion process that is used in generators is a reversible process, that is, the same equipment can change electrical energy to mechanical motion. If we connect the wire of Fig. 17-1 to a 6-volt battery instead of to a galvanometer, the current in the wire will cause the wire to be thrown upward or downward through the magnetic field, direction of motion depending on current direction.

A rotating machine that uses mechanical energy and produces electrical energy is called a generator, but the same machine can act as a motor, putting out mechanical energy when it is driven by electrical energy. The old term "dynamo" means an energy converter, usable as either a generator or a motor.

LEFT-HAND GENERATOR RULE

The relation of direction of motion of wire in a field to the direction of induced e.m.f. may be briefly described this way: With the thumb, forefinger and middle finger of the left hand placed at right angles to each other, Fig. 17-3, the forefinger (or first finger) gives the direction of the field, the thumb gives the direction of motion of the wire, and the center finger gives the direction of the induced current.

This rule does not explain anything, it is merely one of the ways of determining one of the above directions when the other two are known.

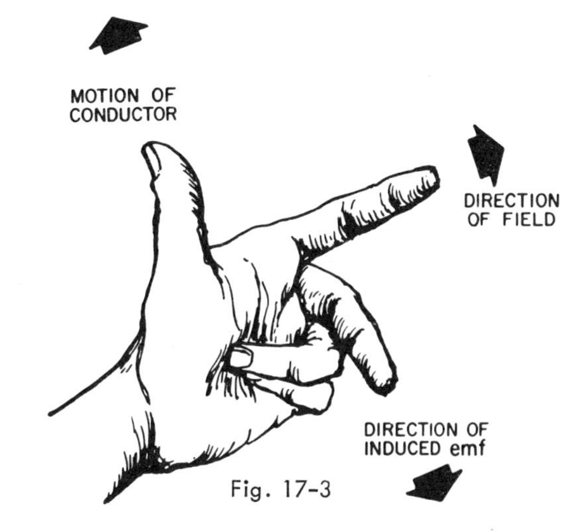

Fig. 17-3

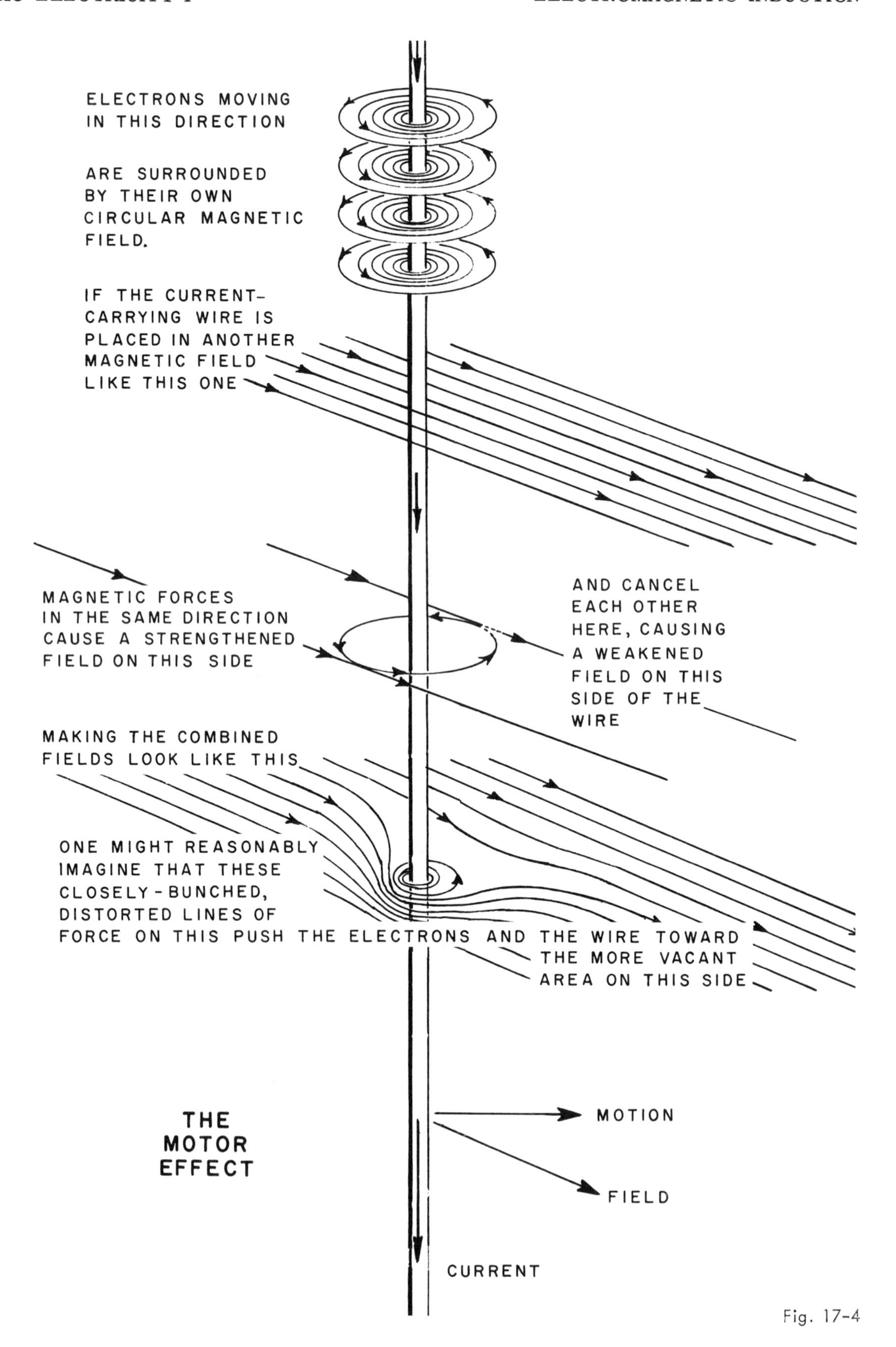
ELECTRONS MOVING IN THIS DIRECTION
ARE SURROUNDED BY THEIR OWN CIRCULAR MAGNETIC FIELD.
IF THE CURRENT-CARRYING WIRE IS PLACED IN ANOTHER MAGNETIC FIELD LIKE THIS ONE
MAGNETIC FORCES IN THE SAME DIRECTION CAUSE A STRENGTHENED FIELD ON THIS SIDE
AND CANCEL EACH OTHER HERE, CAUSING A WEAKENED FIELD ON THIS SIDE OF THE WIRE
MAKING THE COMBINED FIELDS LOOK LIKE THIS
ONE MIGHT REASONABLY IMAGINE THAT THESE CLOSELY-BUNCHED, DISTORTED LINES OF FORCE ON THIS PUSH THE ELECTRONS AND THE WIRE TOWARD THE MORE VACANT AREA ON THIS SIDE
THE MOTOR EFFECT
MOTION
FIELD
CURRENT

Fig. 17-4

Fig. 17-4 shows how a current-carrying wire is pushed sidewise by a magnetic field. At first, this topic may seem to have little to do with generators, because the current in 17-4 may be caused by a battery, and the sidewise force on the wire is the force that is responsible for the operation of an electric motor.

The purpose of this diagram at this point is to emphasize the similarities of the two ways of using this one energy conversion process. Wires in a magnetic field enable us to change energy from mechanical to electrical, or the reverse. If we produce electrical energy, we call the machine a generator; if we produce mechanical energy, we call the machine a motor.

The distorted magnetic field shown near the bottom of the diagram at the left seems to be the only satisfactory way of forming a mental picture of the development of a force against the wire. Recalling the properties that we assign to lines of magnetic force: the arrows on the magnetic lines merely represent the direction that the N-pole of a compass would point; magnetic lines pushing sidewise against each other and trying to straighten out lengthwise cause a pressure against the left side of the wire in Fig. 17-4. (See also Pages 228, 229.)

But what has this to do with a generator? Summarizing Fig. 17-4, electrons moving downward through the magnetic field are kicked sidewise to the right by the field.

In Fig. 17-5, below, electrons again are being moved downward through a magnetic field, moving downward because they are part of a wire that is being moved downward by two hands. The magnetic field is toward the observer, as it was in Fig. 17-4. Again, electrons are kicked sidewise to the right by the field. This same sidewise kick, now being in the same direction as the wire itself, can cause a current; and we call this sidewise kick on the electrons "induced electromotive force."

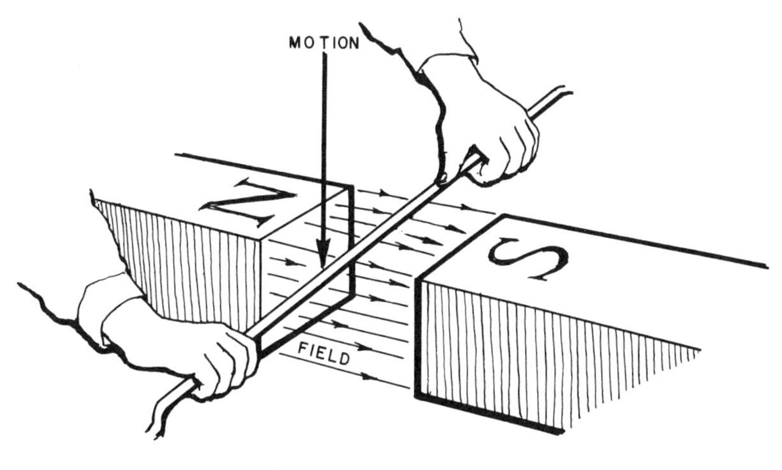

Fig. 17-5

Compare Fig. 17-5 with Fig. 17-1; reversing the direction of the field, as we look at it, also reverses the direction of the induced e.m.f. Try applying the left-hand rule, Fig. 17-3, to three induced-e.m.f. diagrams, (17-1, 17-2, 17-5).

Figs. 17-1, 17-2 and 17-5 show the generation of an e.m.f. by moving a wire so that it cuts across a magnetic field. It is often just as practical to produce e.m.f. by moving the magnetic field so that it cuts across stationary wires.

An e.m.f. is produced in a stationary coil (Fig. 17-6) when a bar magnet is withdrawn from or inserted into the coil. The lines of force, moving along with the magnet, cut across the wires of the coil.

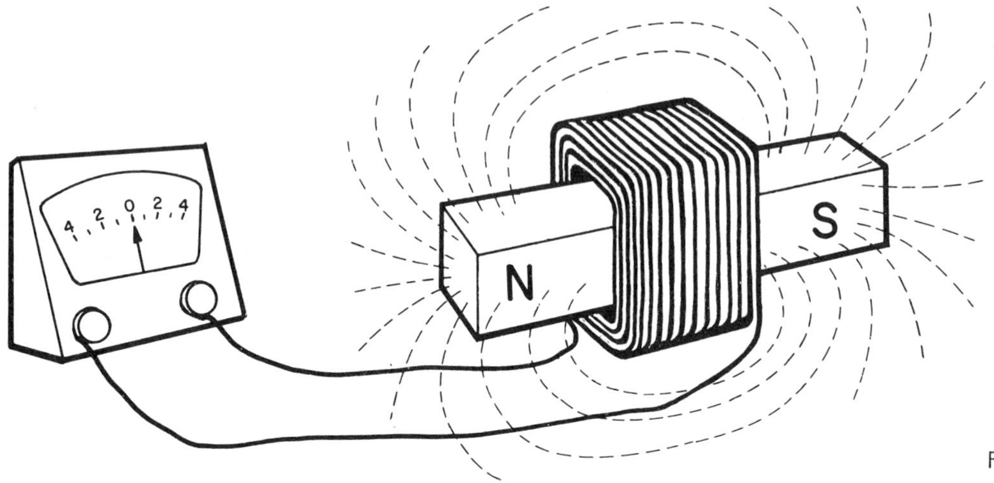

Fig. 17-6

With several magnets of various strengths available, one may show that a greater voltage is produced by a stronger magnet.

By trying the effect with several coils that differ in number of turns, it is seen that more turns produce more e.m.f. This last effect may be explained in either of two ways, both amount to the same thing:

1. A coil of ten turns has ten loops that are in series with each other. If one volt is produced in each turn, then a total of ten volts is produced in ten turns.

2. The amount of voltage depends on the amount of cutting of lines of force. One line of force cutting across ten wires does as good a job as ten lines cutting across one wire. The total amount of "cutting-across" is the same.

While the above equipment is available, it is easy to demonstrate that moving the magnet slowly produces a small e.m.f.; faster motion causes more e.m.f.

Amount of induced e.m.f. depends on the rate of cutting of lines of force with wires. The induced e.m.f. is proportional to the product of these three factors which determine the rate of cutting: (1) number of lines of force; (2) number of turns of wire; (3) speed of movement (relative motion of wires and field).

The relationship of voltage measurements to magnetic field measurements is this:

One volt is produced when 100,000,000 lines of force are cut by wire per second.

If 50,000 lines of force are cut by a coil of 2000 turns in one second, the total cutting is $50{,}000 \times 2000 = 100{,}000{,}000$ lines cut per second, so one volt is induced.

If 300,000 lines of force are cut by a coil of 5000 turns in two seconds, the total cutting is $300{,}000 \times 5000 = 1{,}500{,}000{,}000$ lines in two seconds. That's a rate of 750,000,000 lines cut each second, which, being 7 1/2 times as much as 100,000,000, produces 7 1/2 volts.

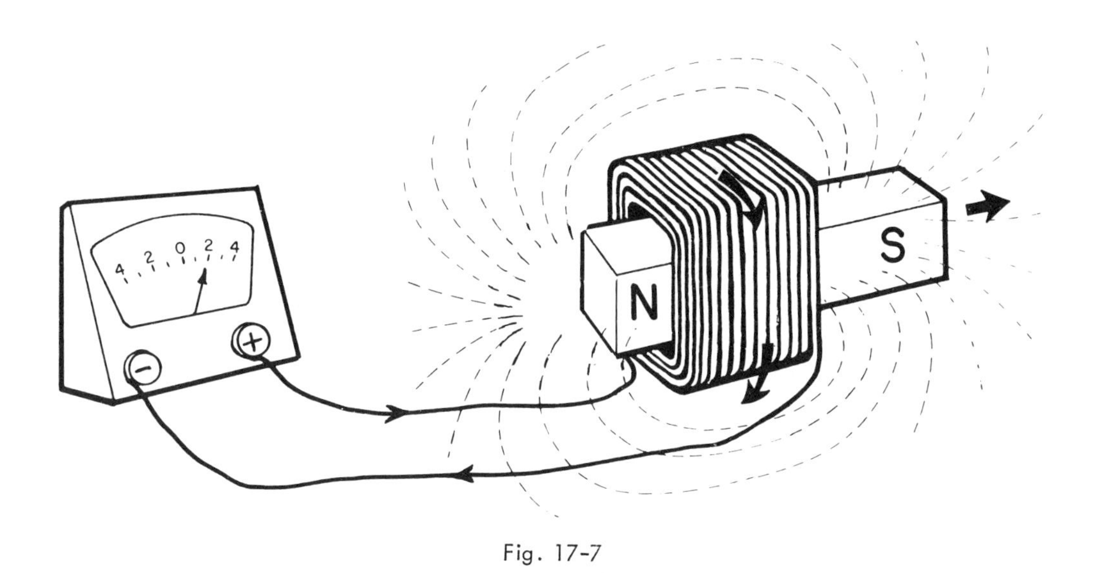

Fig. 17-7

This sketch shows the withdrawal of the magnet from the coil. The magnetic field of the N-pole is moving to the right, cutting across the wires of the coil. If one wishes to determine the direction of induced e.m.f. by using the left-hand rule (Fig. 17-3), it must be remembered that the hand rule is based on relative motion of the wire. Pulling the magnet to the right is equivalent to moving the coil of wire to the left. To use the hand rule, the thumb must therefore point to the left, representing the relative motion of the wire through the field. To find the direction of e.m.f. over the top of the coil, the thumb points to the left, the forefinger (for field) upward, and the center finger then gives the current direction toward the observer at the top of the coil. At the bottom of the coil, the thumb still points to the left, the field is downward, and the center finger points away from the observer, giving the current direction around the coil as shown by the arrows on the wire in the diagram.

There is a fundamentally more important way of determining the current direction that may be described with the help of Fig. 17-7. As pointed out before, electrical energy is produced at the expense of mechanical energy; the hand that removes the magnet from the coil must do some work. The magnet does not push out of the coil by itself, the hand must pull it out.

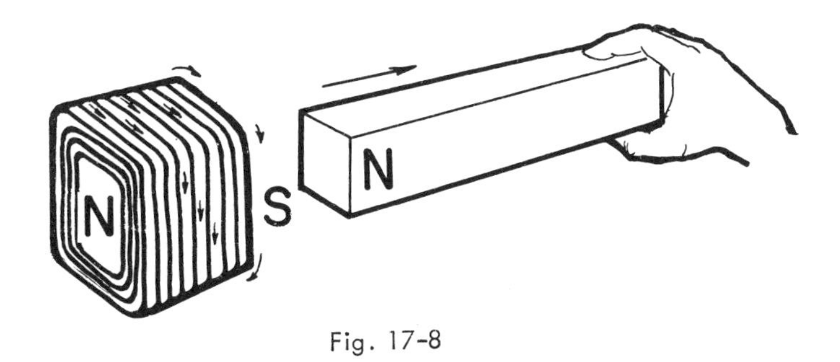

Fig. 17-8

How can the coil make it difficult to remove the magnet? By creating magnet poles of its own that tend to draw the magnet into the coil. See Fig. 17-8, showing the magnet a little more removed from the coil. The induced current in the coil is in such a direction as to develop poles on the coil as shown (recall left-hand rule for a coil), which poles try to pull the magnet toward the coil.

If the motion of the magnet is reversed, that is, pushed into the coil, the induced current reverses also, developing poles on the coil that try to repel the approaching magnet.

This general idea, recognized years ago by Lenz, is summarized in Lenz's Law, which states, briefly, that:

> An induced current opposes the motion that causes it.

Before we leave Figs. 17-6 to 17-8, they can be used to illustrate another view of Lenz's Law, which will be useful in determining induced current direction in more complex machinery. Note that in Fig. 17-6, the coil is surrounded by the magnetic field of the bar magnet. The field is like this: The removal of the magnet is the removal of this magnetic field. The induced current in the coil tries to maintain a field of the same strength and direction as the field that is being removed. (Apply hand rule to coil in Fig. 17-8, determine direction and shape of field of the coil due to current in it.)

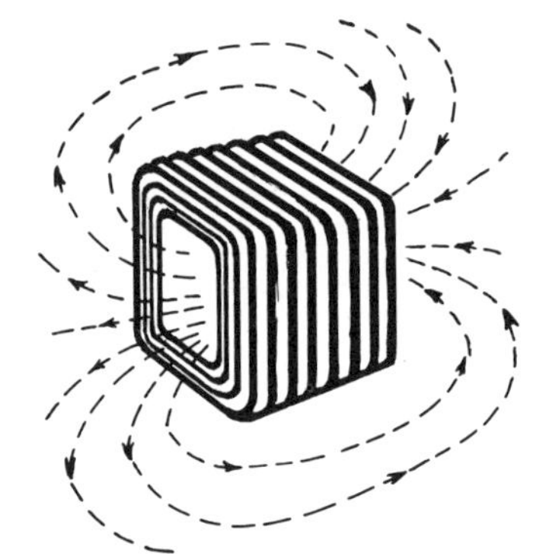

Fig. 17-9

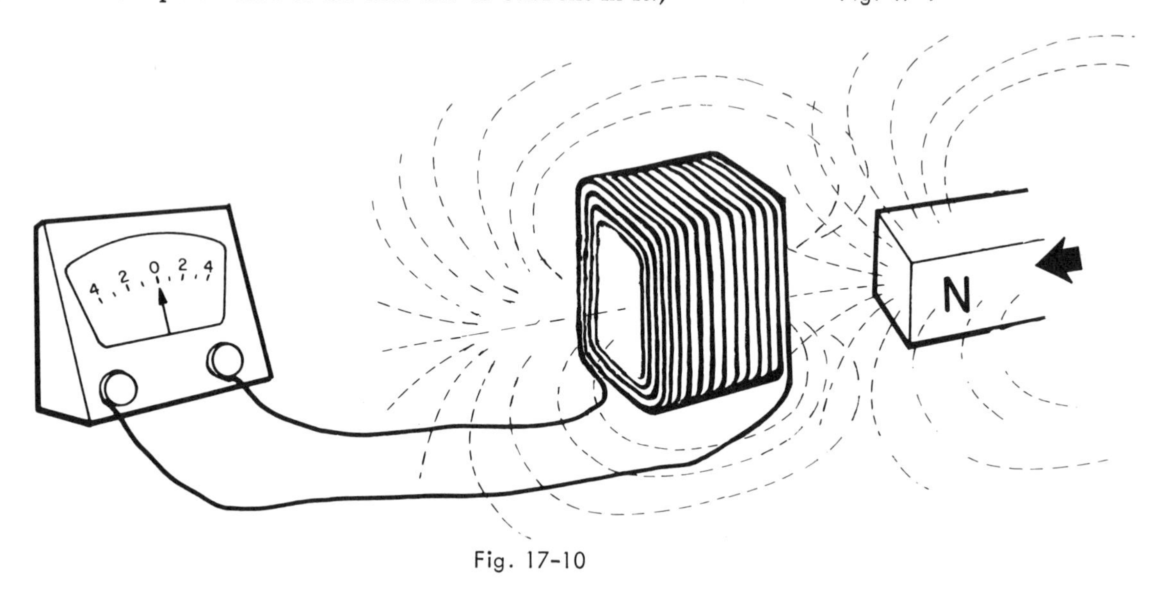

Fig. 17-10

Consider now (Fig. 17-10) a coil affected by the approach of a magnet. Originally, the coil had no magnetic field in it. As the approaching magnet's lines of force enter the coil, the coil develops a field of its own that tends to restore conditions in the coil to the original zero-field condition, that is, tends to cancel out the oncoming field.

Another way of saying Lenz's Law is:

> Induced voltages, and induced currents, oppose change of magnetic field.

In the preceding discussion, the terms "induced voltage" and "induced current" may seem to have been used interchangeably. One should understand that the relative motion of wire and magnetic field always induces a voltage, or e.m.f.; and this induced e.m.f. causes a current if there is a closed circuit.

ROTATING MACHINES

Commercial generators produce electrical energy either by rotating coils of wire in a stationary magnetic field, or by rotating a magnet inside a stationary coil of wire.

The largest generators built contain stationary coils in which the useful current is induced by a rotating magnet. Fig. 17-11 shows one stationary coil. The cylindrical rotating magnet is magnetized along a diameter.

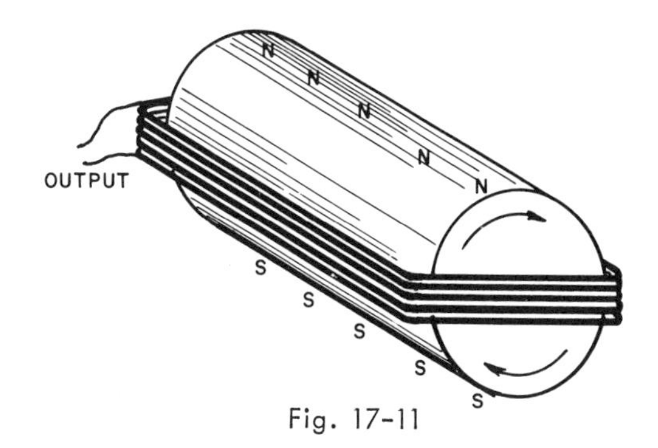

Fig. 17-11

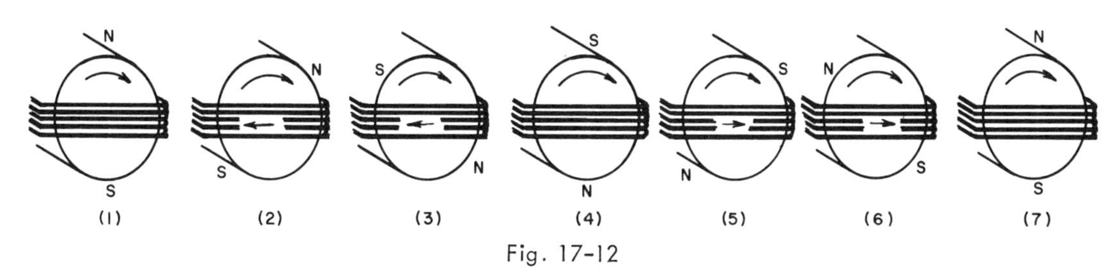

Fig. 17-12

Sketches 1 - 7 show the direction of induced voltage in the coil at successive instants during one rotation of the magnet. In position (1) there is no induced voltage. During the first quarter-turn, the voltage increases, reaching a maximum as the poles sweep close by the wires, then decreasing during the next quarter-turn. At position (4) the induced voltage is instantaneously zero, then surges in the opposite direction. A generator of this type produces alternating current. A complete rotation of this simple 2-pole magnet produces one cycle of induced alternating current. Rotating this magnet at a speed of 60 revolutions per second (3600 r.p.m.) produces our ordinary 60-cycle alternating current for distribution to homes and industry.

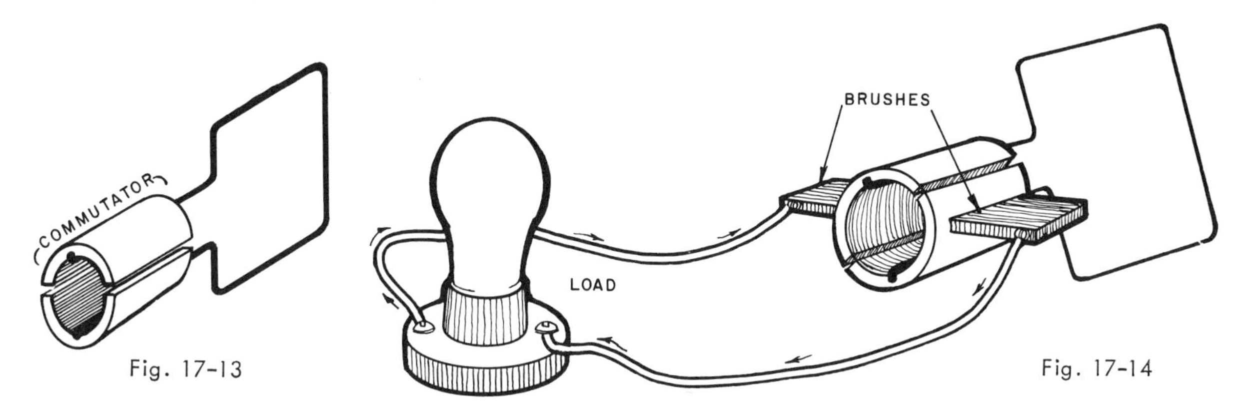

Fig. 17-13

Fig. 17-14

D.C. generators use stationary field magnets, the induced current being generated in rotating coils. The basic principle of producing D.C. may be shown by following in detail what happens when one loop of wire is rotated in a magnetic field. In order to produce a direct (one-way) current in the outside circuit that is served by the generator, the ends of this loop are fastened to semicircular metal strips, insulated from each other, which rotate along with the loop. These two half-circle segments form the part of this generator called the commutator.

Two stationary conductors (often blocks of graphite) called brushes, are held in contact with the commutator. These brushes carry the generated D.C. to the outside circuit.

The following series of diagrams shows successive positions of the steadily rotating loop. N and S represent poles of a horseshoe magnet.

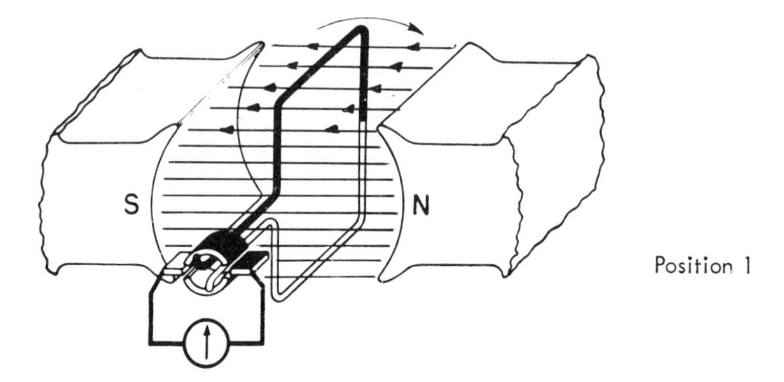

Fig. 17-15 Rotating Loop

At the instant represented by position (1), no e.m.f. is produced, because the wires are moving parallel to the field and there is no cutting of lines of force. (Half of the loop is blackened for later identification.)

As the loop moves from position (1) to position (2), lines of force are cut at an increasing rate, even though the rotation rate is steady. Notice how a, b, c, and d in diagram below show the relative number of lines cut during small equal time intervals between (1) and (2).

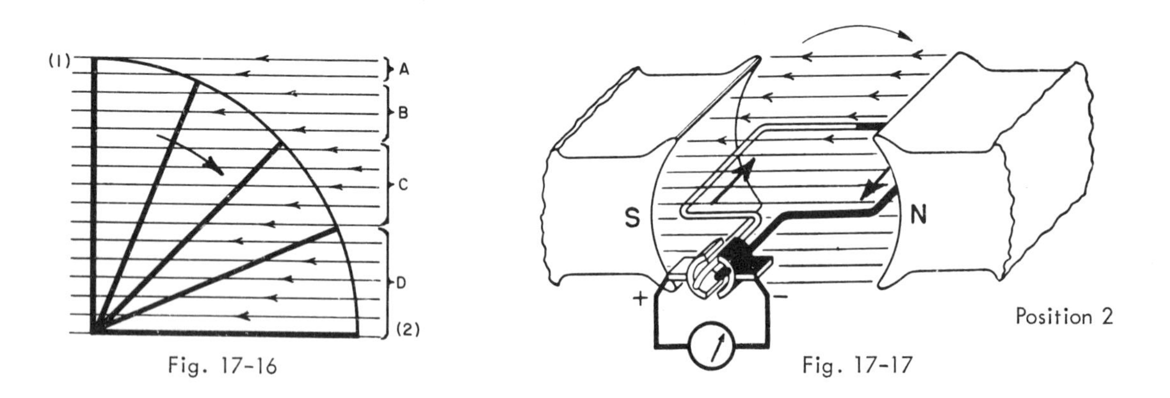

Fig. 17-16

Fig. 17-17

At position (2) the sides of the loop are cutting lines of force at the maximum rate. The induced current <u>in the loop</u> (found by either left-hand rule or by Lenz's Law) is a flow of electrons directed toward the brush on the right and away from the brush on the left. This forcing of electrons from the rotating coil toward the right-hand brush makes this brush negative-charged. The removal of electrons from the left-hand brush makes it positive-charged. In the stationary wiring of the external circuit, electrons flow from the negative brush to the positive brush.

Between positions (2) and (3), current continues to be induced in the same direction, but decreases in amount as the wire approaches position (3). At this position the two segments of the commutator are short-circuited, but with no ill effect, because at this instant no e.m.f. is being generated. At position (3) no lines of force are being cut.

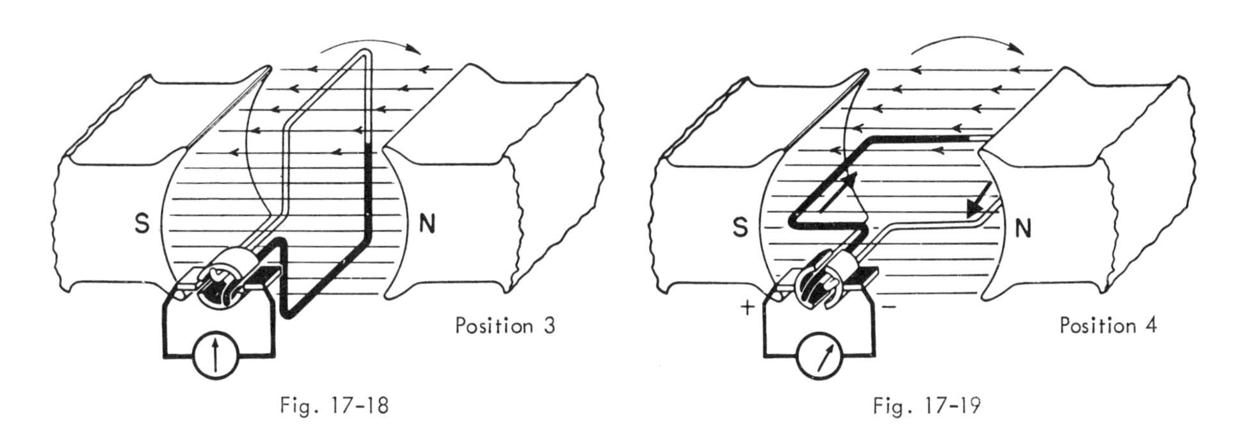

Fig. 17-18 Fig. 17-19

Between positions (3) and (4), increasing voltage and current is produced, just as happened between positions (1) and (2). But notice that the black side of the loop, previously moving downward through the field, is now moving upward, so the current direction in the black side has been reversed. (Compare diagrams for positions (2) and (4)).

However, the black side of the loop is now taking electrons from the left brush, forcing them around through the white side of the loop toward the right-hand brush, so the charges on each brush are the same as before.

Reviewing the above diagrams, note that in the rotating loop itself the generated current alternates in direction. Watch the black half of the commutator as it rotates. In position (2), the black segment is negative and supplies electrons to the right-hand brush. In position (4), the black segment has become positive, but just as it becomes positive it slides away from the right-hand brush and contacts the left brush. Likewise the white segment of the commutator changes position as the current direction in the loop changes, so that the right-hand brush is always supplied with electrons and the left-hand brush is always losing electrons into the rotating loop. Thus the electron flow through the outside load is kept one-directional.

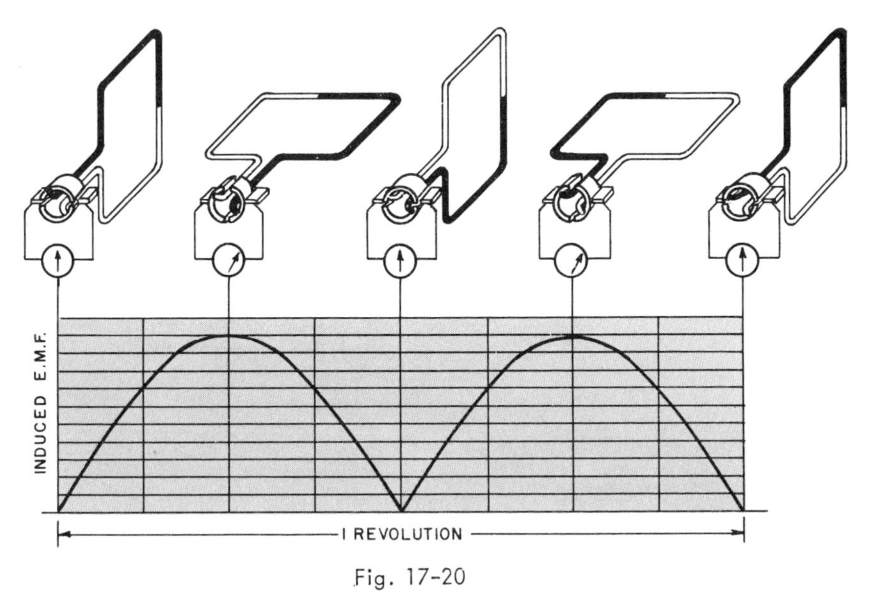

Fig. 17-20

This graph shows how the voltage (or current) changes in amount during one revolution of the loop. This type of current is called pulsating D.C.

In the next Unit we shall see how the addition of more loops and more commutator segments can make the generated current more steady and continuous, as well as producing a greater amount of voltage than can be made in one loop of wire.

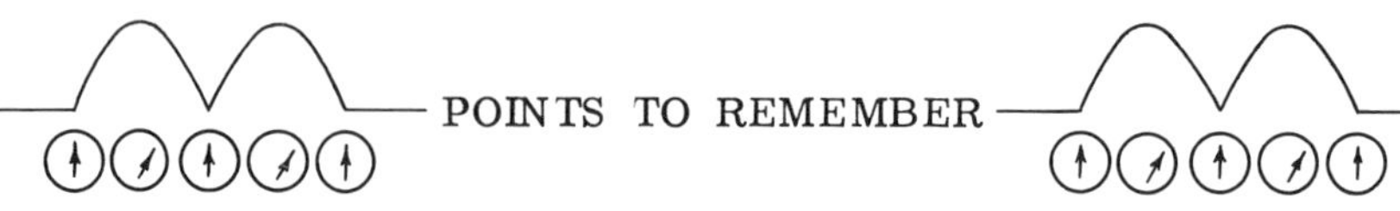

POINTS TO REMEMBER

- The voltage produced by generators is called "induced e.m.f.". This name is given to the e.m.f. that is produced by the motion of wires across a magnetic field, or by the motion of magnetic field across wires.
- This "induction" process in a generator converts mechanical energy into electrical energy.
- The amount of induced e.m.f. depends on the strength of the magnetic field, the number of turns of wire in the device, and the speed of movement.
- To produce one volt, lines of force must be cut by wire at the rate of 100,000,000 per second.
- Lenz's Law: An induced current opposes the motion that causes the induced current. Induced voltages and currents oppose change of magnetic field.
- Alternating current is generated in stationary coils by rotating a magnet inside the coil.
- When coils are rotated in a stationary magnetic field, an alternating current is generated in the coil. By means of a commutator this current is fed into the outside circuit as direct (one-way) current.

REVIEW QUESTIONS

1. A wire is moved through a field, as sketched below. What is the direction of the induced e.m.f.?

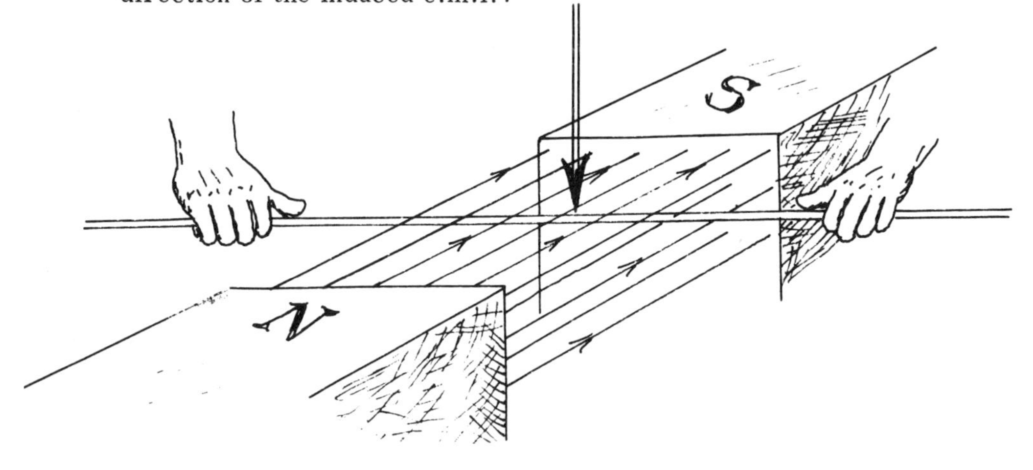

2. In a generator, where does the electricity come from?

3. In 1912, some folks took short trips in their electric automobile, powered only by storage batteries and an electric motor. The necessity of frequent battery-charging helped make these cars obsolete. Wouldn't a generator, belt-driven from the wheels of a trailer, charge the batteries and make a longer trip possible?

4. State three factors on which the amount of induced voltage depends.

5. In a certain generator, like Fig. 17-15, the loop of wire in position (1) encloses 10,000 lines of force. Numerically, how much cutting of lines of force occurs during one complete rotation of the loop?

6. In the generator of question 5, if the loop is rotated at a speed of 2400 r.p.m., how many lines of force are cut each second? How much voltage is produced?

7. From the sketch, determine which brush is positive and which is negative.

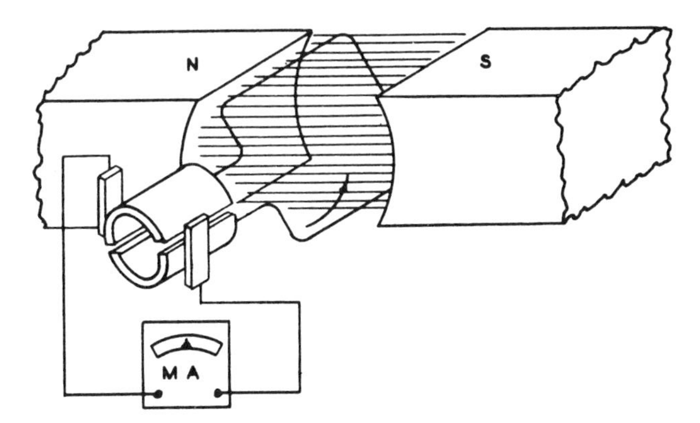

8. State Lenz's Law. State the left-hand generator rule. Which one of these is the more important fundamental principle?

9. Fig. 17-7, Page 177, shows the effect of pulling a magnet from a coil, the magnet being pulled out to the right. If the magnet were pulled out to the left, would the induced current be in the same direction as shown in Fig. 17-7? Why?

10. See Fig. 17-11 and 17-12, Page 179. When the magnet is rotating, is there any torque tending to move the coil?

11. A copper disk is supported between magnet poles so it can be rotated. What happens in the disk as it rotates?

12. Does the strength of the magnet have any effect on the amount of force needed to turn the disk?

13. A coin spinning on the end of a thread is lowered into a magnetic field. What happens? Why?

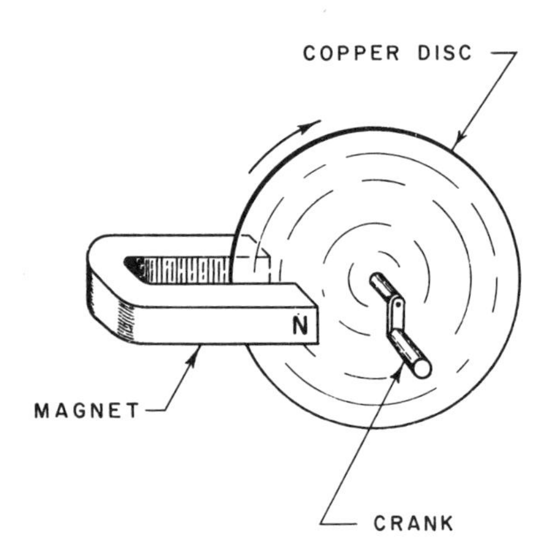

14. An aluminum cup is hung upside down on a pivot over a rotating magnet. What happens to the cup?

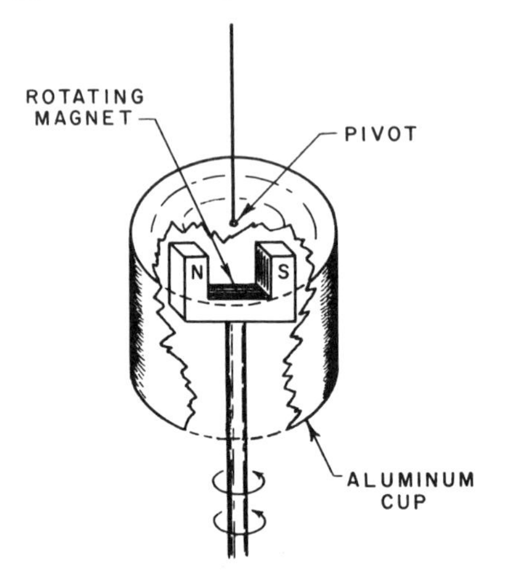

Unit 18 D.C. GENERATORS

In Unit 17, the single loop of wire, rotating in a magnetic field, was used to illustrate the principle of generation of e.m.f. However, one loop of wire makes such an ineffective generator that it is not useful, even as a toy. The first improvement that might come to mind is to use a coil of several turns instead of a single loop. A 100-turn coil will make 100 times as much voltage as a one-turn coil, at the same r.p.m. and field strength.

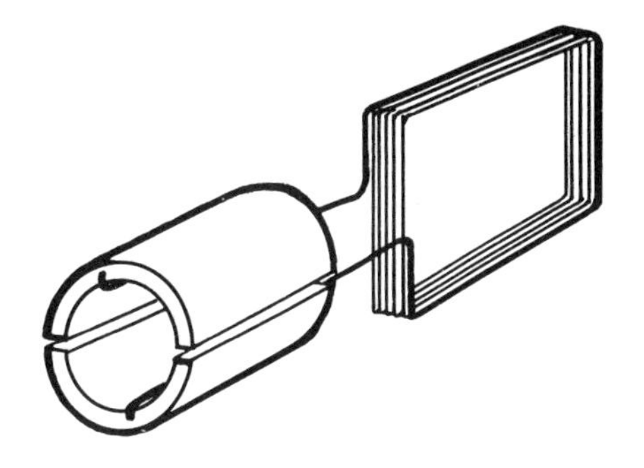

Fig. 18-1

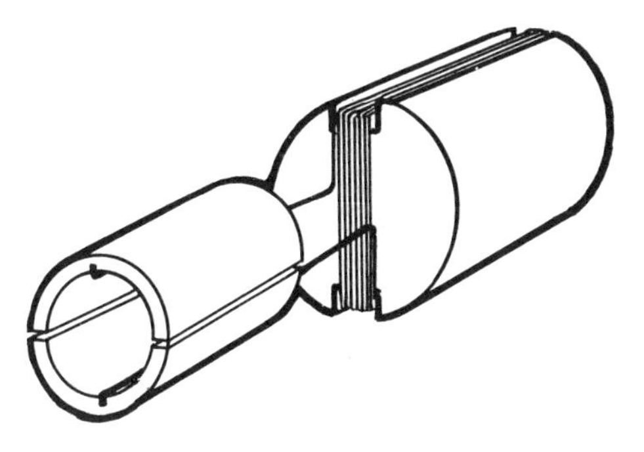

Fig. 18-2

Another improvement is the use of an iron core around which the generating coil is to be wound. The use of this iron core immediately creates a stronger magnetic field for the coil to operate in. With the same field magnet, the placing of the iron core between its poles increases the number of lines of force by several times (see Pages 82 and 95).

One disadvantage of the simple generator still needs correcting. This coil of wire, rotating in a strong field still produces an e.m.f. that rises and falls to zero twice during each rotation, (Fig. 17-20). Mechanically, this is like a one-cylinder gas engine; electrically, current that varies in this fashion causes difficulties in the generator and in the circuit that it feeds.

To produce a smoother and steadier e.m.f. and current, more coils are placed on this rotating iron core, and they are connected to a several-segment commutator in such a fashion that the voltage produced by the generator is the sum of several individual coil voltages. At certain instants, the voltage generated in one coil still drops to zero, but other coils in series are then producing voltages high enough so that the total output voltage is fairly constant.

This rotating assembly of coils, placed in slots in an iron core, and connected to commutator segments, is called the armature of the generator.

Small D.C. armatures are easy to obtain for study and disassembly; there are millions of them in use in automobiles and aircraft. Armatures from D.C. motors, and from universal (A.C.-D.C.) motors used in vacuum cleaners and hand drills are similar in construction.

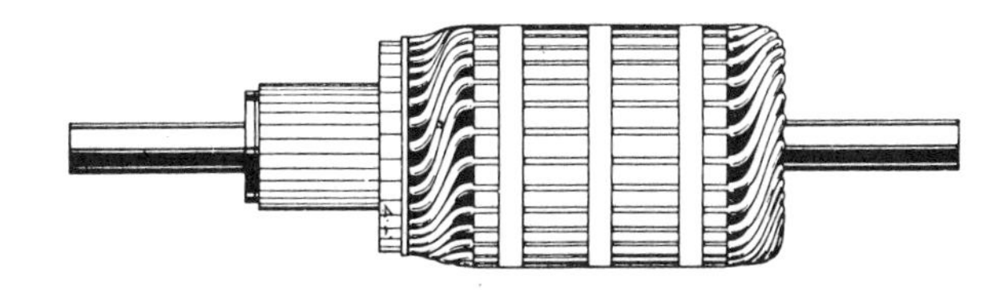

Fig. 18-3

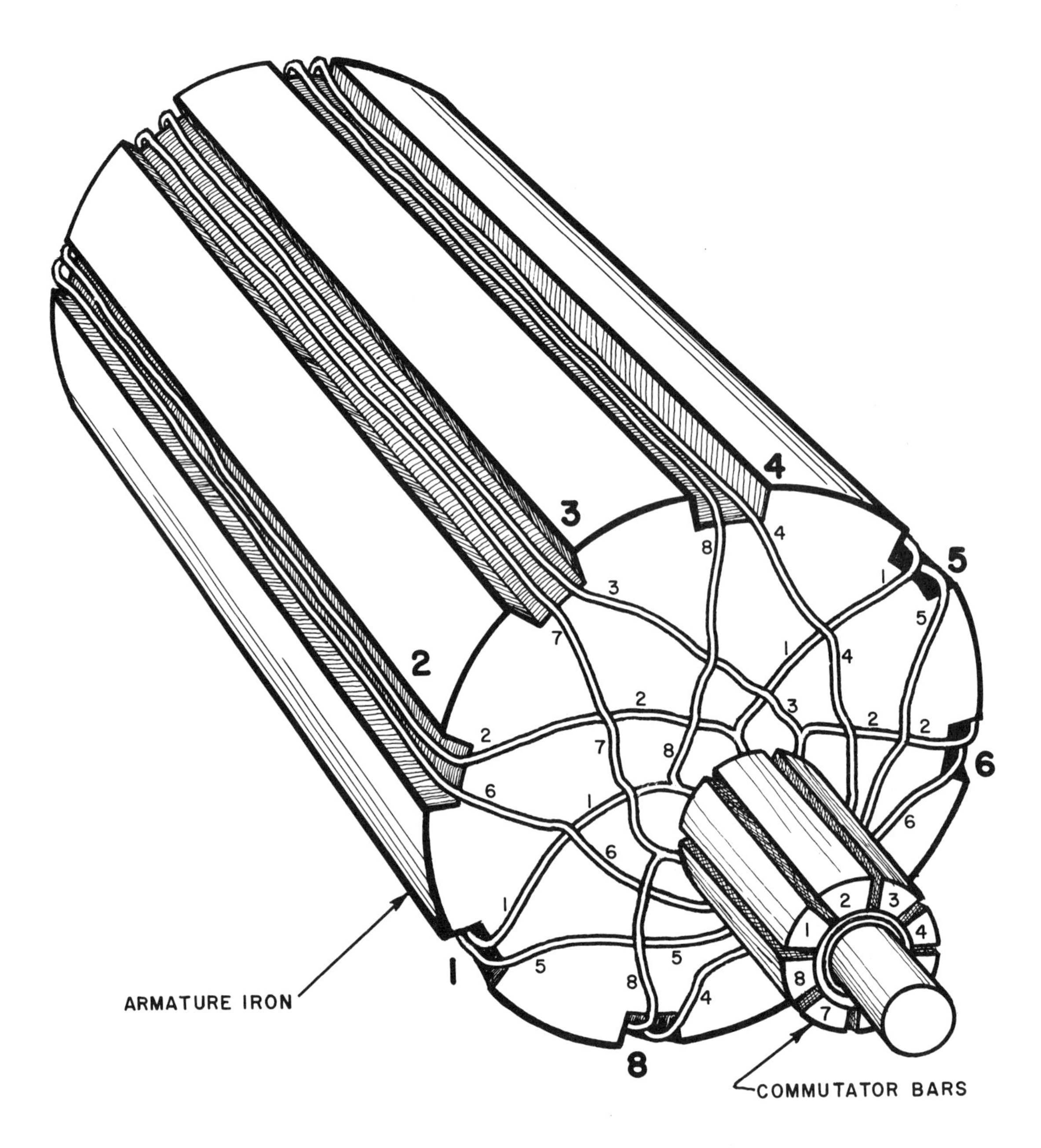

Fig. 18-4

The above diagram shows the wiring of an armature suitable for use in a simple generator that has one pair of field-magnet poles. At first glance, this sketch may seem complicated, but, like everything else, it becomes simple after one takes a few minutes to trace out the circuit and understand it.

To trace out the wiring — start on commutator bar 1. Wire 1 leads to the left through slot 1, is brought over to slot 5 at the back end of the armature, through slot 5 to the front end, where it connects to bar 2. This traces one loop of coil 1. In actual practice, wire 1, starting from bar 1, is wound through slots 1 and 5 many times, forming the coil. The finish end of the coil connects to bar 2.

Similarly, trace coil 2. Starting on bar 2, wire 2 leads to slot 2, across the back of the armature to slot 6, (and around through slots 2 and 6 many times) with the finish end of the coil connecting to bar 3. Coil 3 uses slots 3 and 7; its ends connect to bars 3 and 4. Coil 4 uses slots 4 and 8; it connects to bars 4 and 5. Coil 5 uses slots 5 and 1; it connects to bars 5 and 6. Coil 6 uses slots 2 and 6, along with coil 2, but coil 6 connects to bars 6 and 7. Coil 7 uses slots 3 and 7, and connects to bars 7 and 8. The last coil, 8, may be traced starting on bar 8, through slot 8, around the other end of the armature and through slot 4, after which it connects to bar 1.

TYPES OF ARMATURE WINDINGS

There are several ways, many of them obsolete, of arranging wire and iron to make an armature; the so-called drum winding is the only one now in extensive use. Drum windings may be arranged in several ways:

(1) Low-voltage, moderately high-current generators have a lap winding. Fig. 18-4 shows a simplex lap winding. Two simplex windings on the same armature form a "duplex" winding. Some generators have more than one pair of field poles, which changes the armature coil layout, because each coil must be placed so that when one side of the coil is passing an N-pole, the other side is passing an S-pole. Lap-wound generators have as many pairs of brushes as pairs of poles.

(2) High-voltage, low-current machines use a somewhat different pattern of wires on the armature drum called a wave winding.

(3) The largest D.C. generators are built with a combination of lap and wave winding which is called a frogleg winding.

Each of these three types can be subdivided into many varieties, depending on voltage and current requirements, number of commutator segments, number of field poles, etc. A complete discussion of them fills entire textbooks on armature wiring, one of which should be sought by anyone who needs to know more details.

Returning to the drum-wound armature of Fig. 18-4, let's see how it will behave when rotated between the poles of its field magnet. Imagine the N-pole of a large magnet placed at the left of the armature in Fig. 18-4, and the S-pole at the right, so the armature is in a magnetic field directed from left to right. Assume the armature is rotated counterclockwise; the wires in slots 1, 2 and 3 will be moving downward through the field. Applying the left-hand rule to these wires (forefinger . . . field, toward the right; thumb . . . motion, downward; center finger . . . current, away from the observer) we find the direction of e.m.f. in these wires is away from the commutator, and toward the back of the armature. In slots 5, 6, and 7, the wires will have an induced e.m.f. toward the commutator. (Use 3-finger left-hand rule again.)

But to get a more complete view of all of the wires, and what is going on in them, we can use a different type of diagram. Let's flatten out the armature of Fig. 18-4.

The front (commutator) end stays in place, and the back end wiring is spread and stretched so that it forms the outside circumference of the pancaked armature of Fig. 18-5. Near the center are the numbered ends of the eight commutator segments, as in Fig. 18-4. Around the commutator are the commutator-end wiring connections, just as in 18-4. The eight almost-rectangles are the remains of the eight cylindrical-curved faces of the iron armature. The outside petals of the pancake are the expanded cross-overs of the coils at the back, not visible in Fig. 18-4.

The tracing-out of individual coils can be followed on this diagram, using the same directions as on the preceding page.

As Fig. 18-5 is drawn, the wires in slots 1, 2, 3, and 8 are moving downward at the instant shown, and all of the wires lying in these slots have an e.m.f. directed away from the commutator.

The wires in slots 4, 5, 6, and 7 are moving upward, and their e.m.f. is toward the commutator. (Note directions marked on wires in the numbered slots in Fig. 18-5.)

Tracing these wires to the commutator, we find that commutator bar 1 has electrons brought to it by coil 8, but they are carried away from this bar through coil 1, so there is not much point in locating a brush-connection to the outside circuit on segment 1. Segments 2 and 3 are similar, but commutator bar 4 has electrons brought to it by coils 3 and 4.

The position now occupied by bar 4 is the place to locate a brush to pick up these electrons and take them out to the external circuit. This electron supply is the negative brush, which in the generator rests against the outside of the commutator (although diagram has to show it inside).

Continuing the current-tracing, we find segment 8 losing electrons in two directions, so a brush in contact with bar 8 will have electrons taken away from it; this brush then is the positive terminal of the generator.

After 45° more rotation, segments 4 and 8 no longer touch the stationary brushes; segments 1 and 5 occupy the positions formerly held by segments 4 and 8. Segment 1 will be positive, because as the wires in slot 4 move over to the left, their current direction changes. Segment 5 will be negative, and supply electrons to the negative brush, because of the reversal of current in coil 4 when the coil tips past the vertical position.

What happens when slots 4 and 8 are vertical, as originally shown in Fig. 18-4?

At this instant no e.m.f. is generated in coils 4 and 8. The negative brush touches both segments 4 and 5. Segments 4 and 5 are connected to coils 3, 4, and 5, but coil 4 is temporarily dead. Coils 3 and 5 bring electrons through segments 4 and 5 to the negative brush, hence the outside circuit is still supplied with electrons. At this same instant, the positive brush is losing electrons through segments 1 and 8 to coils 1 and 7.

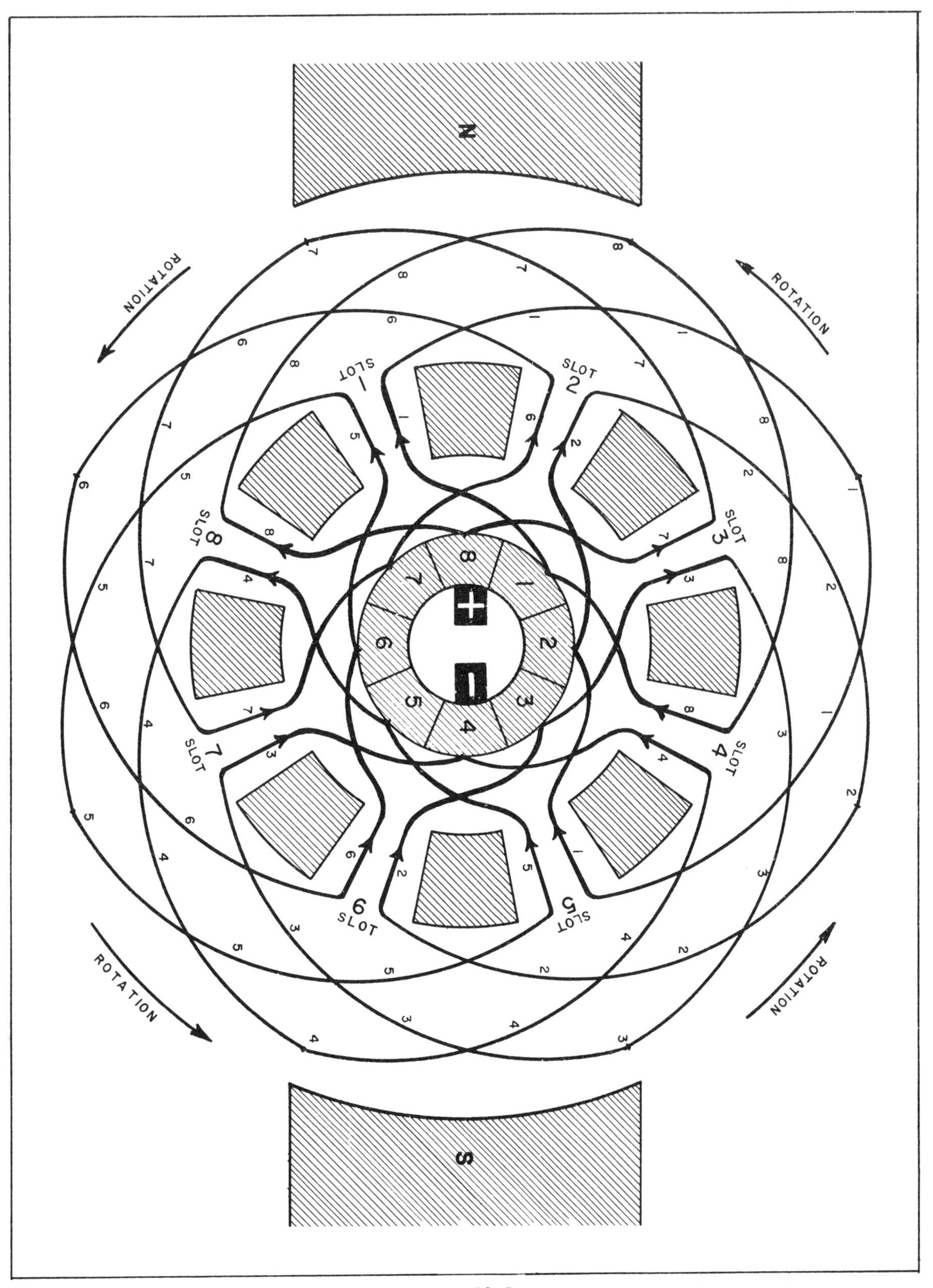
N
S
ROTATION
ROTATION
ROTATION
ROTATION
SLOT 1
SLOT 2
SLOT 3
SLOT 4
SLOT 5
SLOT 6
SLOT 7
SLOT 8
+
-

Fig. 18-5

PATHS THROUGH THE ARMATURE

Fig. 18-6, taken from 18-5, is intended to show the series-parallel arrangement of the coils in which e.m.f. is generated. At the instant pictured in 18-5, for example, coils 1, 2, 5, and 6 might be generating 9.2 volts each, and coils 3, 4, 7 and 8 generating 3.8 volts each.

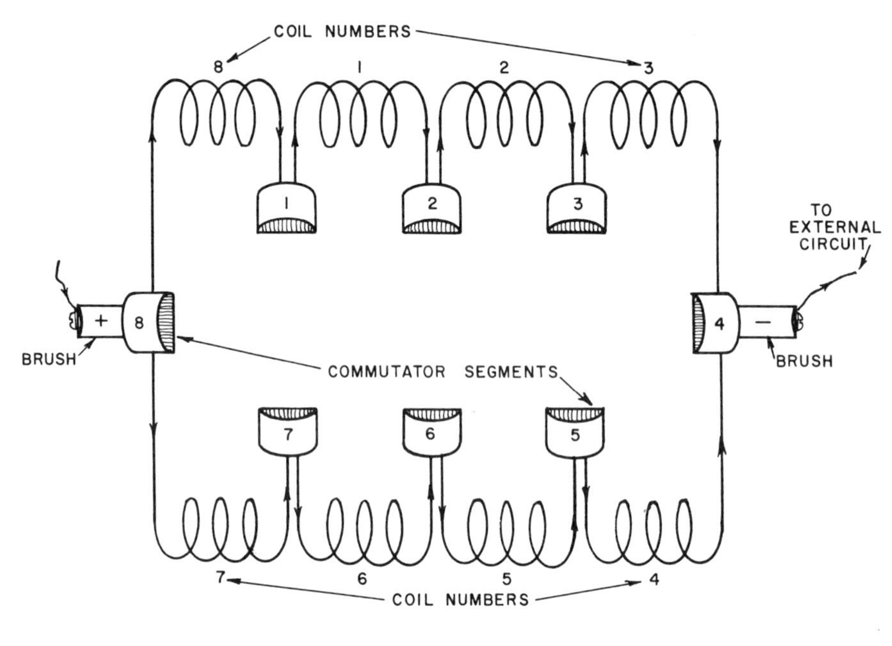

Fig. 18-6

Referring now to Fig. 18-6, notice that coils 8, 1, 2, and 3 are in series, so their individual voltages add, 3.8 + 9.2 + 9.2 + 3.8 = 26 volts. Coils 7, 6, 5, and 4 in series also produce 26 volts. With the two sets of coils in parallel, the total instantaneous voltage is still 26. (Compare cells in series and parallel.)

The current (amps) delivered by this generator is the sum of two equal currents in the two parallel sets of coils. If the generator delivers 10 amps to the external circuit, then the current in each coil is 5 amps.

Fig. 18-6 may be puzzling to someone who has memorized the fact that "electrons flow from minus to plus." They do, in the external circuit. Inside the generator, electrons whipped by lines of force are driven from the positive terminal toward the negative terminal. Their motion is the cause of the positive and negative charges being developed.

Lap-wound armatures require as many brushes as there are field poles, and have as many parallel paths through the armature as there are brushes. This is advantageous in low-voltage high-current armatures, since the total current output can be large without using excessively large wire on the armature. For example, a six-field pole lap-wound generator has six brushes and six paths through the armature. In order to produce 180 amps, each coil in the armature need carry only 30 amps.

Wave windings have only two parallel paths, regardless of the number of field poles.

FIELD STRUCTURE FOR GENERATORS

In a few low-power applications, permanent magnets provide the magnetic field for the generator. The voltage of such generators is used for controls or signaling.

Ordinarily, the field structure is of the general shape shown at the right. The circular frame, or yoke, is often of cast steel, fitted with pole-pieces of laminated iron.

This stationary iron is magnetized by current in the field coils that surround the pole pieces. In most generators, this current is supplied by the generator itself. Only a small fraction of the generated power (about 3% or less) is used to supply this magnetizing, or "exciting" current.

Fig. 18-7 Two-Pole Field

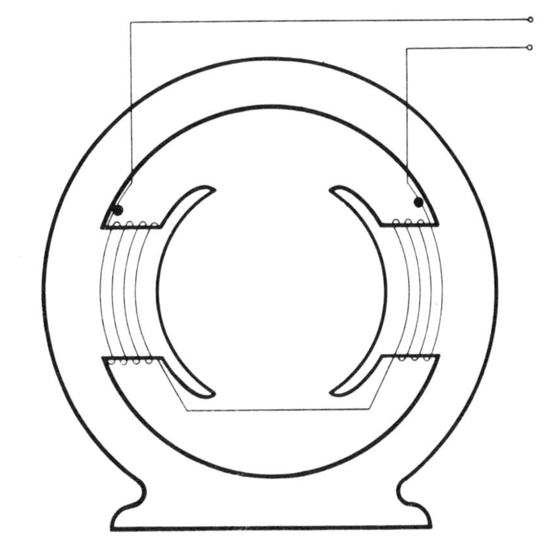

Fig. 18-8 Two-Pole Field Windings

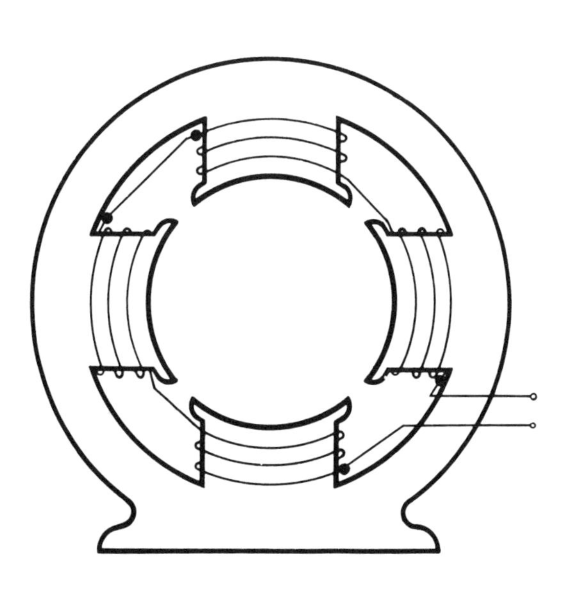

Fig. 18-9 Four-Pole Field Windings

FIELD CONNECTIONS FOR SELF-EXCITED GENERATORS

There are three possible arrangements for field coils, so that they may be energized by current generated in the armature of the same machine:

1. Series: The field coils may be in series with the external load circuit. Series coils consist of relatively few turns of large wire, since they must carry the entire output current. Of these three types, this series generator is of least use.

2. Shunt (or parallel): The field coils may be connected across the brushes of the generator, which puts the coils in parallel with the external load. Shunt coils consist of a large number of turns of small wire, and carry only a small current.

3. Compound: The field-magnet iron may be magnetized by the combined effect of two sets of coils. One set of low-resistance coils is in series with the load, and one set of high-resistance coils is in parallel with the load circuit.

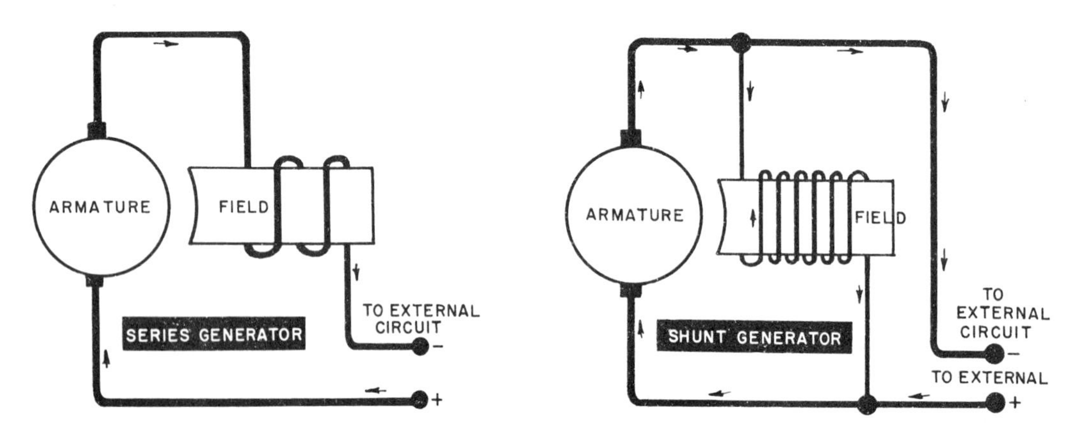

For simplicity in showing the circuit relations, the "field" is shown as only a single magnet. In actual practice, the armature is surrounded by two, four, or more field poles.

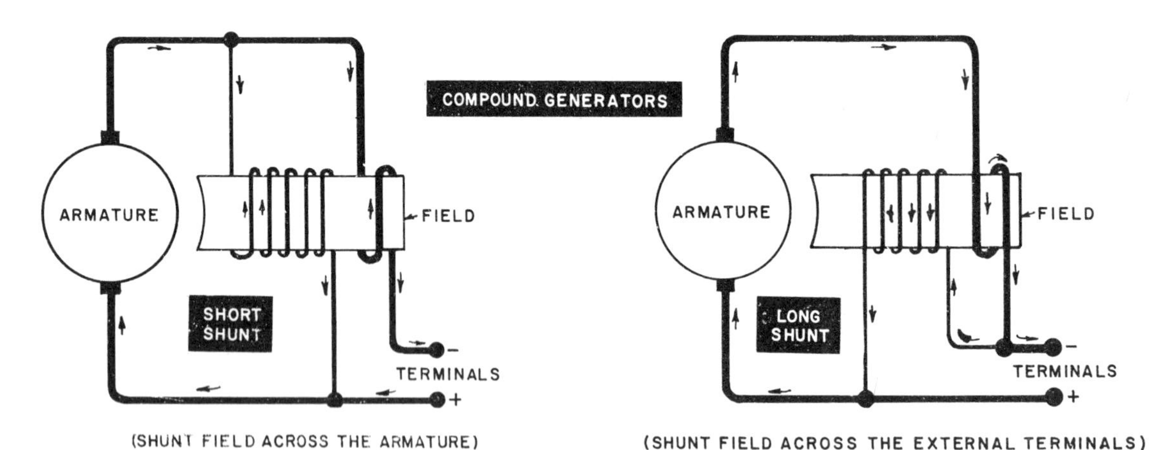

Fig. 18-10

In both of the compound generators shown above, the series field aids the shunt field in magnetizing effect. This is the usual arrangement, called cumulative compounding. Connecting the coils so that they oppose each other, called differential compounding, makes a less-often used machine.

ARMATURE REACTION

Before further discussion of the behavior of these types of generators, one of their common internal ailments must be described. "Armature reaction" is the name given to the distortion or bending of the main magnetic field of the generator, caused by the magnetic field of the current in the armature.

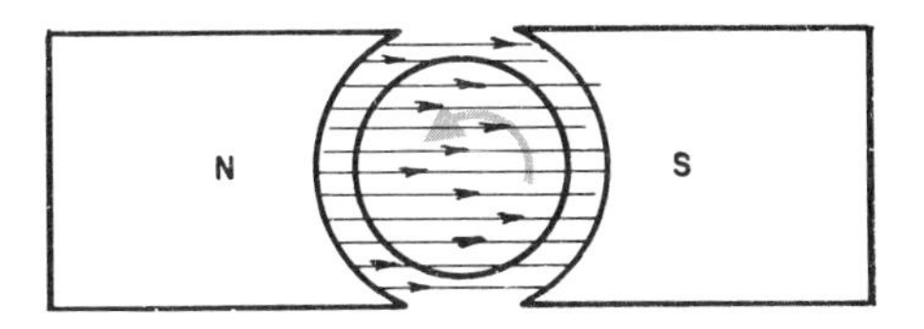

Ideally, the magnetic field in a generator has a straight, uniform pattern.

But the current generated in the armature causes another magnetic field . . . .

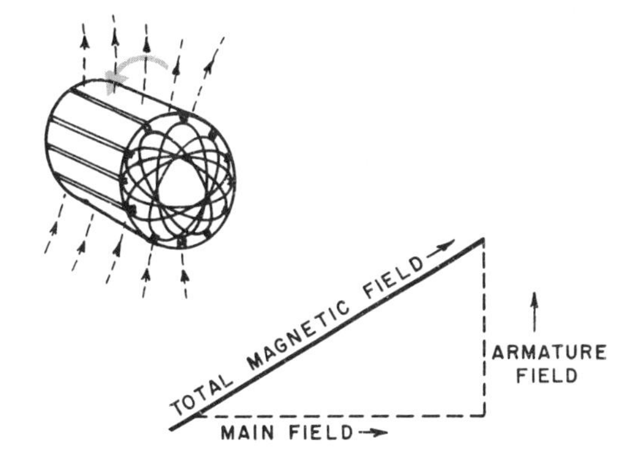

Both magnetic fields combine, main field and armature field, making the total magnetic field take the direction shown.

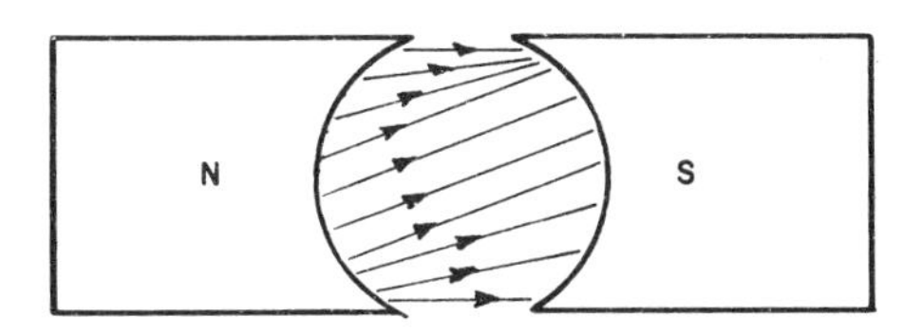

So, when the armature is producing current, the actual field in the generator appears as shown left, unless something is done about it.

The Ill Effects of a Twisted Field

The bunching of lines at the corners of the field poles causes an irregularity in the voltage output. More important, the field iron is not used effectively, and the total flux is less, making the average voltage output low.

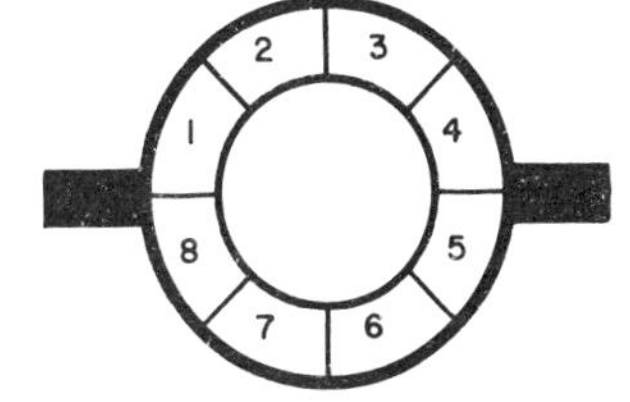

Furthermore, the twisted field changes the timing of the current reversals in the armature coils. In connection with Figs. 18-4 and 18-5, it was stated that no harm was done by the brushes at certain instants, because at those times no e.m.f. was generated in the coil connected to the pair of segments involved. That statement is true only if the magnetic field is not disturbed. When the field is distorted, there will be an e.m.f. between the commutator segments at the instant when both touch the same brush, resulting in a brief high current that causes excessive sparking and arcing as the commutator rotates.

The first-used remedy for this condition was rotation of the brush-holder by an amount equal to the twisting of the field, so that commutator segments would break contact with the brush at the instant of no e.m.f. This was an unsatisfactory remedy, because the amount of field distortion changes when the armature current (load current) changes.

To improve commutation, the brush holder of a generator is turned forward, in the direction of rotation of the armature. In a motor, backward rotation of brushes improves commutation.

A better remedy is the addition of small field poles, called interpoles, or commutating poles, between the main field poles.

Previous sketches showed the armature current causing a vertical flux that tipped the main magnetic field. The interpoles create another downward flux that tends to tip the main field back where it belongs.

The interpole coils of the generator are connected into the circuit so that the interpoles have the same polarity as the main poles directly ahead of them (ahead in the sense of direction of armature rotation). In Fig. 18-11, if rotation were reversed, the polarity of the interpoles must be reversed also.

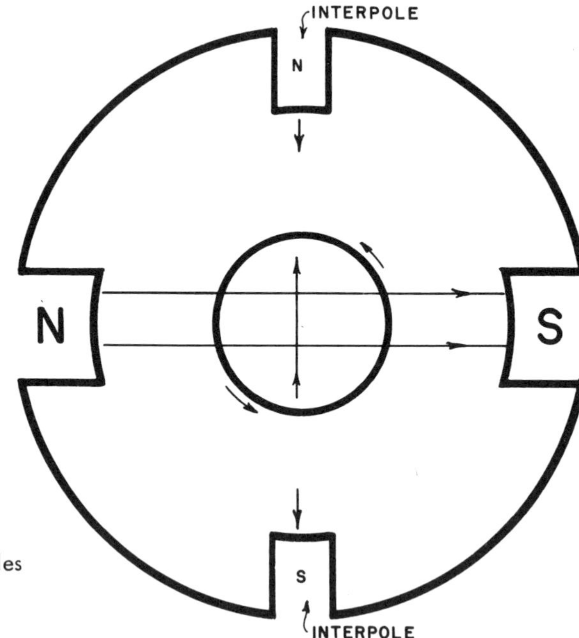

Fig. 18-11 Generator with Interpoles

To make the strength of the interpoles appropriate for their changing duty as the armature and load current changes, the interpoles are energized by coils in series with the armature, and therefore carrying the same current as the armature. These interpoles take care of the commutator difficulties, so that stationary brush holders can be used, with the brushes at the geometrical axis as shown originally. However, these interpoles overcome the field distortion only in their immediate neighborhood, so that much of the overall field-weakening effect is still present. Large generators carry their output current through a few wires lying in the pole face, placed parallel to the armature wires. This pole-face winding, called a compensating winding, is the most complete way of overcoming the field-weakening effect of armature reaction.

It should be noted that armature reaction is advantageous in automotive generators, which must operate over a wide range of speeds. If the field-strength is constant, the e.m.f. is proportional to r.p.m., which would be highly undesirable in the automotive generator. At moderate current output, the armature current distorts and weakens the average field sufficiently to help keep the e.m.f. at a reasonable value at high speed.

BUILD-UP OF MAGNETIC FIELD IN SELF-EXCITED GENERATOR

The successful starting up of a generator depends on the existence of residual magnetism in the field iron, that is, a little magnetism remaining from the effect of previous current in the field coil. When the armature of a shunt or compound generator starts rotating, a very low voltage is generated in it, due to the weak field in which the armature rotates. This low voltage causes a small current in the shunt field coils, increasing the strength of the field slightly, which causes the generated voltage to increase slightly. This increased voltage causes more current in the field, increasing the field strength still more, so still more voltage is generated in the armature.

This building-up of voltage, current, and field strength goes on until a limit is reached, which may be shown with the help of this graph.

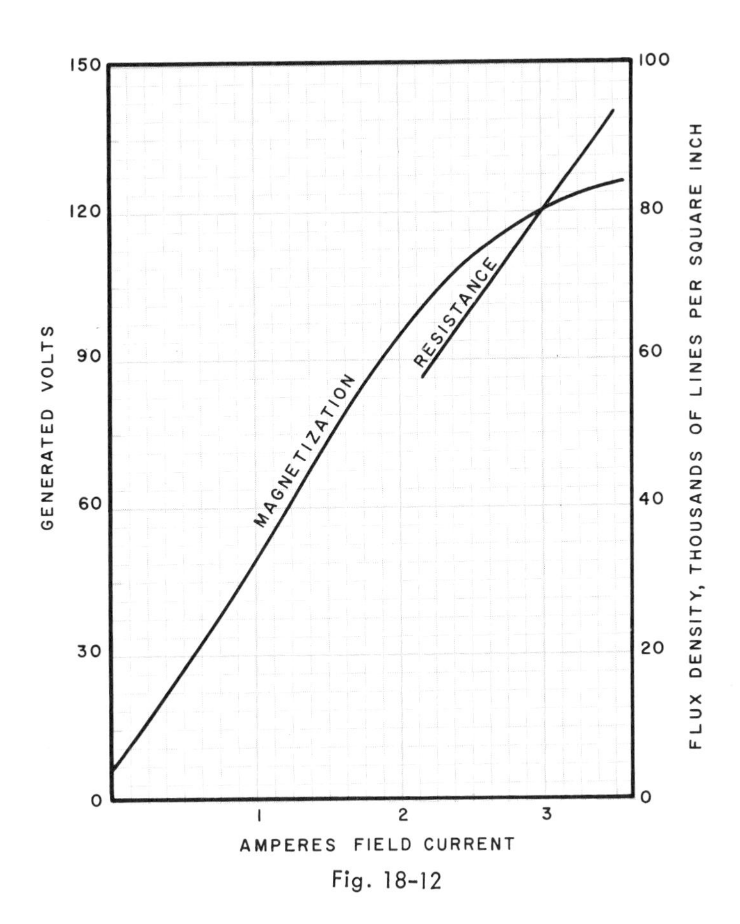

Fig. 18-12

The "magnetization" curve, like Fig. 11-3 on Page 105, shows the increase in field strength as the field current increases. Assume we have a generator, rated 120 volts output, which has a 40-ohm field coil. When the generator is started, the magnetization starts at a point above the zero line, a point representing residual flux density of, say, 5000 lines per square inch. According to the scales at the left, 5000 lines/square inch will cause a generated voltage of 7.5 volts, provided the armature is rotating at rated speed. The small current in the field ($I = 7.5/40 = 0.19$ amp), adds to the field strength, and the build-up continues to a field strength of 80,000 lines per square inch, at which time the generated 120 volts is putting 3 amps through the field. This 3 amps is needed to maintain the field at 80,000, so that the 120 volts can be generated. At 3 amps, no more than 120 volts can be generated, and the build-up has stopped. This limit is indicated by the "resistance" line on the graph; points on this resistance line give values of volts and amps for a 40-ohm resistance.

The previous discussion has assumed constant speed. The generator output could be increased or decreased by increasing or decreasing the r.p.m. Also, the operating voltage of this shunt generator could be lowered to some other value, say 100 volts, by putting a little more resistance in the field circuit by using a rheostat in series with the field coil. Voltage output on a shunt generator is commonly controlled by such a field rheostat.

THE SERIES GENERATOR

A glance at Fig. 18-10 can remind one that the field of the series generator carries the entire load current to the external circuit, so, the greater the load current, the greater the magnetic field strength. If the generator is started with the external circuit disconnected from the generator terminals, there is no build-up of field, because the small voltage (due to residual magnetism) cannot produce any current at all in the open circuit. If a small load-current is taken from the generator, its output voltage is low; at a reasonably high load-current the output voltage is high. This would produce weird results if an ordinary parallel-wired lighting circuit were used as the load; with two or three lamps turned on, the lamps are dim. The more lamps that are turned on, the brighter each lamp would become. However, a little of this voltage-increasing effect can be a good thing, and illustrates the effect of the series field of a cumulative compound generator.

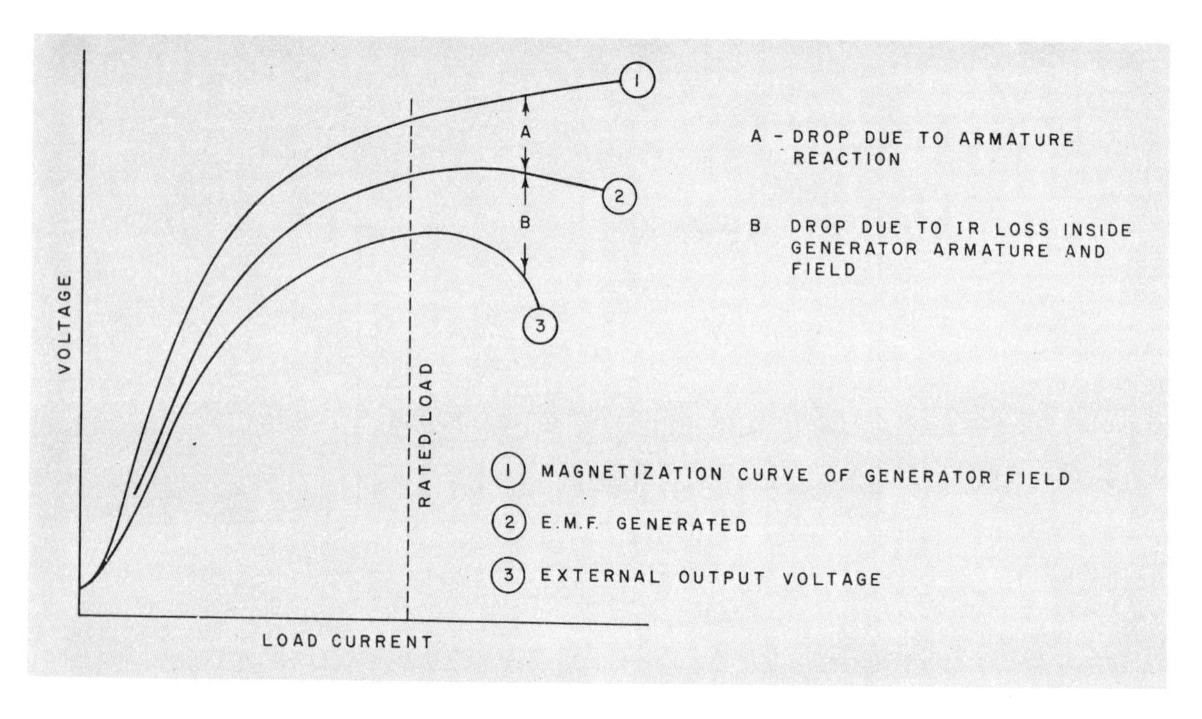

Series Generator Load-Voltage Characteristic Curve

The series generator, impractical for most jobs, does have one interesting application: it can be used in a simple motor-control system, driving a series motor at nearly constant speed with changing load on the motor (Unit 22).

THE SHUNT GENERATOR: Voltage Losses

Assume that we have a shunt generator, with armature resistance equal to 0.4 ohm, rated 10-amp output current. When operating with no load, (open external circuit) we find that the e.m.f. is 121 volts. When operated at its rated 10-amp load, there is a 4-volt drop, or waste, in the armature. ($V = IR = 10 \times 0.4 = 4$ v.) 4 volts is used in pushing electrons through the generator itself. This 10 amps in the armature also distorts and weakens the field, so that there is a decrease in generated e.m.f. of 3 volts. Due to all of these voltage deficiencies, the field current and flux is reduced somewhat, so that the generated e.m.f. is less, by another 4 volts. Due to these last two items, armature reaction and reduced field current, $121 - 7 = 114$ volts is generated, less 4 volts used in the armature, leaving 110 volts for the output voltage at the terminals.

Summarizing the voltage reductions given in the preceding numerical example:

As the load current increases,

1. Armature reaction weakens the field, so that less e.m.f. is generated.

2. IR drop in the armature uses up some of the e.m.f. that is produced.

3. Both of the above effects reduce the output voltage. Reduced output voltage causes reduced field current, therefore the field flux is less. With less field flux, there is a further reduction in generated e.m.f.

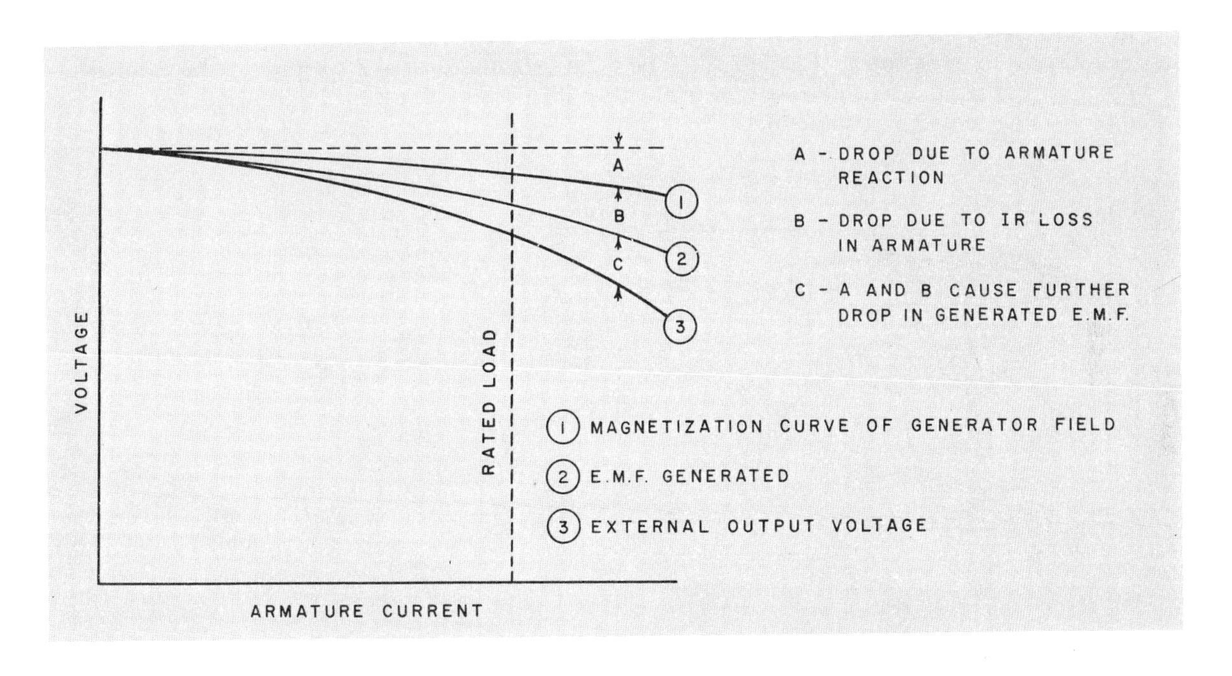

Shunt Generator Load-Voltage Characteristic Curve

If the generator is overloaded, for example, by drawing 15 amps from it, increased armature reaction and further reduction in field current may bring the generated e.m.f. down to 109. 15 amps through the 0.4 ohm armature uses 6 volts, so the terminal voltage is down to 103 v.

Voltage Regulation

As a measurable quantity, the term "voltage regulation" means the percentage change of voltage from rated-load to no-load conditions.

$$\text{Regulation} = \frac{\text{Open-circuit voltage - Voltage at rated load}}{\text{Voltage at rated load}}$$

Using numbers from the above example: $\text{Regulation} = \frac{121 - 110}{110} = .1 = 10\%$

Line Drop

The actual voltage delivered at the load itself may be considerably less than the terminal voltage of the generator, because of voltage (= IR) used on the line connecting the generator to the load, (see Pages 42 and 43). If, in the above example, the generator has to deliver its energy through a line of 0.2-ohms resistance, the voltage at the end of the line, with a 10-amp load, is 110 - 2 = 108 volts, and with a 15-amp load, 103 - 3 = 100 volts.

THE COMPOUND GENERATOR

The purpose of the compound generator is to compensate for the preceding voltage losses by increasing the generated e.m.f. as the current-load increases. Let's examine the effect of series field coils, added to the shunt generator described previously.

At a 10-amp load, with series-field coils present, we still have the field-weakening effect of armature reaction and the 4-volt IR drop on the armature, plus maybe another 1-volt IR drop in the series field. All of these effects can be overcome by the addition of enough turns of the wire to the field, turns in series with the load, so that the 10 amps in these turns can add to the magnetizing effect of the shunt field coil, increasing the generated e.m.f. The generated e.m.f. can readily be brought up to 126, which, less the 5-volt internal IR drops, makes the output voltage 121, the same as at no load. A generator with open-circuit voltage equal to voltage at rated load is called "flat-compounded."

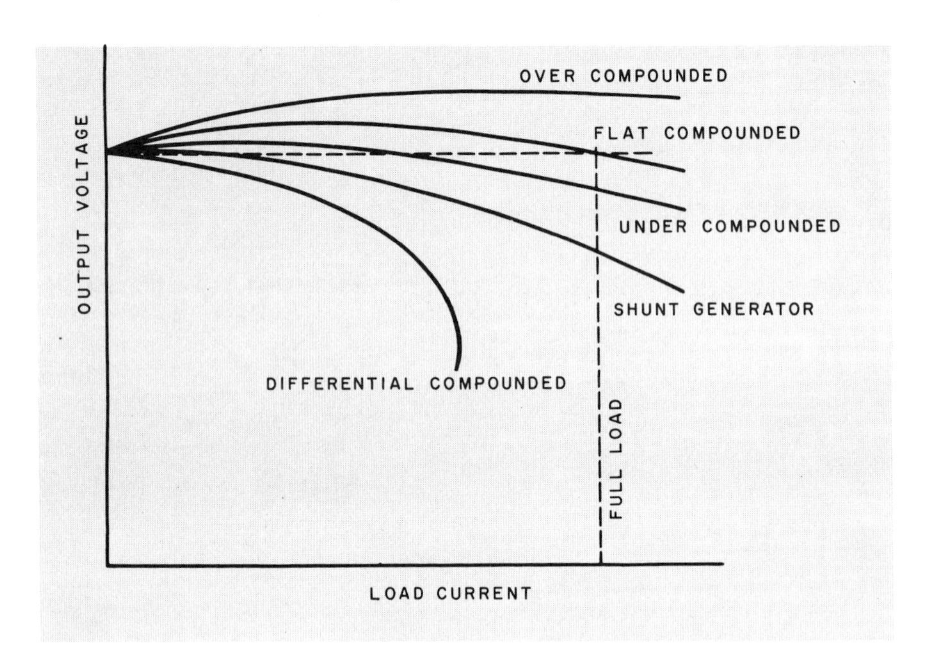

Fig. 18-13
Compound Generator
Load Characteristics

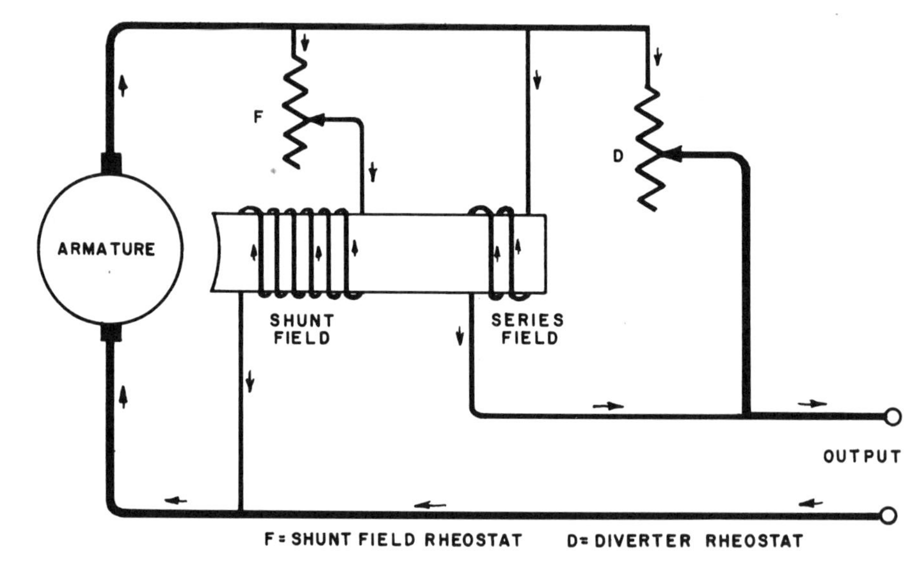

Fig. 18-14
Diverter Rheostat

A generator can be over-compounded, meaning that enough series ampere-turns can be provided to make the output voltage rise above no-load voltage as the output current increases. (Compare series generator.) Usually, compound generators are built with enough series turns to accomplish over-compounding, and the user can adjust the current in the series winding to suit his own operating conditions. The diverter rheostat allows some load current to by-pass the series coils.

SEPARATELY EXCITED GENERATORS

Two general ways of providing a magnetic field for a generator have been mentioned:

1. The use of a permanent magnet, which is of very limited application.

2. Self-excitation — shunt, series, or compound which is the most widely used method.

A third possibility is the use of a separate current source to energize the field coils of the generator. Normally, this method is used only as a part of a specialized motor-control circuit, such as Ward Leonard, Rototrol, or Amplidyne control, to name merely a few systems.

The purpose of these systems is to permit the operator to select any desired speed, after which the system holds the motor at that speed, regardless of variations in load on the motor. Separate-excitation systems of this type are used in mine hoists, steel-mill drives, paper machines, Diesel-electric locomotives, and so forth.

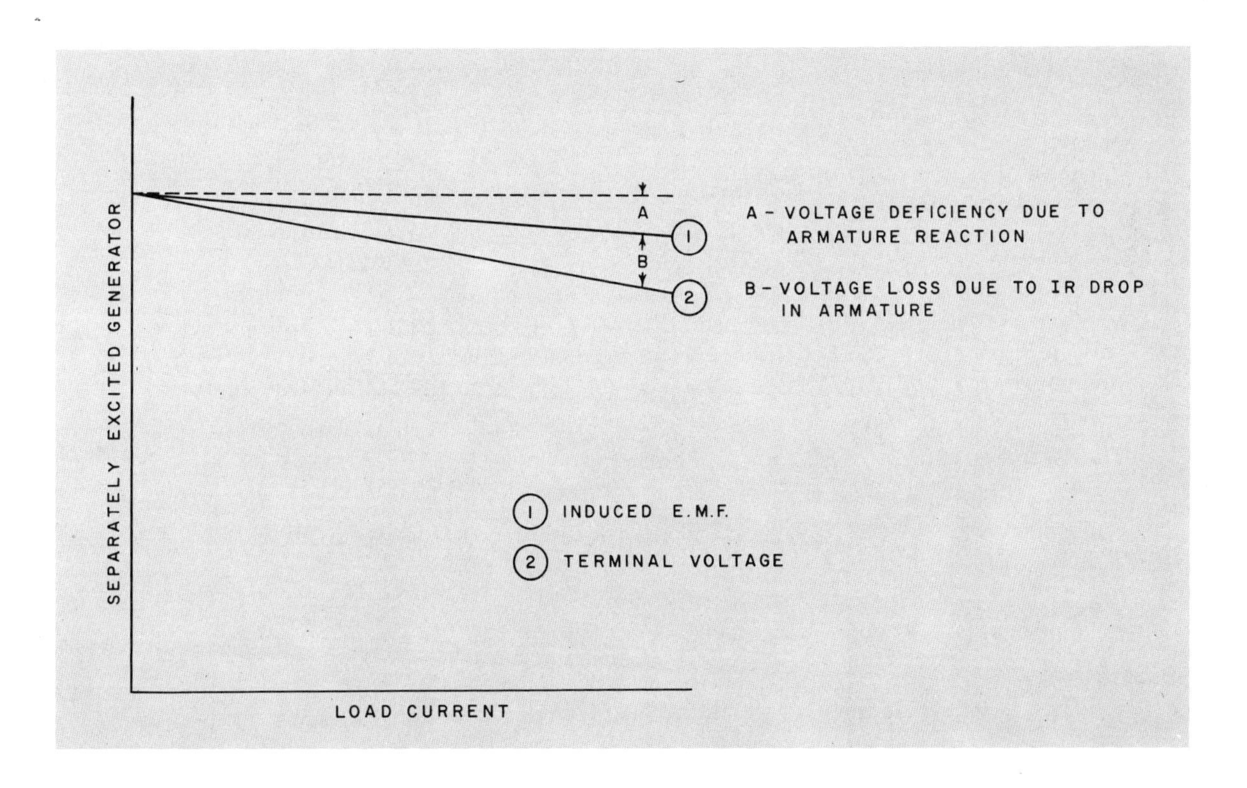

Separately Excited Generator Load-Voltage Characteristic Curve

GENERATOR CALCULATIONS

The following paragraphs are not intended to provide enough details to illustrate all of the factors that must be calculated by someone who is in the generator-building business. They are intended only to point out again the basic principles of the energy conversion that goes on in a generator.

Generated E.M.F.

Generator e.m.f., as stated before, is proportional to field strength, number of wires on the armature, and r.p.m. of the armature. When the field strength, armature windings, and r.p.m. of the armature are known, the number of lines of force cut per second can be found. Because the cutting of 100,000,000 lines by wire each second makes one volt,

$$\text{e.m.f.} = \frac{\text{lines cut by wires per second}}{100{,}000{,}000}$$

Using as an example an armature similar to that of Figs. 18-4, 18-5, 18-6, and given the information that the armature has 8 coils, each coil consisting of 40 turns, operating at 1200 r.p.m. between two field poles, each pole having 15 sq. in. face area and flux density 80,000 lines per square inch, to calculate the generated e.m.f.:

First, Fig. 18-6 shows that the coils are in two paralleled groups, with four coils in series in each group.

The e.m.f. produced is that for four coils in series (not eight), so we need to take into account 4 coils of 40 turns each = 160 turns.

The purpose of this calculation is to find the average e.m.f., so we need not be concerned about differences in instantaneous voltages in the coils.

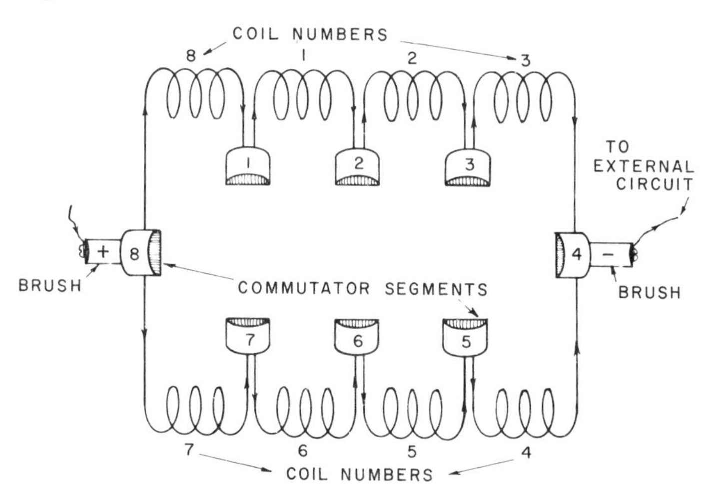

Each turn of wire in the coil has two sides, both of which cut the entire field twice (up and down) for one revolution. The 160 turns, then, has to be multiplied by four to give the number of times that the entire field is cut by wire each revolution. The field is cut 640 times.

The total field flux is 80,000 lines per sq. in. × 15 sq. in. = 1,200,000 lines.

During one rotation 1,200,000 lines are cut 640 times, so the total cutting is 640 × 1,200,000 = 768,000,000.

The coils rotate at 1200 r.p.m., which is 20 revolutions per second.

The total cutting of lines per second is 768,000,000 times 20.

The e.m.f. generated is: $\frac{768{,}000{,}000 \times 20}{100{,}000{,}000} = 153.6$ volts

Summarizing the preceding series of calculations in words:

$$\text{Total cutting of lines per second} = \frac{\text{Total armature turns}}{\text{No. of parallel paths}} \times 4 \times \text{Flux} \times \frac{\text{r.p.m.}}{60}$$

and

$$\text{Generated e.m.f.} = \frac{\text{Turns} \times 4 \times \text{Flux} \times \text{r.p.m.}}{\text{Paths} \times 60 \times 100{,}000{,}000}$$

Planning a generator design to produce a given e.m.f. involves a sensible choice of turns, flux, r.p.m., and type of winding, based on both theory and experience, and taking into account any special demands on the generator in use.

POWER LOSSES

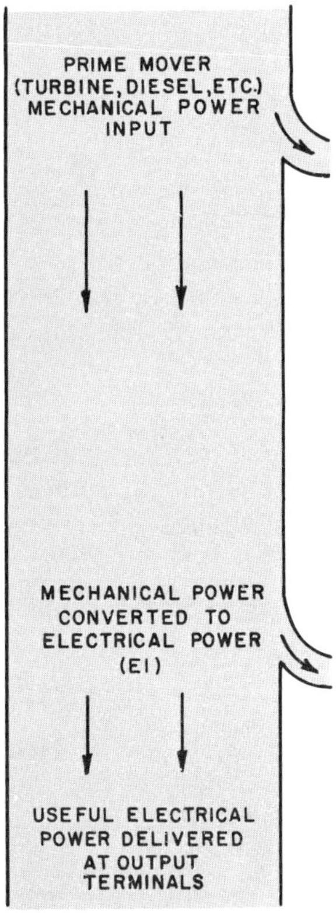

Power losses are divided into two types: (1) "Stray power loss" is mechanical power which is changed to heat power without ever appearing as electrical power generated. (2) "Copper loss" or "I^2R loss" is due to heat production by currents in the armature and field circuits of the machine.

PRIME MOVER (TURBINE, DIESEL, ETC.) MECHANICAL POWER INPUT

MECHANICAL POWER CONVERTED TO ELECTRICAL POWER (EI)

USEFUL ELECTRICAL POWER DELIVERED AT OUTPUT TERMINALS

1. Stray Power Loss

   a. Strictly mechanical losses are those due to friction in bearings and brushes, and in windage, which is air friction. This loss depends on the speed, but is independent of load current.

   b. "Core loss" includes heat produced by molecular friction inside the iron of the armature, due to continual reversal of magnetization. This is called hysteresis loss; it increases with increase in flux density and increase of speed. Core loss also includes heat produced by useless "eddy currents" generated in the armature iron and pole-face iron. Eddy-current losses increase as the square of speed and flux density, and vary slightly with load current.

2. Copper Loss

   a. Copper losses include power lost in heating the shunt field, and also in heating the armature circuit, which includes armature wiring, brush contacts, and series fields. The armature circuit loss is proportional to the square of the load current.

Continuing with the preceding example, if the entire armature has a resistance = 0.4 ohm, brush resistance = 0.05 ohm, and the generator armature is producing 10 amps, there will be 4.5 volts (0.45 × 10 according to Ohm's Law) lost or wasted as "IR drop" inside the machine, and the terminal voltage at the brushes is 153.6 - 4.5 = 149.1 volts.

Output voltage = Generated e.m.f. minus IR drop in armature and brushes

With 10 amps in the armature, the total power generation is at the rate of 153.6 v. times 10 amp = 1536 watts. 4.5 × 10 amp = 45 watts used to heat the armature and brushes. 149.1 v. × 10 amps = 1491 watts delivered at the brush terminals. (1536 - 45 = 1491)

If this is a shunt generator, the field coils might carry 0.4 amps at 149.1 volts, which equals about 60 watts. Subtracting this 60 from the 1491 watts leaves 1431 watts to be delivered to the external circuit.

The electrical efficiency of this generator is:

$$\frac{\text{power output}}{\text{total power generated}} = \frac{1431}{1536} = .932 = 93.2\%$$

If mechanical friction losses in the generator require 50 watts, mechanical energy must be put into the machine at the rate of 1536 + 50 = 1586 watts.

The overall efficiency is:

$$\frac{\text{power output}}{\text{mechanical power input}} = \frac{1431}{1586} = .902 = 90.2\%$$

GENERATOR NAMEPLATE DATA AND RATINGS

The full-load rating of a generator is a statement of conditions which provide efficient operation without exceeding safe limits of speed and temperature. This data, which is supplied on the nameplate of the machine, includes speed, voltage, power output (KW) or current output and allowable temperature rise.

If operated at very low current output, efficiency is low. At too low speed, air circulation is poor and overheating may result. Higher-than-normal current for a long time raises temperature and may damage insulation and burn commutator and brushes. Standard voltages for larger D.C. generators are 125, 250, 275, and 600 volts.

The "temperature rise" allowed in a machine is a rise above 40° C, which is taken as a standard surrounding temperature. For example, the temperature of "Class A" insulation (enamel, oil-impregnated paper and cotton) should not exceed 105° C, for long life. A machine with this insulation will be rated "50° C temperature rise", which allows the average or surface temperature of a coil to be 90° C (40 + 50) while allowing for hot spots in the center of the coil to be 15° higher than 90°, which is the 105° C specified limit.

GENERATORS IN PARALLEL

In most of the larger applications of D.C. power, changing load requirements are met by the operation of two or more generators in parallel. By so doing, low-load requirement is met by operating one or two generators near their high-efficiency full-load rating. This is preferable to operation of one huge machine at a small fraction of its full load. With several generators in use, repairs to one need not interrupt the power supply.

Shunt Generators in Parallel

Because shunt generators' terminal voltage drops when current increases, two such generators in parallel share the total load current in accordance with their own voltage-current characteristics. The graph below, Fig. 18-15, shows voltage-current curves for two different shunt generators of the same voltage rating.

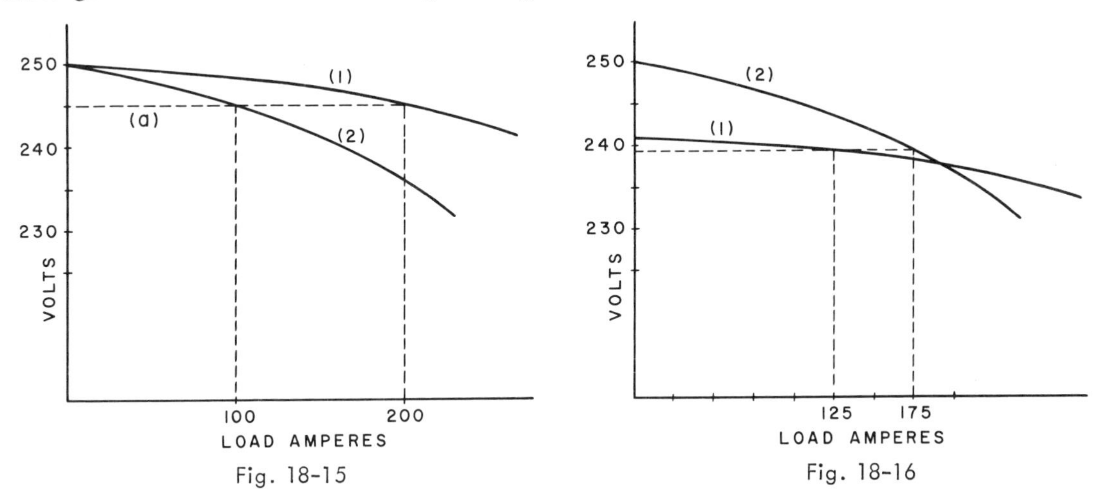

Fig. 18-15

Fig. 18-16

In parallel, both necessarily have the same terminal voltage, represented here by line (A), at 245 volts. Of a total load current of 300 amps, generator #1 supplies 200 amps. If, for some reason, the voltage output of #1 is lowered, either by reduced speed or reduced field, the terminal voltage of both generators drops to the value shown in Fig. 18-16, with #1 now carrying only 125 amps.

Increasing the field current in #1, by field rheostat adjustment, will raise its terminal voltage. In Fig. 18-17 the result of such procedure is shown, with #1 now carrying 225 amps, at about 247 volts. With less current in #2, its terminal voltage has also risen to 247.

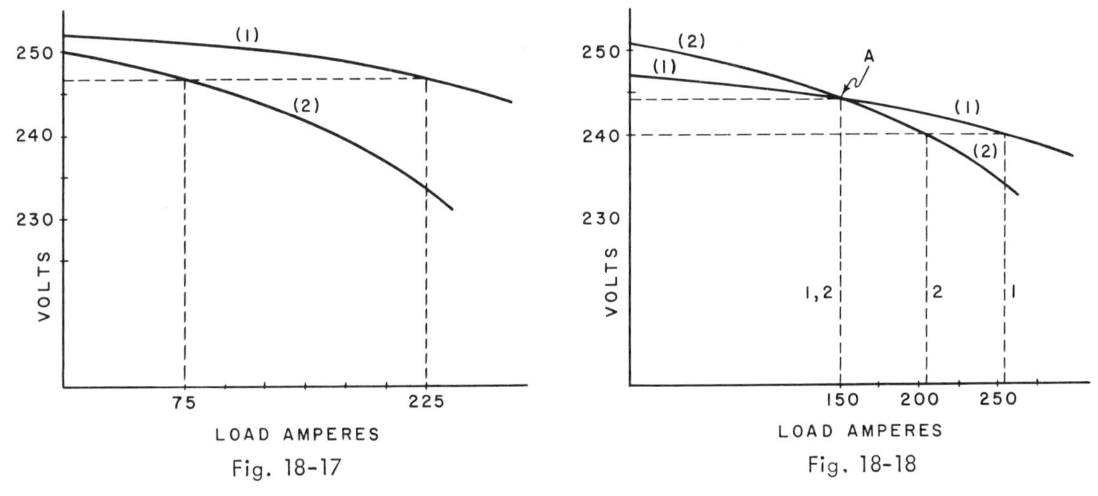

Fig. 18-17

Fig. 18-18

By adjustment of field rheostats on both generators, they can be made to carry the same current, as at point A in Fig. 18-18. If the current load increases, identical generators would continue to carry their equal shares of the increased current. With unlike generators, as shown here, the one with the more drooping characteristic curve will take a smaller part of the increased current. For example, after adjustment of #1 and #2 so that both carry 150 amps, if the load current requirement increases to 460 amps, the terminal voltage of both generators drops to 240 volts, with #1 carrying 255 amps, and #2, 205 amps.

Normally, when machines of different sizes are in parallel, the total load is divided in proportion to the generator ratings, that is, each generator will be operated at about the same percent of its full-load rating.

Compound Generators in Parallel

When flat-compounded or over-compounded generators are connected in parallel, a small addition has to be made to the circuit. To realize its necessity, we must first see how two such generators would behave in a simple parallel connection.

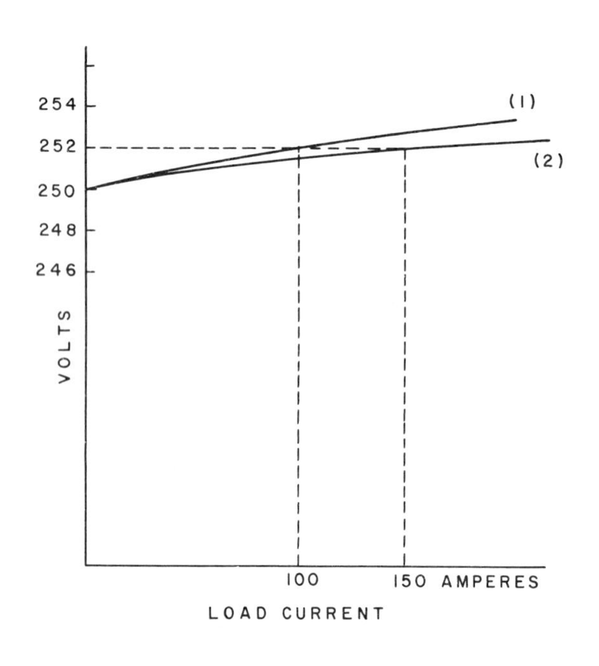

Fig. 18-19

Assume that two compound generators, having a terminal-voltage to load-current relation as shown in Fig. 18-19, are connected to the line at an instant when both have exactly the same terminal voltage, say 252 volts. Soon one of them, say #2, reduces its output voltage very slightly, perhaps due to warm-up of shunt field or a slight speed reduction.

With less terminal voltage, its share of load current drops, perhaps to 140 amps, which requires #1 to produce 110 amps. This increased current in the series field of #1 raises its terminal voltage a little, but #1 is connected across #2 which has a lowered terminal voltage, which is an unstable situation.

The increased terminal voltage of #1 causes it to produce a still larger share of the load current, which in turn causes more increase of series field, more voltage output, and soon #1 is carrying nearly all of the load. Meanwhile, the terminal voltage of #2 is dropping toward 250, for its field is continually weakening due to the decreasing current in its series field.

As its current falls to zero, #1 starts feeding current into the armature and series field circuit of #2; #2's series field reverses, weakening the total field; #2 operates as a motor with a weak field, taking a new unreasonable value of current from #1. Before this sad state of affairs is reached, #1's circuit breaker may have opened, disconnecting it from the line.

This trouble was not experienced with shunt generators, for their characteristic action is to shirk current load, their terminal voltage falling off as they are forced to carry more current. In contrast, over-compounded generators are too enthusiastic; a greater current load causes a voltage rise (series field effect) that results in a runaway action. An increase in load results in the compound generator's trying to take all of the load.

The addition to the circuit that solves this problem is a wire that puts the series fields of the generators in parallel. This line is called the equalizer. Fig. 18-20, while omitting many details, may help show how this equalizer works.

If, for some reason, #2's terminal voltage is reduced, armature #2 carries less current, and #1 carries more. However, the series fields are unaffected; the same potential difference exists across them as before. The series field strength of #1 does not rise, and the output voltage of #1, rather than rising, falls a little due to the increased IR drop in the armature of #1. Therefore, #1 has lost its tendency to run away with all of the load current, and the two (or more) generators can settle down to a reasonable distribution of load current. For successful parallel operation, the equalizer connection must have a very low resistance, and the series fields must have resistances that are inversely proportional to the current rating of the generators.

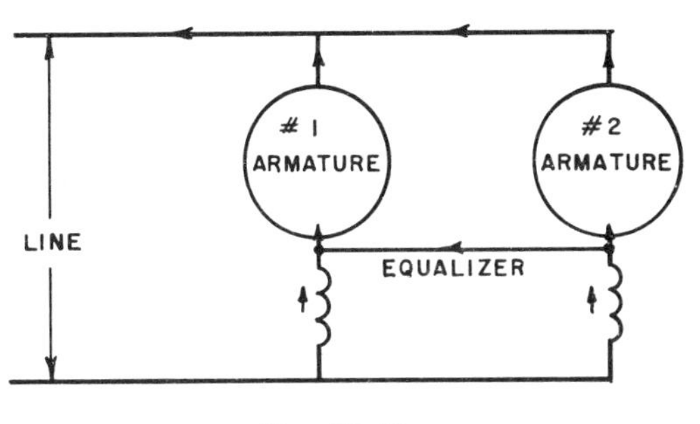

Fig. 18-20

A more complete sketch of the circuit for paralleled compound generators is shown below.

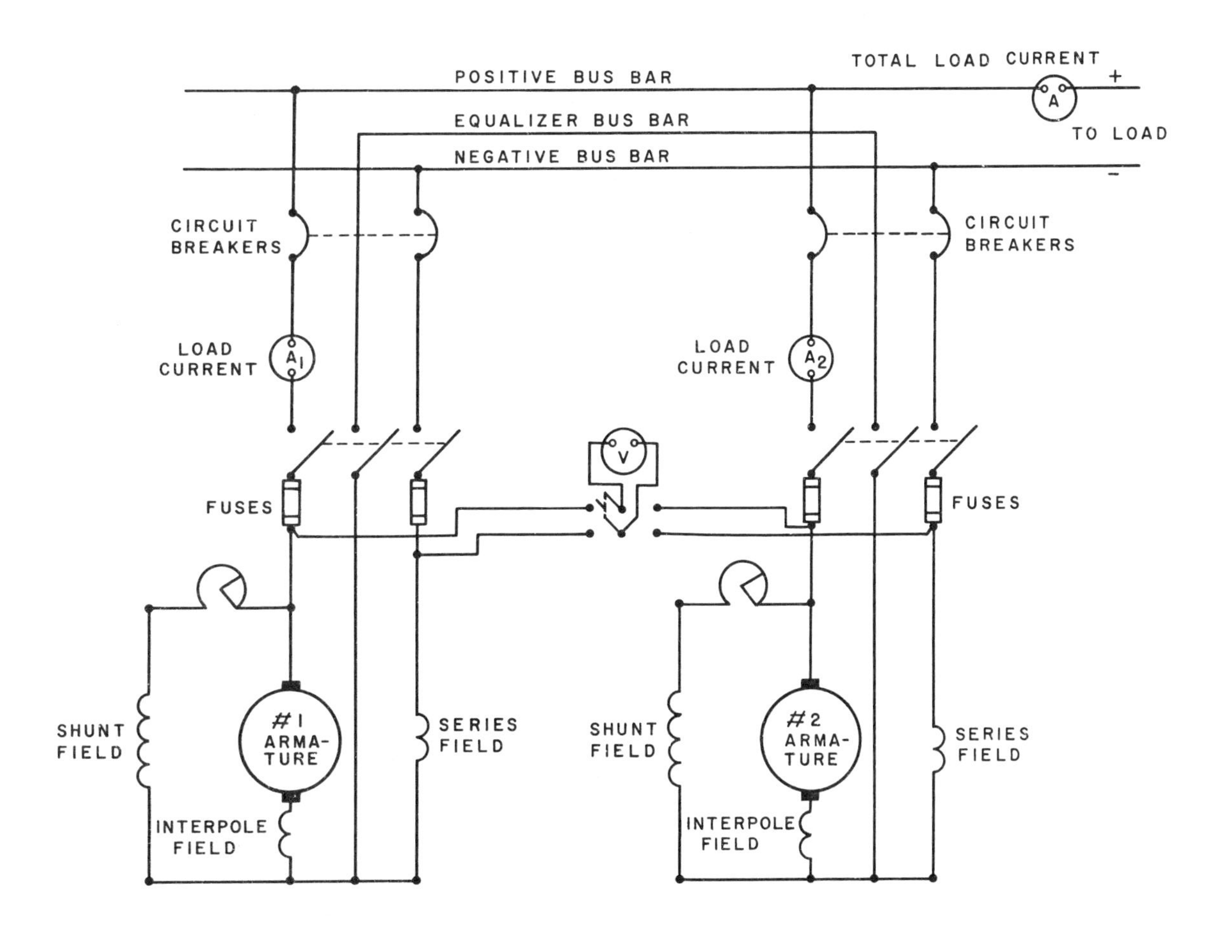

Fig. 18-21

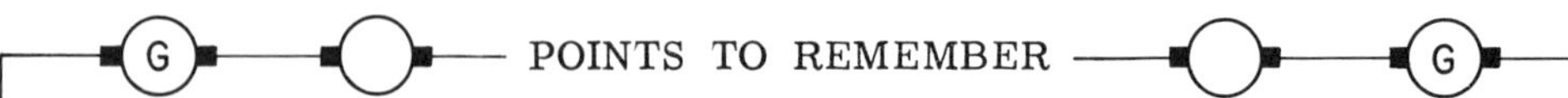

POINTS TO REMEMBER

- D.C. armatures carry coils in a series-parallel arrangement. There are two or more parallel paths through the armature, and each path consists of several coils in series.

- The magnetic field of the generator is usually supplied by current from the generator itself. This process is called self-excitation.

- Shunt field coils, in parallel with the load circuit, produce field magnetism that decreases slightly as current output of the generator increases.

- Series field coils, in series with the load circuit, produce field magnetism that increases in proportion to the output current.

- Compound generators have both series and shunt fields.

- D.C. generators which are a part of specialized motor-control circuits are usually separately-excited.

- Armature reaction, which is field distortion due to armature current, causes commutation difficulties which can be corrected by the use of interpoles. It also causes field weakening which can be corrected by the use of compensating windings.

- Generated e.m.f. $= \dfrac{\text{lines cut by wires per second}}{100{,}000{,}000}$

- In a drum armature, e.m.f. $= \dfrac{\text{turns} \times 4 \times \text{flux} \times \text{r.p.m.}}{\text{paths} \times 60 \times 100{,}000{,}000}$

- Efficiency $= \dfrac{\text{power output}}{\text{power input}}$

REVIEW QUESTIONS

1. A four-pole generator field has a flux density of 75,000 lines per square inch. Each pole face is 5 inches square. Calculate the total flux.

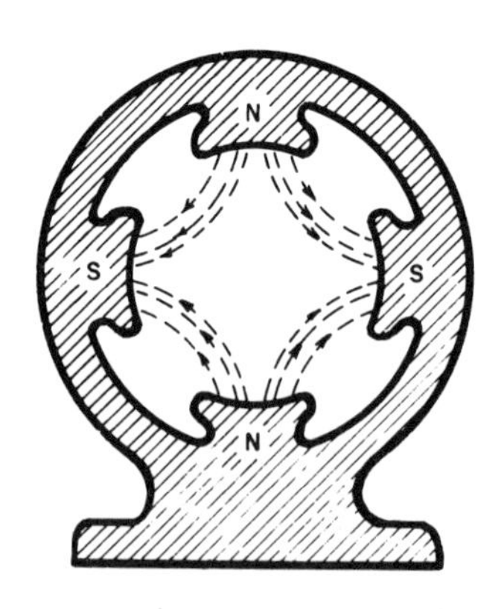

2. Name three types of field-coil arrangement for self-excited generators. Which can give the steadiest voltage output?

3. Name the three factors of greatest influence in determining the e.m.f. produced in a generator armature.

4. What is armature reaction? Name two main disagreeable effects of armature reaction. How may both of these effects be corrected?

5. After standing idle for several weeks, an engine-driven D.C. compound generator is started up. It runs fine, but produces no voltage. Suggest reasonable possible faults and remedies.

6. Considering only the effect of the efficiency of the generator, should the armature resistance be high or low? The shunt field resistance, high or low? The series field coils, high or low resistance?

7. Draw typical load-voltage characteristic curves for:

   a. a shunt generator

   b. an under-compounded generator

   c. an over-compounded generator

   d. a series generator

8. Give three different reasons why the terminal voltage of a shunt generator decreases with an increase in load current.

9. A shunt generator is rated 125 volts, 25 KW. Armature resistance is 0.08 ohm; shunt field circuit resistance is 25 ohms. Determine:

   a. the induced e.m.f. in the armature at rated load

   b. the watts loss in the armature

   c. watts loss in the shunt field circuit

   d. the total power generated in the armature

10. A 10-KW, 120-volt D.C. generator has an output of 120 volts at rated load. With no load, a voltmeter across the output terminals reads 110 volts. Determine the voltage regulation. Is this machine a shunt, cumulative compound, or differential compound generator? How can you tell?

11. A 12-KW, 240-volt, 1500-r.p.m. shunt generator has an armature resistance of 0.2 ohm and a shunt field resistance of 160 ohms. The stray power losses are 900 watts. Assuming shunt field current is constant, calculate:

    a. the efficiency at rated load

    b. the efficiency at half rated load

12. Explain how interpoles accomplish their purpose in a D.C. generator. State the polarity rule for interpoles.

13. A 10-KW, 230-volt long-shunt compound D.C. generator has efficiency = 82%, armature resistance = 0.15 ohm, series field = 0.1 ohm, shunt field = 100 ohms. At rated load, calculate:

    a. armature current

    b. voltage across the brushes

    c. generated e.m.f.

    d. total copper losses

    e. h.p. of the prime mover

14. A separately excited 6-KW generator has a terminal voltage of 135 volts at no load. At full load, the terminal voltage is 120 volts, with speed and field excitation unchanged. Armature resistance = 0.25 ohm. Find:

    a. how much of the voltage decrease is caused by armature reaction

    b. the voltage regulation

15. Complete the internal and external connections for the compound generator illustrated in Fig. 18-20. This generator is to be connected as a cumulative compound long shunt machine. The interpole field windings are to be a part of the armature circuit terminating at the connection points marked A1 and A2. Be sure to have the connections for all main field poles and interpoles correct so that the proper polarities will be obtained.

Fig. 18-20

CUMULATIVE COMPOUND GENERATOR
WITH COMMUTATING POLES

N OR S INDICATE MAIN POLE POLARITY

$A_1 - A_2$ ARMATURE TERMINALS

$F_1 - F_2$ SHUNT FIELD TERMINALS

$S_1 - S_2$ SERIES FIELD TERMINALS

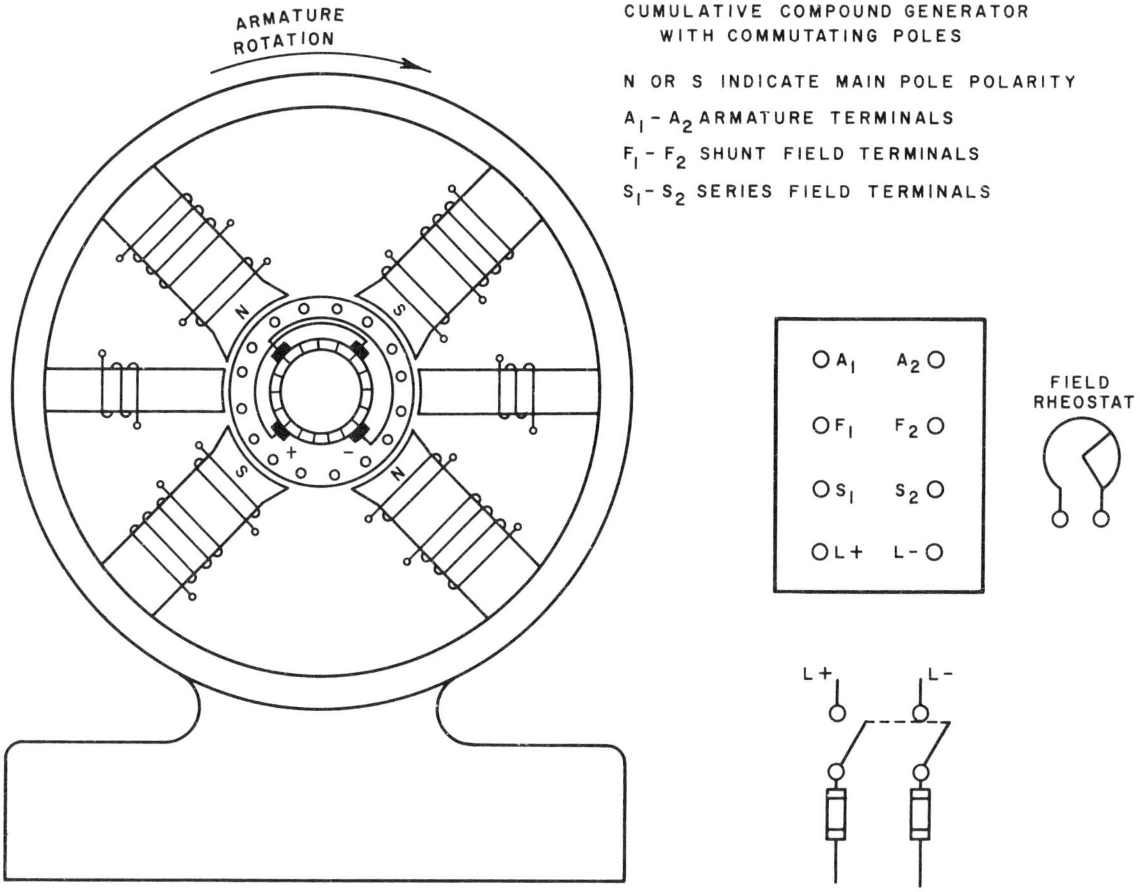

ARMATURE ROTATION

FIELD RHEOSTAT

Unit 19 A SOURCE OF E.M.F. : ENERGY STORED IN A MAGNETIC FIELD

Units 17 and 18 described e.m.f. generated by mechanical motion; mainly, the motion of wires through a magnetic field. There is a large group of devices in which e.m.f. is generated simply by the motion of magnetic lines of force, without the necessity of mechanically rotating pieces of iron. E.m.f. induced by moving fields of force has its greatest application in alternating-current equipment, such as power transformers, or radio antennas, or tuning-coils in a TV set.

E.m.f.'s of this latter type exist in D.C. circuits whenever the current is stopped, started, or changed in amount. Often these e.m.f.'s merely exist, without meriting attention. In some equipment, such as automobile ignition systems, the induced e.m.f. is highly useful.

Fortunately, D.C. circuits provide a good starting point for the study of these induced voltages. We can examine how these voltages are produced, and what their effects are, in some slow-motion situations that give us a chance to understand what is going on.

THE BUILD-UP OF CURRENT IN A CIRCUIT CONTAINING A COIL

When the switch is closed, and electrons start to flow in this circuit, a magnetic field forms in and around the coil. This field is the total effect of all the little circular fields around each turn of wire in the coil, (Pages 79 and 80). The electrons in the circuit take a short time to build up speed, and the magnetic field increases in extent and in number of lines as the current increases.

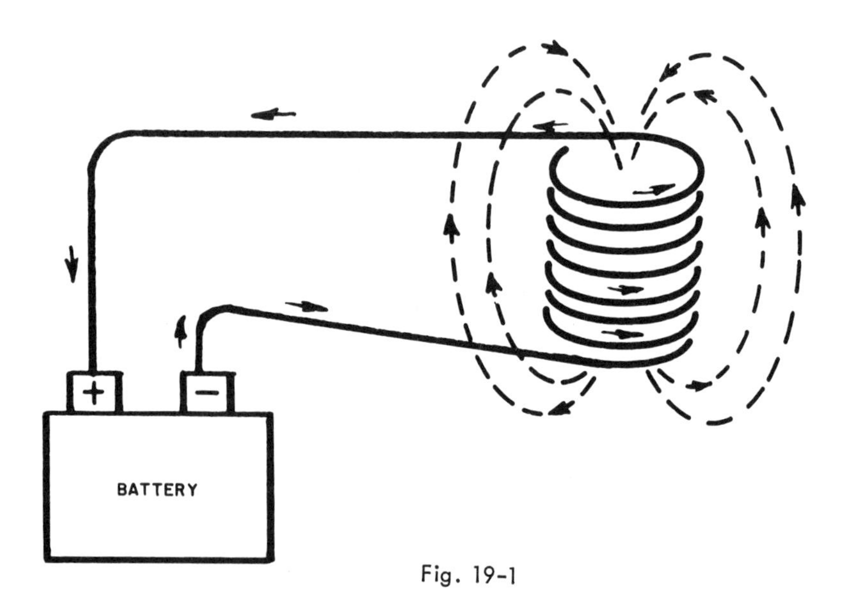

Fig. 19-1

Three successive views of this increasing field may indicate how it expands outward while the current increases. Fig. 19-2.

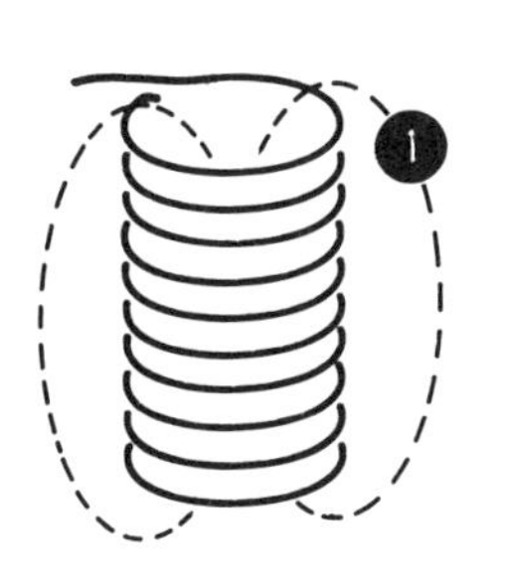

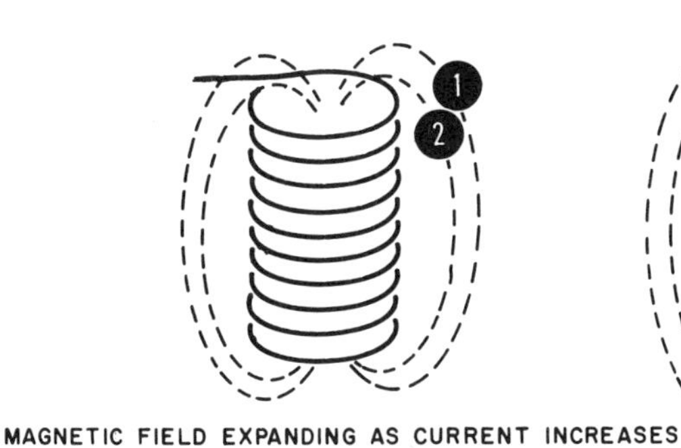

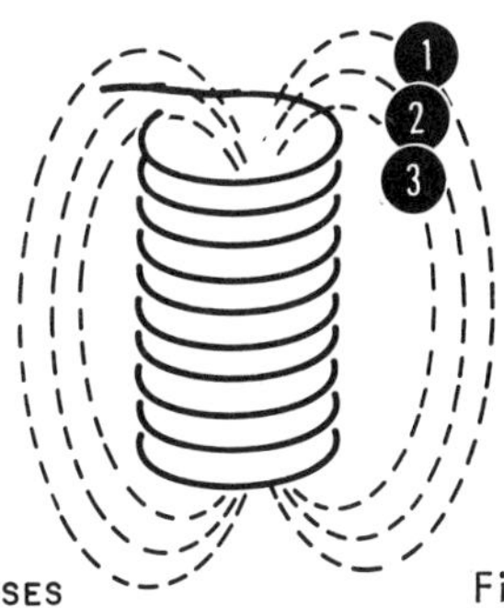

MAGNETIC FIELD EXPANDING AS CURRENT INCREASES Fig. 19-2

As these lines of force expand outward, originating from single wires, they cut across the other wires in the coil, thus producing e.m.f. in all the turns of the coil. The direction of this e.m.f. can be found by Lenz's Law: "The induced e.m.f. opposes the change that causes it." In this case, the change is the starting-up of the current, so the induced e.m.f. opposes the e.m.f. of the battery that is causing the current. The induced e.m.f. produces no current itself, but it hinders the production of current by the battery. It may take a few hundredths or a few tenths of a second for the current to come up to the value that we calculate by Ohm's Law, $I = E/R$.

As always, the amount of the induced e.m.f. depends on the number of turns of wire, the number of lines of force, and the speed of movement of the lines of force; that is, e.m.f. is proportional to the rate of cutting of lines of force by wires. In equation form,

$$E = \frac{\text{turns} \times \text{flux}}{\text{seconds} \times 10^8} \qquad (10^8 \text{ abbreviates } 100{,}000{,}000)$$

Induced E.M.F. Depends on Rate of Change of Current

Note that the "speed of movement of the lines of force" depends on how fast the current in the coil is increasing. Let Fig. 19-2 represent the field due to a current that accelerates gradually from 1 amp to 2 amp to 3 amp. If this current change (1 amp to 3 amp) occurs in two seconds, the rate of change is one ampere per second.

$$\text{Rate of change of current} = \frac{\text{Amount of change in current}}{\text{Time interval}}$$

Fig. 19-2 could as well represent views of the coil taken at 0.01-second intervals, the current increasing from 1 amp to 3 amp in two hundredths of one second. This is a higher rate of change:

$$\text{Rate of change} = \frac{2 \text{ amp}}{.02 \text{ second}} = 100 \text{ amps per second}$$

(Nobody says there is any 100-ampere current. 100 amp/sec is a rate of increase Compare calculation of the pay rate for a boy who gets 50 cents for a 5-minute errand. During that time he is being paid at the rate of $6.00 per hour.)

The importance of the "rate of current change" is this: If the rate of change is 100 amp/sec, the magnetic field is sweeping outward through the coil 100 times as fast as it does when the rate of change is one amp/sec. The faster-moving magnetic field will induce 100 times as much e.m.f. in the coil.

Induced e.m.f. is proportional to rate of change of current.

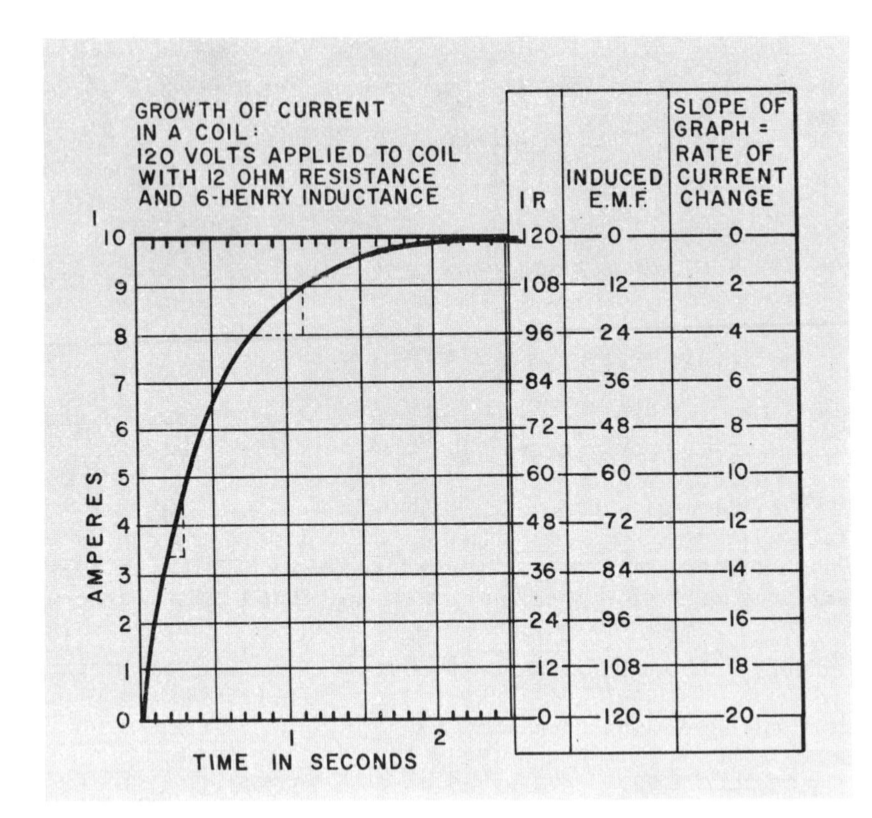

Fig. 19-3
Current Increase
In a Coil

Let's examine a graph that shows an example of the current increase in a coil. For this particular situation, with 120 volts applied to a 12-ohm coil wound on an iron core, the maximum current is 10 amps, according to Ohm's Law. When the circuit is closed (at t = 0) the current increases rapidly at first, then more gradually approaches its final value.

The values listed in the columns at the right of the graph may be calculated from the graph itself.

The "IR" values are voltage drops due to current in the coil, at various values of I. (R is 12 ohms, if I = 2, IR = 24 v.). These IR values are found first, in order to make it easy to find the amount of induced e.m.f. at several different times.

"Applied voltage = induced e.m.f. + IR" is a brief way of saying that the 120 volts applied must overcome the opposing induced e.m.f. and also overcome the resistance of the wire. When the current has risen to 3 amp, for example, 36 volts is used on resistance (IR = 36) and the rest must equalize the induced e.m.f., which therefore must be 84 volts, (120 = 84 + 36).

The last column gives the rate of change of current, in amperes per second, at various points. Graphically, the rate of change of current is represented by the steepness of the curve. When I = 10, the curve has become flat, the "slope" is zero, and the rate of change is zero. At the start, the current became 1 amp in about .05 second. At the start, the rate of change is

$$\frac{\text{Amount of change}}{\text{Time interval}} = \frac{1}{.05} = 20 \text{ amps per second}$$

From the graph, find what is happening to the current during the interval between t = 0.2 and t = 0.3 second. At t = 0.2, current is 3.3 amps; at t = 0.3 second, current is 4.5 amps.

$$\text{Rate of change} = \frac{\text{Amount of change}}{\text{Time interval}} = \frac{4.5 - 3.3}{0.3 - 0.2} = \frac{1.2}{0.1} = 12 \text{ amps/sec}$$

This 12 amp/sec rate is an average value for the 0.1 second interval, and should be thought of as being true only for the instant at the middle of the interval, when t = 0.25 sec and I = 4 amp.

Any of the values listed for "slope" of the graph can be found by this method. To find the rate of change at t = 0.95 sec (when I = 8.5 amp), consider a time interval that extends equally on both sides of the value t = .95; say the interval, 0.8 to 1.1 sec. At 0.8 sec, I is 8 amps. At t = 1.1 sec, I is 8.9 amps. The current has increased by 0.9 amp in a 0.3-sec interval, so the rate of increase is 3 amps/sec.

The reason for listing the values of induced e.m.f. and the values for rate of current change is to point out readily that the induced e.m.f. is proportional to the rate of change of current. For this particular coil, it happens that the induced e.m.f. is numerically six times as much as the rate of change of current. (Note that this is true for all values in the list.) For each amp/sec of current change, 6 volts of e.m.f. is induced. This quantity, 6 volts of induced e.m.f. for each ampere/second, is called the inductance of the coil.

Inductance is the ability of a coil to induce e.m.f. in itself when the current in it changes.

The amount of inductance of the above described coil is 6 volts per amp/sec. This clumsy expression, "volts induced for each ampere per second of current change" can be replaced by the term "henry."

A one-henry coil produces one volt of induced e.m.f. when the current changes at the rate of one ampere per second.

The letter "L" is used to represent inductance. The above coil has L = 6 henries.

The length of the above slow-going discussion was not intended to give the idea that the details of the increase of current in a coil are of terrific importance in themselves. The real purpose of the discussion was to arrange a simple situation to introduce the idea of the meaning of "inductance" of a coil.

"Inductance" is the property of coils that is terrifically important in alternating-current devices. The student who understands the meaning of inductance the first time he reads about it is a very unusual person. Most people have to study it over more than once.

Returning to Fig. 19-3, the actual time required for the current to reach its full value (10 amps) is of no particular concern. A time that is of more value in calculations is the time in seconds that is equal to L ÷ R. For this coil, L is 6 h. and R is 12 ohms. For this coil, L divided by R is 0.5 seconds. This value is called the "time constant" for this particular coil.

In any circuit containing both L and R, when the time = L/R, the current has risen to 63.2% of its final value. See Fig. 19-3: at time = 0.5 seconds, I has become 6.32 amps. In a coil with small inductance and large resistance, the time constant is a small number, and the current rises to its final value very quickly.

E.M.F. Induced When Current in a Coil Stops

If a 12-ohm, 5-henry coil, (as used for the graph, Fig. 19-3) is connected in a circuit like Fig. 19-4, a 10-amp current is quickly built up in the coil. When the current becomes a steady 10 amps, the magnetic field around the coil is stationary. If the current in the coil is decreased or stopped for any reason, the magnetic field around the coil shrinks and collapses. As these lines of force return to the wires from which they came, they cut across turns of the coil as they collapse, giving energy back to the circuit by inducing an e.m.f. in the wires of the coil.

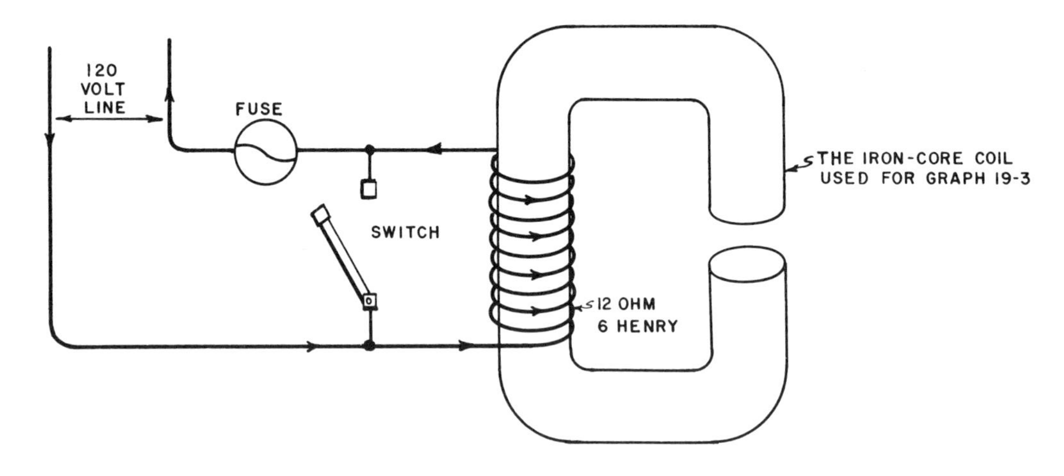

Fig. 19-4

The direction of the e.m.f. when the current stops, according to Lenz's Law, will be in a direction that opposes the change that causes it. The change is now a decrease in current, so the induced e.m.f. will try to maintain the current, trying to keep electrons going in the same direction in which they had been traveling.

In the circuit of Fig. 19-4, closing the switch disconnects the power line from the coil and at the same time completes a low-resistance circuit across the terminals of the coil, giving the moving electrons a good opportunity to slow down and coast to a stop, (see Fig. 19-5).

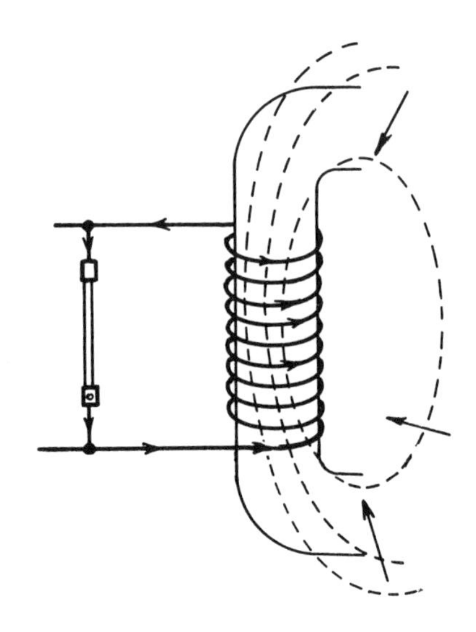

COLLAPSING FIELD INDUCES EMF THAT CAUSES CURRENT TO CONTINUE

Fig. 19-5

The graph that shows how fast the current decreases is exactly like Fig. 19-3 inverted, which is the graph shown in Fig. 19-6.

The current, originally 10 amps, drops by 63.2% of its original value, down to 3.68 amps, in 0.5 seconds. 0.5 seconds is the time constant, which equals $L/R = 6/12 = 0.5$ seconds.

Because the induced e.m.f. is the only source of voltage, the induced e.m.f. must equal IR

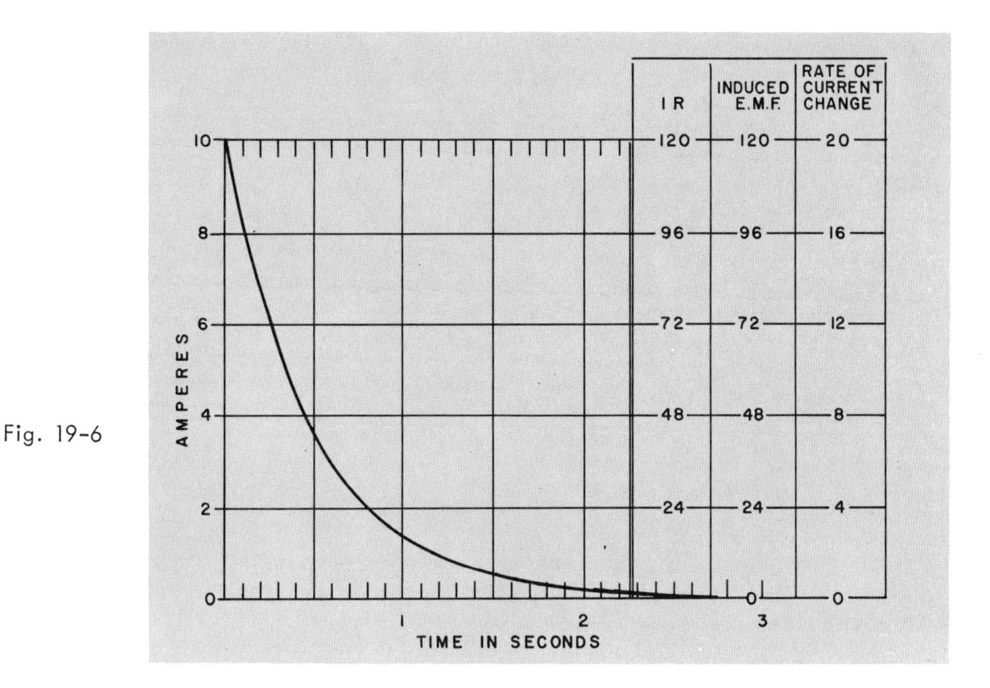

Fig. 19-6

Effect of a Quick Stop of Current

The circuit of Fig. 19-4 allowed the current to take its time in coming to a stop; the field collapsed slowly, inducing a small e.m.f. More often, the current in a coil is stopped by opening a switch in series with the coil. This quick stopping of current causes a fast collapse of magnetic field, which induces a high e.m.f. for a very short time.

A convincing demonstration of the existence of this e.m.f. can be performed by holding the bared ends of a small iron-core "choke coil" (10 henry, 150 ohm, for example) and placing the ends of the wire on the terminals of a 1.5-volt dry cell. Of course, 1.5 volts will not produce enough current in the fingers to be noticeable. Usually, fingers are not sensitive to voltages less than about 50. When the wires are removed from the cell, the collapsing magnetic field of the coil induces an e.m.f. in the coil, which will produce enough current in the fingers to be noticeable. The current exists for only a few millionths of a second, too short a time to affect even a very sensitive voltmeter. Naturally this demonstration should be performed personally by the one who needs evidence of the existence of the induced e.m.f.

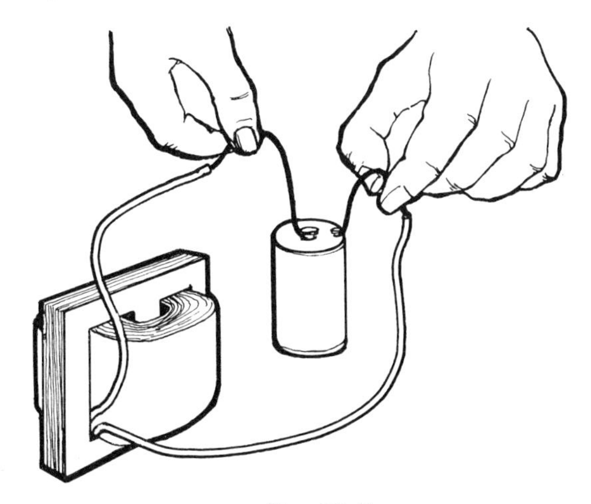

Fig. 19-7

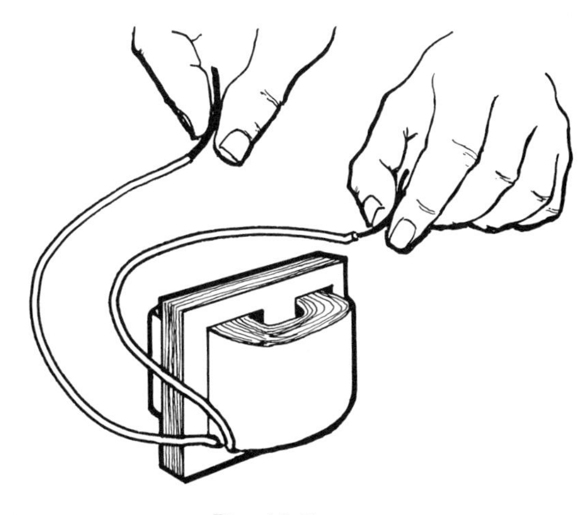

Fig. 19-8

To calculate the amount of this induced e.m.f., we need to know the resistance of the circuit of Fig. 19-8. Assume it is 50,000 ohms.

The time constant of this circuit is L/R = 10 henries/50,000 ohms = .0002 second, which tells that the coil current and the induced e.m.f. lose 63% of their initial values in that short time.

The average induced e.m.f. during the 0.0002 second can be found. Just before the coil was disconnected from the cell, the current was $I = E \div R = 1.5\text{ v} \div 150\text{ ohm} = .0100$ amp. 0.0002 second later, the current had decreased by 63%, a drop of .0063 amp, becoming .0037 amp.

The rate of change of current is: $\frac{.0063}{.0002} = 31.5$ amp/sec

Induced e.m.f. is inductance times rate of change: e.m.f. $= 10 \times 31.5 = 315$ volts

This is an average value, the e.m.f. at the start being even higher. The entire performance is over so quickly that not enough electrical energy is delivered to the fingers to give their owner any cause for complaint.

The above demonstration must be done with a small coil and a low-voltage source, as suggested. The sudden disconnecting of a large coil can cause e.m.f.'s harmful to people and equipment. For example, the shunt field of a 120-volt D.C. generator might have 10-henries inductance and 40-ohms resistance, carrying 3 amps. If that 3 amp current is reduced to 1 amp in 0.01 second, the rate of change of current is 200 amps per second, and the average induced e.m.f. is 10 h. × 200 amp/sec = 2000 volts, with an average current still = 2 amp. The opening of a switch in such a circuit produces a metal-vaporizing arc at the switch, and the induced e.m.f. may break down insulation in the coil. For this reason, a special type of switch is used on the field circuit of large generators, so that if the field circuit must be opened, a low-resistance path is automatically connected across the terminals of the field coil just at the instant the coil is disconnected from the generator. This low resistance across the coil lets the current come to a gradual stop without developing any high induced voltage.

Energy in the Magnetic Field

The source of the energy of the induced e.m.f. is the magnetic field itself. This magnetic-field energy, which necessarily accompanies a current of electrons, is in some ways similar to the "kinetic" mechanical energy possessed by a rotating flywheel, or any moving object.

When a force is applied to a heavy flywheel, (like line voltage applied to a coil), it takes a little time to get the wheel moving. The wheel pushes back against the hand that is pushing on the wheel, (like induced e.m.f. that opposes line voltage when the electron motion starts.)

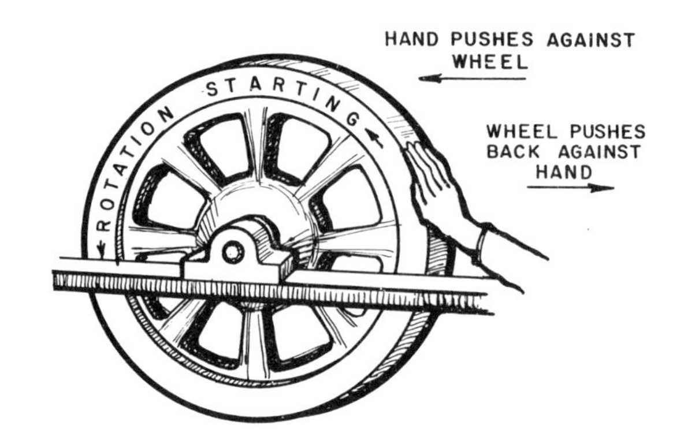

Fig. 19-9

If a 50-pound wheel is rotating at high speed, no one in his right mind would stick his arm through the spokes to stop it because that wheel will exert a force of many times 50 pounds against the resistance that causes it to stop suddenly. Likewise, the sudden stop of current in a coil develops a huge electron-moving force when the resistance of an opened switch appears in its circuit.

The amount of energy in the magnetic field of a coil, measured in joules, is: $1/2\ L\ I^2$. A "joule" is a metric-system unit for measurement of energy. One watt, you will recall, is a rate of one joule per second. In a 15-henry coil carrying 4 amps, the magnetic field energy is $1/2 \times 15 \times 4^2 = 120$ joules. That's enough energy to light a 60-watt lamp for two seconds.

E.M.F. Generated in One Coil by Changing Current in Another

Up to this point, our discussion has been concerned with e.m.f. induced in the same coil in which the current-changes took place, the effect called self-inductance.

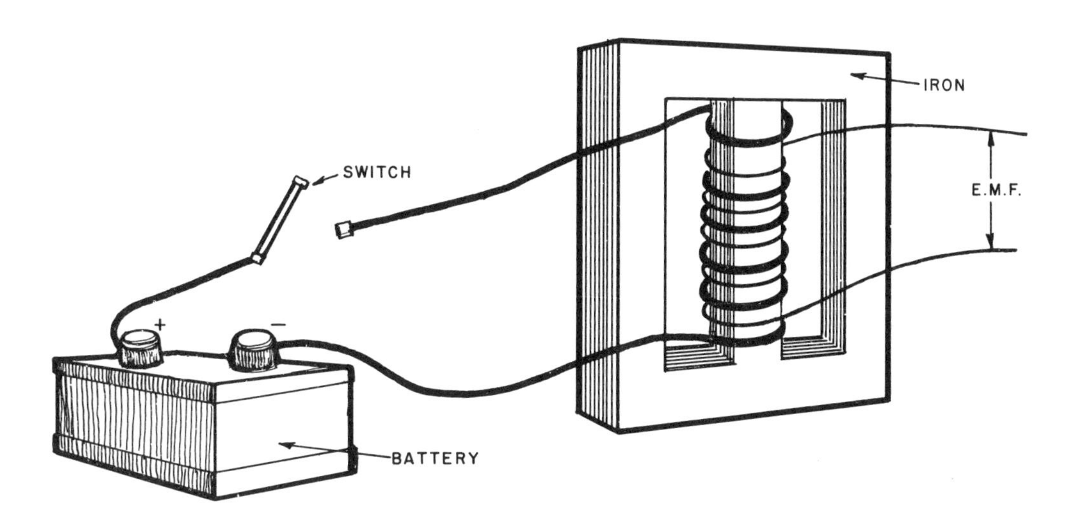

Fig. 19-10

If we place a second coil in a position where it will be cut by the changing flux of the first coil (Fig. 19-10), e.m.f. will be induced in the second coil also.

The effect of one coil on the other is called "mutual inductance." Mutual inductance is defined and measured in much the same way as self inductance — two coils have a mutual inductance of one henry when a rate of change of one amp per second in one coil induces one volt in the other coil.

Fig. 19-10 shows two features of the coil construction that make for a high mutual inductance:

1. Both coils are wound on the same iron core, so that each coil is in a position to be cut most effectively by the changing magnetic field of the other. If the coils are separated, some lines of force of one would not cut the other coil.

2. The coils are surrounded by iron, making a low-reluctance, easy magnetic path so that a lot of lines of force will be produced by a small current in one coil.

3. A third feature, not indicated on the diagram, is that the mutual inductance is increased by using a large number of turns on each coil.

An arrangement of two coils, as in Fig. 19-10, is called a transformer. It is especially useful in alternating-current circuits, but also has several applications in direct-current equipment.

Induced E.M.F. in the Gasoline-Engine Ignition System

The basic principle of an automobile ignition system may be described with the help of Fig. 19-10. When the switch is closed, a current builds up in the "primary" coil which is connected to the battery. The slowly-expanding magnetic field induces a small and useless e.m.f. in the other coil, the "secondary" coil, which is wound on the same iron core.

When the primary-circuit switch is opened, the current stops suddenly. The quickly-collapsing magnetic field induces a large and useful e.m.f. in the second coil.

The primary winding uses a wire-size large enough to create enough ampere-turns to effectively magnetize the iron (Unit 11) and enough turns so that the resistance of the winding is large enough to limit the rate of heat production. Since the purpose of the ignition system is to produce a high voltage, the secondary coil consists of a very large number of turns. The more turns of wire cut by the collapsing field, the larger the e.m.f. produced. Since the current in the secondary is very small, very small wire can be used.

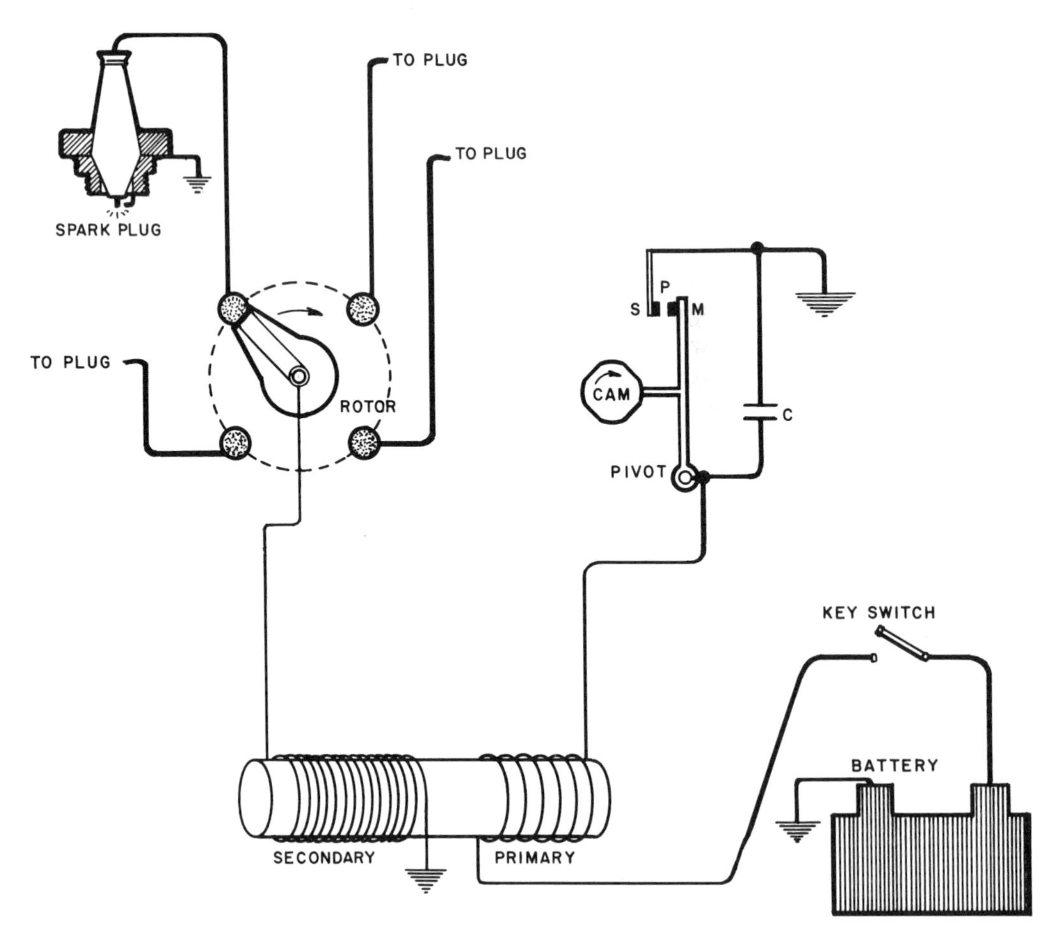

Fig. 19-11

Fig. 19-11 is a more complete diagram of the ignition system for a four-cylinder gasoline engine. The added complications are mostly mechanical, rather than electrical. The rotor and its four contacts, the timer cam, the contact points P, and the capacitor C, are all associated with the distributor. The timer cam and rotor are mounted on the same shaft, which is gear-driven by the engine, and turns at one-half of the speed (r.p.m.) of the engine.

When the engine is to be started, the key-switch is closed. If the cam happens to be in the position shown in the diagram, the contact points P are open, and there is no current in the primary coil. When the engine is cranked by the starter motor, the timer cam rotates. A spring, not shown, pushes the movable contact arm M to the left and holds it against the rotating cam. As the cam rotates, the movable contact point is alternately permitted to touch the stationary contact S, then is pushed away from the stationary contact, so that the primary circuit is alternately closed and opened. These contact points accomplish the necessary closing and opening of the primary circuit that was done by the switch in Fig. 19-10. When the points close, the expanding field of the primary induces a small e.m.f. in the secondary, too small to be useful. When the points open, the collapsing field induces a useful large e.m.f. in the secondary coil, provided the current in the primary stops suddenly enough.

In the diagram, the two coils are separated in order to emphasize the absence of wire-connection between them. As actually assembled, the secondary consists of several layers of wire-turns, extending the entire length of the core. The primary coils surround the secondary, and also extend as far as the ends of the core. The symbol ⏚ represents a so-called "ground" connection, which in this case is a connection to the metal frame of the automobile.

The purpose of the condenser C is to help the primary current to stop suddenly. An electrical condenser (also called capacitor, described more fully in Unit 25) consists of two pieces of metal foil, separated by waxed paper or some other kind of insulation. The symbol in the diagram uses the two parallel lines to represent the two pieces of metal foil, which are connected to the circuit. The vacant space between the two lines indicates that one metal foil does not touch the other, so there is no conducting path through the condenser itself.

To find the value of the capacitor in the ignition circuit, let's first see what would happen without it: The primary coil has inductance of its own, so that when the points start to open, the collapsing field induces an e.m.f. that tends to keep electrons flowing through the primary coil and through the points P. This e.m.f. will be enough to start an arc as the points first open. The vaporized metal in the arc permits enough conduction so that the primary current gradually comes to a stop. This gentle stop means that the magnetic field contracts slowly, inducing only a small e.m.f. in the secondary coil. A small e.m.f. produced by the coil means that the voltage at the spark plugs will not be enough to make sparks, so the engine won't start.

Now put the capacitor in the circuit, in parallel with the contact points. When the points start to open, a little resistance (air) appears at that part of the circuit. Assuming for a moment that the current direction is from the primary coil toward the contact points, the electrons driven toward the pivot connection now have a choice of paths: either the difficult path through the opening contacts, or the wire leading to the lower metal foil of the capacitor. The large area of metal offers, for awhile, lots of room for electrons, so most of the electrons rush on to that metal foil, soon charging it negatively, (and repelling electrons from the top plate, incidentally.) In a short time the capacitor foil is loaded with electrons and will take no more. During this same short time the points have opened a little farther without starting a conducting arc. Cold air between the points is a good insulator, and the primary current comes to a smashing halt. The flux collapses abruptly, inducing a high e.m.f. (maybe 20,000 volts) in the secondary coil, which causes a spark at the gap in the spark plug. During one rotation of the timer cam and rotor, the contact points close and open four times. The turning rotor delivers energy to each of the four spark plugs in order.

The spark plug itself is a simple device; if its porcelain insulator is unbroken and reasonably clean and the spark gap is the right distance, it cannot fail to perform its function when supplied with high-voltage e.m.f.

Other D.C. Applications of Induced E.M.F.

The automobile ignition system and other induced e.m.f. devices are adaptations of the "Induction Coil" of Fig. 19-12. The armature A is a springy metal strip, held fast at the bottom. At the top is a small iron disk. The spring itself tends to stay over to the right, against the contact point P. When the primary coil is connected to a battery, the armature vibrates, just as in the electric bell (Fig. 10-8, Page 92).

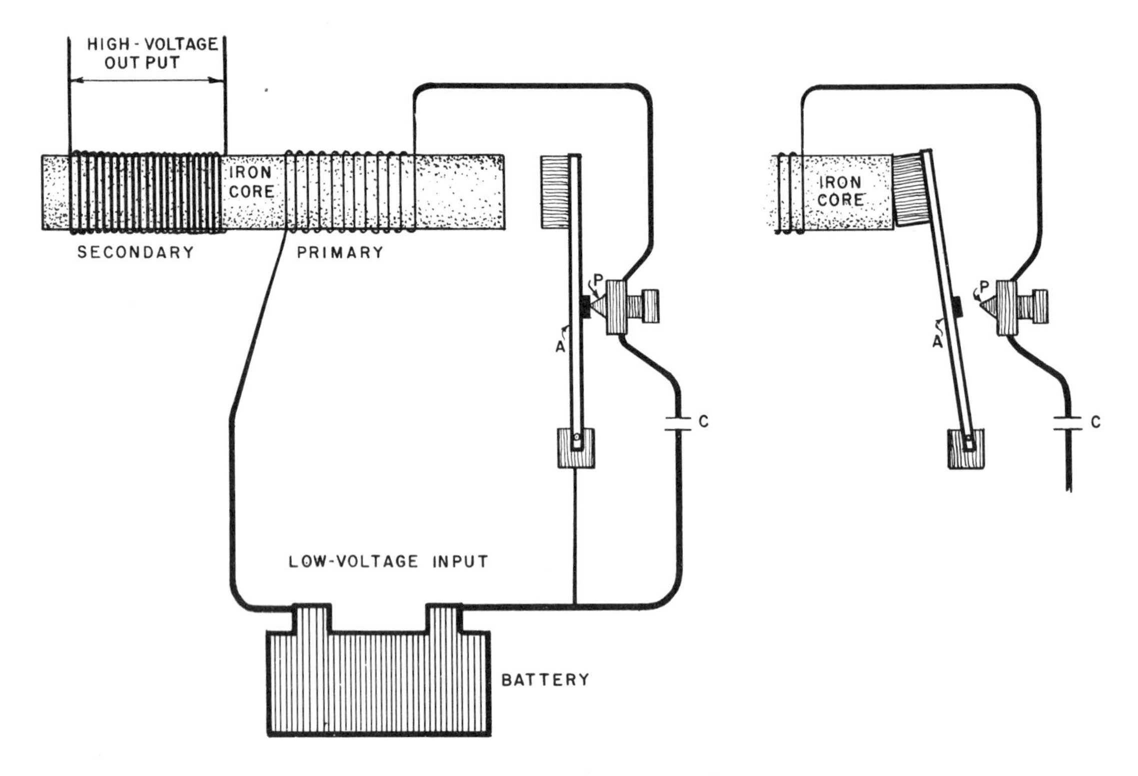

Fig. 19-12 Induction Coil

Magnetic attraction pulls the armature spring away from the stationary contact point P, but as soon as the spring leaves the contact, the primary circuit is broken, and the soft iron core loses enough magnetism to permit the spring to fly back to the contact point, re-establish current and magnetic field, and repeat the whole process continually. The capacitor across the armature and contact point serves the same purpose as it does across the contacts in the auto ignition system — that is, helping the primary current to stop suddenly, so that a large e.m.f. is induced in the secondary.

For many years this simple induction coil was the most-used source of high-voltage direct current. It powered early X-ray tubes, horseless-carriage ignition, and experimental equipment for electron-investigators. Thousands of these coils were sold to gullible citizens, with the claim that practically all known bodily ailments could be cured by applying the coil's tingling current to the afflicted parts. Doubtless many people did feel better after the treatment stopped.

The induction-coil is adapted for electric-fence charging by replacing the speedy vibrator with a slow-motion, balance-wheel operated contact, which closes the primary circuit for an instant at few-second intervals. Brief pulses of voltage every two seconds are enough to train the cattle, without too-rapid discharge of the storage battery. (A.C. fence chargers are also used.)

The majority of automobile radios are powered by an adaptation of the induction coil. Customary vacuum tubes require a source of 75 to 300 volts D.C. to enable the tubes to perform their various amplifying functions in the radio receiver.

The diagram below shows the principle of operation of the vibrator and transformer in a battery-powered receiver.

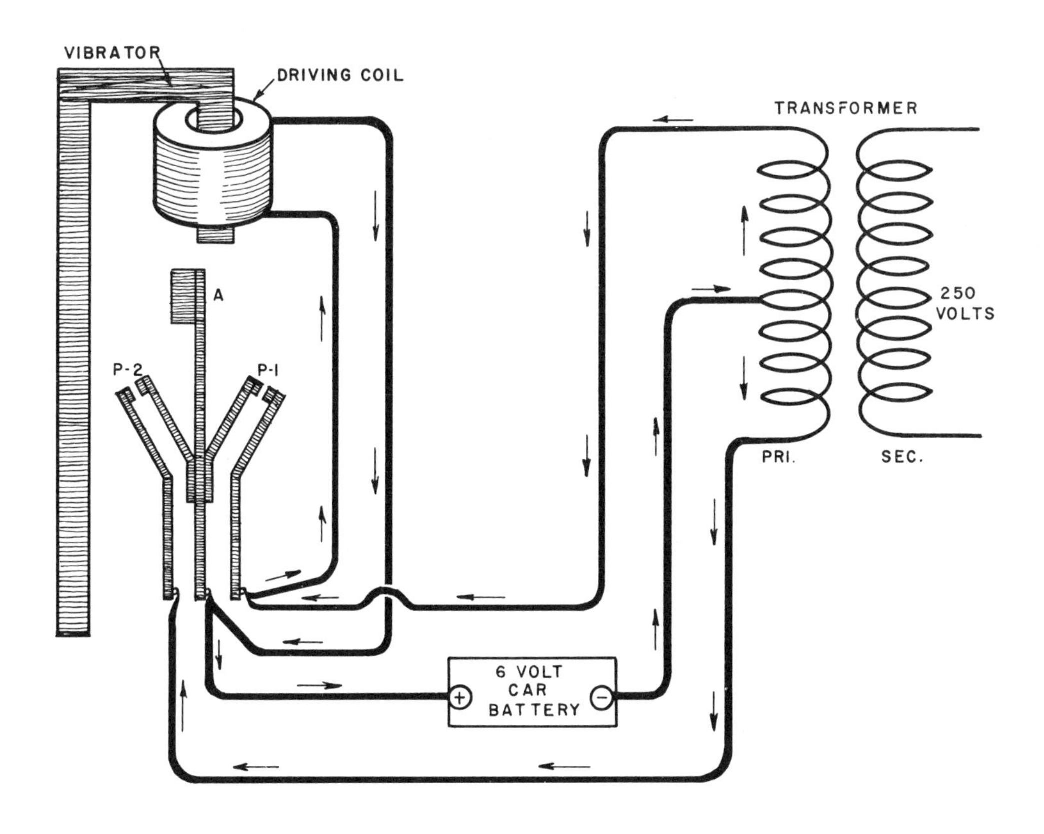

Fig. 19-13

The armature A is shown in its rest position. Contact points P-1 and P-2 are both open. When the circuit is first closed, there is a small current through the top half of the primary coil and through the driving coil of the vibrator, these coils being in series. The magnetic pull of the driving coil pulls the springy armature A to the right, closing P-1. Contacts P-1 are in parallel with the driving coil, so when they are closed they form a no-resistance bypass. With P-1 closed, there is more current in the top half of the primary of the transformer, building magnetic field to cut the secondary. And with P-1 closed, there is practically no current in the driving coil, which releases its magnetic pull on A, so that A flies back past its rest position, closing P-2 and opening P-1. Current in the top half of the primary is reduced, current in the bottom half of the primary is at a high value and opposite in direction to the old current, so the original field collapses and a new field builds up as P-1 opens and P-2 closes. This change of magnetic field induces a surge of voltage in the secondary. Also, the opening of P-1 allows the driving coil to again become magnetic, so it yanks A back to the right, opening P-2 and repeating the whole process. The purpose of the vibrator is to rapidly reverse the current in the primary of the transformer, creating there a rapidly alternating magnetic field that can induce a high e.m.f. in the large number of turns of the secondary coil. This high-voltage A.C. then has to be converted to D.C. through a rectifier, to be described in Unit 26.

CALCULATION OF INDUCTANCE OF A COIL

Most often, if one wishes to find the inductance of a given iron-core coil, his calculations are based on measurements of current and voltage taken when the coil is operated on an alternating-current circuit. The calculations that follow are intended to show how the inductance can be found by calculation alone. This calculation should also help in securing understanding of the meaning of inductance.

Three types of coil-and-core arrangements are to be considered: iron-core, iron-core with air gap, and air-core. First, a few preliminary notions that apply to all coils should be reviewed.

Self-inductance has already been defined as the ability of a coil to induce e.m.f. in itself. A coil is said to have one henry of inductance if one volt is induced when the current changes at the rate of one ampere per second. In a 5-henry coil, 5 volts are induced if the current changes at the rate of one ampere per second.

To induce one volt, the total cutting of wires by lines of force (flux × turns) must be 100,000,000 per second. Combining this with the above definition of a henry, a one-henry coil has a cutting rate of 100,000,000 lines per second if the current in the coil changes at the rate of one ampere per second.

For our present purpose, the above expression can be simplified. A one-henry coil undergoes a cutting of 100,000,000 lines of force when the current changes by one ampere. (The time in which this change takes place is not now specified, because this calculation does not involve the number of volts induced by the change.)

The formula —

$$\text{henries} = \frac{\text{flux} \times \text{turns}}{\text{amps change} \times 10^8}$$

puts the above statement into a form that we can use for calculation. 10^8 abbreviates 100,000,000. Flux × turns gives the "total cutting of lines of force."

Assume that the flux in a 200-turn coil changes from 400,000 lines to 250,000 lines when the current changes from 5 amperes to 3 amperes. The flux decreases by 150,000, these 150,000 lines cut 200 turns of wire, so the total cutting is 150,000 × 200 = 30,000,000. The ampere change is 2 amps.

$$\text{henries} = \frac{150{,}000 \times 200}{2 \times 10^8} = 0.15 \text{ henry}$$

In order to calculate the henries of inductance for a coil then, we need only to know:

(1) the number of turns in the coil, and

(2) how much change of flux is caused by some amount of change in current.

1. Calculation of Inductance of an Iron-Core Coil

The coil at the right consists of five layers of wire, with 120 turns in each layer. The iron core is 1/2″ × 1/2″. To find its inductance, we must first find the relation between flux and current, by reference to a graph like Fig. 11-3, Page 105. Part of such a graph for a typical soft-iron is shown in Fig. 19-15.

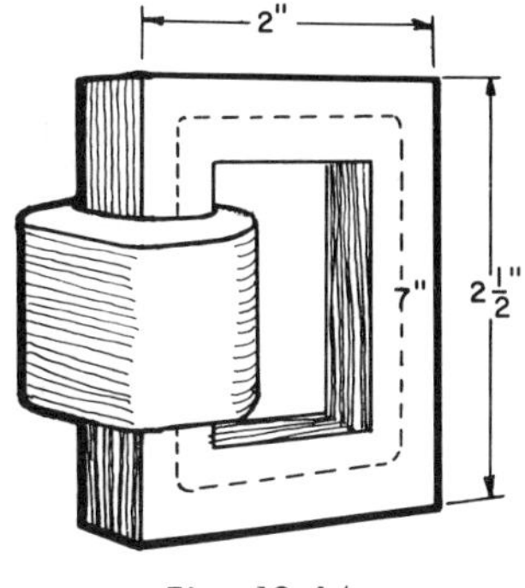

Fig. 19-14

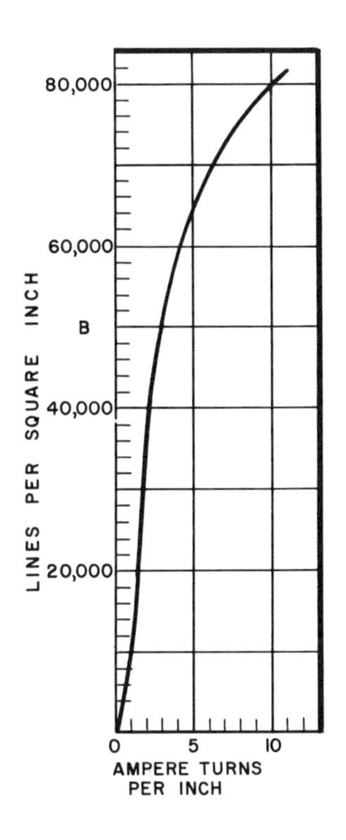

Fig. 19-15

The inductance of the coil is greatest when a small change of current produces a large change of flux. The graph shows that this condition exists for values of B between 20,000 and 60,000 lines per square inch. Therefore this range of flux values will be used in the computation. At values of B above 80,000, the iron is near saturation, large changes in current cause small changes in flux, and therefore the inductance is less for high values of current.

According to the graph, 1.5 amp-turns per inch produce 20,000 lines per square inch, 4 amp-turns per inch produce 60,000 lines per square inch. The magnetic path in the iron is 7 inches long, so, at B = 20,000, amp-turns is 10.5; to have B = 60,000, amp-turns must be 28. Dividing each of these amp-turn values by the 600 turns, we find .0175 amp and .0467 amp for the necessary currents at the two values for flux density.

The actual flux lines depend on B, the flux density, and on the cross-section area of the iron core, which is 1/4 sq. in. When B is 20,000 lines per sq. in., the flux is 5000 lines. When B is 60,000 lines per sq. in., the flux is 15,000 lines. Therefore, the flux that cuts wires is the difference between 5,000 and 15,000, that is, 10,000 lines.

$$\text{henries} = \frac{\text{flux cut} \times \text{turns}}{\text{amp change} \times 10^8} = \frac{10{,}000 \times 600}{(.0467 - .0175) \times 10^8} = 2 \text{ henries}$$

This is the maximum inductance for this coil. If the coil is operated at higher currents, the inductance could be found by calculating the ampere-turns at the higher values, and finding the flux change from Fig. 11-3. At best, this answer should be called a good estimate rather than an exact calculation, for in a large coil not all of the flux cuts across all of the turns; some lines of force stray from the ideal path. And not all iron follows the chart of Fig. 19-15.

2. Calculation of Inductance for a Coil on an Iron Core with an Air Gap

Taking the same coil and core used in the calculation above, a slot 0.05″ wide is sawed through the core, giving the core-iron the appearance of Fig. 19-16. (We keep the same coil, 600 turns.) In calculating the inductance, we use the same 20,000 - 60,000 range of flux density, which requires 10.5 to 28 amp-turns to magnetize the iron.

Fig. 19-16

Additional amp-turns are needed to maintain the flux in the air gap. As in Unit 11, the formula used is: amp-turns for air = flux density × .313 × length of air gap.

When B on the graph is 20,000, amp-turns for air will be 20,000 × .313 × .05, which equals 313. Total amp-turns for air and iron will be 313 + 10.5 = 323 amp-turns, which requires .538 amps in 600 turns.

When B is 60,000, amp-turns for air equals 60,000 × .313 × .05 = 939. Total amp-turns at 60,000 will be 939 + 28 = 967 amp-turns, requiring 1.61 amps.

When B is 20,000, the flux is 5,000, as before; and when B is 60,000, the flux is 15,000 so we still use 10,000 as the change in flux.

$$\text{Inductance} = \frac{10{,}000 \times 600}{(1.61 - .538)\ 10^8} = .056 \text{ henry}$$

Although the inductance is lowered by the presence of the air gap, coils that are used primarily for their inductance-effects (choke coils) often have an air gap. With it, the coil is useful over a much wider range of current values. Larger inductance is obtained by using several thousand turns of wire.

Provided one uses iron with properties shown in the graph, Fig. 19-15, calculation (1) can be abbreviated to this:

$$\text{henries} = \frac{N^2 \times 8 \times \text{area}}{50{,}000 \times \text{length}}$$

in which N is the number of turns, "area" is square inch cross-section area of the iron core, and "length" is the length in inches of the magnetic path through the iron, which must have no air gap.

Provided that the amp-turns for iron are small enough to be neglected compared with the amp-turns for the air gap, calculation (2) can also be abbreviated to:

$$\text{henries} = \frac{N^2 \times \text{area}}{\text{length} \times 31{,}500{,}000}$$

in which length = length of the air gap (in inches)

area = square inches cross-section area at the air gap

N = number of turns

Both of these shortened formulas point out the fact that the inductance is proportional to the square of the number of turns, a fact that may have been concealed in the original calculations. Originally, turns was used in finding amps from ampere-turns, then used again in "flux × turns" which put it into the computation twice.

3. Calculating Inductance of Air-Core Coils

With no iron to form a magnetic path of definite length and area, the above methods are not useful. This formula for an air-core coil is based more on experience than on definitions:

$$\text{Inductance in Millihenries} = \frac{d^2 N^2}{5000 \times (3d + 9L + 10r)}$$

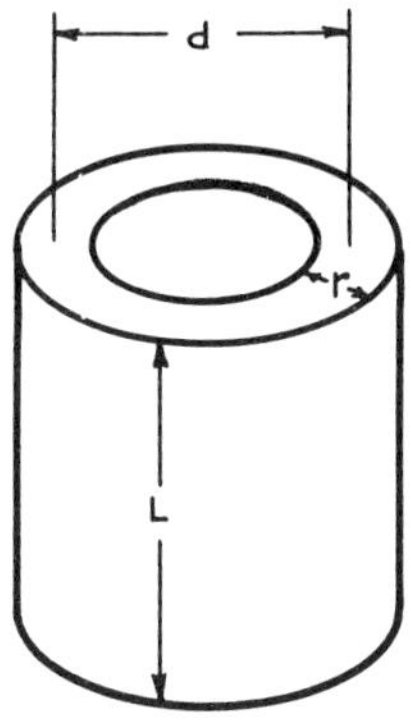

As shown in Fig. 19-17, d is the average diameter of the coil, r is the thickness of the windings, and L is the length of the coil, all in inches. N is the number of turns. Millihenries (mh) are thousandths of a henry. 40 millihenries may be rewritten as .04 henries or as 40,000 microhenries.

If the coil consists of only one layer of wire, "10r" in the above formula is omitted.

d

r

L

Fig. 19-17

BUILDING A COIL THAT WILL HAVE A GIVEN INDUCTANCE

Radio experimenters often find it convenient to make coils that they need — air-core coils of low inductance. Using the formula just described, possible values of the coil dimensions are estimated and substituted in the formula along with the desired value of inductance, and the number of turns is calculated. If the number of turns is unreasonable, new dimensions must be assumed and the calculation repeated.

Coil manufacturers have a great variety of information available in the form of graphs and tables, but the amateur can still be permitted some trial-and-error methods.

The building of an iron-core coil to have a desired inductance may be complicated by limitations on size, resistance, current, or heat. A coil that is to be used mainly for its inductance effect normally requires an air gap to avoid magnetic saturation of the iron, and thereby maintain the inductance at usefully-high values of current.

Assume one plans a coil to fit a core similar to Fig. 19-16, that will have an inductance of 10 henries. Cross-section area of the core is put at 1/2″ × 1/2″ for a trial, and air gap is estimated as .04 inches. (A .02″ or .1″ gap is not unreasonable.)

$$\text{Using the formula, henries} = \frac{N^2 \times \text{area}}{\text{length} \times 31{,}500{,}000}$$

$$10 = \frac{N^2 \times 1/4}{.04 \times 31{,}500{,}000}$$

$$N = 7200$$

Whether this result can be used will depend on current-carrying requirements of the coil. To avoid unreasonable bulk on a 1/2″ square core, the coil must use small wire, say #32, which can cause a heating problem. Using a larger cross-section, such as 3/4″ × 3/4″ = .56 sq. in. and recalculating gives N = 4750. Use of the wires-per-sq. in. table, size limitations and any necessity for insulation between layers makes an estimate of wire size possible. From length of wire used, and current expected, the voltage drop across the coil and the watts rate of heat production can be found.

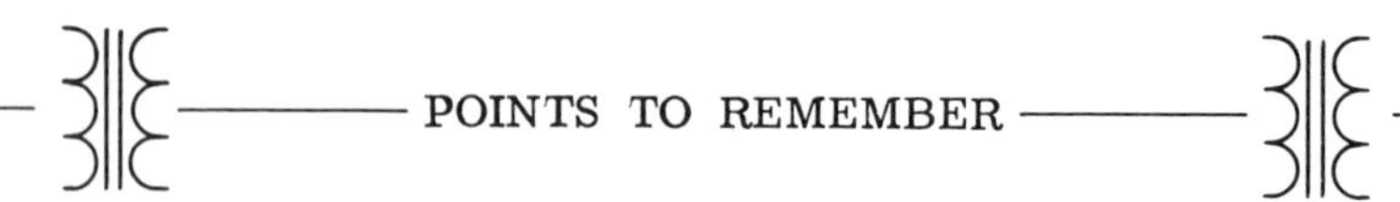

- Induced e.m.f. opposes the change that causes it.
- An increasing current in a coil generates an e.m.f. in the coil that hinders the increase.
- A decreasing current in a coil generates an e.m.f. in the coil that hinders the decrease, attempting to maintain the current.
- The amount of induced e.m.f. depends on the rate at which magnetic lines of force cut wires.
- The cutting of 100,000,000 lines by wires, per second, induces one volt.
- A one-henry coil produces one volt of induced e.m.f. when the current changes at the rate of one ampere per second.
- Two coils have a mutual inductance of one henry when one volt is induced in one coil by a current-change rate of one ampere per second in the other.
- Induction coils, useful in gas-engine ignition, generate a high-voltage pulse in one coil when its many turns are cut by the quickly-collapsing magnetic field of the D.C. primary coil.

REVIEW QUESTIONS

1. Calculate the "time constant" of a 3-henry 100-ohm coil. Calculate the current in the coil .03 seconds after it is connected to a 120-volt D.C. line.

2. In a certain 1200-turn coil, the flux changes from 40,000 to 30,000 when the current changes from .05 amp to .03 amp. Calculate the inductance of the coil, over this range.

3. In a given coil, will 6 amps cause more lines of force than 3 amps? In the example of Fig. 19-3, why isn't the induced e.m.f. greater when the current is 6 amps?

4. In the diagram of the automobile ignition system, which terminal of the battery should be the negative?

5. In the automobile ignition system, are there induced e.m.f.'s in both the primary and the secondary when the points open? If so, in which coil is the induced e.m.f. greater? Why?

6. On an electric bell, there is a contact continually opening and closing. Would it work better with a capacitor across these contact points?

7. A 15-henry 600-ohm coil has been connected to a 60-volt D.C. line for several minutes. Calculate the current. The circuit is opened, and the current stops in 0.01 seconds. Find the rate of change of current during this .01 second interval. Find the average induced e.m.f. during this interval.

In Unit 17, it was pointed out that when a wire carries electrons across a magnetic field, the wire is pushed sidewise.

The current in the wire has a magnetic field of its own. The wire's magnetic field combines with the externally-applied magnetic field, making the resulting field shown in Fig. 20-1.

To apply this effect in an electric motor, let's examine the effect of an external magnetic field on a rectangular loop of wire which is supplied with D.C. from a battery. For our present purposes, assume that the external magnetic field is supplied by a permanent magnet.

The sections of the loop that lie parallel to the field are not affected by the field. The side of the loop marked A will be pushed upward; the side marked B will be pushed downward. Let's see why.

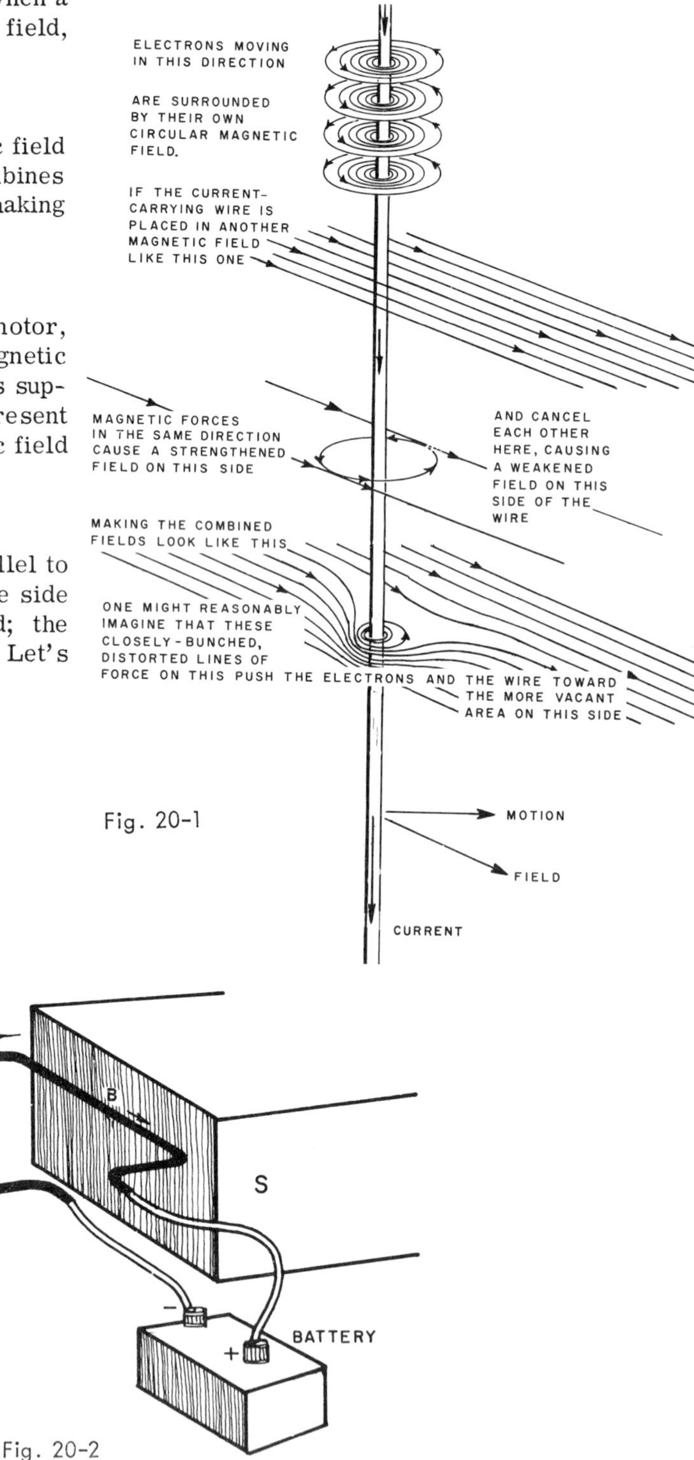

Fig. 20-1

DIRECTION OF FIELD

A

B

N

S

BATTERY

Fig. 20-2

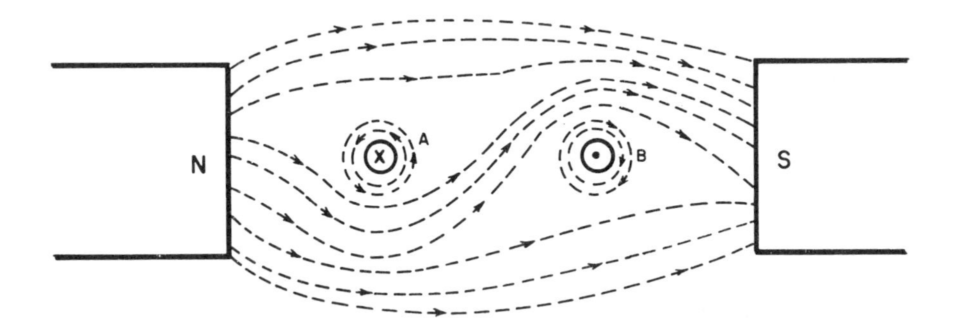

Fig. 20-3

Fig. 20-3 represents a vertical cross-section of the loop in the magnetic field. At A, the heavy circle represents wire A of Fig. 20-2. The X in the circle represents electrons moving away from the observer (like the tail of an arrow flying away). The dot in the circular section of wire B represents electrons moving toward the observer (the point of an approaching arrow). The circular pattern around A and B represents the magnetic field of the current in these wires. (Using the left-hand rule, check the correctness of these directions.)

Underneath A, the N→S magnetic field combines with the field of the wire, making a strong field under the wire. Above A, the field of the magnet and the field of the wire are in opposite directions; they cancel, making the weak field represented by the less-concentrated lines above A. Wire A is lifted by the strong magnetic field beneath. Think of the N→S lines of force as both repelling each other and attempting to straighten themselves, to account for this lifting effect.

A similar effect at B pushes wire B downward. B is pushed down by lines of force, much as the round stick in Fig. 20-4 is pushed down by the string.

Note that the direction of motion of the wire can be quickly found by using a 3-finger right-hand rule: With first finger, middle finger and thumb at right angles to each other, _forefinger = _field, _center finger = _current, thu_mb = _motion.

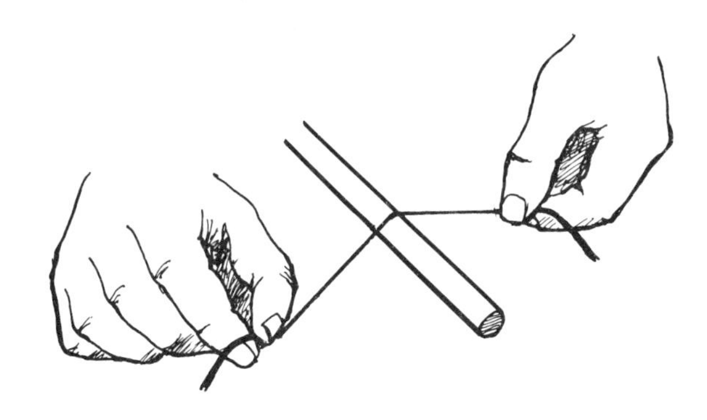

Fig. 20-4

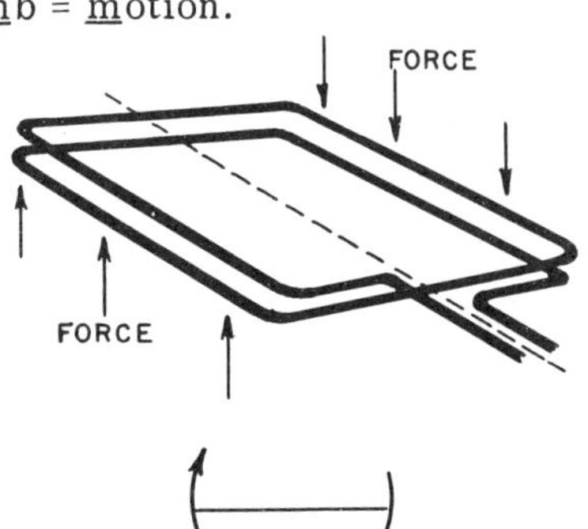

Fig. 20-5 Torque

The lifting of one side of the loop and the pushing down of the other side creates a turning effect, or torque, on the loop of wire.

This combination of forces is the torque that turns the armature of electric motors. This same method could have been used to explain the turning effect on the moving coil in a voltmeter or ammeter (Unit 12).

As drawn in Fig. 20-2, the loop would rotate only about a 1/4-turn from the position shown, until A and B were vertical. Continued lifting on A and pushing down on B are useless. In order to achieve continued rotation, the current direction in the loop must reverse at the time that the loop reaches its vertical position.

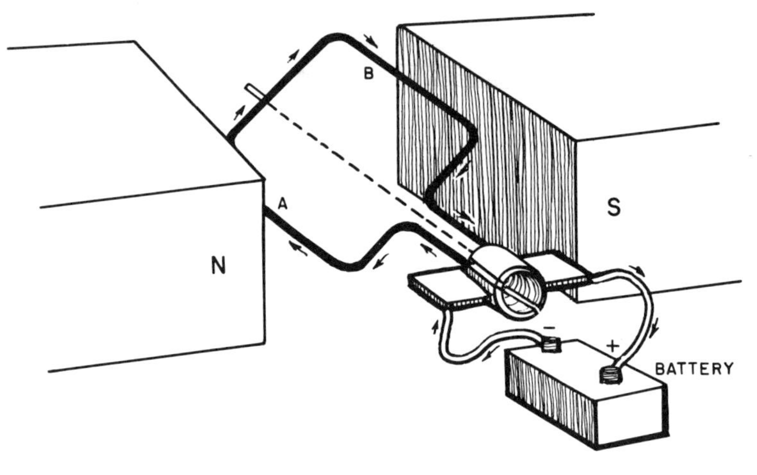

Fig. 20-6

This reversal can be accomplished, for a single coil, by a two-segment commutator, as shown in Fig. 20-6. At the instant shown, electrons flow from the negative brush through A and return through B to the positive brush. As A is lifted to the top of its rotation, the commutator segment that supplied electrons to A slides away from the negative brush and touches the positive brush. Thus the current in the loop is reversed; the momentum of the loop carries it past the vertical position; A is then pushed downward to the right, B is lifted to the left, and another half-turn of rotation continues.

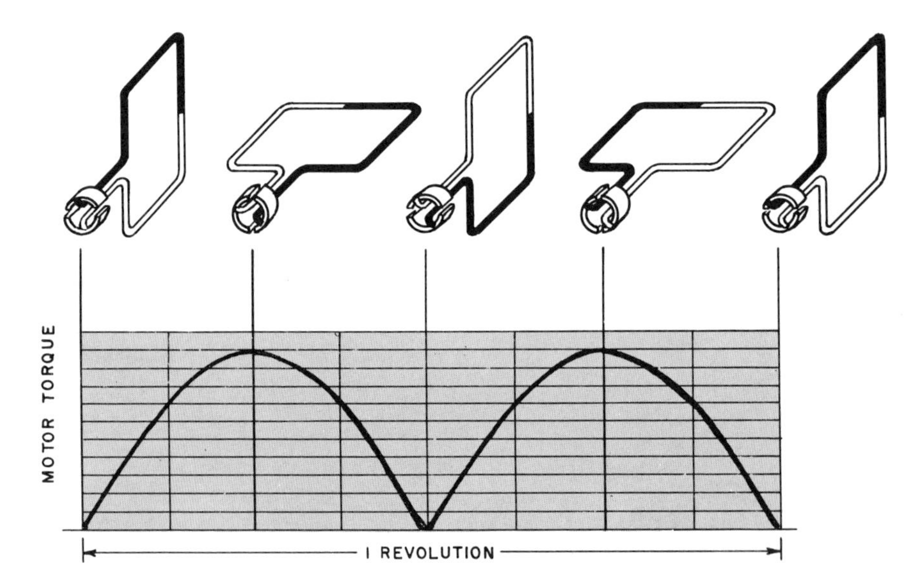

Fig. 20-7

This impractical single-coil armature has a variety of faults, one of which is the irregularity of the torque that it produces. When the loop is horizontal, the force on the wire is at its greatest; when the loop is vertical, there is no force on the wire.

A steadier torque is achieved by using the several coils of a drum-wound armature. The armature shown in Unit 18, Pages 186-190, is just as appropriate in a motor as it is in a generator.

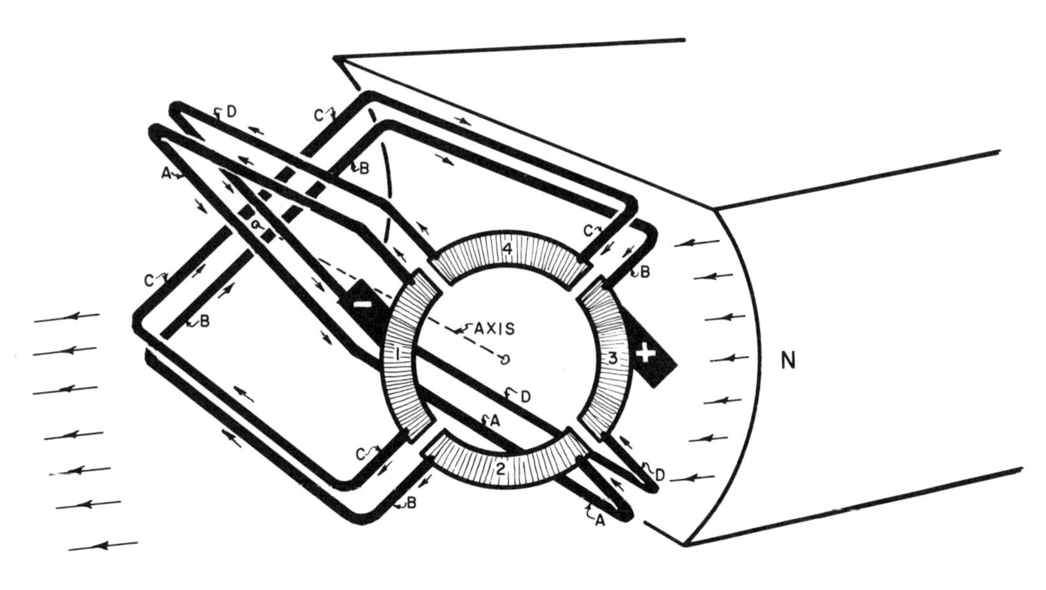

Fig. 20-8

Fig. 20-8 shows a similar but simpler drum winding. Assume that the S-pole of the field magnet is at the left; it has been omitted from the diagram in order to show the windings clearly.

Trace incoming electrons from the ⊖ brush through commutator segment number 1 through coil A to segment 2, then through B to segment 3, where the positive brush leads to the completed circuit (not shown) through a source of D.C. and back to the negative brush. From the ⊖ brush, another circuit can be traced through armature coils C and D to the positive brush. Compare this drum-winding with that shown in Fig. 18-4 to note the similarity in principle.

The circuit of Fig. 20-8 is re-drawn in more schematic fashion in Fig. 20-9. (The term "schematic diagram" means one that lays out the electrical circuit plainly, without regard to the actual appearance of the device. A photograph, or a "pictorial diagram" shows what the device looks like, without regard to showing electrical circuits.)

Two parallel circuits exist through this armature. All four coils contribute their torque to aid rotation of the armature.

In Fig. 20-8, a further rotation of 45° will bring coils B and C to a vertical position. At that instant, the negative brush will touch both segments 1 and 4; segments 2 and 3 contact the positive brush.

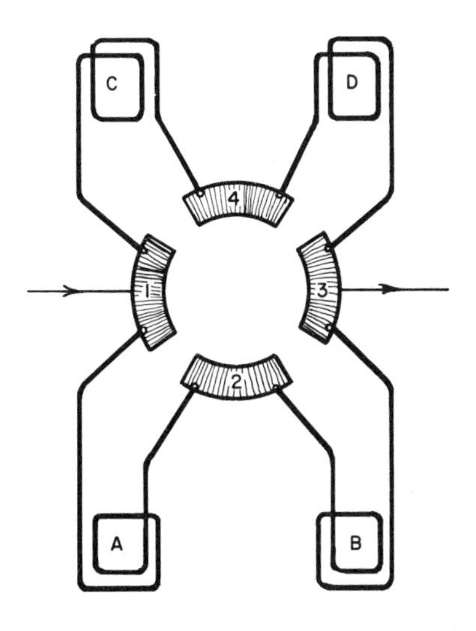

Fig. 20-9

As shown in Fig. 20-10, there is no current in coil C, because both ends of it touch the same brush. Likewise, there can be no current in coil B. This condition exists at the instant when coils B and C are in a vertical position, and, even if there were current in coils B and C, it would produce no torque. So the absence of current in the coils during this short interval is no disadvantage. At this same instant, coils A and D are in a horizontal position, where they are producing maximum torque.

In a more complicated drum winding, for example, one with twelve coils, there would be ten coils carrying current and producing torque during the short time that two of the coils were inactive, like B and C in Fig. 20-10.

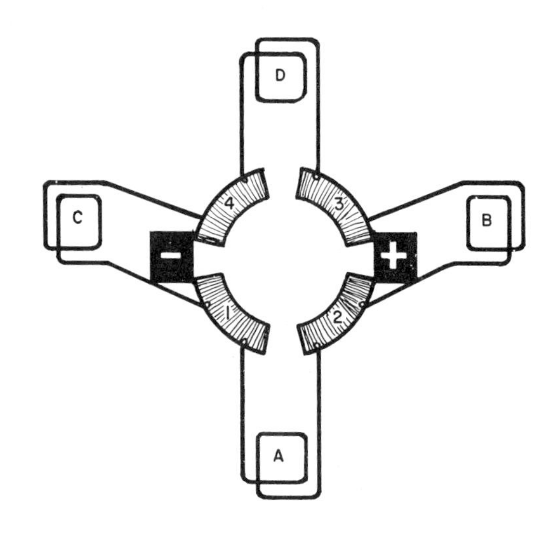

Fig. 20-10

OTHER EXAMPLES OF THE "MOTOR EFFECT"

The sidewise force on a current (Fig. 20-1), due to the interaction of an external magnetic field with the field of the current, has other applications than its use in D.C. and A.C. motors. The motion of the coil in a loudspeaker can be explained on this basis.

Since the force on the moving electrons exists whether or not the electrons are confined to a wire, the path of electrons moving in a vacuum tube can be controlled by magnetic forces.

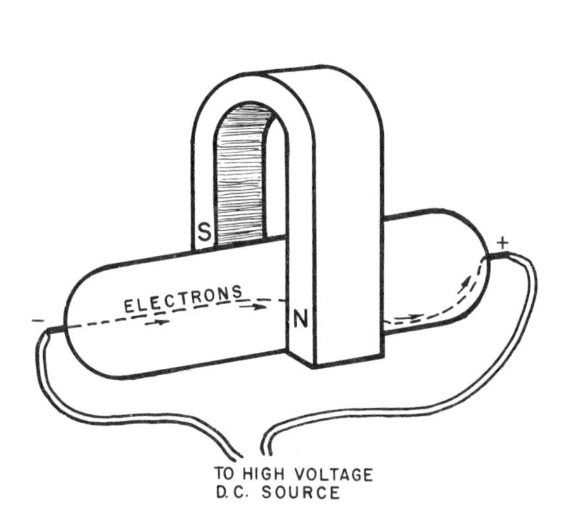

Fig. 20-11

Fig. 20-11 shows a simple type of vacuum tube, in which electrons tear loose from the end of the negative wire and tend to follow a straight path through the vacuum to the positive terminal. (The negative terminal of a tube is sometimes called the "cathode." Before electrons were known, old-timers called the mysterious beam observed in such tubes by the name "cathode-ray", since it was a ray coming from the cathode.)

The electrons themselves are invisible, but they may produce a faint glow in a trace of air left in the tube. When a magnet is brought near the tube, the electron stream is pushed up, sidewise, or down, according to the direction of the magnetic field.

The N → S horizontal field of Fig. 20-11 pushes the electron beam down; reversal of the magnet poles would push the beam upward.

The picture on the fluorescent coating on the face of a TV picture tube is caused by an electron beam, which sweeps across the screen horizontally 15,750 times per second, and vertically 60 times per second. This motion of the beam is accomplished by magnetic fields.

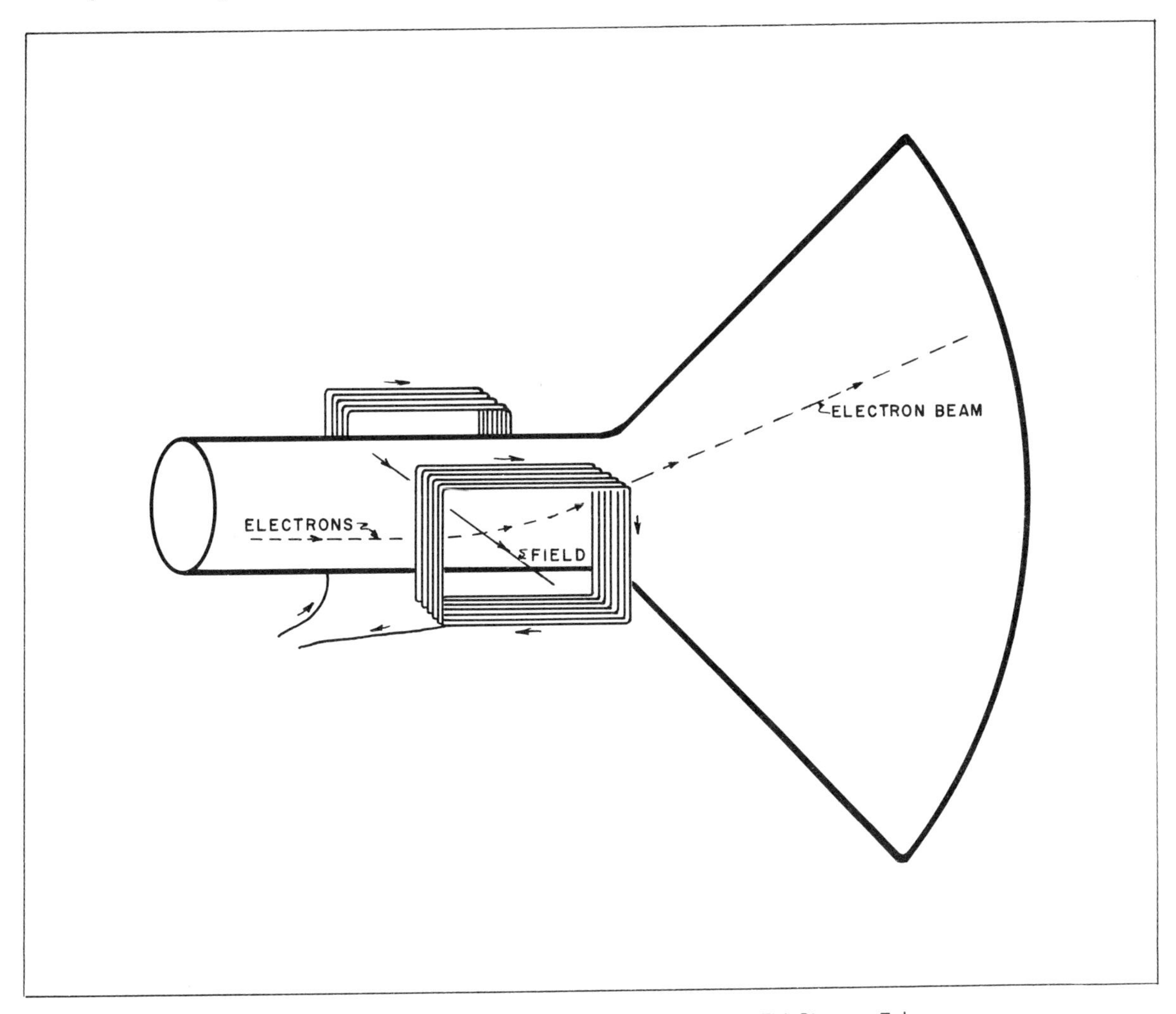

Fig. 20-12 Deflection of Electron Beam in a TV Picture Tube

Fig. 20-12 shows the "vertical deflection coils"; the current in this pair of coils controls the vertical position of the electron beam.

A similar pair of coils, one above and one below the neck of the tube, controls the horizontal movement of the electron stream.

A coil encircling the neck of the tube focuses the electron beam, again using a magnetic field to control electron movement.

Electric arcs in air are also deflected by magnetic fields. In arc welding, the sidewise push of a field tends to "blow out" the arc and produce a spattery welding job; hence some iron objects are demagnetized before welding. When a switch carrying a high current is opened, as in a circuit-breaker, an undesirable arc tends to form. By arranging a strong magnetic field at the contacts, the arc can be pushed out into a long path and thereby be extinguished.

POINTS TO REMEMBER

- Electrons moving through a magnetic field are pushed sidewise, in a direction at right angles to the field and at right angles to their original direction.

- The above fact explains the motion of armatures of D.C. and A.C. motors, and the controlled movement of electron streams in electric arcs or in vacuum tubes.

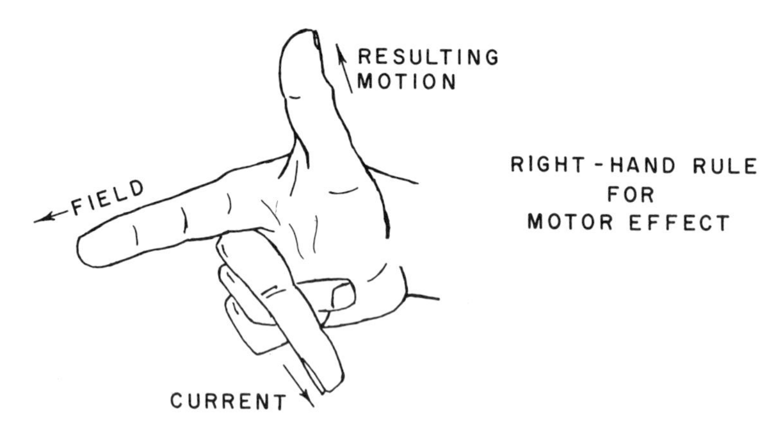

RIGHT-HAND RULE FOR MOTOR EFFECT

- The drum armature is an effective way of arranging coils to produce a continuous torque in a motor.

REVIEW QUESTIONS

1. How should magnet poles be placed so that the wire will be moved upward when the switch is closed?

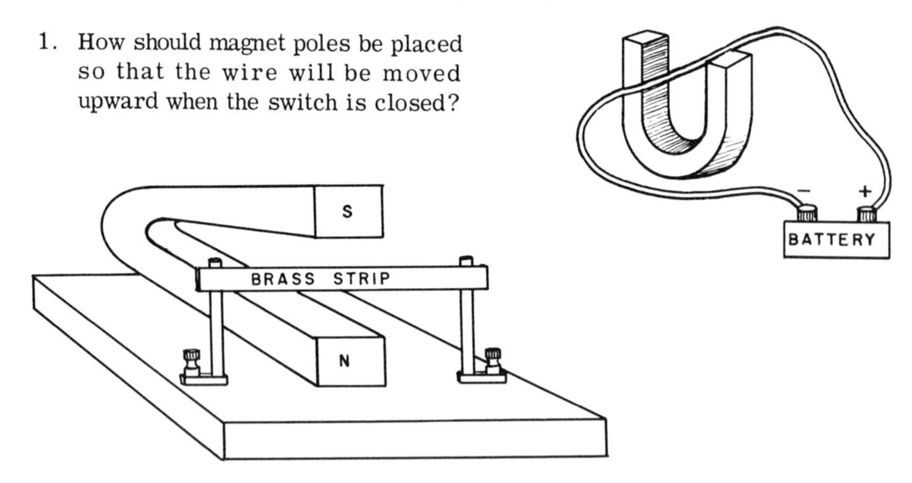

2. A brass strip is fastened to the left terminal above, and rests in loose contact with the right-hand terminal. What happens when a battery is connected to the terminals (a) so that the left one is negative? (b) reversed, with right negative?

3. What happens to the wire of question 1 if an alternating current (60 cycle) is sent through the wire?

4. Determine the direction of rotation of the armature of Fig. 20-8, Page 231.

5. a. What is torque?

   b. What factors would determine the amount of torque on a coil placed in a magnetic field?

6. a. Determine the necessary battery polarity to produce rotation as indicated.

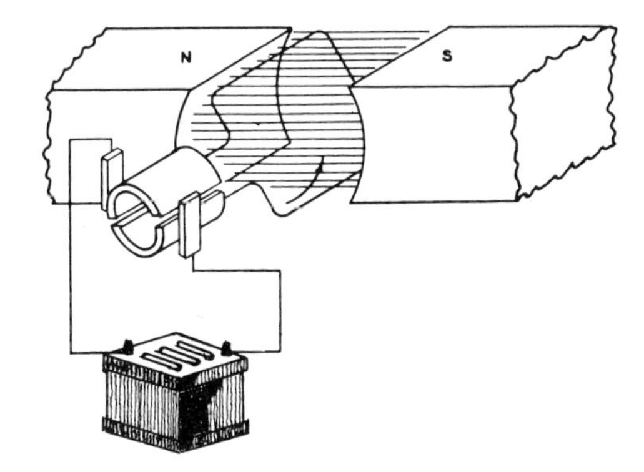

   b. Is this the same polarity as found for question 7 on Page 183?

   c. Is the current direction in the loop of wire the same in this sketch as it was on Page 183? Why or why not?

Unit 21 D.C. MOTOR CALCULATIONS

The purpose of this unit is to provide a more detailed understanding of the conversion of electrical energy to mechanical energy in the electric motor. The previously described motor-force experienced by a wire in a magnetic field can be calculated:

$$F = \frac{B \times L \times I}{11,300,000}$$

F is pounds of force on the wire

B is flux density in lines per square inch

L is the length of wire in the field

I is amperes of current

(The derivation of this formula, and the following torque formula, are given in the Appendix, Page A-4.)

The "torque" delivered by a motor is a more useful quantity than the simple force against the wires. Torque is turning effect, calculated by multiplying the applied force by the radius of the turning circle. Torque is measured in pound-feet.

The torque exerted on the armature of a motor can be found from:

$$\text{Torque (lb.-ft.)} = \frac{\phi \times Z \times I_a}{425,000,000 \times m}$$

ϕ is the flux passing through the armature

Z is the number of wires in the armature

I_a is the total armature current

m is the number of parallel paths through the armature

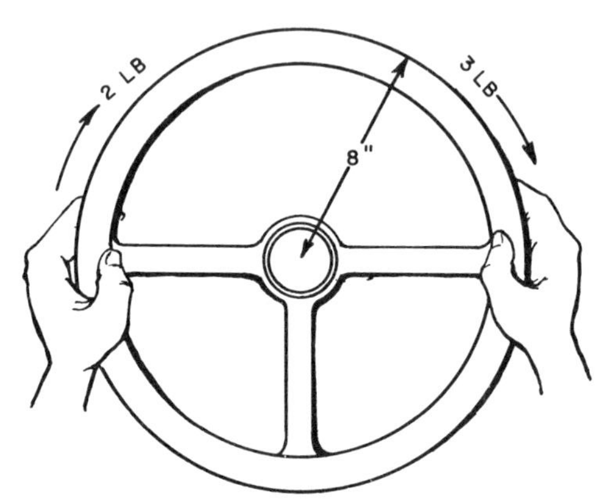

Fig. 21-1 Torque

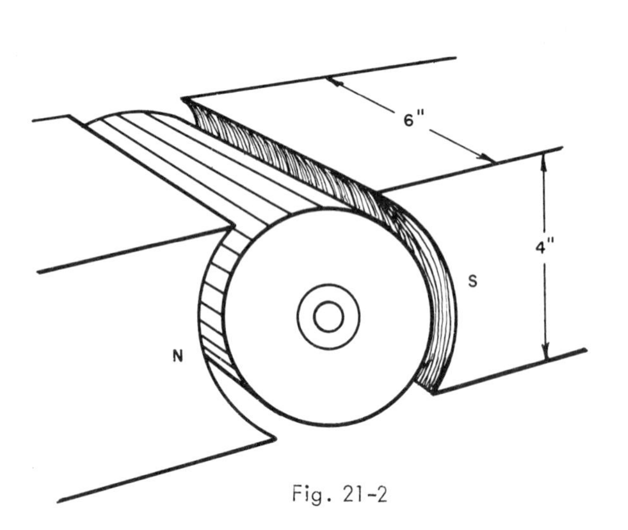

Fig. 21-2

To illustrate the use of this formula, assume an armature 6" long is placed between magnet poles as in Fig. 21-2. The armature carries 200 turns of wire; that's 400 wires for Z in the formula. B in the field magnet is 50,000 lines/sq. in., so 24 × 50,000 = 1,200,000 lines leaving the N-pole and passing through the armature. The total armature current is 10 amps, which passes through two parallel paths in the armature, as in Fig. 20-9.

$$\text{Torque} = \frac{1,200,000 \times 400 \times 10}{425,000,000 \times 2} = 5.65 \text{ lb.-ft.}$$

Horsepower Output

The preceding calculation of torque does not in itself tell the power of the motor; speed must be taken into account also. One horsepower is defined as a rate of doing work equal to 33,000 foot-pounds per minute, (Unit 8). From this definition, h.p. can also be calculated from torque and r.p.m., (true for all machines, not limited to electric motors.)

$$\text{h.p.} = \frac{2\pi \times \text{torque} \times \text{r.p.m.}}{33{,}000}$$

The above formula may be rewritten: $\text{h.p.} = .00019 \times \text{torque} \times \text{r.p.m.}$

or

$$\text{torque} = \frac{\text{h.p.}}{.00019 \times \text{r.p.m.}}$$

Assuming that the armature developing 5.65 lb.-ft. of torque in the previous example is operating at 1250 r.p.m., we can find h.p.:

$$\text{h.p.} = \frac{2 \times 3.14 \times 5.65 \times 1250}{33{,}000} = 1.34 \text{ h.p.}$$

Incidental to this discussion of power, 746 watts = 1 h.p., and 1.34 h.p. = 1000 watts. We had assumed that this armature has a current of 10 amps, so, if it were 100% efficient, a power input of 100 volts × 10 amps = 1000 watts would produce the 1.34 h.p.

Experimentally, the torque of a motor is measured directly by a device called a Prony brake. Tightening the bolts makes the brake tend to turn along with the motor pulley. The brake arm is restrained by the stationary spring scale, so a torque load is placed on the motor. The torque is the product of the net force on the scale times the effective length (L) of the torque arm in feet.

$$T = F \times L \text{ (lb.-ft.)}$$

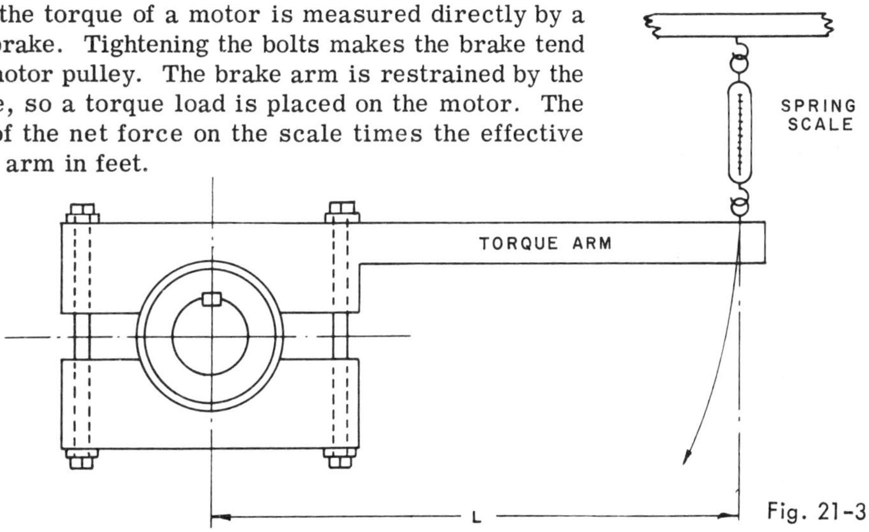

Fig. 21-3

Speed of the motor can be found by the use of a revolutions-counter and stopwatch, or a tachometer, or a calibrated stroboscopic light. Thus the true mechanical horsepower output (or "brake horsepower") can be determined from measurements of torque and speed.

If the horsepower output is known originally, from electrical data, torque can readily be calculated for any known value of r.p.m. by using

$$T = \frac{\text{h.p.}}{.00019 \times \text{r.p.m.}}$$

E.M.F. Generated in a Motor

It's time we noted that whenever an electric motor is running, its wires are cutting lines of force; therefore, an e.m.f. is generated in the armature. Using numbers from the previous example, we can calculate that e.m.f., using the generator formula, (Unit 18):

$$\text{e.m.f.} = \frac{\text{turns} \times 4 \times \text{flux} \times \text{r.p.m.}}{\text{paths} \times 60 \times 100{,}000{,}000} = \frac{200 \times 4 \times 1{,}200{,}000 \times 1250}{2 \times 60 \times 100{,}000{,}000} = 100 \text{ volts}$$

This generated 100 volts is necessarily in a direction opposite to the direction of the current through the armature of the motor. This conclusion can be reached in either of two ways:

(1) With the help of the 3-finger rules for motor and generator, it can be seen that the motion caused by current in a wire will cause an e.m.f. that opposes the current.

(2) If the generated voltage were in the same direction as the current, we wouldn't need the Power Corporation; we'd just give the armature a spin, short-circuit the brushes, and let the motor run itself. Things don't work that way.

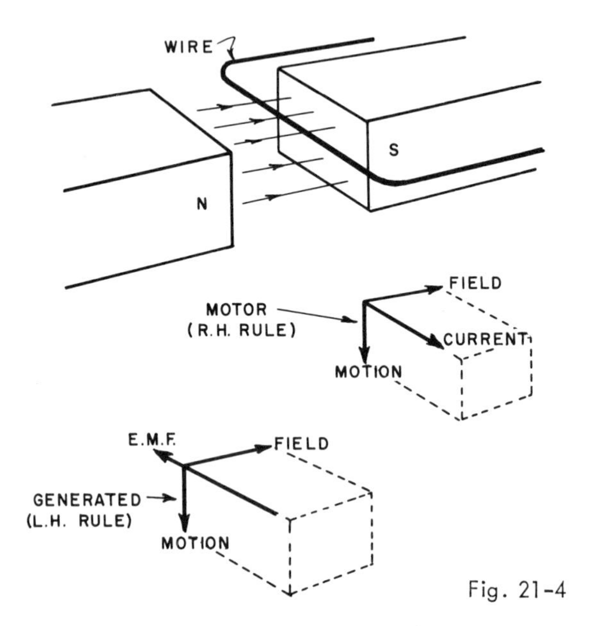

Fig. 21-4

Importance of Generated E.M.F. in a Motor

It is sometimes difficult for a beginner to realize the value of this e.m.f. that a motor generates. The generated e.m.f. is a measure of the useful mechanical energy obtained from the electrons passing through the armature.

Sometimes this e.m.f. is called "Back e.m.f.", which emphasizes the fact that it opposes the voltage applied to the motor. But this is a useful sort of opposition. The generated "Back e.m.f." hinders the movement of the incoming electrons in the same way that the weight of a sack of groceries opposes the efforts of a boy carrying the sack up a flight of stairs. If there were no opposition, no useful work would be done. If the boy left the groceries on the sidewalk, he could run upstairs a lot faster, but that doesn't get the groceries delivered. An electric heater-element generates no Back e.m.f.; therefore the electrons may run through it rapidly, but they produce no mechanical work.

It is easy to make an adjustment on an electric motor so that it will generate no Back e.m.f.: merely bolt down the armature so that it cannot turn. Then electrons can run through the motor much easier and faster; and the motor has been converted into an electric stove.

Returning to the numerical example used previously, we have an armature rotating at 1250 r.p.m., generating 100 volts, and taking a current of 10 amps from the power line. Assume that the armature wiring has 2-ohms resistance, and now find out the total (line) voltage needed to operate the motor.

The power line has two jobs to do: (1) it must supply 100 volts which is converted to mechanical energy, and (2) it must supply enough additional voltage to force the 10-amp current through the 2-ohm wire resistance. It takes 20 volts to put 10 amps through 2 ohms, so the line voltage must be 100 + 20 = 120 volts.

Total voltage applied to the armature	=	"Back e.m.f." generated in the armature	+	Voltage (IR) used to overcome wire resistance

Carrying this calculation one step further: If we multiply the total applied voltage (120 volts in the example) by the current (10 amps), we find the total power input, 1200 watts.

Multiplying the generated e.m.f. (100 volts) by the 10 amps, we get 1000 watts, which is the useful mechanical power output. Note that this same figure has already been found once before — from the 1.34 h.p. output that was found from torque and r.p.m.

The power input is 1200 watts; the output is 1000 watts. Where does the other 200 watts go? By multiplying the 20 volts used on resistance by the 10 amps, we get 200 watts. This represents the rate at which energy is converted into heat in the armature. 200 watts is the rate of heat production.

Total input power (Applied volts × amps)	=	Useful mechanical power output (Back e.m.f. × amps)	+	Heating rate (IR × amps)

Observe that, in the preceding discussion, we have not said that the Back e.m.f. produces the useful mechanical energy, but we have said that the useful power produced can be calculated from the Back e.m.f. and the current. This is just like saying that the useful power (working rate) accomplished by the grocery boy can be calculated from the weight of the sack and the speed that he lifts it. The weight is not doing the work, but the greater the weight, the more work is done by the boy.

One more sample calculation: Given a 5-ohm armature that takes 6 amps on a 115-volt line when operating at its normal rating, find (a) Back e.m.f. generated, (b) power input, (c) useful power output, (d) heating rate, (e) efficiency, (f) current and heating rate if the motor is stalled.

(a) 6 amp × 5 ohm = 30 v. used on resistance
115 - 30 = 85 volts Back e.m.f.

(b) Power input = 115 × 6 = 690 watts

(c) Power output = 85 × 6 = 510 watts

$$\frac{510 \text{ watts}}{746 \text{ w/h.p.}} = .68 \text{ h.p.}$$

(d) Heating rate = 30 v. × 6 amp = 180 watts

(e) Efficiency $= \frac{\text{power out}}{\text{power in}} = \frac{510}{690} = 0.74 = 74\%$

(This is the "armature efficiency", not the overall efficiency of the entire motor. The armature efficiency can also be found from Back e.m.f. ÷ line volts = 85 ÷ 115 = 0.74)

(f) If motor stalls, current becomes
115 v. ÷ 5 ohms = 23 amps

(Power input becomes 115 × 23 = 2645 watts, all of which is the heating rate.)

ARMATURE WINDINGS

As pointed out in Unit 18, two main types of drum-armature winding are in use: the lap winding and the wave winding. In Fig. 21-5 (as in Fig. 18-5) the innermost circle of numbered rectangles represents an end view of commutator bars. The next circle of twelve distorted rectangles represents sections of the face of the armature (Fig. 21-6).

Outside of the rectangles representing the cylindrical armature face are lines showing the coil connections at the back of the armature, which information would not be visible when drawn in a diagram such as Fig. 21-6. The "field poles" in Fig. 21-5 represent a four-pole field in which this armature is to rotate; Fig. 21-6 gives a simplified view of the actual appearance of the field structure.

Fig. 21-5 Lap Winding

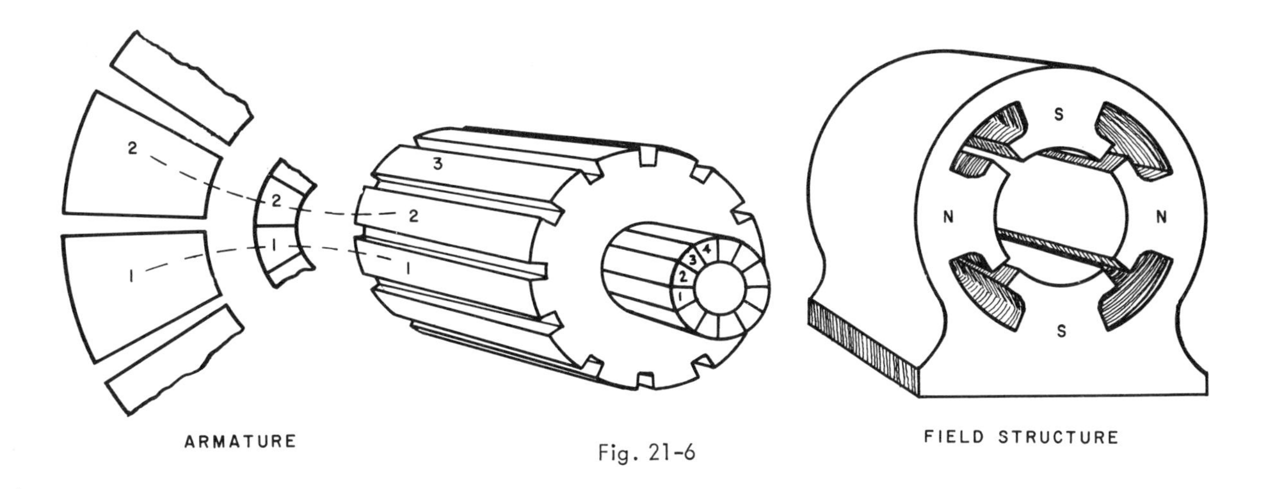

Fig. 21-6

The Lap Winding

A few minutes spent in tracing out the wiring in Fig. 21-5 will make the pattern seem less complicated for the 12 coils on this armature are all alike. Starting from a negative brush, say the one touching bar #1 (brushes are shown inside rather than in their actual outside position), electrons flowing from the D.C. supply line to bar #1 can escape into the winding by either of two paths.

Let's follow the heavy-shaded wire through slot No. 1, and back through slot No. 4. The main feature of the lap winding is that the finish end of this coil, coming through slot No. 4, is connected to the commutator bar (#2) next to the one from which we started (#1). From bar #2 the current path is through slot No. 2, back by slot No. 5 to bar #3, then out slot No. 3 and back by slot No. 6 to bar #4, which is in contact with a positive brush that completes the circuit to the D.C. power source. Returning again to bar #1, another path can be traced through slots Nos. 3, 12, 2, 11, 1, and 10, back to the other positive brush.

Note that under both N-poles, the current is away from the commutator; under both S-poles, the current is toward the commutator. With the help of Fig. 21-6 and the 3-finger right-hand rule, one may determine the direction of rotation of the armature.

Fig. 21-7 is another schematic view of the circuits through this 4-pole armature. Each numbered rectangle corresponds to a numbered commutator bar of Fig. 21-5. The purpose of this sketch is to show that there are four parallel paths through this armature.

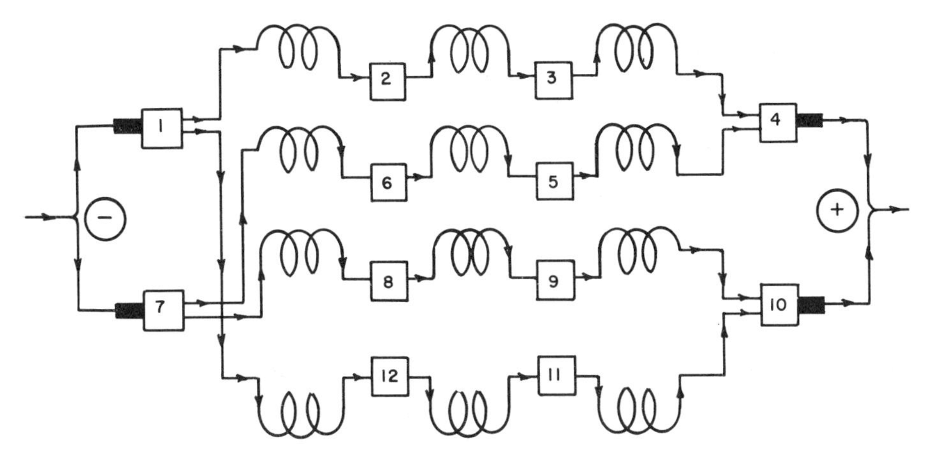

Fig. 21-7

There are so many variations in armature windings that the subject can merely be introduced in these few pages; for the whole story one should consult a text dealing only with armatures.

In general, lap windings require

(1) as many brushes as there are poles.

(2) as many parallel paths through the armature as there are poles.

The Wave Winding

Fig. 21-8 shows another pattern, called the wave winding. Comparing it with the lap winding, one may notice that the wave winding also accomplishes a similar control of current direction in the wires under each field pole, so that rotation is produced. (One need not be concerned because the wires in slot No. 7, Fig. 21-8, carry currents in opposite directions, which are therefore of no effect. At the instant shown, slot No. 7 is between field poles, so there would be no force on those wires anyway.)

Seeking differences between this winding and the previous lap winding, one may note first, observing the heavy-shaded wire that starts from bar #1, that the ends of the coil are spread apart, connecting to widely-separated bars, rather than to adjacent bars.

Secondly, eleven bars and slots are used, rather than twelve, because a 4-pole wave winding will not fit on a 12-bar, 12-slot armature. The reason for this, as well as the reasons for locating the commutator connections, is involved in some arithmetic that will not be discussed here.

The winding should be traced out (or better, re-drawn, starting with a sketch that does not show the wiring) starting at bar #1, through slot No. 1, over to slot No. 4 to bar #6, out slot No. 6 to slot No. 9 to bar #11, and so on around the armature until bar #4 is finally reached. Also, from bar #1, there is another path, out slot No. 10, in slot No. 7, and so forth, again finally arriving at bar #4.

Fig. 21-9 shows, in schematic fashion, that there are only two parallel paths through this armature. (The numbered rectangles correspond to the commutator bars in Fig. 21-8.)

Wave windings require

(1) only two brushes, but they may have as many brushes as poles.

(2) only two parallel paths through the armature in one complete wave winding, regardless of number of brushes.

Comparing uses of the two windings, lap windings are good for high-current, low-voltage motors, since they have more parallel paths for the current. High-voltage low-current machines (motors or generators) can better employ a wave winding.

21-8 Wave Winding

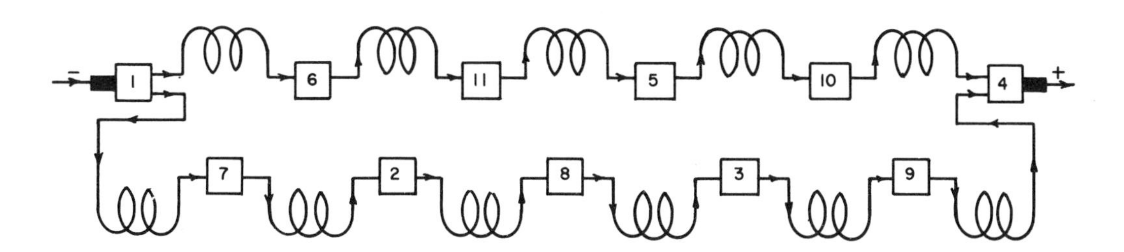

Fig. 21-9

Up to this point, we could have assumed that the armature rotates in the field of a permanent magnet. Permanent magnet-fields are actually of limited use only in a few small motors; the great majority of useful motors use electromagnets for the field structure.

As in generators, the field magnet coils may be either in series or in parallel, or two sets of windings (one in series, one in parallel with the armature) may be used, making a compound-wound motor.

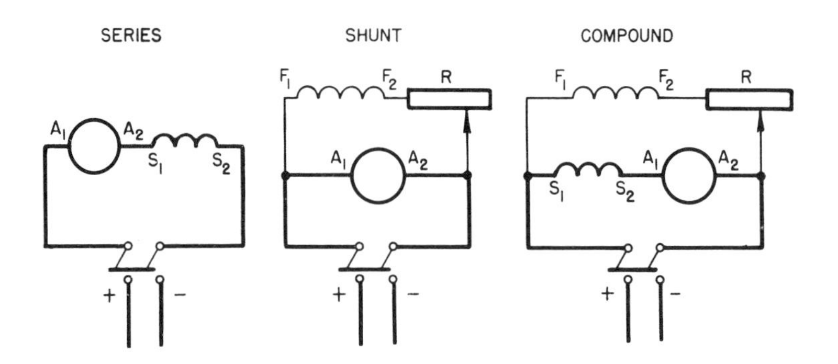

Fig. 21-10 Motor Field Connections

The behavior of these magnetic-field windings and their effect on motor performance is the subject of the next Unit.

Field Distortion

Much as in generators, (see Pages 193,194), the current in the armature of a motor produces a magnetic field of its own, which is in a direction at 90° to the main magnetic field in which the armature rotates. To counteract this warping of the magnetic field, large D.C. motors are often built with interpoles, (or "commutating poles") the windings of which are in series with the armature. These interpoles produce a field that counteracts the armature field. Without interpoles, decreased efficiency and excessive sparking at the commutator would result, when the motor is operated under conditions requiring high armature current. In the motor shown in Fig. 21-11, the four large poles are the main field poles, the four small ones are the interpoles.

Fig. 21-11 Shunt Motor Field with Interpoles

In a motor, the interpoles must have the same polarity as the main poles directly back of them (back, in the sense of direction of rotation of the armature). Note that this is just the reverse of the situation in a generator.

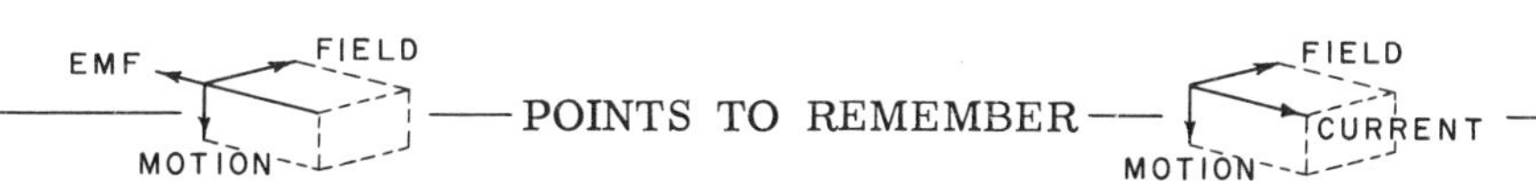

POINTS TO REMEMBER

- Torque means turning effect. It is calculated as force × radius and is measured in pound-feet.

- Torque of a motor depends on flux, number of wires, and current according to the formula:

$$\text{torque} = \frac{\phi \times Z \times I_a}{425{,}000{,}000 \times m}$$

- One horsepower is defined as a rate of working. It equals 33,000 ft.-lb./min.

$$\text{h.p.} = \frac{2\pi \times \text{torque} \times \text{r.p.m.}}{33{,}000}$$

- The total voltage applied to the armature of a motor does two things:
  1. Part of it (= IR) produces heat by causing current through resistance.
  2. The other part (equal to the generated e.m.f.) runs the motor, producing mechanical energy.

- Applied voltage = e.m.f. + IR

- Power input = useful power output + I^2R heating rate.

REVIEW QUESTIONS

1. Calculate the torque produced on a lap-wound armature of 300 wires. Total armature current is 40 amps, flux is 2,125,000 lines.

2. This torque (Question 1) produces how much force at the rim of a four-inch diameter pulley?

3. The armature of Question 1 rotates at 990 r.p.m. Calculate h.p.

4. Calculate e.m.f. generated in 300 wires (150 turns) rotating at 990 r.p.m. through 2,125,000 lines, if there are two parallel paths through the armature.

5. An armature, resistance 0.47 ohms, is supplied with 124 volts D.C. and 40 amperes. Calculate.

   a. volts used to overcome resistance of armature
   b. volts used to make mechanical energy (= back e.m.f.)
   c. h.p. output
   d. efficiency
   e. watts heating rate

6. If the above armature stalled due to overload, calculate current in armature.

7. Determine the direction of rotation of the armatures shown in Figs. 21-5 and 21-8.

8. What is the polarity of interpoles in reference to main field poles in a direct current motor?

9. Complete the external and internal connections for the shunt motor illustrated in Fig. 21-12 for counterclockwise rotation. The interpole field windings are to be a part of the armature circuit which terminates at the connection points marked A1 and A2. Be sure to have the proper connections for the interpole field windings and the main field windings so that their polarities will be correct for counterclockwise rotation.

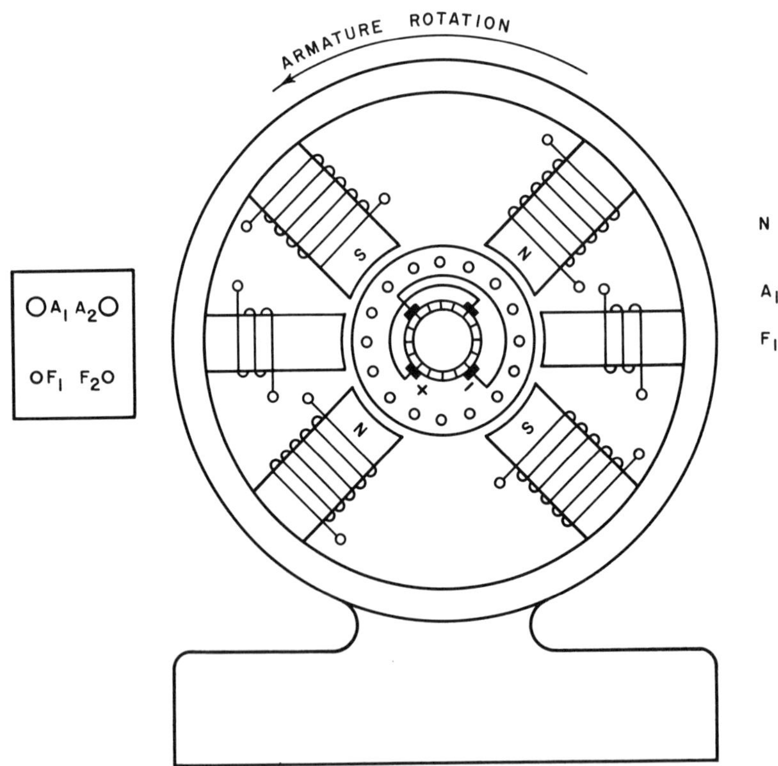

Fig. 21-12

SHUNT MOTOR WITH INTERPOLES

N OR S INDICATE MAIN POLE POLARITY

A_1 - A_2 ARMATURE TERMINALS

F_1 - F_2 SHUNT FIELD

Unit 22 D.C. SHUNT AND SERIES MOTORS

The speed and torque of a motor depend not only on the current in the armature, but also on the strength of the magnetic field in which the armature rotates. A shunt field coil, connected across the D.C. line that feeds the armature, maintains a practically constant magnetic field. A series field coil carries the same current as the armature, a current that varies as the load on the motor changes. It is the purpose of this unit to find how certain useful self-regulating characteristics can be achieved in a motor by the use of a shunt field, a series field, or a combination of both. In addition to the motor's own self-regulating features, further control of speed and torque can be obtained by external control of current in the field and armature.

For convenience in the discussion that follows, two long formulas from the previous unit will be abbreviated:

$$\text{Torque} = a \times \phi \times I_a$$

Formula 22-1

As before, ϕ is flux through the armature. I_a is the current in the armature and 'a' combines the quantities of the previous formula, $\frac{Z}{425{,}000{,}000\,m}$

$$\text{e.m.f.} = b \times \phi \times \text{r.p.m.}$$

Formula 22-2

'a' is a fixed number for a given armature, once it is assembled in the motor.

'b' is, for a given armature, a constant term that combines the quantities previously expressed as: $\frac{\text{turns} \times 4}{\text{paths} \times 60 \times 10^8}$

THE SHUNT MOTOR

As long as the line voltage is constant, the unchanging field-coil current maintains a steady magnetic field, regardless of variations in armature current.

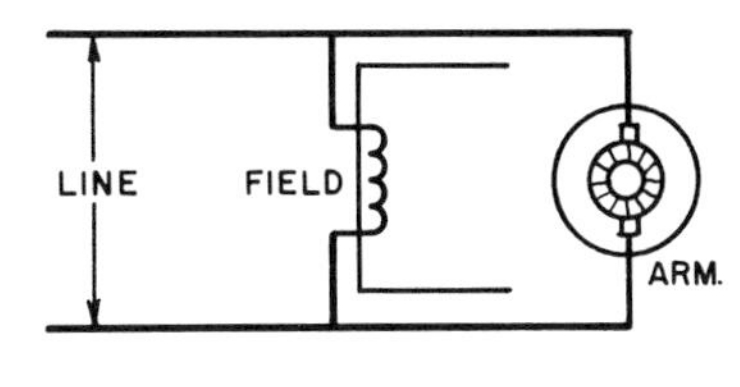

Fig. 22-3

To see just how such a motor will behave under changing load conditions, let's get some exact information by using a numerical example:

Assume $\phi = 2{,}000{,}000$; $a = 6 \times 10^{-7}$; $b = 8.5 \times 10^{-8}$; line volts = 220; armature resistance = 4 ohms.

Using Formula 22-1 —

$$\text{Torque} = a \times \phi \times I_a$$
$$\text{Torque} = 6 \times 10^{-7} \times 2{,}000{,}000 \times I_a$$
$$\text{Torque} = 1.2 \times I_a$$

From Formula 22-2 —

$$\text{e.m.f.} = b \times \phi \times \text{r.p.m.}$$
$$\text{e.m.f.} = 8.5 \times 10^{-8} \times 2{,}000{,}000 \times \text{r.p.m.}$$
$$\text{e.m.f.} = 0.17 \times \text{r.p.m.}$$

From these results, and the use of the idea that line volts = e.m.f. + I_aR, the current and r.p.m. of the motor can be calculated for several torque loads.

For example, we give this motor work to do that requires that the motor exert a torque of 4.8 lb.-ft. Since torque = 1.2 × I_a for this particular motor, an armature current of 4 amps will be required to produce the 4.8 lb.-ft. of torque.

IR for the armature is 4 amp × 4 ohm = 16 volts.

220 (line) - 16 = 204 volts for e.m.f.

Inserting 204 volts into "e.m.f. = 0.17 × r.p.m."

$$204 = 0.17 \times \text{r.p.m.}$$

$$\text{r.p.m.} = 1200$$

Torque	I_a	$I_a R_a$	E.M.F.	R.P.M.	Armature			Overall	
					Input (watts)	Output (watts)	Efficiency	Input (watts)	Efficiency
0	0	0	220	1294	0	0	--	110	0
1.2	1	4	216	1270	220	216	.98	330	.65
2.4	2	8	212	1247	440	424	.96	550	.77
3.6	3	12	208	1223	660	624	.945	770	.81
4.8	4	16	204	1200	880	816	.93	990	.824
6.0	5	20	200	1176	1100	1000	.91	1210	.825
7.2	6	24	196	1153	1320	1176	.89	1430	.822
8.4	7	28	192	1129	1540	1344	.87	1650	.815
9.6	8	32	188	1106	1760	1504	.855	1870	.805
10.8	9	36	184	1082	1980	1656	.84	2090	.79
12.0	10	40	180	1059	2200	1800	.82	2310	.78
13.2	11	44	176	1035	2420	1936	.80	2530	.765
14.4	12	48	172	1012	2640	2064	.78	2750	.75
15.6	13	52	168	988	2860	2184	.765	2970	.735
16.8	14	56	164	965	3080	2296	.745	3190	.72
18.0	15	60	160	941	3300	2400	.73	3410	.70
33.0	27.5	110	110	647	6050	3025	.50	6160	.49

The results of a series of such calculations are tabulated on the preceding page. Sets of values for torque, armature current, IR in armature, e.m.f. and r.p.m. were calculated as in the sample given. Power input for the armature is 220 volts × the armature current. Power output for the armature is e.m.f. × the armature current.

In order to obtain illustrative figures for the total power input to the whole shunt motor, the field coil is assumed to require 0.5 amps from the 220 volt line. This 110 watts is added to the armature input to get total power input.

The armature efficiency is: $\frac{\text{e.m.f.}}{\text{line volts}}$ or $\frac{\text{power output of armature}}{\text{power input to armature}}$

The overall efficiency of the entire motor is: $\frac{\text{power output of armature}}{\text{total power input to motor}}$

Note from the table that, at the 4.8 lb.-ft. torque used in the example given, the motor runs at 1200 r.p.m., produces 816 watts of mechanical power, and uses 64 watts (880-816) in heating the armature.

Suppose now that the load on the motor is suddenly increased, putting a torque drag of 12 lb.-ft. on the motor pulley, tending to slow the motor. The motor must either develop 12 lb.-ft. of torque, or stall.

> As the shunt motor slows a little, the reduced r.p.m. results in a reduced e.m.f., which permits more current through the armature.
>
> By slowing down to 1059 r.p.m. (see table) only 180 volts e.m.f. is generated, armature current becomes 10 amps, which produces 12 lb.-ft. of torque.
>
> Although the power output of the motor has increased, this is not an advantageous load for this motor.
>
> Efficiency has dropped to 78%, and the 400 watts (2200 - 1800) heating rate in the armature may raise the armature temperature beyond a safe limit.

One more change: Assume that while operating at 12 lb.-ft. torque, the belt breaks, reducing the load on the motor to zero.

> 10 amps in the armature is still producing 12 lb.-ft. of torque, which now accelerates the motor armature.
>
> If the r.p.m. gets to 1294, 220 volts e.m.f. is generated, so the armature current becomes zero and no torque is produced, so the motor accelerates no further.

Of course, this assumes a friction-free motor. Actually the armature must produce a small torque to overcome friction, so that the actual top speed for the motor may be 1290 instead of 1294.

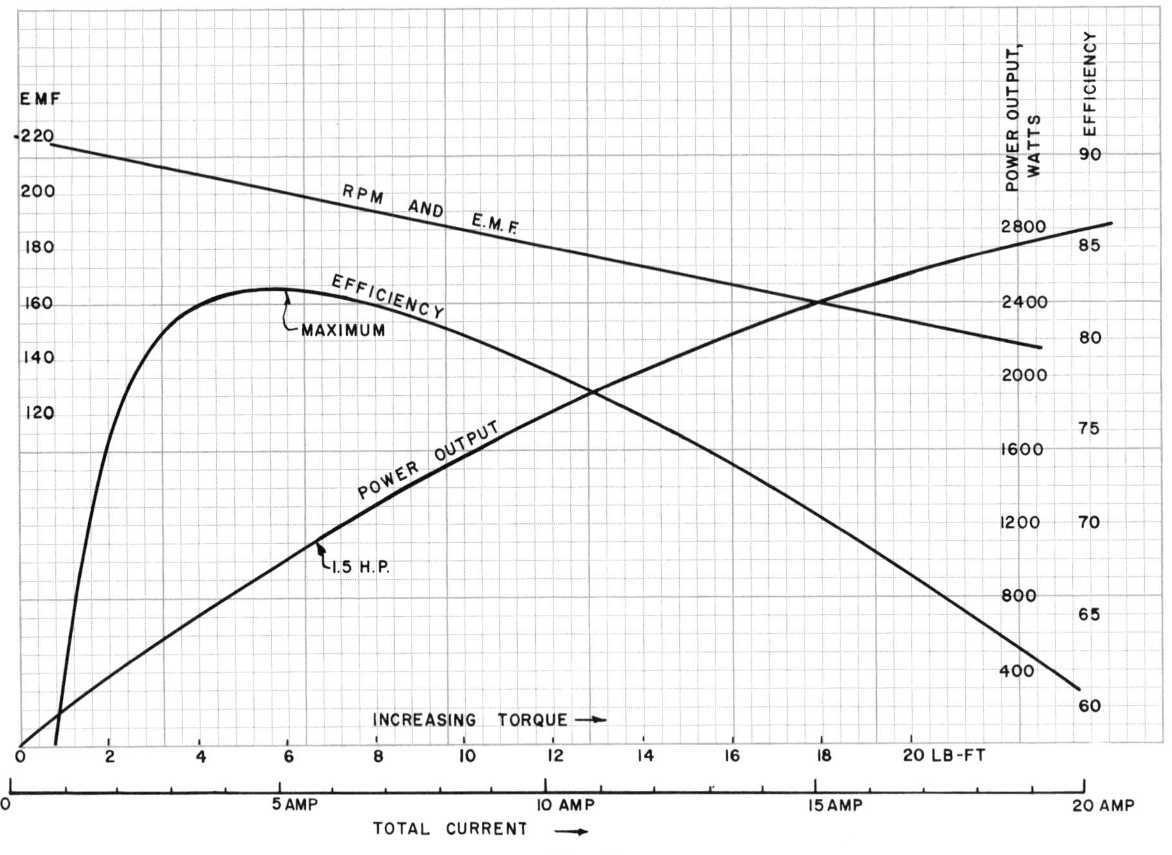

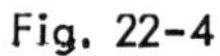
Fig. 22-4

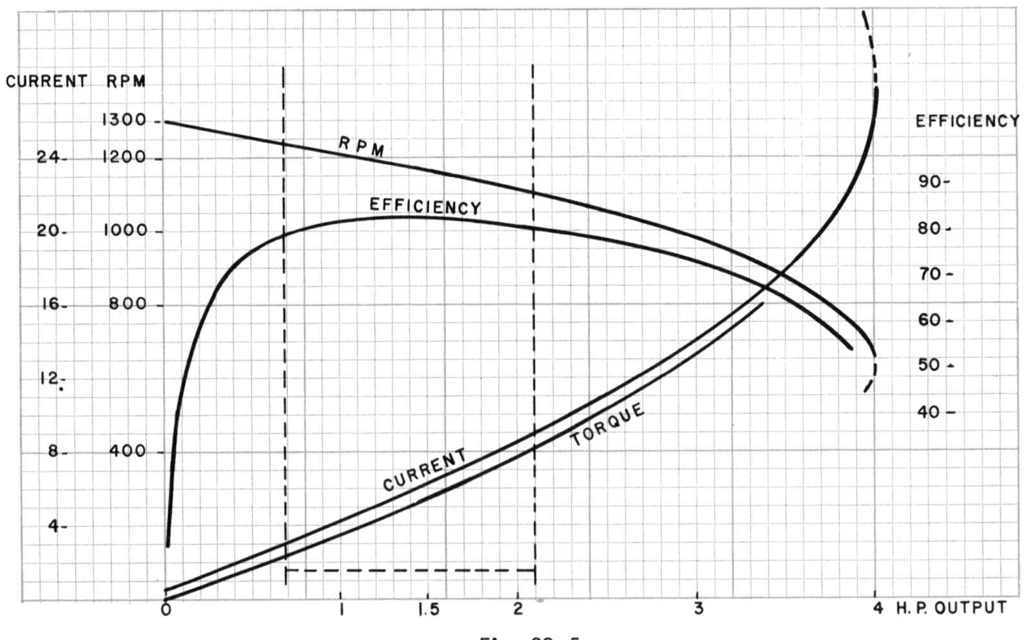

Fig. 22-5

Fig. 22-4 summarizes information from the table on Page 248, showing how r.p.m., efficiency, and power output change as the torque-load (and current) is increased. The scale for efficiency is chosen to emphasize the efficiency change.

Normally the rated load for the motor is the h.p. output at peak efficiency; for example, a 10 h.p. motor would be designed to have its maximum efficiency at 10 h.p. output. The overall electrical efficiency is greatest when I^2R in the armature = I^2R for the field.

Fig. 22-5 summarizes the tabulated information in a different form, relating the changes in r.p.m., efficiency, and current to the h.p. output. Some portions of this graph may be more of theoretical interest than of practical interest, for the graph covers a far wider range than that in which a 1.5 h.p. motor would be sensibly operated.

Below 3/4 h.p., the efficiency is low, but no harm is done. Above 2 h.p., current increases rapidly, increasing the heat production in the armature. The maximum possible power output for this particular motor is about 4 h.p., at 50% efficiency. At still lower efficiency, current increases still further, and h.p. output is reduced. Anyone planning on operating this motor at such overloads should also plan on replacing the motor with a new one every few minutes.

Speed Regulation

The speed of this motor does not change excessively with change in load over a reasonable range; therefore, the shunt motor is sometimes called a constant-speed motor, in comparison with the series motor to be described later. This self-regulating effect, called "speed regulation", is a characteristic of the motor itself. The speed regulation is expressed numerically by defining regulation as equal to:

$$\frac{\text{No-load speed minus full-load speed}}{\text{Full-load speed}}$$

For example, if full-load speed for the above motor is 1170 r.p.m.,

$$\text{Regulation} = \frac{1294 - 1170}{1170} = .106 = 10.6\%$$

The lower the armature resistance, the better the speed regulation of the shunt motor.

From formula 22-2, it may be noted that speed is proportional to counter e.m.f., when field flux is constant.

Calling the speed at no load = S_1, and full load speed = S_2,

$$b \times \phi \times S_1 = \text{e.m.f. at no load}$$

$$b \times \phi \times S_2 = \text{e.m.f. at full load}$$

Dividing the above two equations, with b and ϕ constant, they cancel, leaving

$$\frac{S_1}{S_2} = \frac{\text{e.m.f.}_1}{\text{e.m.f.}_2}$$

in which e.m.f._1 means e.m.f. at no load,
e.m.f._2 means e.m.f. at full load

SPEED CONTROL OF SHUNT MOTORS

Control implies adjustment of the speed by external adjustment of the armature current, or field current, or both.

Field Control

Using the same motor data from the previous examples, let's find out what happens to the speed of the motor when the magnetic field is weakened by inserting resistance into the field circuit. The result may not turn out as one first expects.

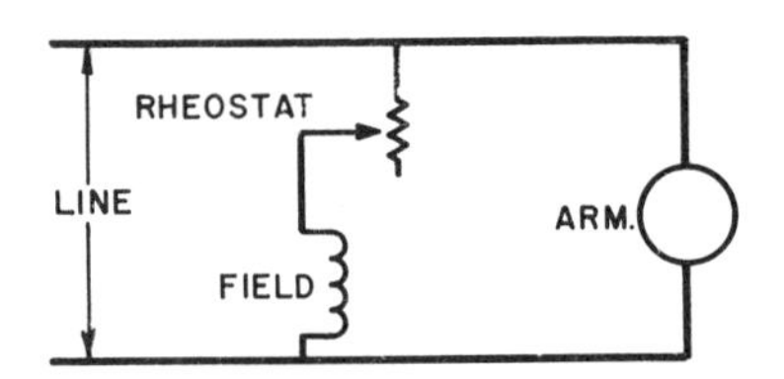

Assume the motor has been operating steadily at 1176 r.p.m., taking 5 amps and producing 6 lb.-ft. torque, (see table Page 248). Suddenly the field current is reduced from 0.5 amp to 0.4 amp, which reduces the flux from 2,000,000 lines to 1,600,000 lines.

When rotating at 1176 r.p.m., the armature was originally cutting 2,000,000 lines and generating 200 volts. Since e.m.f. is proportional to flux cut, if speed remains at 1176 for a moment after flux is reduced, the cutting of 1,600,000 lines will generate only 160 volts.

If only 160 volts is generated, that leaves 60 volts (220 line volts - 160 volts) which pours 15 amps through the 4-ohm armature. (Volts = IR, $60 = 4 \times 15$) This change in current, along with the changed flux, will affect the torque.

$$\text{Torque} = a \times \phi \times I_a$$

$$= 6 \times 10^{-7} \times 1{,}600{,}000 \times 15$$

$$= 14.4 \text{ lb.-ft.}$$

This new torque, 14.4, is a lot more than is needed to manage the 6 lb.-ft. load, so the armature will accelerate. Increased speed increases the generated e.m.f., which in turn reduces the current input. With reduced field, the motor picks up speed until the suddenly-larger current is reduced to a value just enough to maintain the 6 lb.-ft. torque load.

Using the torque formula again, with $\phi = 1{,}600{,}000$, we can find that a current of 6.25 amp will produce the 6 lb.-ft. of torque.

IR in the armature becomes $6.25 \times 4 = 25$ volts.

The generated e.m.f. is $220 - 25 = 195$ when the armature arrives at its new steady speed.

This new r.p.m. can be found from:

$$\text{e.m.f.} = b \times \phi \times \text{r.p.m.}$$

$$195 = 8.5 \times 10^{-8} \times 1.6 \times 10^{6} \times \text{r.p.m.}$$

$$\text{r.p.m.} = 1434$$

Comparing conditions before and after changing the field strength:

Flux	Torque	I_a	R.P.M.	E.M.F.	Power Input	Power Output
2,000,000	6 lb.-ft.	5	1176	200	1100 watts	1000 watts
1,600,000	6 lb.-ft.	6.25	1434	195	1375 watts	1219 watts

Armature Control

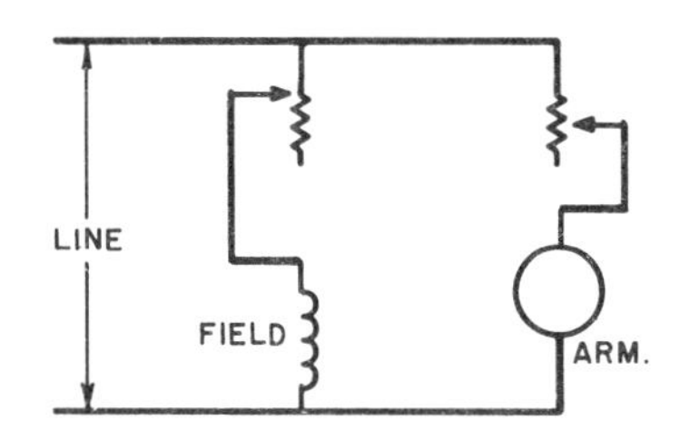

Using the same figures (torque = 6 lb.-ft., I_a = 5 amps, ϕ = 2,000,000, etc.) let's determine the effect of adding one ohm resistance in series with the 4-ohm armature. At this instant of adding resistance, r.p.m. is still 1176, generating 200-volt e.m.f. which leaves 20 volts available to overcome the resistance of the armature circuit. Since the armature circuit now has 5 ohms instead of 4, the current in the armature is momentarily reduced to 4 amps, from the previous 5 amps. This reduced current produces less torque (4.8 instead of 6) so the motor slows down, being unable to maintain the 6 lb.-ft. load. This slowing reduces the e.m.f., which makes more voltage available for producing current through the armature circuit. As soon as 5 amps is again available, the 5 amps produce the 6 lb.-ft. torque which will carry the load at a reduced speed. To calculate the new speed: 5 amps through a 5-ohm armature circuit needs 25 volts; generated e.m.f. can be only 220 - 25 = 195 volts; this 195 volts runs the motor at 1147 r.p.m.

Compare:

Flux	Armature-Circuit Resistance	I_a	R.P.M.	E.M.F.	Power Input	Power Output
2,000,000	4 ohm	5 amp	1176	200 v.	1100 watts	1000 watts
2,000,000	5 ohm	5 amp	1147	195 v.	1100 watts	975 watts

Field control is used much more often than armature control. The addition of resistance is unsatisfactory for two reasons: it causes increased power loss and poorer speed regulation. However, both armature control for below-normal speeds and field control for above-normal speeds can be used on the same machine. For example, manual speed controllers with above- and below-normal speed control facilities are used with shunt and cumulative compound motors. Also, electronic control units are used with D.C. motors to obtain above- and below-normal speeds where the currents are controlled by means other than rheostats.

Shunt motors are used in those industrial applications where a relatively constant speed is required from no-load to full-load and where there are no severe mechanical overload conditions. Shunt motors are often used with fans and blowers; as a prime mover or motor unit for motor-generator sets; as the motor unit for such metalworking machines as lathes, shapers, milling machines, and grinders; in the textile industry for spinning frames and looms; or in any industrial application where the speed must be kept relatively constant at various load points.

THE SERIES MOTOR

Unlike the shunt motor, in which field magnetization was attained by a small current in many turns, the series motor field carries the entire current in a low-resistance coil of few turns. Shunt field magnetization is independent of armature current; series field magnetization changes as the motor current changes under varying load.

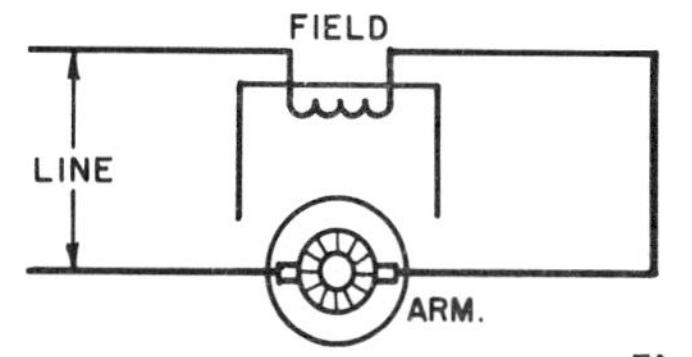

Fig. 22-6

A numerical example may help establish some accurate ideas on the behavior of a series motor.

Assume we have a series motor in which field resistance is 2.4 ohms, armature resistance is 4.0 ohms (total 6.4 ohms), $a = 48 \times 10^{-8}$, $b = 6.8 \times 10^{-8}$, $\phi = 2{,}000{,}000$ when $I = 6.25$ amps (rated current). Line volts = 220.

When $I = 6.25$, the voltage drop due to resistance is $6.25 \times 6.4 = 40$ volts.

Counter e.m.f. generated is $220 - 40 = 180$.

Torque $= a \times \phi \times I = 48 \times 10^{-8} \times 2{,}000{,}000 \times 6.25 = 6$ lb.-ft.

Since e.m.f. $= b \times \phi \times$ r.p.m., we can find r.p.m. from $180 = 6.8 \times 10^{-8} \times 2{,}000{,}000 \times$ r.p.m.; r.p.m. = 1320

In order to calculate changes that occur when the torque-load on this motor is changed, we must take into account the fact that the field flux changes when the armature current changes. In Fig. 22-7, the "flux" curve indicates that the field increases as the current increases, up to about 12 amps, at which point saturation is reached, and the flux is assumed to be constant for higher values of current. (Not exactly true, but satisfactory for this example.)

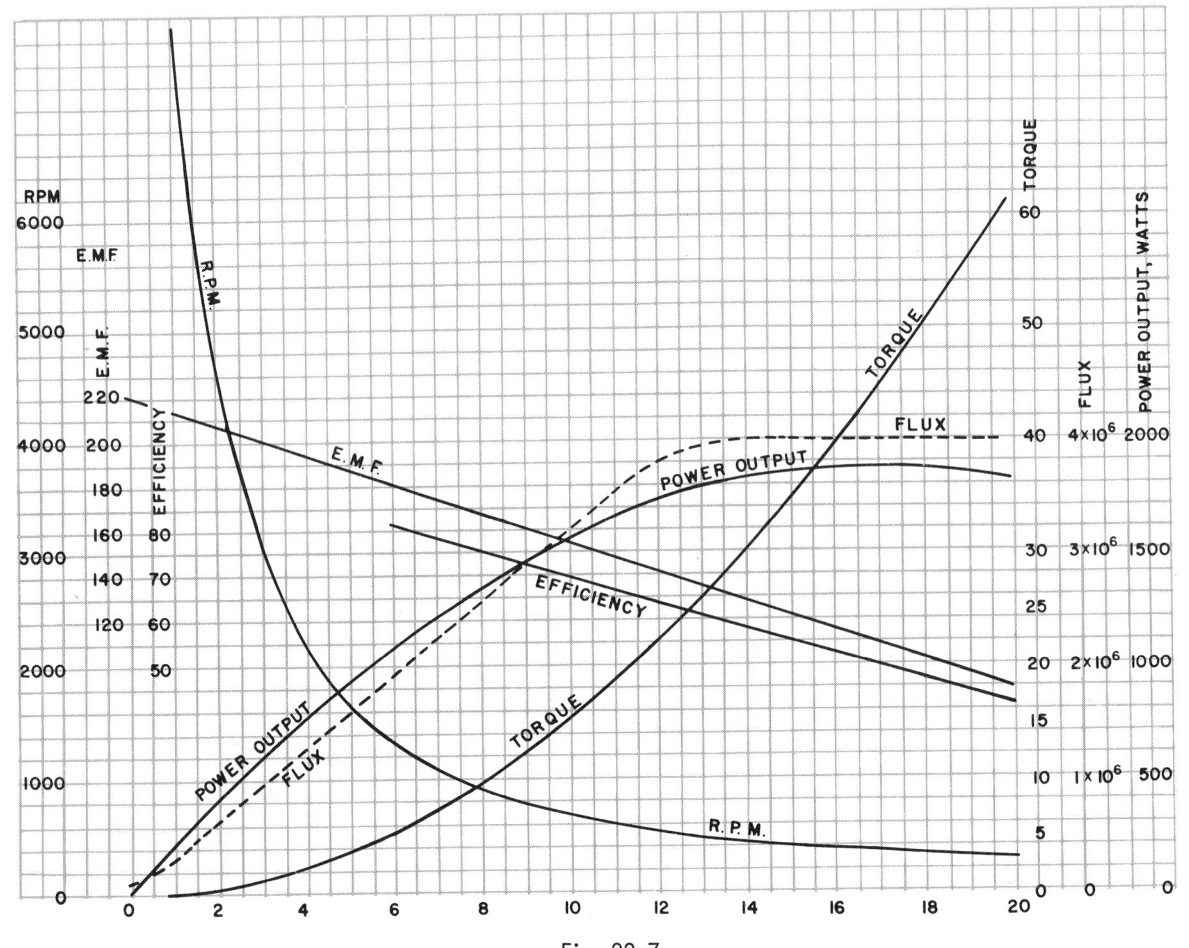

Fig. 22-7

The values in the table below are found as follows: For various values of current from 0 to 20, flux is determined from Fig. 22-7. IR is the voltage used on resistance; IR = current × 6.4 ohms. E.m.f. is found by subtracting each value of IR from 220. Torque is found from a × ϕ × I; r.p.m. is found from e.m.f. = b × ϕ × r.p.m. Watts output is e.m.f. × amps; watts input is 220 × amps.

I (amp)	Field Flux	Total IR	E.M.F.	Torque	R.P.M.	Output (watts)	Input (watts)	Electrical Efficiency
0	Low	0	220.	0	--	0	0	
0.5	160,000	3.2	216.8	0.04	19,800	108	110	
1	320,000	6.4	213.6	0.15	9,800	214	220	
2	640,000	12.8	207.2	0.60	4,750	414	440	
3	960,000	19.2	200.8	1.38	3,180	602	660	
4	1,280,000	25.6	194.4	2.46	2,230	777	880	.87
5	1,600,000	32.	188.0	3.84	1,725	940	1,100	.855
6	1,920,000	38.4	181.6	5.53	1,390	1,090	1,320	.825
6.25	2,000,000	40.0	180.0	6.0	1,320	1,125	1,375	.82
7	2,240,000	44.8	175.2	7.5	1,150	1,226	1,540	.795
8	2,560,000	51.2	168.8	9.8	970	1,350	1,760	.77
9	2,880,000	57.6	162.4	12.4	830	1,462	1,980	.74
10	3,200,000	64.0	156.0	15.4	716	1,560	2,200	.71
11	3,520,000	70.4	149.6	18.6	607	1,646	2,420	.68
12	3,840,000	76.8	143.2	22.1	550	1,718	2,640	.65
14	4,000,000	89.6	130.4	30.1	480	1,826	3,080	.59
16	4,000,000	102.	117.6	39.3	432	1,880	3,520	.535
18	4,000,000	115.	104.8	49.8	385	1,885	3,960	.475
20	4,000,000	128.	92.0	61.5	338	1,840	4,400	.42

Our first calculation on the series motor showed 6 lb.-ft. of torque produced, with the motor operating steadily at 1320 r.p.m., on 6.25 amps. Suppose the torque-load is suddenly increased to 12.4 lb.-ft. This slows the motor, which reduces e.m.f. because of the r.p.m. reduction. Reduced e.m.f. permits more current, and a little more current causes a lot more torque, which carries the increased load. Notice that torque depends on current and on flux; increasing the current also increases the flux, so that the torque is proportional to the square of the current, unless the field iron reaches saturation. R.p.m. has been reduced considerably, down to 830 from 1320, due to the increased flux. At this load, the motor can run no faster than 830; if it did, it would generate so much e.m.f. that the necessary current could not be maintained.

One more change: Reduce the torque load, say to 2.46 lb.-ft., at a time when the motor had been operating at 6 lb.-ft. torque, 1320 r.p.m. This reduction makes the armature turn easier, so its first response would be to speed up a little. Increased speed generates more e.m.f. More e.m.f. reduces current input. Reduced current reduces the flux. If the speed increases from 1320 to 1390 (table) the current is reduced to 6 amps, which is enough to keep the motor accelerating. (5.53 lb.-ft. produced; load is 2.46). When the speed has risen to 2230, e.m.f. is up to 194.4, which lets in 4 amps to produce the 2.46 lb.-ft. that carries the load at a steady 2230 r.p.m. Notice that e.m.f. does not rise as fast as the speed does, because as the speed goes up, there is less field flux.

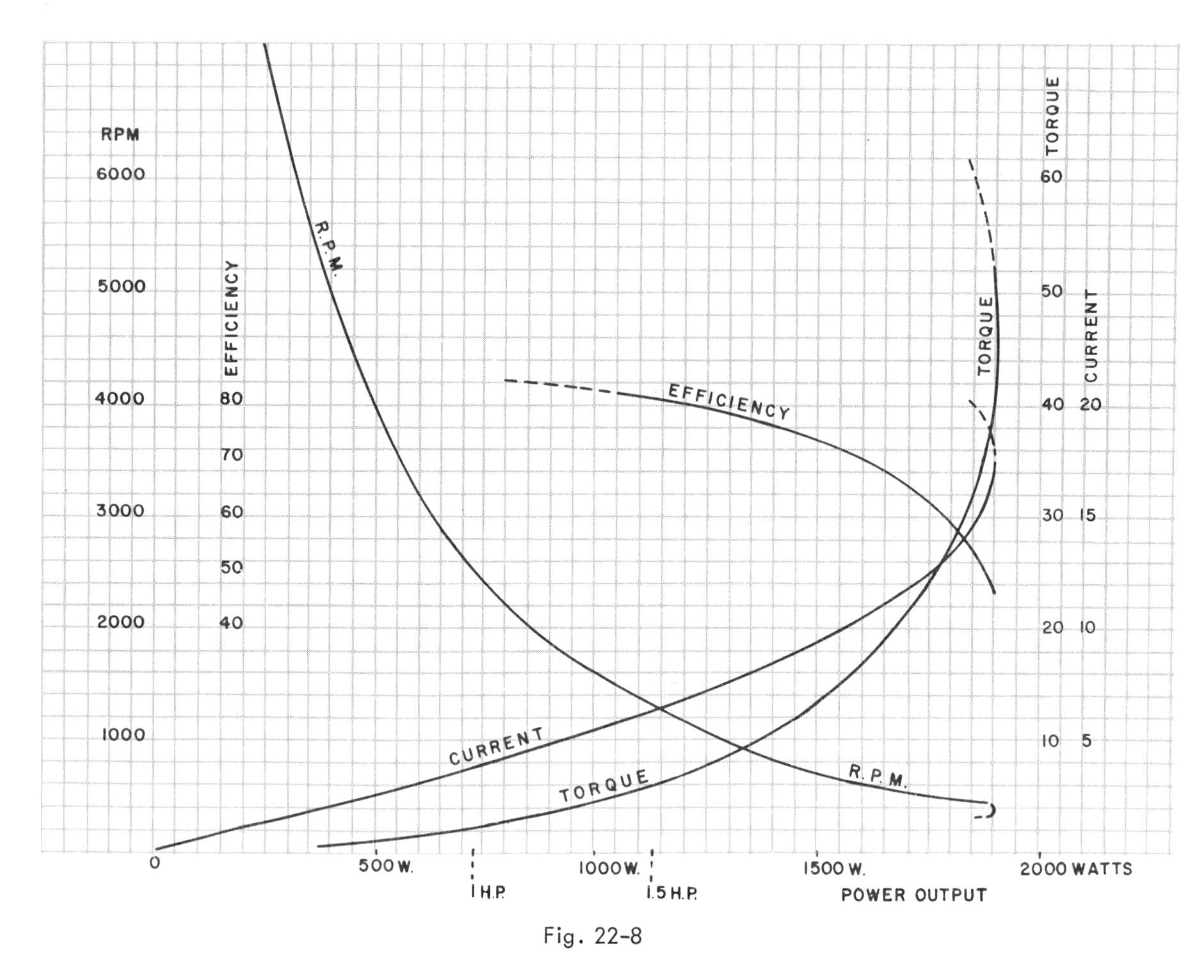

Fig. 22-8

In the shunt motor, since flux is constant, a small increase in r.p.m. produces enough increase in e.m.f. to reduce the current to such a value that there is not enough torque to accelerate the motor further. (Compare tabulated values for series motor and shunt motor.) When the load is removed from a shunt motor, it accelerates a little, and e.m.f. rises to a value sufficient to shut off the torque-producing current.

When the load is removed from a series motor, speed and e.m.f. also increase, but, due to decreased flux, e.m.f. does not increase rapidly enough to shut down on the torque-producing current. This torque accelerates the motor further, without theoretical limit. (See series motor table.) If the load is removed, speed may rise to 9800 r.p.m.; at 9800 r.p.m. the one ampere input produces 0.15 lb.-ft. of torque. If the friction in the motor is equivalent to less than 0.15, speed builds up further.

In actual practice the top speed of series motors is limited:

1. Friction (bearings, brushes, windage) limits the speed of small series motors. At 10,000 r.p.m. the entire power input may be expended on friction, so the speed increases no further.

2. In large motors, high speed produces inertial forces that disassemble the armature; this stops the motor. At 5000 r.p.m., the surface of an 8″-diameter armature is traveling at about 2 miles per minute, and each ounce of copper wire in the slots requires a force of 180 pounds to hold it in place.

On the preceding graphs, efficiency at low power output is not plotted. Values for electrical efficiency, calculated from e.m.f. ÷ line volts, would be misleading. When current is 1 amp, calculated electrical efficiency is .97, but if 50 watts is used on mechanical friction, actual efficiency is .745. Actual efficiency is not a subject for calculation: rather it is found by test on the motor.

The series motor is used in any industrial application where extremely high torque is required and where very heavy overload is suddenly applied while operating. This motor, however, cannot be used in those applications where a relatively constant speed is required from no-load to full-load as the series motor has a poor speed regulation and, if operated at no-load, may reach a dangerously fast speed.

The series motor is used on cranes, hoists, subway railway cars, electric locomotives, and similar applications requiring extremely high starting torque.

POWER LOSSES IN A MOTOR

Just as in a generator (Page 201) power losses in a motor are classified into two types. In the previous discussion, the I^2R losses (copper losses) in field and armature have been taken into account in the calculations of electrical efficiency. Stray power losses (core losses and friction losses) have to be found by test on the motor.

For example: A shunt motor has a 200-ohm field and the armature circuit resistance is 0.4 ohms. At no load, the motor takes 3 amps on a 220-volt line. Find the stray power loss.

Field current: 220/200 = 1.1 amp

Armature current: 3.0 - 1.1 = 1.9 amp

Armature circuit: uses $1.9 \times 220 = 418$ watts

I^2R in armature is about 1.4 watts ($1.9 \times 1.9 \times 0.4 = 1.44$), so stray power losses must be 418 - 1.4 = 416.6 watts

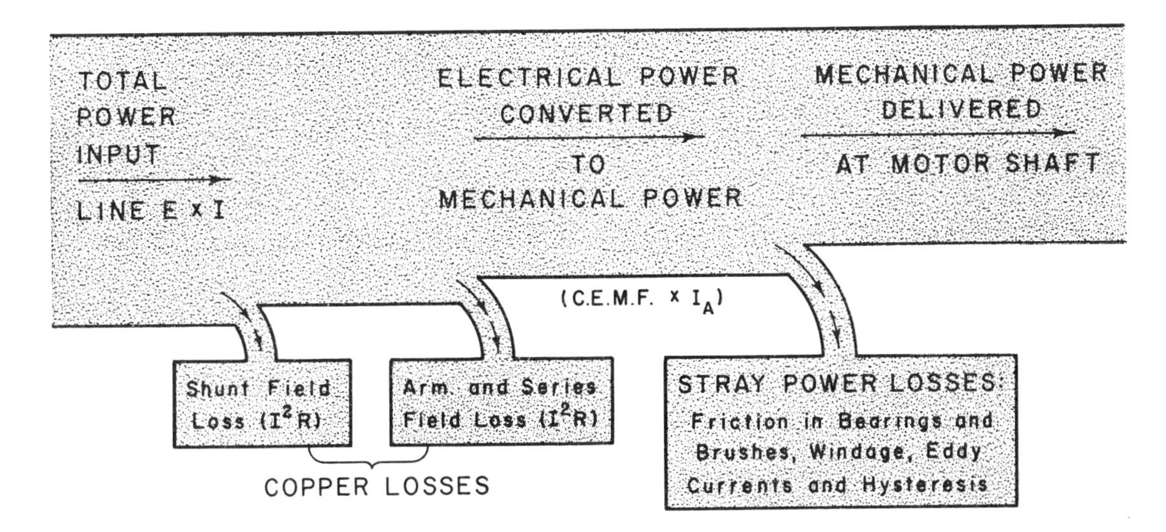

COMPOUND MOTORS

Comparing the advantages of series and shunt motors, we find (1) the shunt motor has a more constant speed, but (2) a series motor of the same power rating can exert a much greater torque, when necessary, without a terrific increase in current.

These two desirable features can be obtained in the same motor by placing both a series-field winding and a shunt-field winding on the field-poles of the motor, which is now termed a compound motor. Usually, connections are arranged so that the series-field current is in the same direction around the field magnets as the shunt-field current, both windings aiding each other in producing flux. Such a connection forms a cumulative-compound motor.

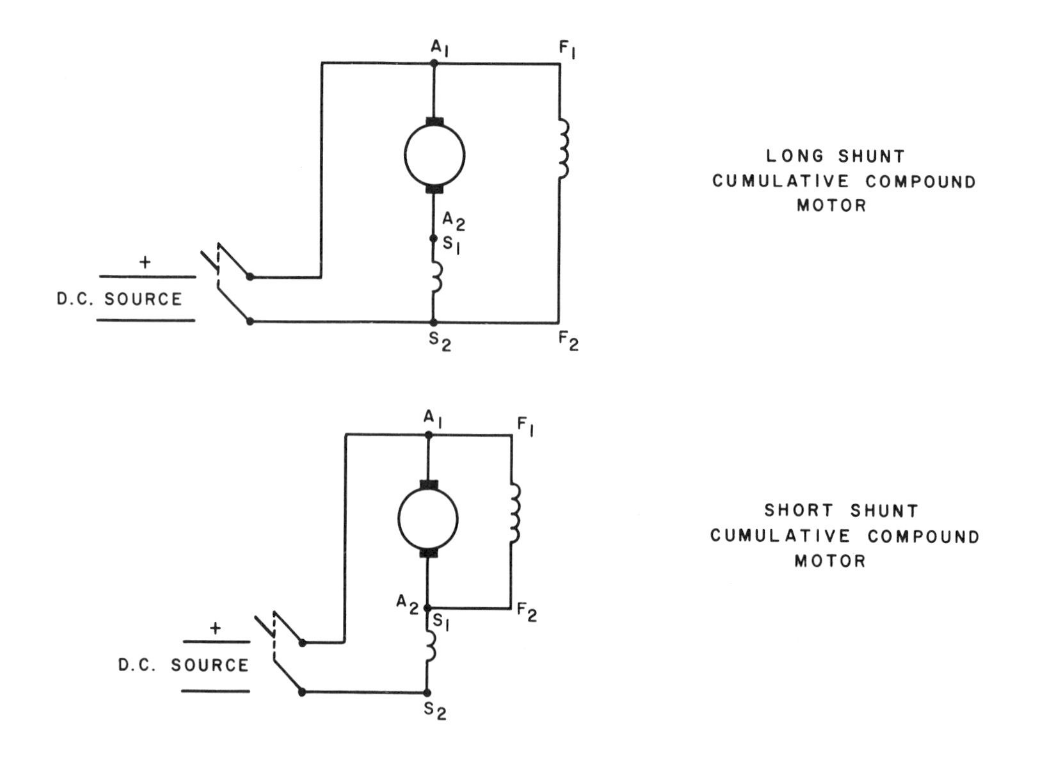

Fig. 22-9 Compound Motor Field Connections

When the shunt field is connected across both the armature and the series field, the cumulative compound motor is connected long shunt. When the shunt field is connected directly across the armature the cumulative compound motor is connected short shunt. Usually cumulative compound motors are connected long shunt. Figure 22-9 shows schematic connections for both long and short shunt cumulative compound motors.

Consider the effect of adding a few series-field turns to an existing shunt motor: At heavy loads, when the motor slows down, the increased current through the series field boosts the field strength, which gives added torque.

Or consider a series-motor, to which a shunt-field has been added: At light loads, the series motor tends to over-speed, due to decreased field flux. But the added constant-flux shunt field is independent of armature variations, providing enough flux to put a reasonable limit on the top speed, just as the speed of a shunt motor is limited.

The graphs below compare the characteristics of the three types of motors: series, shunt, and cumulative compound. Compound motors can be built with characteristics closely approaching either the series or the shunt characteristics, according to the relative division of ampere-turns between series and shunt coils.

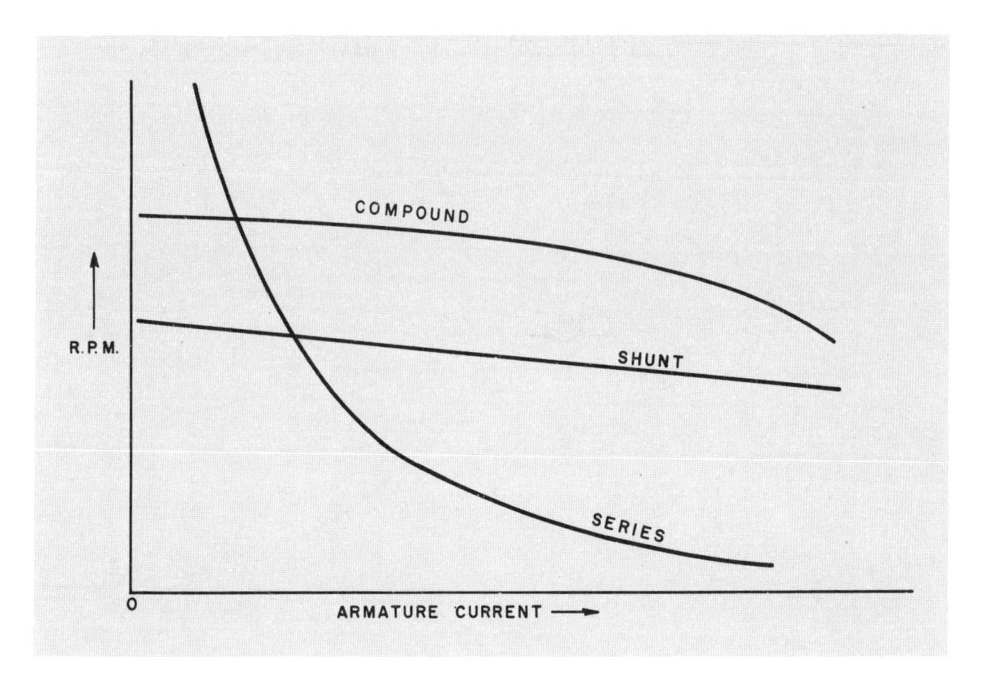

Fig. 22-10 A

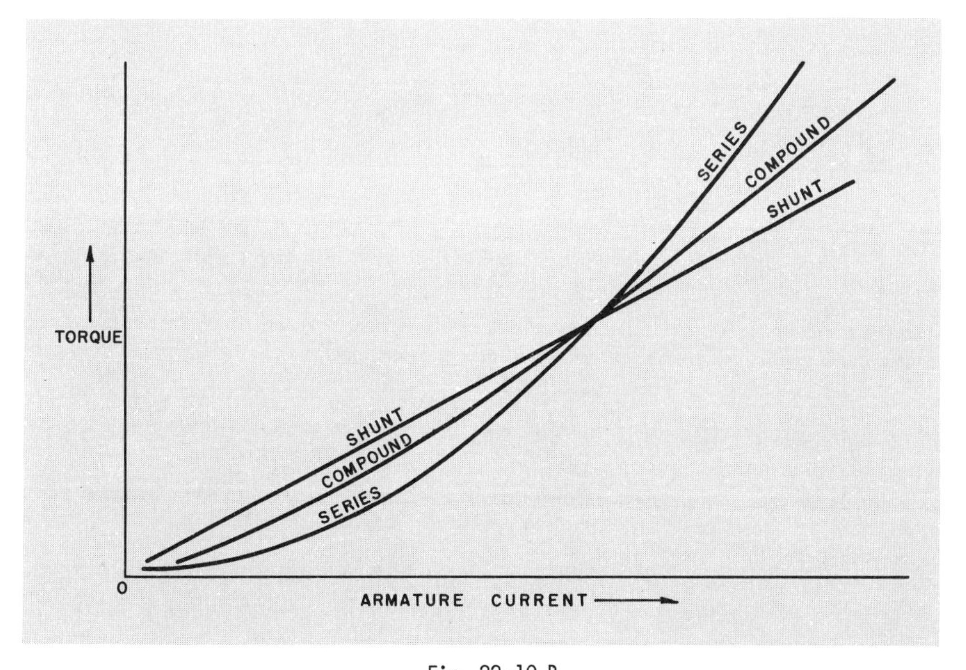

Fig. 22-10 B

Cumulative compounding is generally used, hence the term "compound motor" means cumulative. Infrequently, a motor may be used with its series field opposing the shunt field; this type is called "differential compound." The shunt field establishes the direction of the field flux, increased current in the series field weakens the field. Excellent speed regulation can be obtained with this type of motor, for the tendency to slow down under load is compensated for by this sequence of reasons: a little slowing permits more armature current, which also weakens the total field, which reduces counter e.m.f., which permits still more armature current, which produces added torque to run the increased load at practically constant speed.

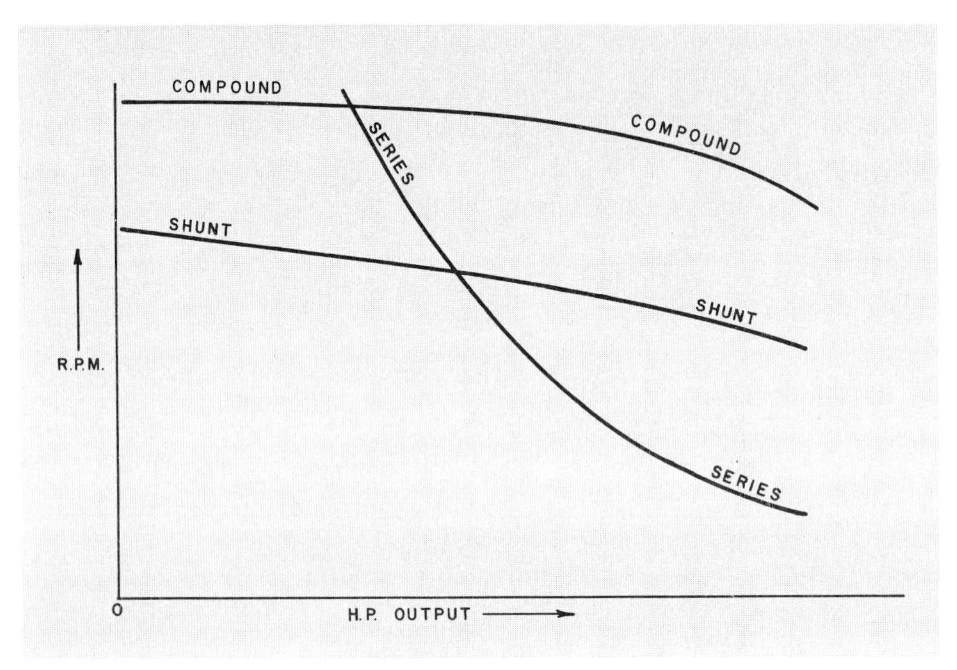

Fig. 22-10 C

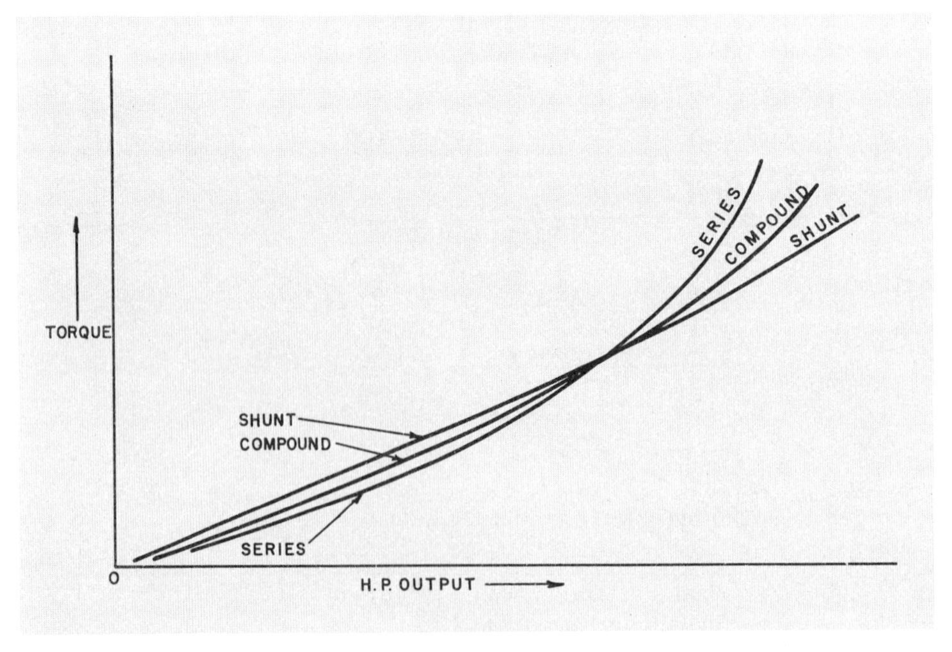

Fig. 22-10 D

The cumulative compound motor will develop a high torque with a sudden increase in load. This motor also has the advantage of having a definite no-load speed so it will not race to an excessively high speed if the load is removed.

Some of the industrial applications for this motor are as the motor unit for passenger and freight elevators, as the motor unit on metal stamping presses, motor drive for rolling mills in the steel industry, motor unit on metal shears and similar applications.

POINTS TO REMEMBER

- Torque is proportional to flux and armature current. Increase of either increases torque.
- Counter e.m.f. is proportional to flux and r.p.m. Increase of either increases e.m.f.
- The shunt motor has its field-coils in parallel with the armature. Its constant field strength limits input current and speed at no-load.
- The series motor has its field-coil in series with the armature. At no-load, reduced field permits enough current to produce torque that accelerates motor greatly. At heavy-load, torque is high, speed low.
- Weakening the field speeds up the shunt motor; reduced armature current slows the shunt motor.
- Comparing advantages of series and shunt motors: The shunt motor has the more constant speed, but a series motor of the same h.p. rating can exert a much greater torque, when necessary, without a terrific increase in current.
- Compound motors have both series and shunt fields. Relative amp-turns of the two fields determine speed and torque characteristics of the motor.

REVIEW QUESTIONS

1. (a) Show with characteristic curves the speed and torque performance for a shunt motor.

   (b) List four industrial applications for a shunt motor.

2. (a) Show with characteristic curves the speed and torque performances for a series motor.

   (b) List four industrial applications for a series motor.

3. (a) Show with characteristic curves the speed and torque performance for a cumulative compound motor.

   (b) List four industrial applications for a cumulative compound motor.

4. A shunt motor is required to carry an additional load. List the sequence of steps in their proper order showing how this motor will adjust itself to carry the additional load.

5. The armature of a D. C. shunt motor carries 15 amperes. The resistance of the armature circuit is 0.7 ohms. Line volts = 220. Find the counter e.m.f. generated in the armature. Find the power output, in watts and in h.p.

6. A 3-h.p., 120-volt shunt motor takes 23 amps at full load and 3 amps at no load. Shunt resistance is 150 ohms; armature resistance is 0.25 ohms; no-load speed is 1600 r.p.m. Find (a) counter e.m.f. at no load; (b) counter e.m.f. at full load; (c) full-load speed; (d) percent speed regulation.

7. Explain the meaning of the following terms:

   (a) speed regulation (b) speed control

8. Explain what happens under each of the following conditions:

   (a) The load is removed from a series motor.

   (b) Resistance is added to the armature circuit of a shunt motor.

   (c) The rheostat in series with the shunt field of a shunt motor operating at no-load becomes open-circuited.

   (d) The field rheostat in series with the shunt field of a shunt motor is adjusted so that all the resistance of the rheostat is cut out and the shunt field current increases.

9. (a) Itemize the losses that reduce the efficiency of a motor and state in what parts of the motor each loss occurs.

   (b) State which of these losses are considered to be constant and independent of the load.

   (c) When the constant losses are grouped together, what term is used?

10. A motor with an input of 1000 watts delivers an output of one horsepower. If the copper losses are 134 watts, compute the constant or fixed losses which are independent of the load.

11. A 50-h.p., 220-volt shunt motor has a full-load efficiency = 83%. Field resistance is 110 ohms; armature resistance is .08 ohm. At full load, determine (a) total power input, in watts; (b) line current; (c) total copper losses; (d) stray power loss.

12. A D.C. shunt motor takes 40 amp at full load when connected to a 115-volt line. At no load, the motor current is 4.4 amp. Shunt field resistance = 57.5 ohms, armature circuit resistance is 0.25 ohms. Full-load speed is 1740 r.p.m. Find: (a) stray power loss; (b) copper loss at full load; (c) efficiency at full load; (d) h.p. output at full load.

13. The generator of a motor-generator set is delivering its full load output of 10 kilowatts. The generator has an efficiency of 88.5%. The motor operates on a 230-volt line. Determine:

    (a) The output of the motor in horsepower.

    (b) The number of amperes the motor is taking from the line when the generator is delivering at rated load. The efficiency of this motor-generator set at rated load is 85%.

14. A motor operating on a 120-volt D.C. supply drives a direct-current generator which is delivering 1 kilowatt at 240 volts. Under these conditions the motor has an efficiency of 78% while the generator has an 85% efficiency. Determine:

    (a) The output in horsepower of the motor.

    (b) The line current drawn by the motor.

15. Reduced line voltage may cause a shunt motor to overheat. Why?

The sudden connection of a large armature to a D.C. power line would cause unreasonably-high current through the line and armature, since, at the moment of starting, no counter e.m.f. exists to limit the current. Without the addition of external resistance, this high current would put a great stress on armature windings, burn brushes and commutators, and cause line-voltage drop to interfere with other machines on the line.

For the gentle starting of large motors, a "motor starter" is used. It is merely a variable resistance, placed in series with the armature. Its primary purpose is to limit the armature current to a safe value during the starting and accelerating period. Along with the starting rheostat, there is usually some arrangement for automatically disconnecting the motor, and leaving it disconnected, if line voltage fails.

There are two common types of manual starting rheostats used with shunt and compound motors: (1) Three-terminal starting rheostat, (2) Four-terminal starting rheostat.

Three-Terminal Starting Rheostat

The three-terminal starting rheostat has a tapped resistor enclosed in a ventilated box. Contact buttons located on a slate panel mounted on the front of the box are connected to the tapped resistor. A movable arm with a spring reset can be moved over the contact buttons to cut out sections of the tapped resistor.

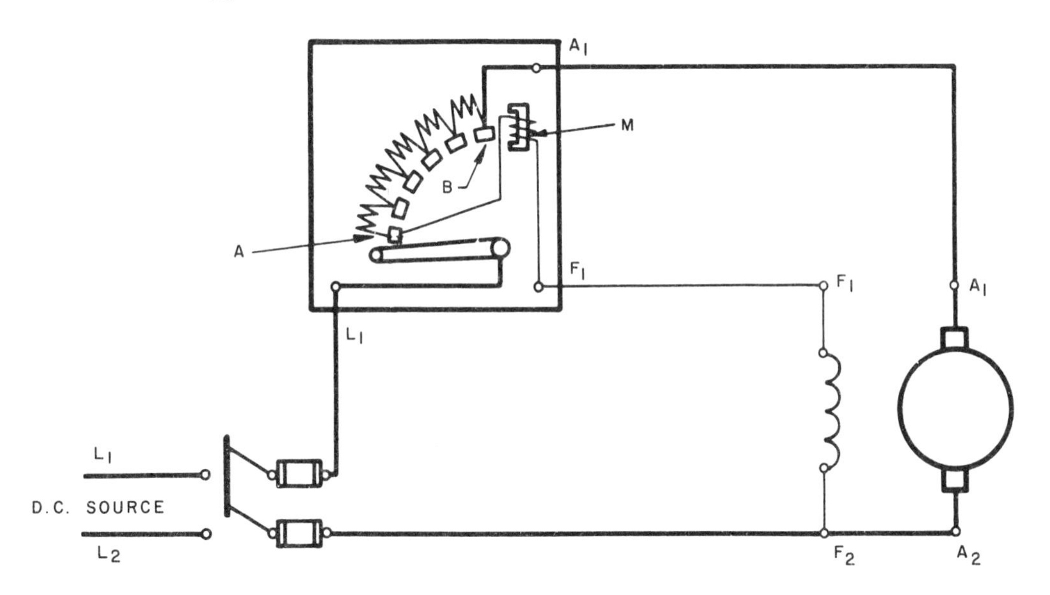

Fig. 23-1 Three-Terminal Starting Rheostat

After the line switch is closed, the handle is moved to the first contact, A. The shunt field is now connected to the line, and is at full strength. All of the starting resistance is in series with the armature; this resistance, in accepted practice, is calculated to limit the starting current to 150% of the full-load current rating of the motor.

As the motor speeds up, the operator moves the handle gradually toward contact B, the time required being dependent on the time needed for the machine to build up speed. At B, the armature is connected directly across the source voltage, and the magnetic holding coil, M, holds the handle in the full "on" position. A spring (not shown) tends to return the handle to the "off" position. If the shunt field current became greatly less, the motor would race if the armature circuit remained connected; however, this is prevented by having the holding coil in series with the shunt field. Reduced current in the holding coil lets the handle fly back to the "off" position. Also, if the line voltage is interrupted, the holding coil releases the handle, requiring the motor to be re-started when line voltage is restored.

The starting resistance is in series with the shunt field when the arm is in the run position, at contact B. This additional resistance is so small, when compared with the field resistance, that it has practically no effect on field strength and speed.

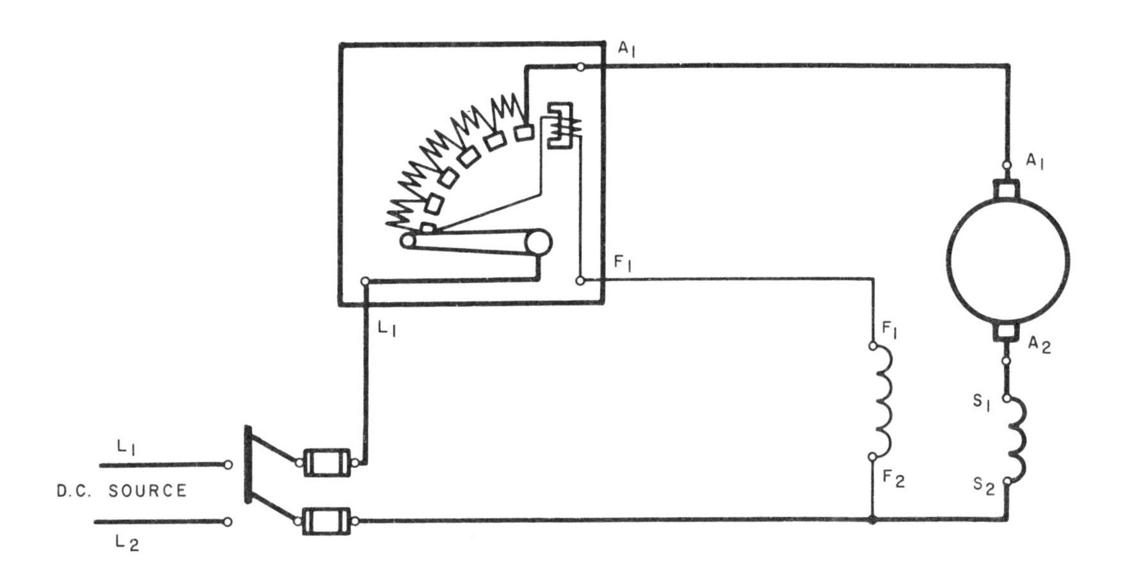

Fig. 23-2 Three-Terminal Starting Rheostat Connected to a Compound Wound Motor

Fig. 23-2 illustrates the connections for a three-terminal manual starting rheostat used with a cumulative compound motor. Note that the only difference in this circuit and the connections for a shunt motor is the addition of the series field.

Starting rheostats are designed to carry the starting current for only a short time; they are not intended for speed-control. An attempt to obtain below-normal speed by holding the arm on an intermediate contact is likely to burn out the starting resistor.

The three-terminal starting box is not suited for use where it is desired to obtain above-normal speeds by use of a field rheostat, since reduced field current may release the handle and shut the motor down. With field control, a slightly different arrangement is used, called a four-terminal starting box.

Four-Terminal Manual Starting Rheostat

Four-terminal manual starting rheostats have two functions which are also common to the three-terminal starting rheostat:

1. To accelerate a motor to rated speed in one direction of rotation.
2. To limit the starting surge of current in the armature to a safe value.

However, this starting rheostat may be used along with a field rheostat, the field control being used to obtain above-normal speeds.

Fig. 23-3 represents a four-terminal starting box connected to a shunt motor.

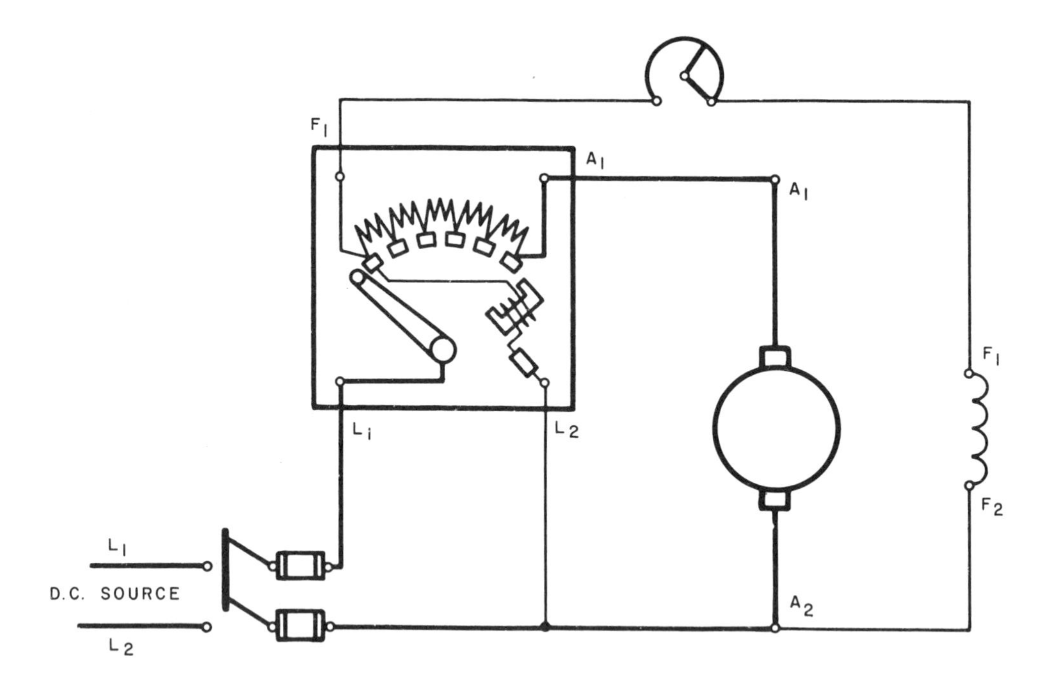

Fig. 23-3 Connections for a Four-Terminal Starting Rheostat

Note that the holding coil is not connected in series with the shunt field, as it is in the three-terminal starting box. In this four-terminal starter, the holding coil, in series with a resistor, is connected directly across the source voltage. The holding coil current is independent of field current, but still serves as a no-voltage release. If line voltage drops, the attraction of the holding coil is decreased, and a reset spring (not shown) returns the movable arm to the "off" position.

A motor is started with a four-terminal starter in the same manner as with a three-terminal starter. Any desired above-normal speed of the motor is obtained by adjustment of the field rheostat in series with the shunt field.

When the motor is to be stopped, all resistance in the field rheostat is cut out, so that motor speed decreases to its normal value; then the line switch is opened. This procedure ensures that, the next time the motor is started, it will be with a strong field and resultant strong starting torque.

Reversal of Rotation

Reversal of a motor is usually accomplished by a reversing switch so placed as to control only the armature current. Reversing current to the entire motor (field + armature) accomplishes nothing, since with both field and armature current reversed, rotation continues in the same direction. In connection with some types of motor-control systems that require a quick stop, the armature current may be reversed momentarily to provide reverse-torque to stop the motor; this method of achieving a sudden stop is called "plugging."

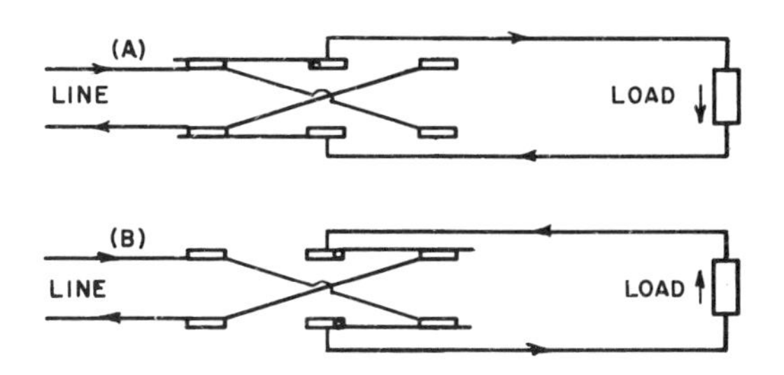

Fig. 23-4 Double-Pole Double-Throw Switch Used as a Reversing Switch

In practice, reversal of a motor is usually accomplished by interchanging the connections of the two armature leads.

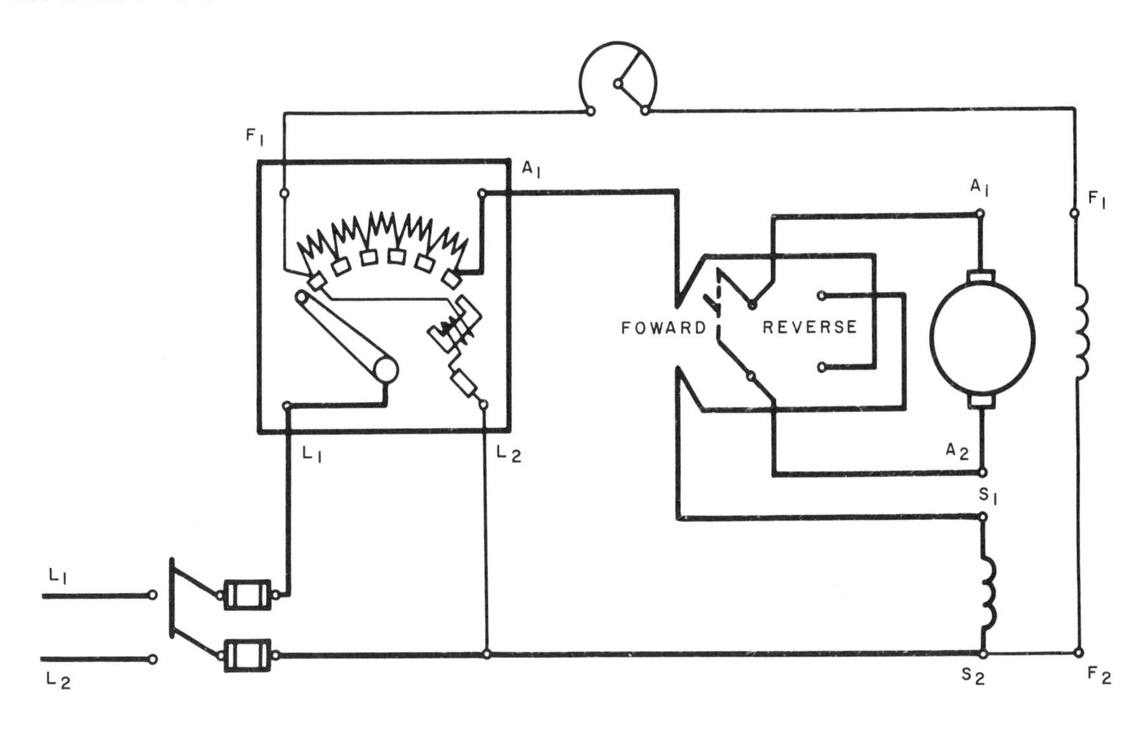

Fig. 23-5 Four-Terminal Starting Rheostat Connected to a Cumulative Compound Motor

In the above circuit, the D.P.D.T. switch, with connections for a compound wound motor, is used to reverse the direction of rotation of the armature. It does so by reversing armature current, but the current in both the series and shunt fields is not affected. Therefore the motor operates as a cumulative compound motor in either direction, for both field circuits are working together. It would be possible to reverse rotation by arranging a circuit in which armature current was kept constant in direction, and field currents were reversed. Since both the connections of the shunt and series field windings would have to be reversed, this would make the motor control connections quite complicated.

MANUAL SPEED CONTROLLERS

It is often necessary to vary the speed of D.C. motors. As pointed out before, speeds of above-normal rating are obtained by inserting resistance in the shunt field, while below-normal speeds can be obtained by adding resistance to the armature circuit.

Two types of manual speed controllers are used with shunt and cumulative compound motors: (1) Above-normal speed controllers, and (2) Above- and below-normal speed controllers.

The National Electrical Manufacturers' Association defines a manual speed controller as a device for accelerating a motor to normal speed with the additional function of varying speed. Manual speed controllers must not be confused with manual starting rheostats which simply accelerate a motor to normal speed.

Above-Normal Speed Controller

This controller combines the functions of a starter and a field rheostat. The starting resistance is used in the armature circuit only during the starting period, limiting the armature current while the motor accelerates to normal speed. The field control circuit is effective only after the motor has been brought up to normal speed, after which insertion of resistance weakens the field, producing higher speed. The controller illustrated in Fig. 23-6, then, has three functions:

1. To accelerate the motor to rated speed by reducing the resistance in the armature circuit.
2. To limit the current surge in the armature circuit to a safe value.
3. To obtain above-normal speed control by varying the resistance in series with the shunt field.

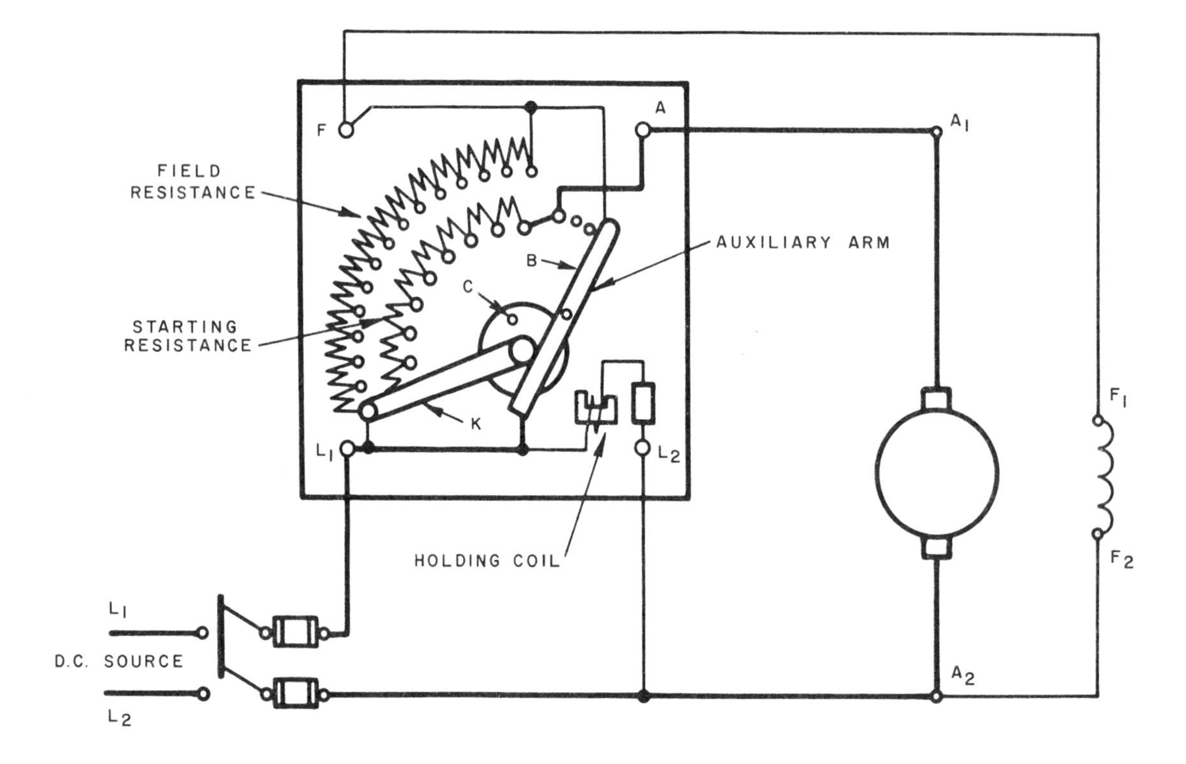

Fig. 23-6 Above-Normal Speed Controller (Start Position)

Two rows of contacts are mounted on a slate panel. The top row of small contact buttons connects to a tapped resistor, which is the field rheostat. The bottom row of larger contacts connects to a tapped resistor in series with the armature. The control arm K connects to both sets of contacts.

In the 'start' position, arm B bypasses the field rheostat, so that full line voltage is applied to the shunt field. Arm K, when moved clockwise, cuts out starting resistance as the motor accelerates. When arm K approaches the normal-run position, pin C pushes arm B counter-clockwise until it is secured against the holding coil. The motor will now have accelerated to normal speed.

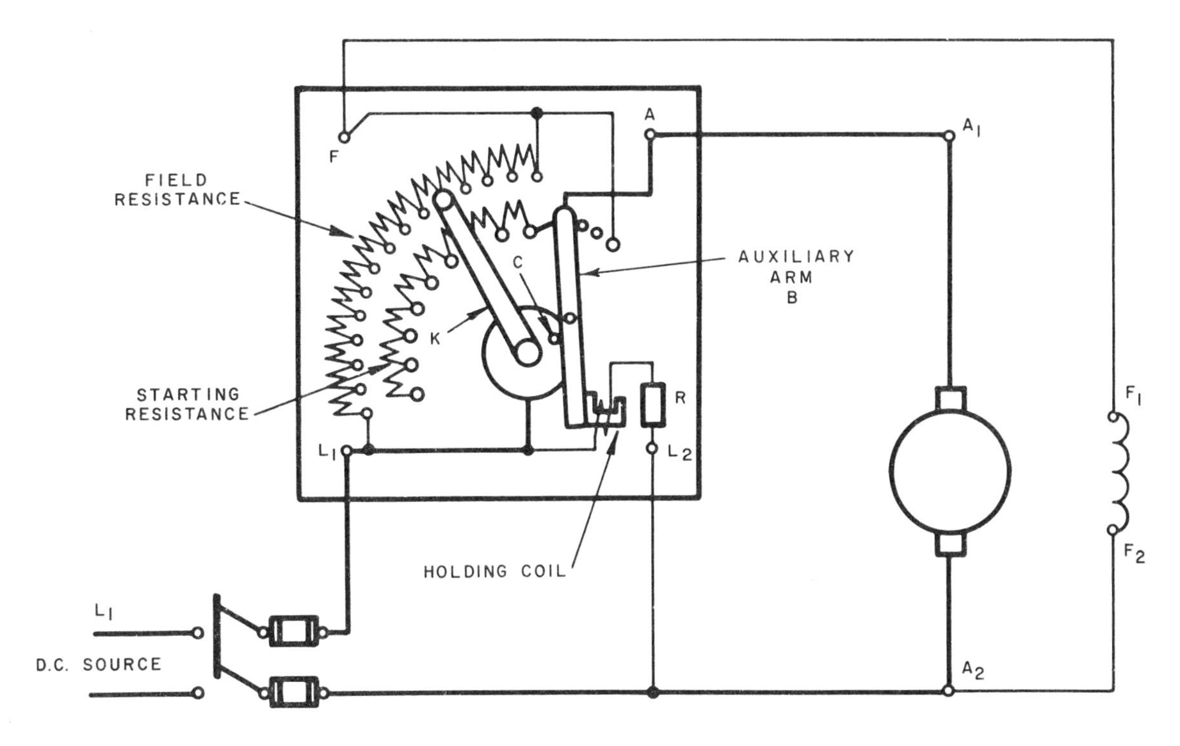

Fig. 23-7 Above-Normal Speed Controller (Run Position)

In the above sketch, note that arm B has been removed from the field circuit so that it no longer short-circuits the field rheostat. Instead, arm B now bypasses the starting resistance, providing a direct path from the supply line to the armature.

If it is necessary to increase the speed of the motor to some value above normal, arm K is moved counterclockwise. This has no effect now on armature current, but it does result in resistance being inserted in the shunt field circuit. Motor speed now increases. Arm K may be left in any intermediate position to obtain desired above-normal speed.

When the line switch is opened, the holding coil releases arm B, which is returned to its original "start" position by a spring. Pin C is now released and permits arm K to return to the "off" position, K being returned by a reset spring.

This type of controller may be used with either a shunt or a compound motor.

Above- and Below-Normal Speed Controller

In some motor installations it is necessary to have a wide range of speed control, including both below-normal and above-normal speeds.

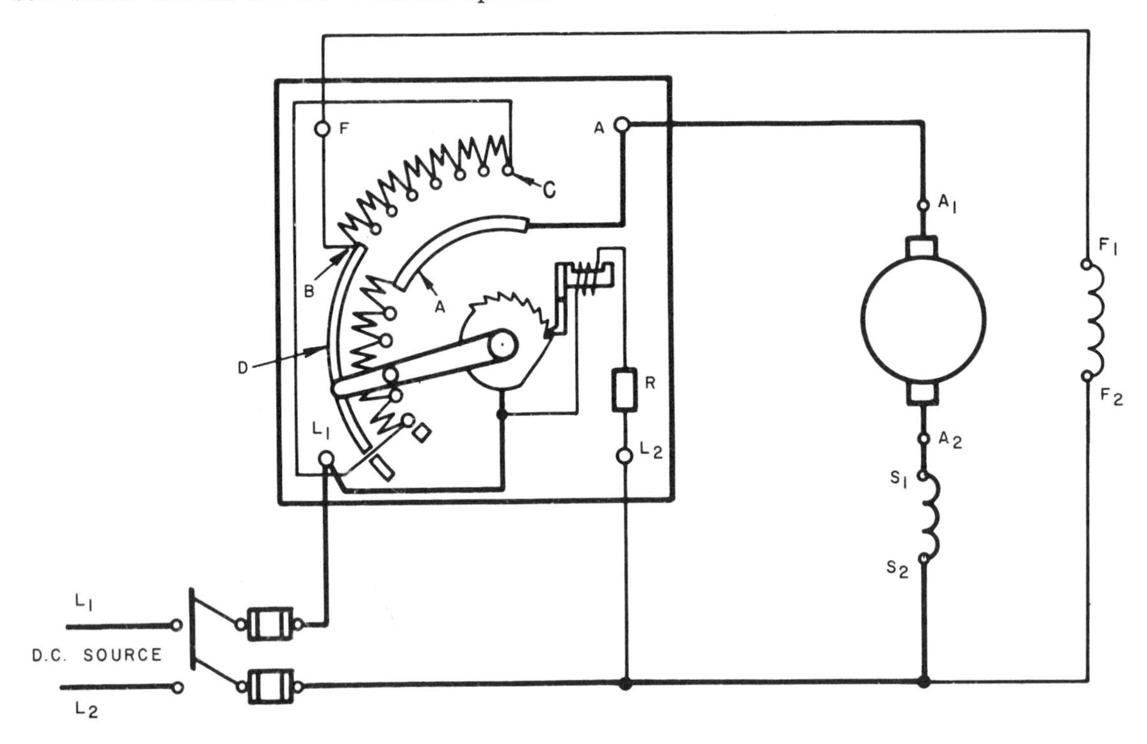

Fig. 23-8 Above- and Below-Normal Speed Controller (Set for Below-Normal Speed)

Fig. 23-8 illustrates a typical above- and below-normal controller. The movable arm connects to two rows of contacts, the lower row of contacts connecting to taps on the armature-circuit resistor, and the upper row connecting to taps on the field resistor. The contacts are mounted on the front of a slate panel, while the armature and field resistors are housed in a ventilated box in back of the panel. Continued clockwise movement of the arm results in continued increase of speed, at first by removing armature-circuit resistance, then by inserting resistance in the field circuit.

In the position shown in Fig. 23-8 there is considerable resistance in series with the armature. The arm also contacts the radial conductor D which connects full line voltage to the shunt field. With the arm in this position the speed is below normal. Once the movable arm is set on any contact point it will lock in that position until moved to some other point. This is done by a unique gear and latch system operated with the aid of the holding coil.

When a motor is operating under heavy load at slow speed, there is considerable current in the armature circuit, requiring the armature resistors to be of large size to radiate the heat produced by the large current. This makes the physical size of this controller larger, for a given H.P. rating, than an ordinary manual starting rheostat.

As the arm is slowly moved clockwise to the upper end of the armature rheostat, it still contacts conductor D (at point B) and also comes in contact with the curved conducting strip marked A. This is the normal speed position. Full line voltage is applied to both the armature and the shunt field.

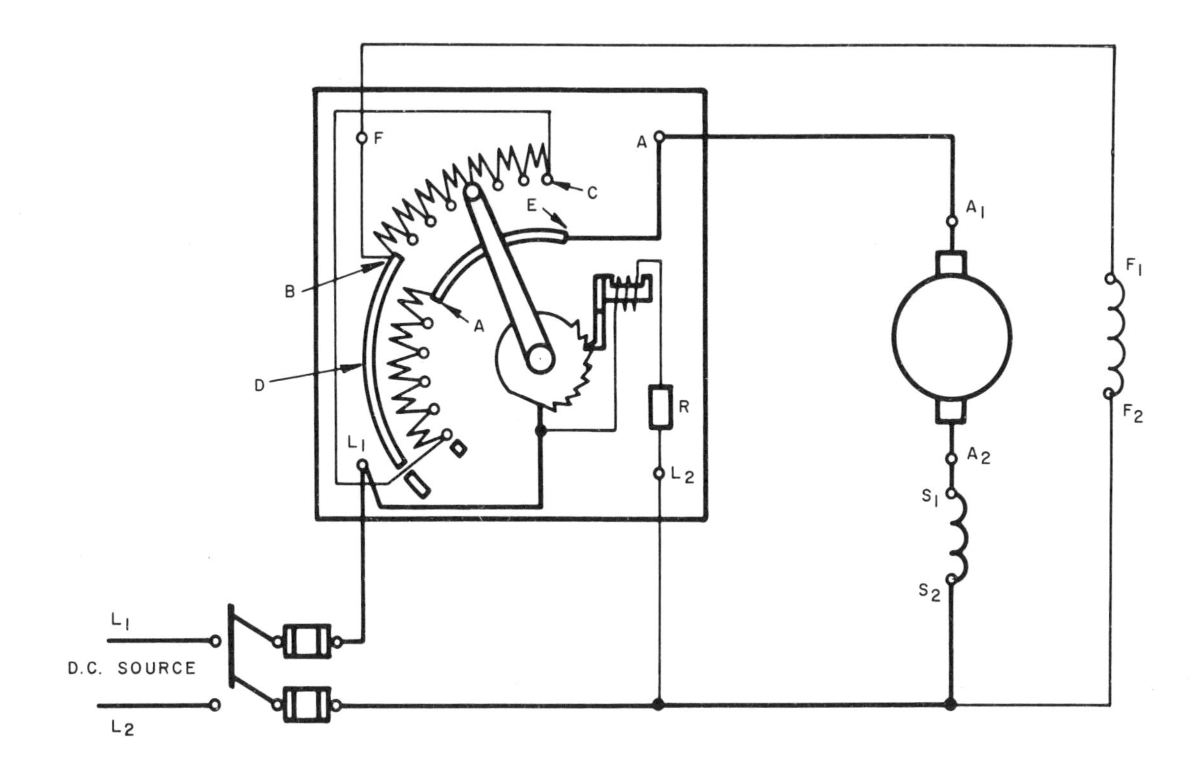

Fig. 23-9 Above- and Below-Normal Speed Controller (Set for Above-Normal Speed)

In an above-normal speed position, full line voltage is still applied to the armature, through strip A-E. The outer end of the control arm now contacts a point on the field rheostat, so that the resistance between the arm and point B has been inserted in the field circuit. If the arm is moved to point C, all of the field rheostat is in use, producing maximum speed by field weakening.

When the line switch is opened, the holding coil releases the latch, and the reset spring returns the arm to the 'off' position. This type of controller may be used with either a shunt or a compound motor, connections for a shunt motor differing only by the omission of the series field.

Manual Starting Rheostats for Series Motors

Series motors require a special type of manual starting rheostat called a series motor starter. These starting rheostats serve the same purpose as the three- and four-terminal manual starting rheostats used with shunt and compound motors. However, series motor starters have different internal and external connections.

There are two types of series motor starters. One type of starter has no-voltage protection while the other has no-load protection.

A series motor starter with no-voltage protection is illustrated in Fig. 23-10. The holding coil is connected across the source voltage. This starter is used to accelerate the motor to rated speed. In case of voltage failure the holding coil will no longer act as an electromagnet. The spring reset can then quickly return the arm to the off position. This protects the motor from damage caused by low voltage conditions.

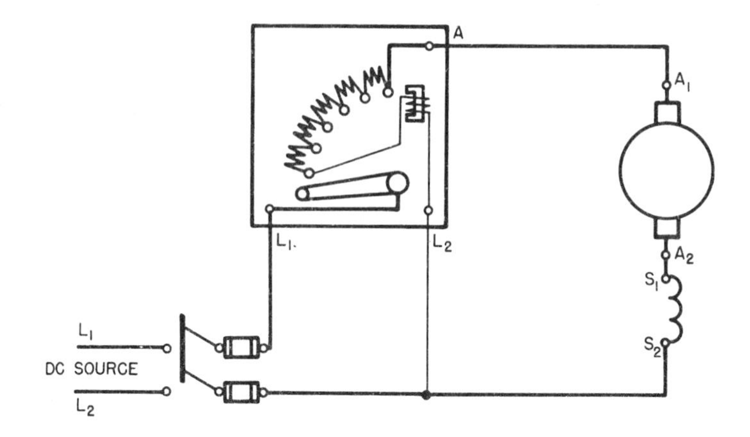

Fig. 23-10 Series Motor Starter With No-Voltage Protection

Another type of series motor starter illustrated in Fig. 23-11 has "no-load" protection. The holding coil is in series with the armature. Because of the large current in the armature circuit, the holding coil consists of only a few turns of heavy wire.

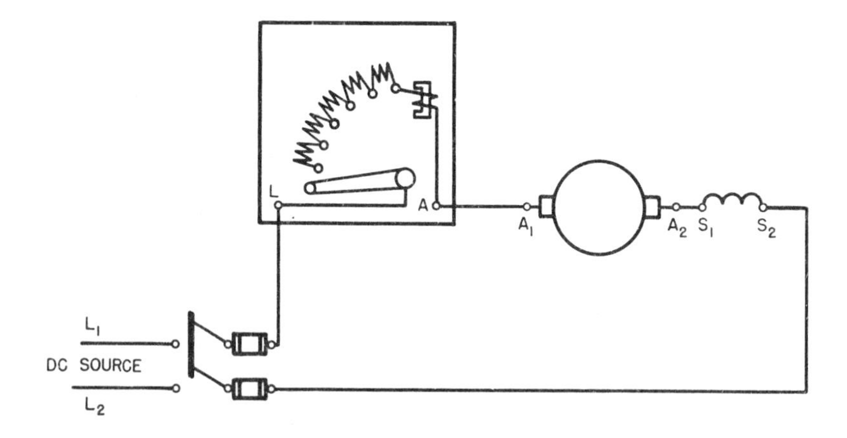

Fig. 23-11 Series Motor Starter With No-Load Protection

The same care is used in starting a motor with this type of starting rheostat as is used with three- and four-terminal starting rheostats. The arm is slowly moved from the off position to the run position, pausing on each contact button for a period of one to two seconds. The arm is held against the tension of the reset spring by means of the holding coil connected in series with the armature. If the load current to the motor drops to a low value the holding coil will weaken and the reset spring will return the arm to the off position. This is an important protective feature. It will be recalled that a series motor may reach a dangerously high speed at light loads. Therefore, if the motor current drops to such a low value that the speed becomes dangerous, the holding coil will release the arm to the off position. In this way damage to the motor caused by excessive speeds is avoided.

Drum Controllers

Series and cumulative compound motors are often used on cranes, elevators, machine tools, and other applications, where the motor is under the direct control of an operator. In these applications, frequent starting, varying of speed, stopping and reversing may be necessary. A manually operated controller, more rugged than a starting rheostat, called a drum controller, is used.

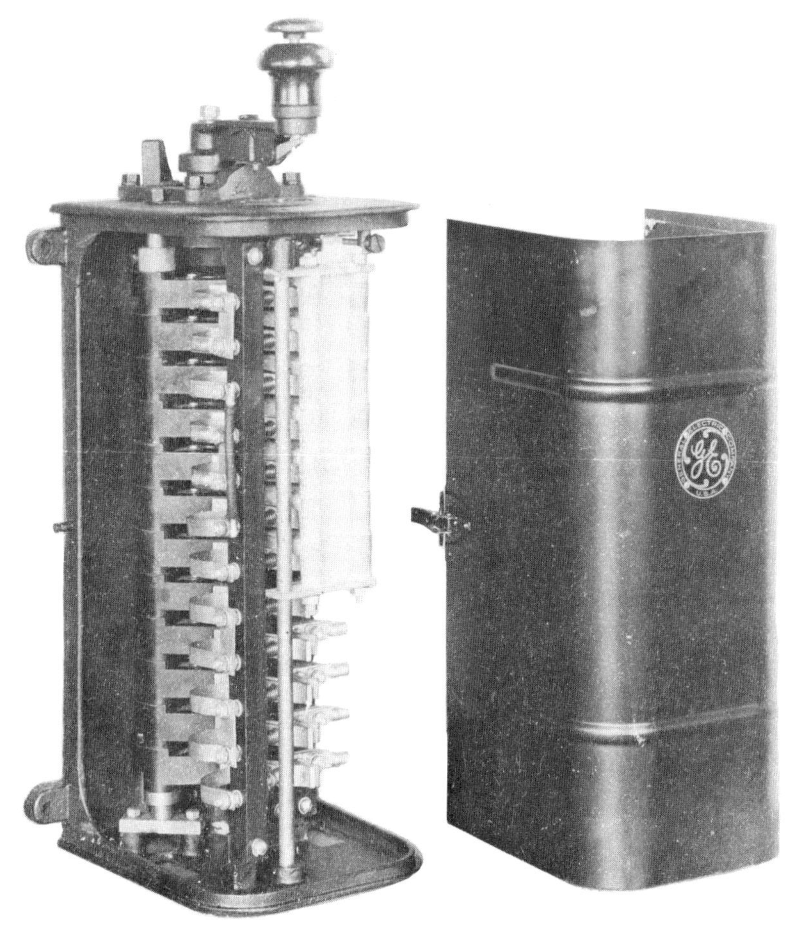

Fig. 23-12 Drum Controller

A typical drum controller is illustrated above. Inside the switch is a series of contacts mounted on a movable cylinder. These contacts, insulated from the cylinder and from each other are the movable contacts. There is another series of contacts located inside the controller, called stationary contacts. These stationary contacts are arranged to make contact with the movable contacts as the cylinder is rotated. On top of the drum controller is a handle which is keyed to the shaft for the movable cylinder and contacts. This handle can be moved in either a clockwise or counterclockwise direction, giving a range of speed control in either direction or rotation. Once set, a roller and notched wheel arrangement keeps the cylinder and movable contacts stationary until the handle is turned by the operator.

A drum controller having two steps of resistance is shown in Fig. 23-13. In this wiring diagram, the contacts are shown in a flat position to make it easier to trace connections. For operating in the forward direction, the set of contacts on the right make contact with the center stationary contacts. For operation in the reverse direction, the movable contacts on the left touch the stationary contacts in the center.

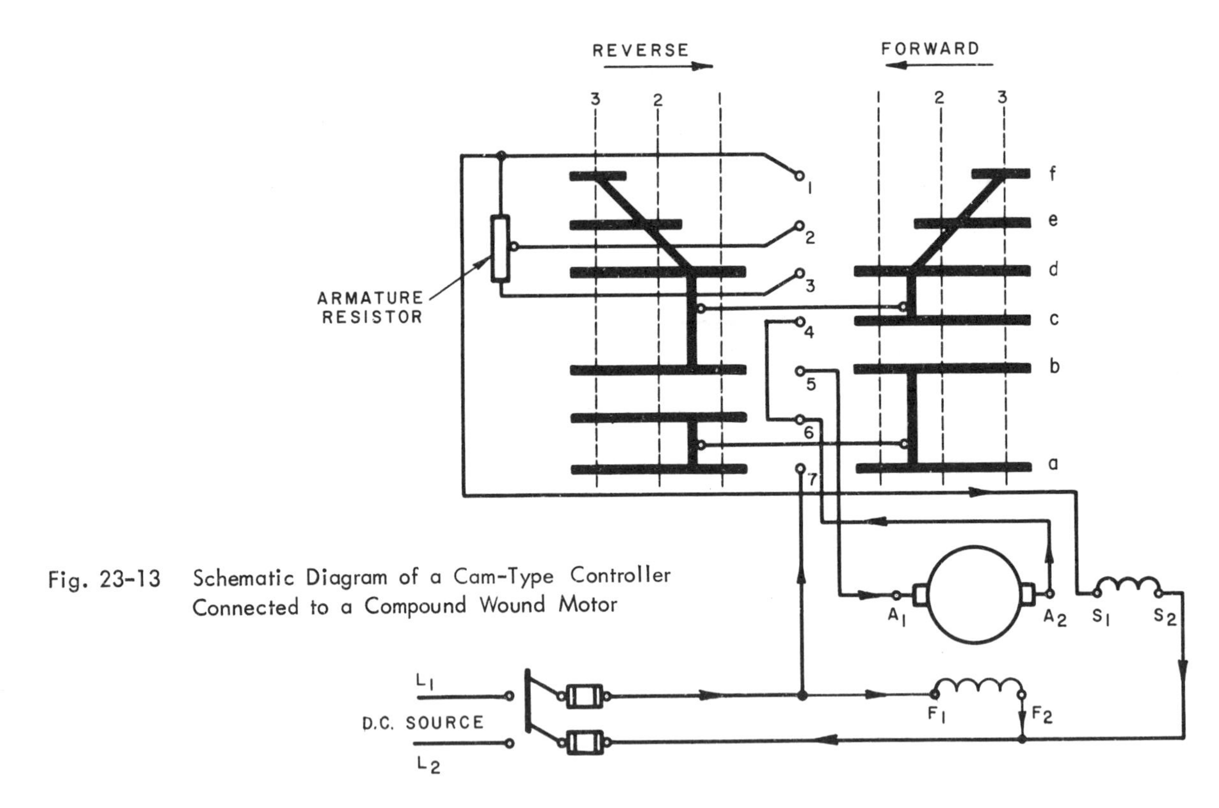

Fig. 23-13 Schematic Diagram of a Cam-Type Controller Connected to a Compound Wound Motor

In Fig. 23-13 it will be noted that there are three forward positions and three reverse positions to which the controller handle can be set. In the first forward position all resistance is in series with the armature. Tracing the circuit for the first forward position:

1. Movable fingers a, b, c, and d contact the stationary contacts 7, 5, 4, and 3.
2. The current path is from 7 to a, from a to b, from b to 5, and then to armature terminal A_1.
3. After passing through the armature winding to terminal A_2 the current path is to stationary contact 6, and then to stationary contact 4.
4. From contact 4 the current path is to contact c, to d, then to 3.
5. The current path is next through the entire armature resistor, through the series field, and then back to the line.

On the second position, part of the resistance is cut out by the connection from d to e. The third forward position bypasses all resistance and puts the armature circuit directly across the source voltage.

In the first reverse position all resistance is again inserted in series with the armature. Fig. 23-14 illustrates the first position of the controller in the reverse direction. A study of this circuit will show that the current in the armature circuit is reversed. However, the current direction in the shunt and series fields is the same as for the forward direction. It was shown earlier that changing current direction only in the armature results in a change of rotation.

On the second position, part of the resistance circuit is cut out. The third reverse position cuts out all resistance and puts the armature circuit directly across line voltage. More elaborate drum controllers can be obtained with more positions for a greater control of speed. However, they all use practically this same circuit arrangement.

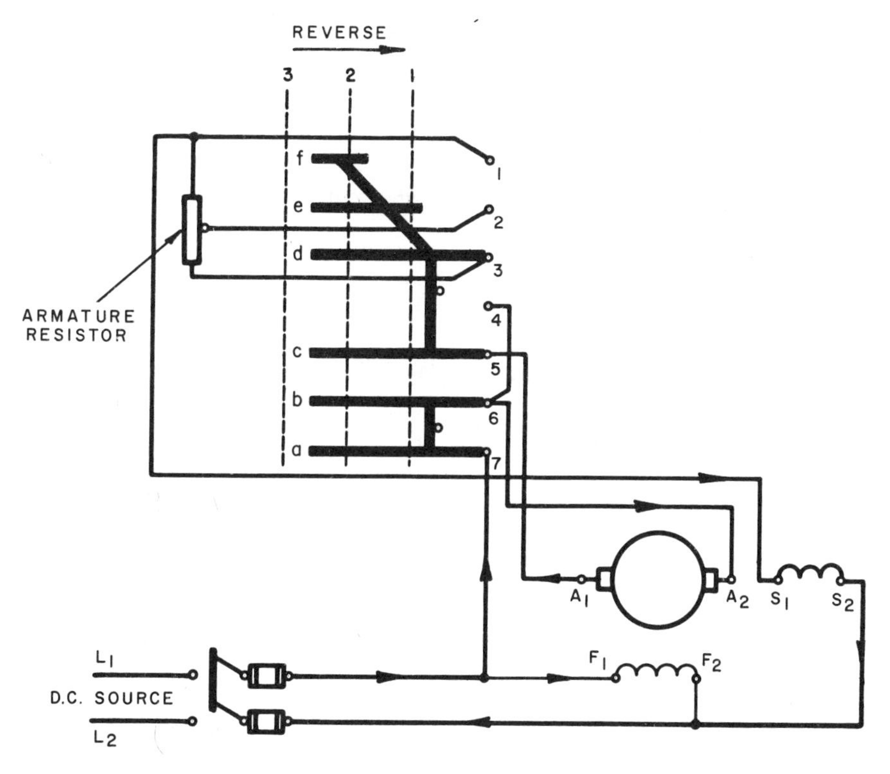

Fig. 23-14 First Position of Controller for Reverse Direction

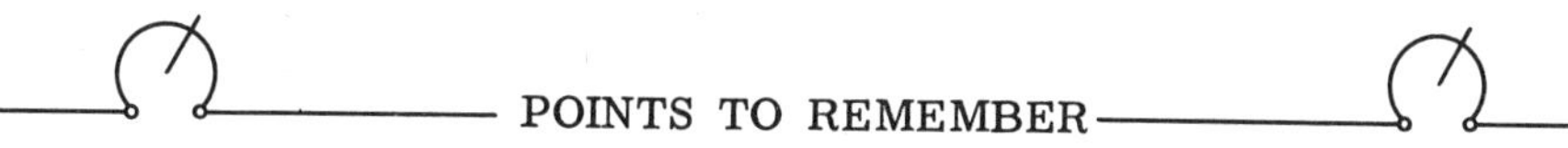

POINTS TO REMEMBER

- Definition of a manual starting rheostat as defined by N.E.M.A.

- The internal and external connections of a three-terminal manual starting rheostat and its specific functions and the internal and external connections of a four-terminal manual starting rheostat and its specific functions.

- The difference between a manual starting rheostat and a manual speed controller as defined by N.E.M.A.

- The internal and external connections for above-normal speed controllers and above- and below-normal controllers.

- The internal and external connections for the no-voltage manual series motor starting rheostat and the no-load manual series motor starting rheostat.

- The specific uses for drum controllers in industry and an understanding of the circuit arrangements used to obtain the desired control of speed and direction of rotation.

REVIEW QUESTIONS

1. Show the connections for a three-terminal manual starting rheostat connected to a shunt motor.

2. Give one advantage and one disadvantage of a three-terminal manual starting rheostat.

3. Show the connections for a four-terminal manual starting rheostat connected to a cumulative compound motor. Include a separate field rheostat in the shunt field circuit for speed control.

4. Give one advantage and one disadvantage of a four-terminal manual starting rheostat.

5. A three-terminal manual starting rheostat has a resistance of 5.2 ohms to its starting resistor. The holding coil resistance is 10 ohms. This starting rheostat is connected to a shunt motor. The resistance of the armature is 0.22 ohm while the resistance of the shunt field is 100 ohms. The line voltage for this motor circuit is 220 volts.

   (a) Determine the starting surge of current taken by the motor.

   (b) The motor has a full-load current rating of 30 amperes. The National Fire Underwriters require the starting surge of current to be not greater than 150% of a motor's full-load current rating. Show with computations whether this manual starting rheostat complies with this requirement.

6. Using the data in Problem 5, determine:

   (a) The current in the holding coil with the movable arm in the run position.

   (b) The counterelectromotive force with the movable arm in the run position if the armature current is 20 amperes.

7. Explain the difference between a manual starting rheostat and a manual speed controller.

8. Why does one type of manual starting rheostat used with series motors have no-load protection?

9. State applications of the drum controller. Why is it desirable in these applications?

10. Explain why a shunt motor's direction of rotation will not change if the connections of the two line wires are reversed.

11. What is the function of a holding coil in a manual starting rheostat?

12. Explain how you would reverse the direction of rotation of:

    (a) A shunt motor

    (b) A series motor

    (c) A cumulative compound motor.

13. Complete the internal and external connections for the above normal-speed controller and cumulative compound motor shown in the following diagram.

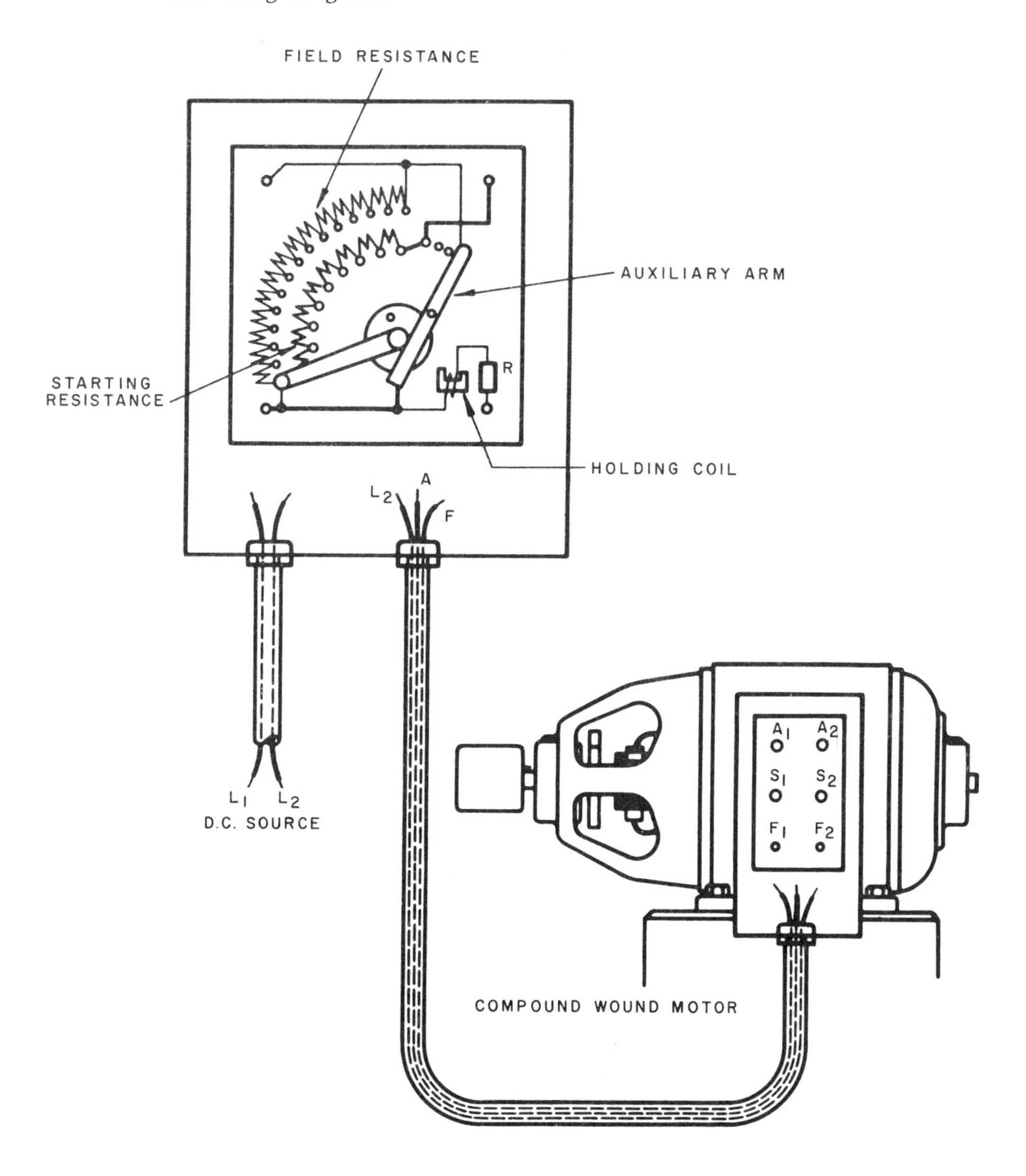

14. Complete the internal and external connections for the above- and below-normal speed controller and cumulative compound motor illustrated in the following diagram:

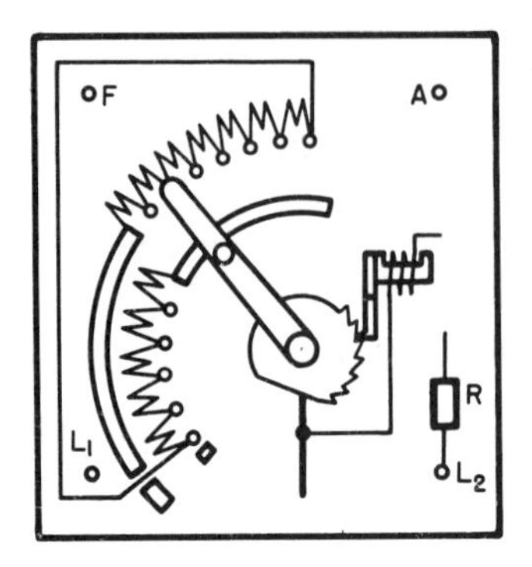

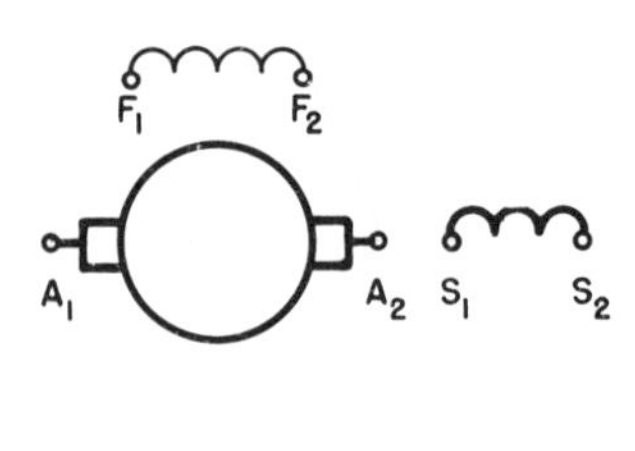

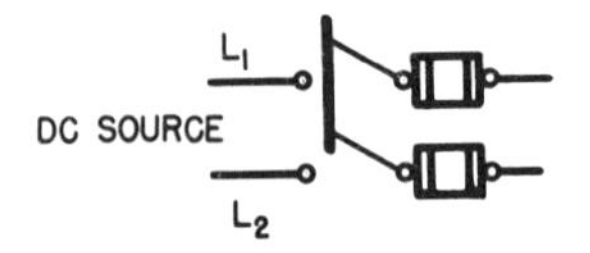

Unit 24 AUTOMATIC MOTOR CONTROL

In present industrial practice, each individual machine is operated by its own motor, with increasing use of pushbutton starting and stopping. Pushbutton-operated automatic starting and control equipment is convenient and has the added advantage of reducing damage caused by human misjudgment. Many of these automatic systems control D.C. motors, which are used because of their wide speed range and excellent torque characteristics.

Two types of circuit diagrams are used in automatic controller work: schematic diagrams and panel wiring diagrams. Schematic diagrams, using symbols rather than pictures of equipment, indicate as clearly as possible how separate pieces of equipment are connected in a circuit. Schematic diagrams are used in the study of a scheme of control and the sequence of operations of electrical devices. Panel wiring diagrams show the physical parts of the controller in their normal physical position on the panel, with each wire shown in its actual correct location. External connections from the controller to the motor are also shown. The wireman uses this type of diagram in the actual wiring of the control panel. The panel-wiring maze is difficult to use in studying the operation of the controller; therefore the schematic is used for understanding the sequence of operations and also as an aid in locating troubles in the controller. The symbols for relay coils, contactors, pushbutton stations, overload devices and other components are used in the schematic and panel-wiring diagrams which follow in this Unit.

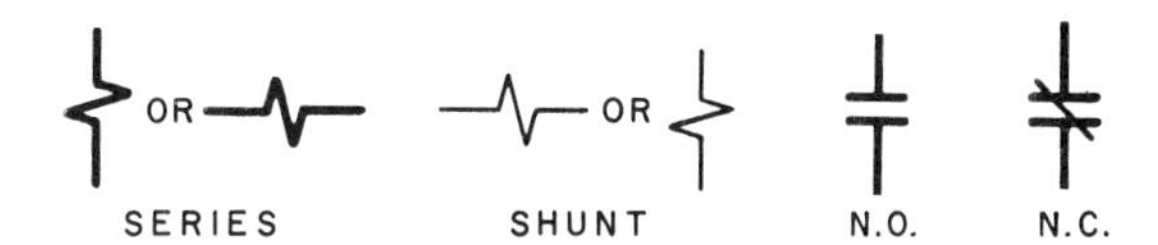

Fig. 24-2 Symbols of Contactor Elements

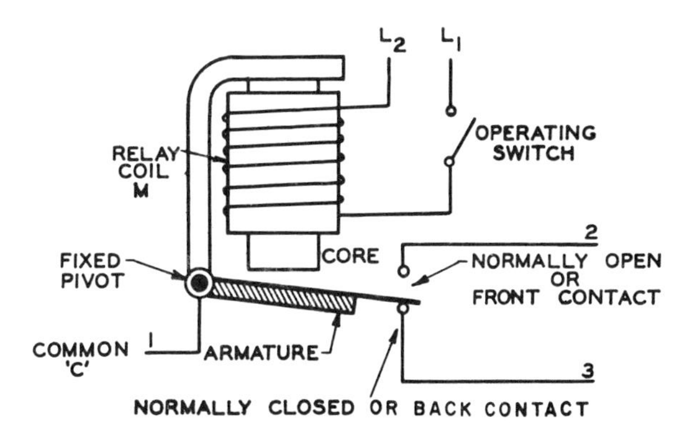

Fig. 24-1 D.C. Magnetic Time Delay Relay

Contactors operated by relays are an important part of any automatic motor controller. A contactor is a switch which is closed or opened by the magnetic pull of an energized relay coil. Fig. 24-1 shows a relay coil with contactors. A relay coil connected in series in the circuit is normally represented by a heavy line (see Fig. 24-2). If the relay coil is connected in parallel, a lightweight line symbol is used. Contactors which are open when the coil is de-energized are known as normally open (N.O.) contactors and are indicated by two short parallel lines. Normally-closed (N.C.) contactors, which are closed when the coil is de-energized, are represented by a slant line drawn across two parallel lines.

When contactors interrupt a large current, a very severe arc forms, which can burn the surface of the contactor. To reduce this burning effect, a "magnetic blowout coil" in series with the contactors extinguishes the arc by electromagnetic action.

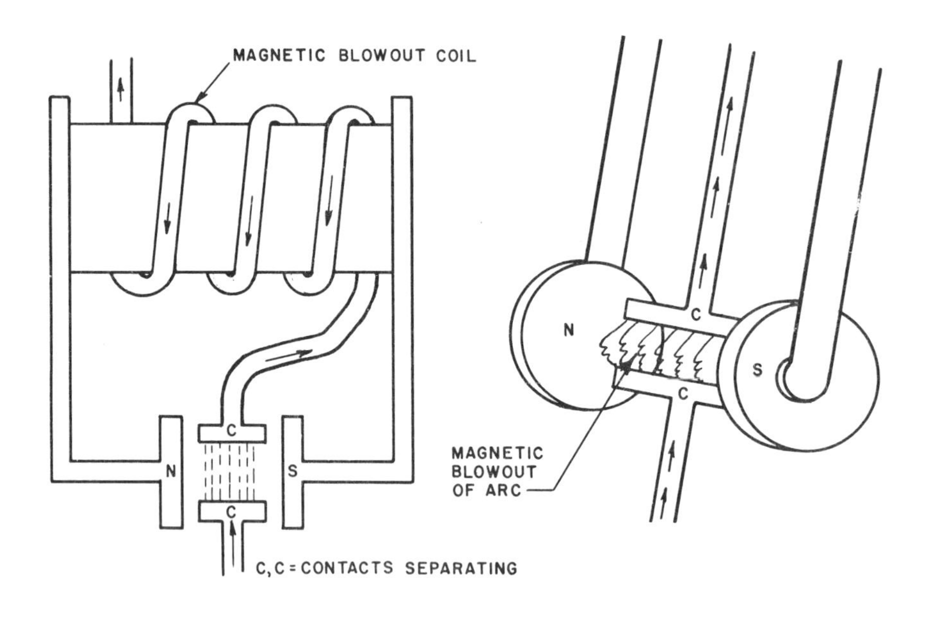

Fig. 24-3 Electromagnetic Action of Magnetic Blowout Coil with Contactors

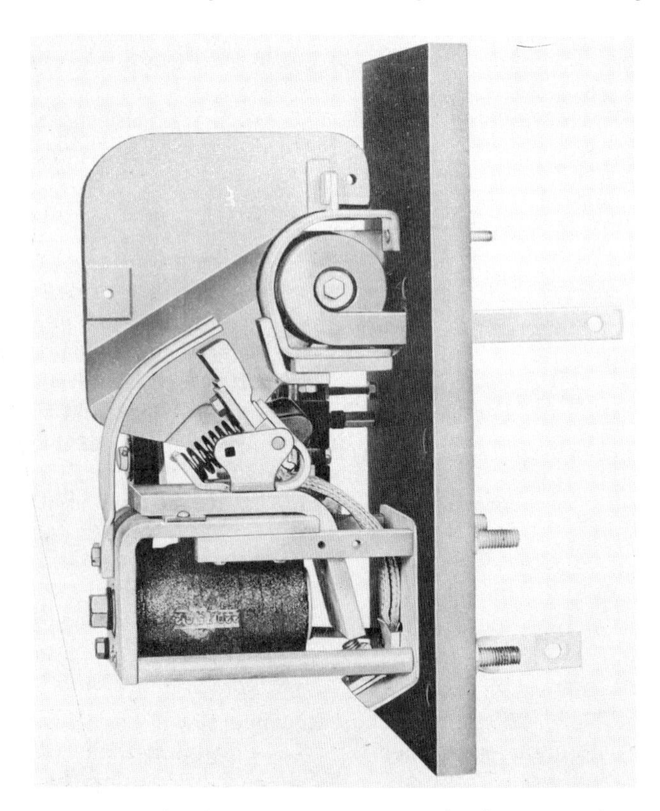

Fig. 24-4 Magnetic Contactors with Blowout Coil and Arc-chute

Fig. 24-4, left, shows a typical relay coil with contactors and a blowout coil with arc chute to minimize heavy arcing.

Fig. 24-5, below, shows its schematic symbol.

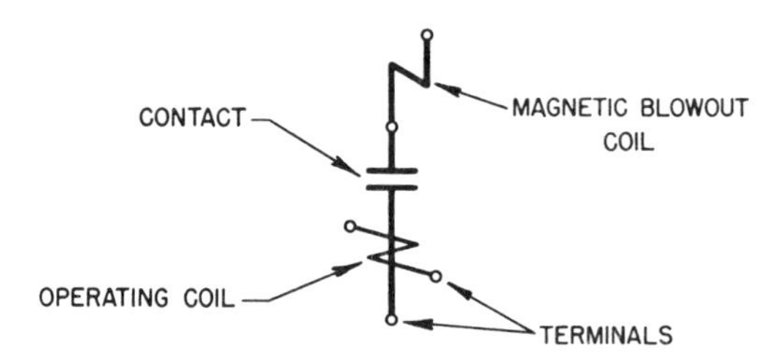

Fig. 24-5 D.C. Magnetic Contactor Symbols

Fig. 24-6 A Typical Pushbutton Station

N.C.

OPEN AND CLOSED

Fig. 24-7 Pushbutton Symbols

Fig. 24-6 shows a typical pushbutton station used with an automatic controller. The push-buttons are really spring-controlled switches. Pressure on the normally-open "start" pushbutton closes the switch contacts and when the button is released, the spring re-opens the switch. The "stop" button is a normally closed switch; finger pressure opens the contacts, which close again when pressure is released.

These pushbuttons generally are used in connection with a relay coil, as shown below. This diagram represents part of an elementary control circuit.

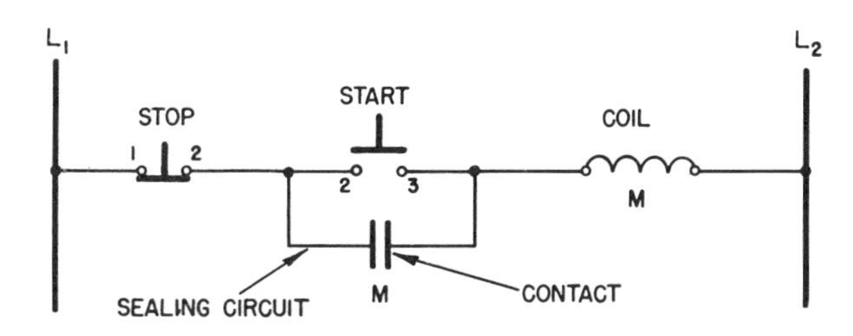

Fig. 24-8 A Control Circuit with Start and Stop Buttons and Sealing Circuit

When the 'start' button is pressed, closing contacts 2-3, there is a circuit from line L_1 through normally-closed contacts 1-2, through 2-3, and through relay coil M to supply line L_2. The current in relay coil M causes contact M to be held closed, so that when the 'start' button is released, opening contacts 2-3, there is still a circuit through the 'stop' button 1-2, through contacts M, and through coil M to L_2. This arrangement, called a "sealing circuit", is a part of control circuits soon to be described. Momentary pressure on the "start" button energizes the relay coil, and sealing contacts M keep the coil energized. In control circuits, coil M also closes other contactors, as well as the sealing contact.

When the 'stop' button is momentarily pressed, the circuit is broken, coil M loses its magnetic pull, contacts M open, and the release of the 'stop' button, closing 1-2, does not re-establish the circuit. Both contact M and the start button are open, so coil M cannot be energized until the 'start' button again closes the circuit at 2-3.

There are so many types of automatic controllers used for special applications that it would be impossible to cover all of them in this unit. Therefore, three standard types will be described in some detail:

1. The Counter Electromotive Force Controller
2. The Voltage Drop Acceleration Controller
3. The Definite Time Limit Controller

THE COUNTER ELECTROMOTIVE FORCE MOTOR CONTROLLER

This is a commonly used method for automatic acceleration of a D.C. motor.

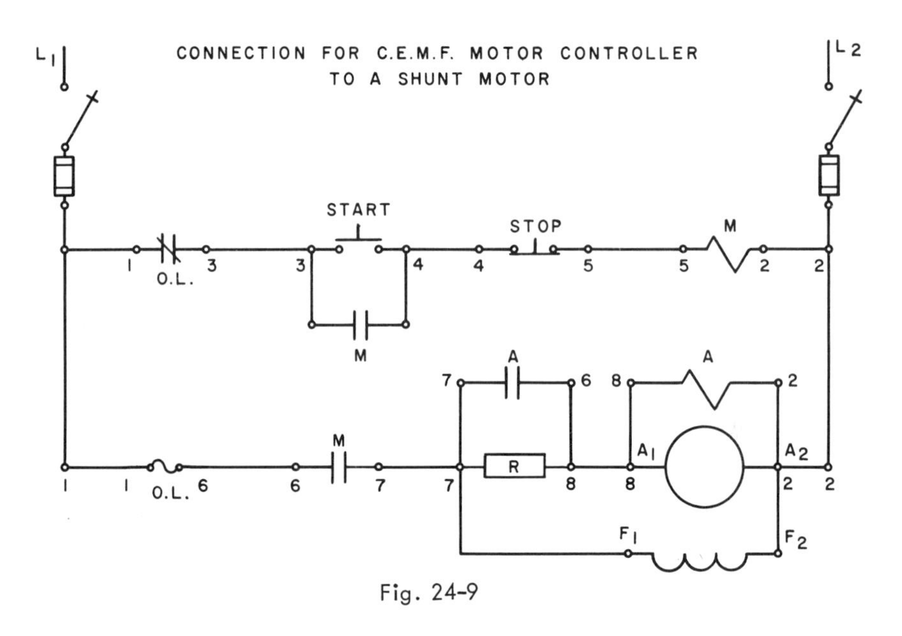

Fig. 24-9

In operating this controller, the line switch is first closed. When the "start" button is pressed, relay coil M is energized. This control circuit remains energized, due to closing of the sealing contacts as previously described.

When coil M in the control circuit is energized, it also closes a heavy pair of contactors (M, 6-7) in the power circuit. The closing of these contacts establishes a circuit from line 1 through the overload device (1-6), through the M contactors, through the current-limiting resistor in series with the armature, and through the armature windings to the other side of the line. The shunt field is directly across full line voltage to assure maximum starting torque.

At the instant the motor circuit is energized, the back e.m.f. is zero and practically all of the line voltage is expended on the current-limiting resistor in series with the armature. As the armature accelerates, counter e.m.f. increases in proportion to the speed. With increased counter e.m.f., more of the line voltage appears across the armature terminals and also across the "accelerating relay" coil A, which is in parallel with the armature terminals. Relay coil A is calibrated to close its contactors when about 80% of rated line voltage is applied to the coil. When the voltage across the armature terminals reaches this predetermined value (80% of line voltage), coil A closes contactors A which shunt out the resistor in series with the armature. Now the armature is connected directly across line voltage and the motor accelerates to rated speed.

Pressing the "stop" button breaks the control circuit and both sets of M contactors open, disconnecting the motor from the line. As the armature slows down, coil A is unable to hold its contactors closed. With the A contactors open, the current-limiting resistor is again in series with the armature. Now the motor is again ready to be started.

Starting protection for this controller, or any D.C. automatic controller, consists of fuses or circuit breakers rated at 150% of the motor's full load current. Running overload protection is provided by the overload heater unit (O.L. 1-6), overheating of which causes a bi-metal strip to trip open the normally-closed contactor (O.L. 1-3) in the control circuit. This heater unit is rated at 125% of the motor's full load current rating. A continued overload on the motor for 45-60 seconds causes it to operate. The 150% starting current surge does not last long enough (3 to 4 seconds) to heat the thermal element enough to cause it to open its contactors.

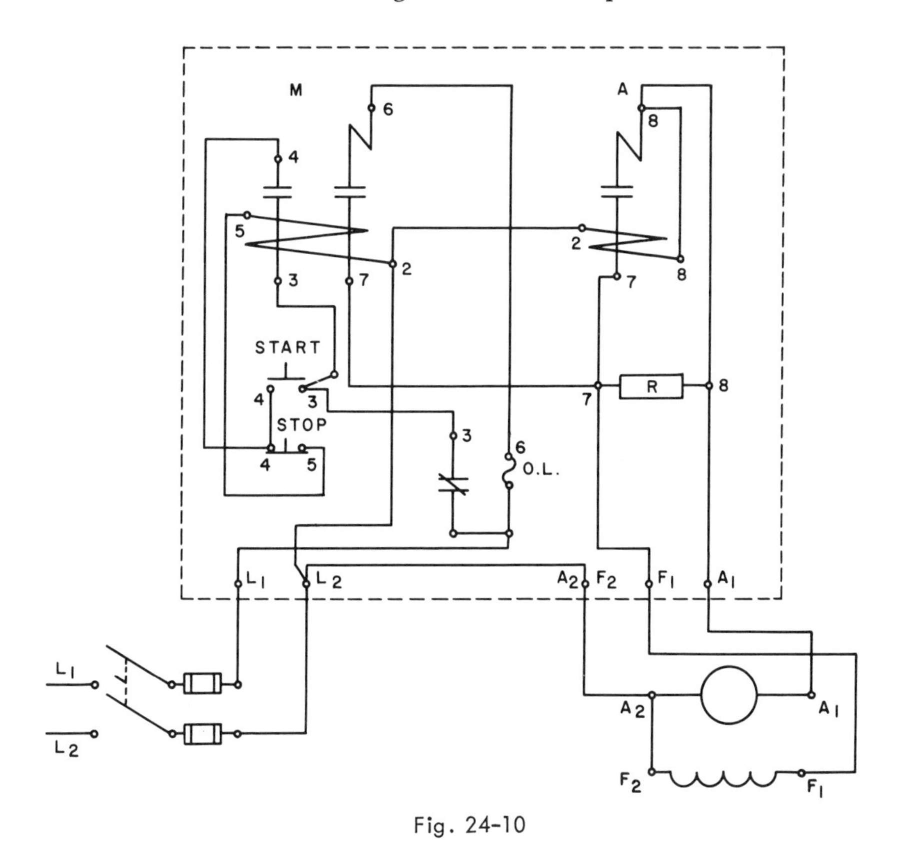

Fig. 24-10

Fig. 24-10 is a panel wiring diagram of the same controller shown in the schematic diagram, Fig. 24-9. Note that the numbering system and scheme of wiring is exactly the same in both diagrams.

DYNAMIC BRAKING

In some installations there is need for quick stopping and immediate reversal of rotation. "Dynamic braking" is a method for quickly using up the mechanical energy of motion of the armature and its mechanical load after the armature circuit is opened. This is done by connecting a resistor across the armature at the instant the armature circuit is disconnected. The disconnected armature, rotating on its own momentum, is cutting flux and acting as a generator. The generated current quickly dissipates this mechanical energy by heating the resistor, and thus stops the motor quickly.

The next Figure shows how dynamic braking facilities can be added to the previously-described counter e.m.f. controller. At starting, the same sequence of events takes place as was described before.

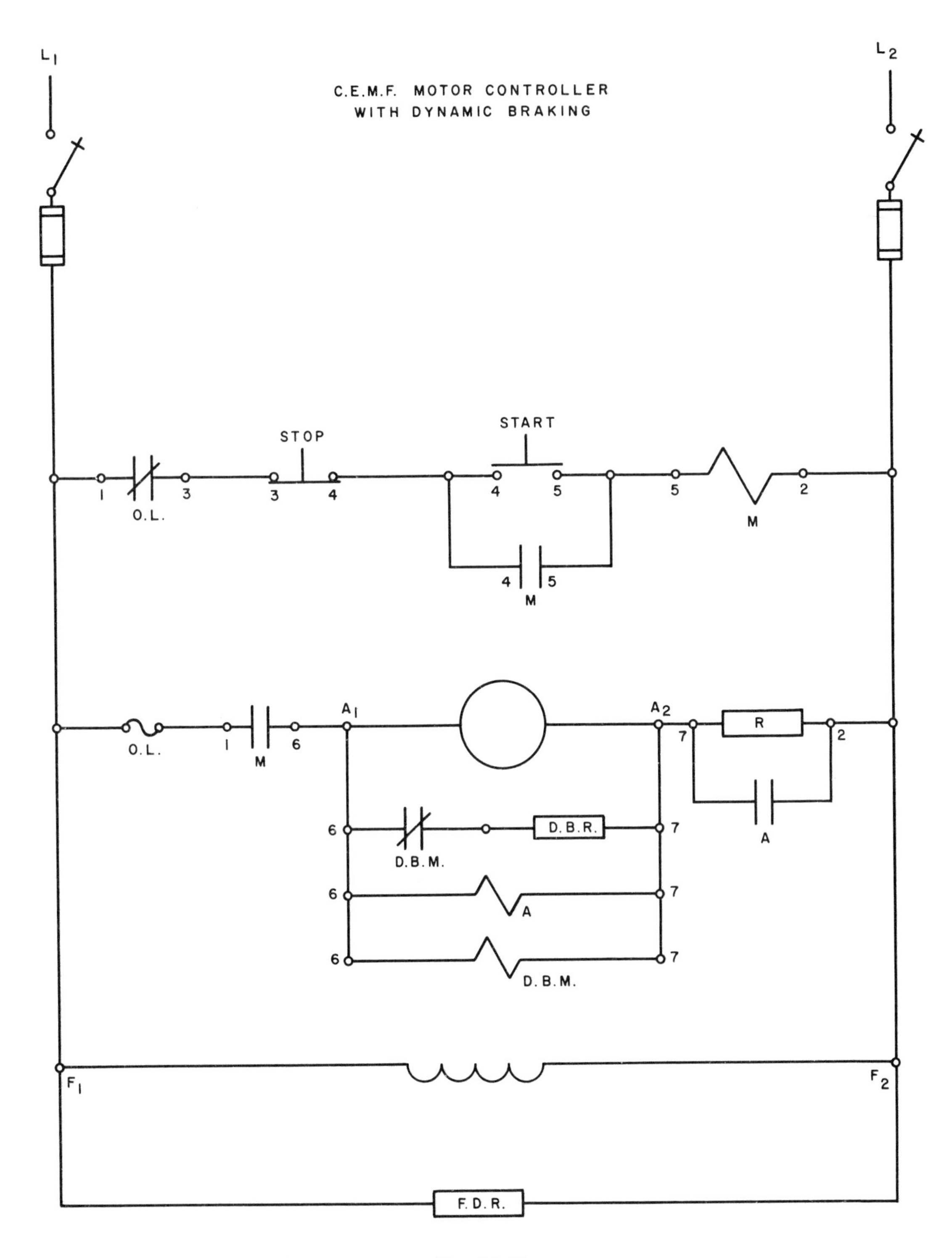

Fig. 24-11

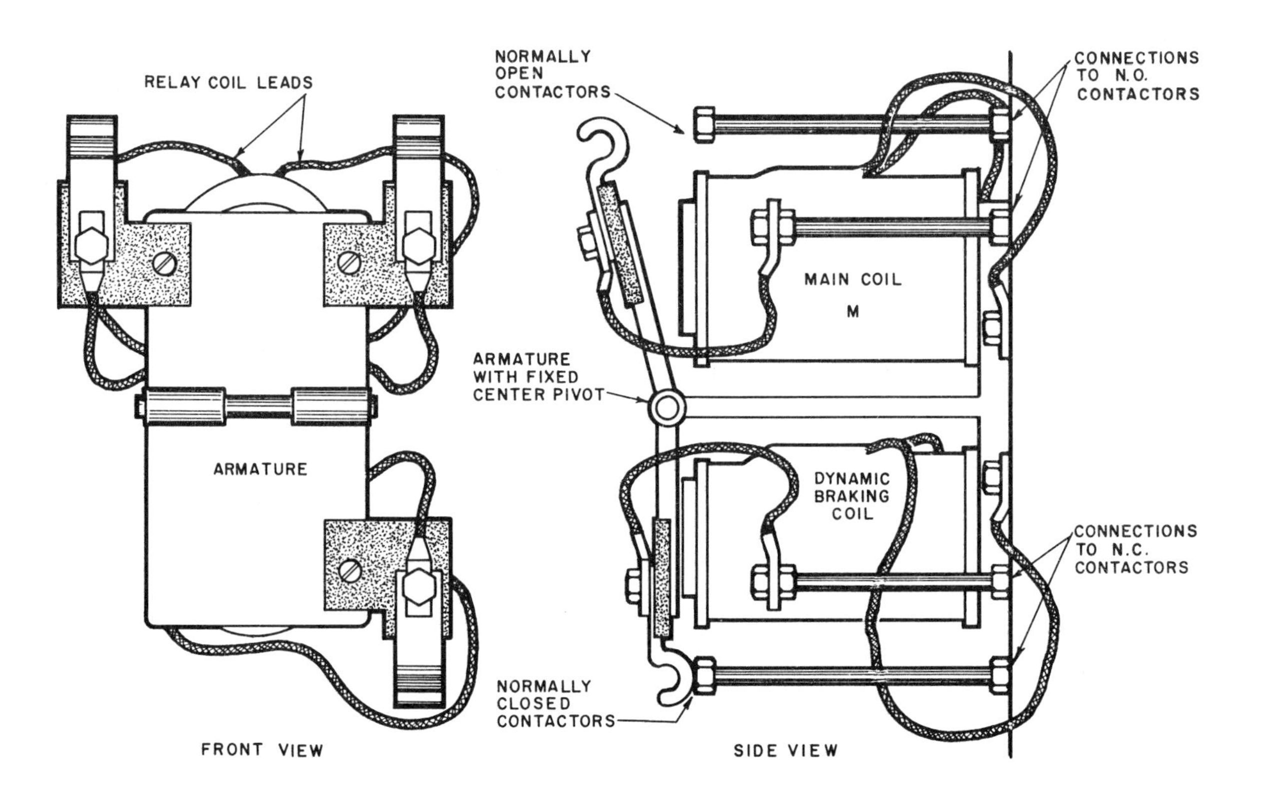

Fig. 24-12 Direct Current Contactor Assembly

Relay coil M and the dynamic braking coil (DBM, 6-7) operate on one pivoted armature, as shown in Fig. 24-12. When the 'start' button is pressed, coil M closes the normally open contactors, pulling open the one set of D.B.M. contactors. As the motor accelerates, relay coil A shunts out the current limiting resistor as before. Although the D.B.M. coil is now energized by full line voltage, coil M has already tipped the pivoted armature clockwise, opening the D.B.M. contact. Coil D.B.M. is not strong enough to bring the armature back to the position shown in Fig. 24-12, so the D.B.M. contactors remain open while the motor operates normally.

When the 'stop' button is pressed, coil M releases the pivoted relay armature. The shunt field of the motor is still connected to the line, so the rotating armature of the motor generates a current that keeps coil D.B.M. energized. Coil D.B.M. is now able to pull contactors D.B.M. to their normally closed position, coil M being de-energized. (Small coiled springs, not shown in Fig. 24-12, help make this action more positive.) With D.B.M. contactors closed, the dynamic braking resistor is connected directly across the motor armature. Now the motor armature, acting as a generator, converts its mechanical energy into electrical energy which is quickly dissipated in the D.B.R. resistor, and the motor armature comes to a quick stop. Coil A releases contactors A, reinserting the current-limiting resistor in series with the armature.

In the circuit of Fig. 24-9, the pressing of the 'stop' button disconnected the entire motor circuit from the line. In that case, the collapsing magnetic field of the shunt field winding delivered its energy to the armature circuit. In the circuit of Fig. 24-11, since the armature is disconnected from the field when the stop button is pressed, a field discharge resistor (FDR) is connected across the field to dissipate the field energy when the line switch is opened.

COUNTER E.M.F. CONTROLLER WITH REVERSING AND DYNAMIC BRAKING

In many applications, it is necessary not only to bring a motor to a quick stop, but also to reverse the direction of rotation immediately. This is usually done by reversal of armature connections, as shown in the circuit below.

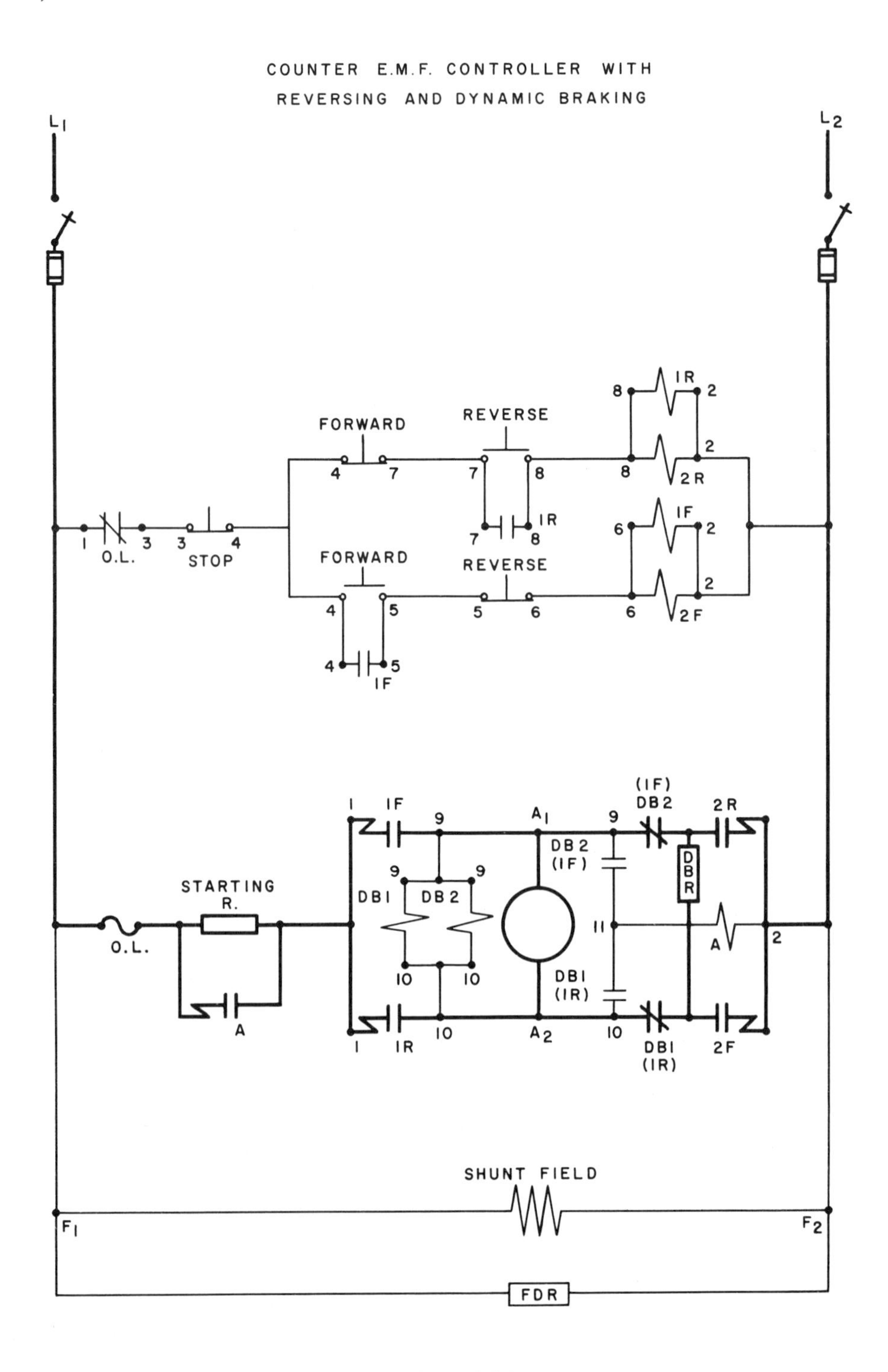

Fig. 24-13

When the "forward" button is pressed, it breaks the normally closed contact (4-7) and makes contact at the normally open terminals (4-5). Relay coils 1F and 2F become energized, closing the 1F sealing contact (4-5), and closing the armature-current contactors 1F and 2F. The normally-closed contactors marked (1F) DB2 are held open by a relay like that of Fig. 24-12, so that the dynamic braking resistor is disconnected when the motor is energized. The normally-open contactors DB2 (1F) at points 9-11 close and connect the accelerating relay coil A across the armature. As the motor accelerates, relay coil A closes contactors A, putting full line voltage on the armature so the motor operates at rated speed.

Pressing the 'stop' button opens the control circuit, so contactors 1F and 2F open and disconnect the armature from the line. Contactors DB2 (1F) also open, de-energizing relay coil A, which opens contactors A. Also, the normally closed (1F) DB2 will reclose and connect the dynamic braking resistor across the armature so that the motor stops quickly.

Following the same starting procedure by noting the sequence of operations when the 'reverse' button is pressed, one finds that the direction of current in the armature is reversed. The motor will accelerate in the reverse direction, and when the armature e.m.f. is high enough, coil A closes contactors A, and the motor operates at rated speed in the reverse direction. Use of the 'stop' button opens contactors A and inserts the dynamic braking resistor in the circuit as before.

In the circuit of Fig. 24-13, the forward and reverse pushbuttons each have a normally closed contact and also a normally open contact. This circuit arrangement makes it impossible to energize the 'reverse' relays (1R and 2R) until the 'forward' relays (1F and 2F) are de-energized. For example, if the 'reverse' button is pressed, it will first break contact at points 5-6 and de-energize coils 1F and 2F before closing across points 7-8 and energizing relay coils 1R and 2R. The same protection exists if relay coils 1R and 2R were energized and the forward button were pressed. This type of connection arrangement, called electrical interlocking, is often used in control circuitry so that when one set of devices are operating, the circuit to a second set of devices cannot be energized at the same time.

THE VOLTAGE DROP ACCELERATION CONTROLLER

Large D.C. motors require controlled steps of acceleration. A series of resistors connected to lockout relays provide the means for smooth and uniform motor acceleration.

Like the counter e.m.f. controller, the voltage drop acceleration controller makes use of these facts:

1. At the instant of starting, armature current is high, voltage across the armature is low, and voltage losses across each of the current-limiting resistors connected in series is high.

2. As the motor accelerates, the counter e.m.f. increases and the armature current decreases. Therefore, the voltage drop across the current-limiting resistors in series with the armature, decreases. Relays connected across these resistors are calibrated to operate and shunt out the starting resistors in a definite sequence as the armature speed increases.

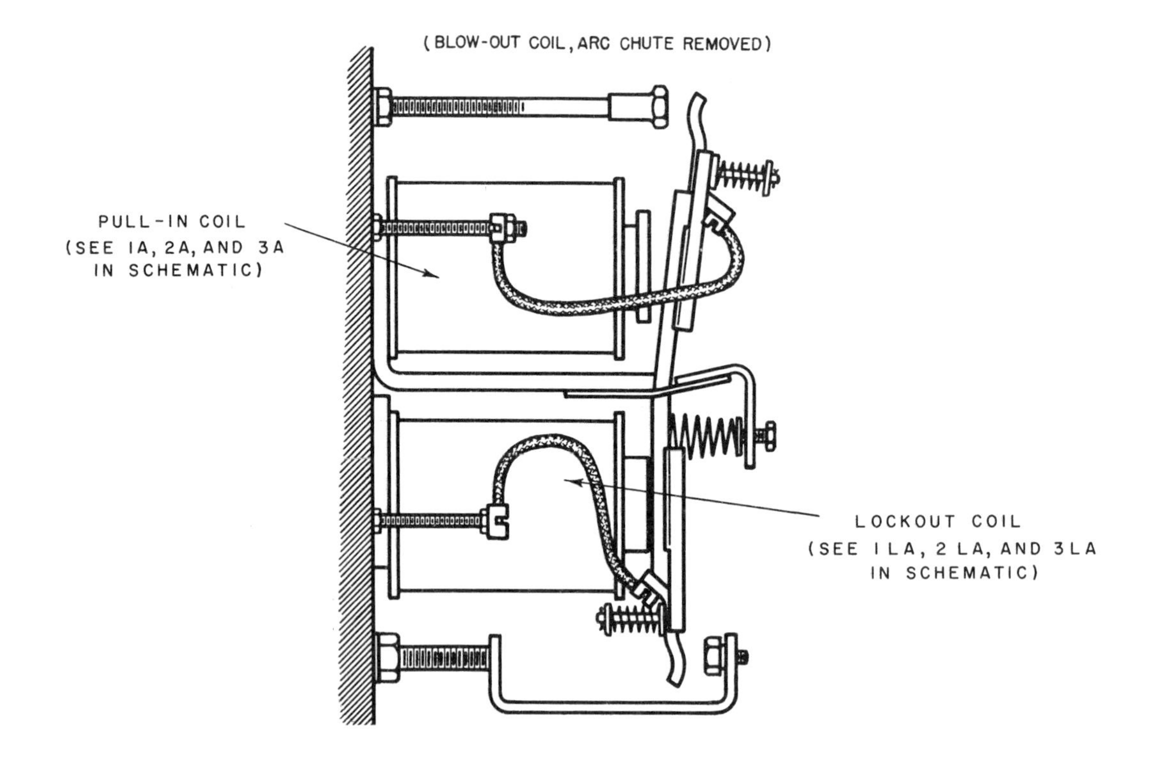

Fig. 24-14 A Lockout Relay

The sketch above shows a typical lockout relay. Two coils affect the one pivoted armature. The normally open contacts can be held open by the lockout coil, even if the pull-in coil is energized. With reduced current in the lockout coil, the energized pull-in coil can tip the armature and close the contacts. Each of the three relays in the schematic diagram (Fig. 24-15) are the same as in Fig. 24-14.

The relay coils marked 1A, 2A, and 3A are pull-in coils. Relay coils marked 1LA, 2LA, and 3LA are lockout coils.

Fig. 24-15 shows a voltage drop acceleration controller connected to a cumulative compound motor. There are three resistors so there are three steps of acceleration. After the line switch is closed, pressure on the 'start' button energizes relay coil M in the control circuit. Coil M closes main contactors M (9-10) which both closes the armature circuit and connects the shunt field across the line. The initial current through the starting resistors (R1, R2, R3) produces a relatively large voltage drop across each section of starting resistance. Therefore, the lockout coil (LA) of each relay has a relatively high voltage across it and can hold the accelerating contactors (1A, 2A, 3A) open. At the instant of starting, coil M also closes the sealing contactors M (3-6) and M (6-4). The short time interval required for closing these contacts insures that the pull-in coils (1A, 2A, 3A) become energized no sooner than the lockout coils.

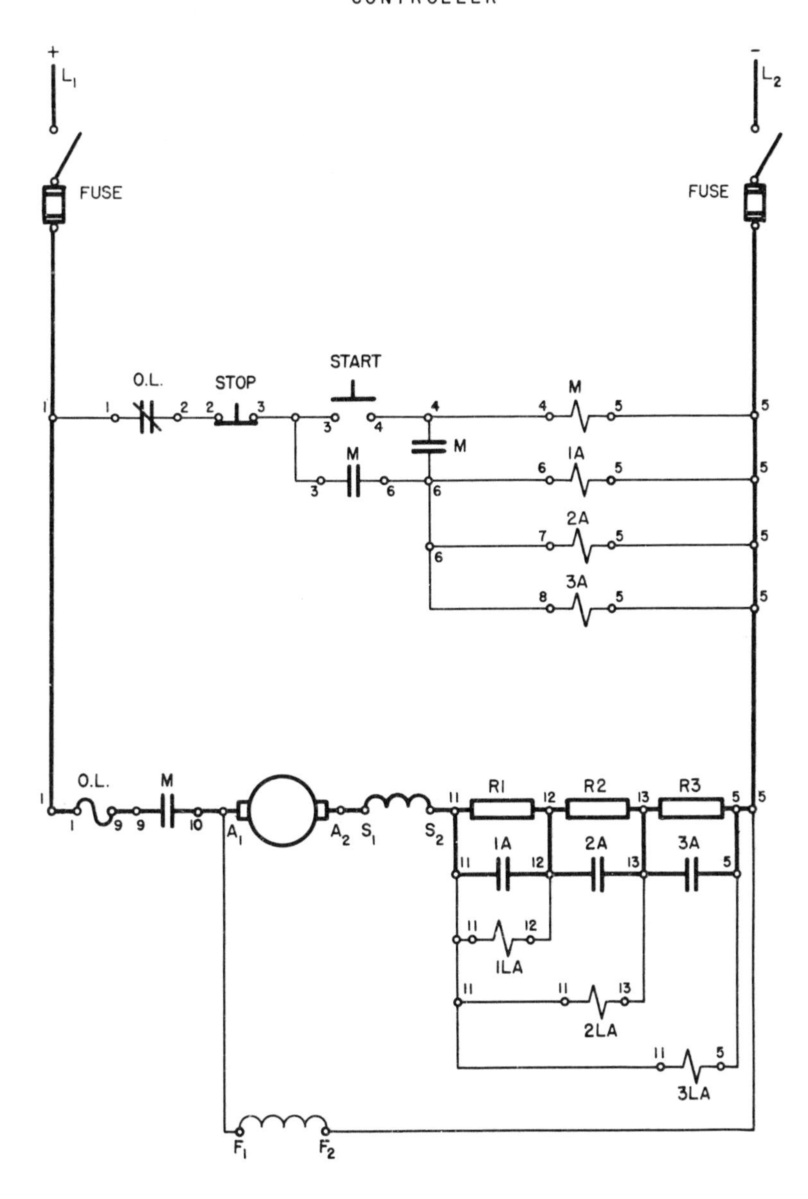

Fig. 24-15

The lockout relays are calibrated to operate and shunt out sections of starting resistance in a definite sequence as the armature accelerates. As current through the series resistors decreases during acceleration, less voltage is impressed on lockout coil 1LA, its pull on the movable contactor becomes less than that of pull-in coil 1A, so that the pull-in coil can close contactors 1A and shunt out resistor R1. As R1 is cut out of the circuit, current increases, but decreases again as the motor continues to accelerate. Soon the voltage across 2LA is low enough to allow pull-in coil 2A to close contactors 2A and shunt out R2. Then R3 is cut out in the same manner as R1 and R2. Thus, the motor is accelerated to rated speed in three steps.

DEFINITE TIME CONTROLLER

The function of this controller is to short out starting resistance, thus connecting the armature across line voltage, at a predetermined time after the pressing of the start button. The closing of contactors after a definite time interval is controlled by either a very small constant-speed motor, or by one of several types of magnetic timing devices. The schematic of Fig. 24-16 shows a definite time controller using a magnetic timer escapement, which controls the closing of contactors by a solenoid type of relay.

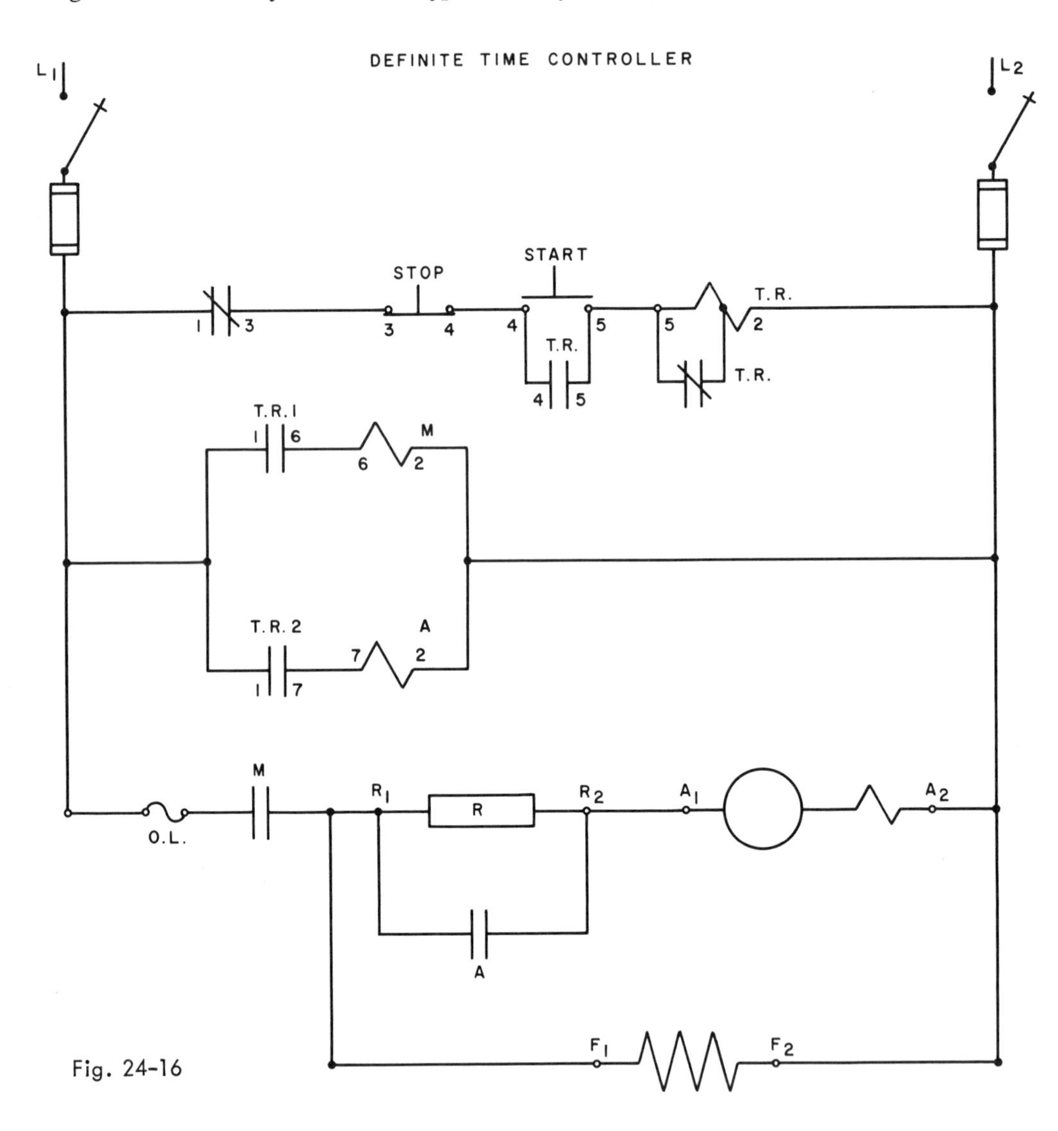

Fig. 24-16

Closing of the start button completes the control circuit from line 1 to point 5, through N.C. contactors which shunt out one part of the time-relay coil, and through the rest of the time relay coil to line 2. As the energized solenoid relay coil TR starts to pull its iron plunger up into the coil (Fig. 24-17) another small set of contactors marked TR1 close, energizing an entirely different relay marked M. Relay coil M closes the heavy M contactors, establishing a circuit path through the series current-limiting resistor and the armature, and also connecting the shunt field across line voltage. The motor now accelerates toward rated speed.

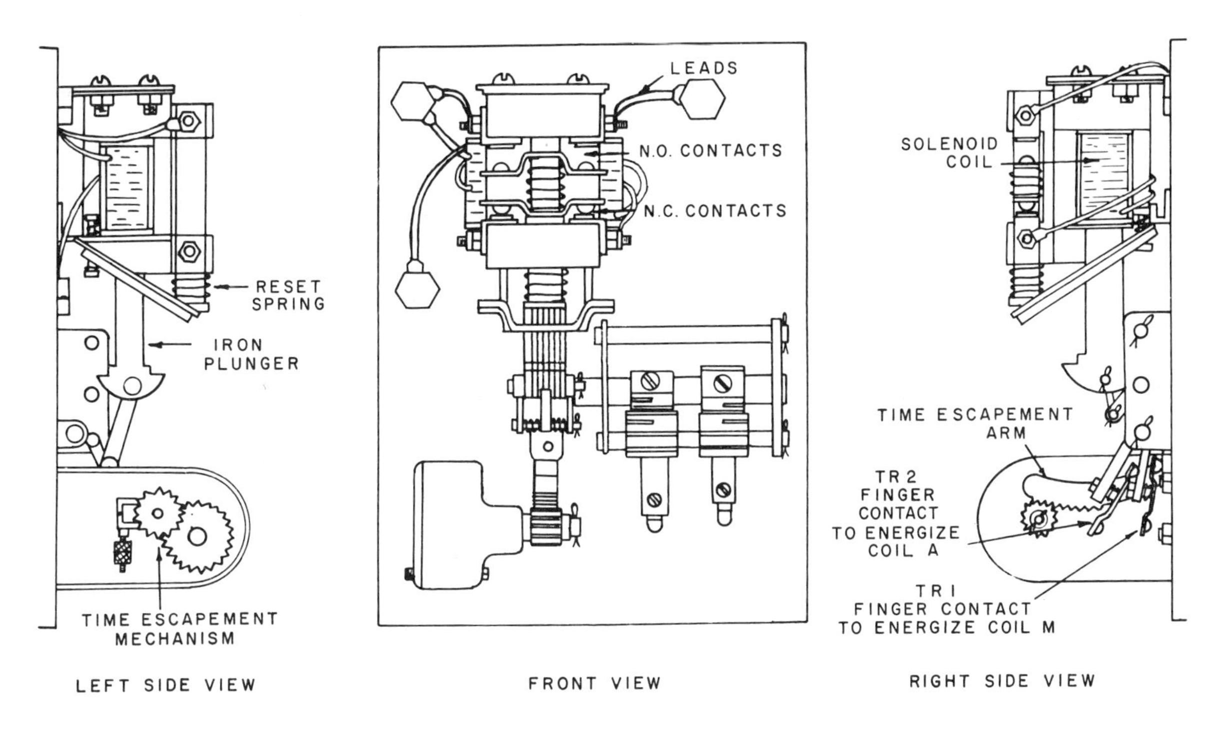

DEFINITE TIME DELAY MECHANISM

Fig. 24-17

Meanwhile, the solenoid relay coil TR is pulling the plunger up into the coil at a rate determined by the time escapement mechanism. Finally, the plunger is pulled up as far as possible, which closes contactors TR2 which energize relay coil A. Coil A closes contactors A, which shunt out the current-limiting resistor and place the armature directly across line voltage. In the definite time interval between the closing of contactors M and contactors A, it is assumed that counter e.m.f. has become sufficient to permit applying full-line voltage to the armature.

Full movement of the plunger into the solenoid coil opens the N.C. contactors TR which had bypassed part of the solenoid relay coil TR. After the plunger has moved fully into the coil, considerably less current is required to hold the plunger in operating position than when the TR coil was initially energized. Therefore, the current in coil TR is decreased considerably by cutting in a high resistance section of the coil, once the plunger is in its final operating position. This eliminates unnessary energy loss.

In Fig. 24-17, left side view, note the escapement mechanism which controls the time required for the solenoid coil to pull up the plunger. TR1 closes first, energizing relay coil M, then after the definite time interval, contactors TR2 close, energizing coil A. The front view and right side view show the normally open TR contactors which act as sealing contactors around the start button. Nearby are the normally closed contacts which are connected across part of the TR solenoid coil.

The starting overload and running overload protection used with this controller functions identically the same as for the other types of automatic controllers previously described.

THE WARD LEONARD CONTROL SYSTEM

As stated before, a rheostat in series with the armature is undesirable for motor control, because the efficiency is lowered by I^2R heat loss in the armature rheostat. The Ward Leonard control system controls armature current by generating a controllable voltage which is applied to the armature of the controlled motor.

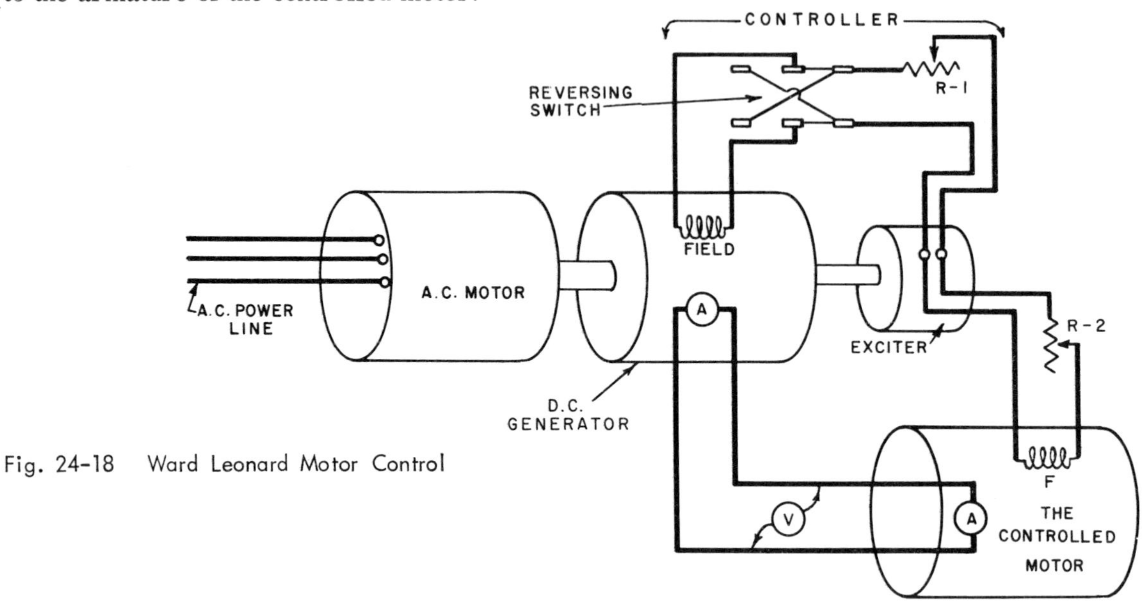

Fig. 24-18 Ward Leonard Motor Control

The large D.C. generator of Fig. 24-18 is driven at fairly constant speed by a three-phase alternating current induction motor. This generator is separately excited, either by a small D.C. exciter generator as shown, or by a separate D.C. line.

Rheostat R1 controls the field strength of the large D.C. generator, thereby controlling the output voltage, V, which is applied to the armature of the controlled motor. This makes possible a wide range of below-normal motor speeds.

Rheostat R2 controls the field of the motor, making a wide range of above-normal speeds possible.

The D.P.D.T. switch in the generator field circuit can reverse the polarity of the generator field, which results in a reversal of the generator output. In this way the direction of current in the motor armature can be reversed, reversing the direction of rotation of the motor.

This system of motor control is used in hoisting equipment and in steel-mill drives, both of which require a wide range of speed control as well as reversal of rotation. In a typical example, the armature control may provide a below-normal speed range from 75 to 750 r.p.m., or a 1 to 10 range of speeds. The motor field rheostat may increase the speed from 750 to 3000 r.p.m., which is four times normal speed. This gives a complete speed control range from 75 to 3000, or a 1 to 40 speed range.

The Ward Leonard control system is very flexible and gives close adjustment of speed over its wide range. Its main disadvantage is its relatively low overall efficiency. There is the efficiency of the A.C. motor, and the D.C. generator, as well as that of the controlled motor to consider, and therefore the overall efficiency of the entire system will be low.

THE ROTOTROL SYSTEM

A Rototrol generator is a special type of exciter (D.C.) generator which supplies the field for a larger generator. The Rototrol itself has three or more field windings; control is established by adjustment of current in these fields. The simplified sketch below shows a "pattern field" which is constant, once its rheostat has been set. The "self-energized field" is produced by the Rototrol armature itself; sometimes a shunt field is used instead of the series field shown here. The "pilot field" opposes the pattern field. In this example, the pilot field is supplied by a small generator, which is driven by the controlled motor, incidental to the motor's main job of driving a machine.

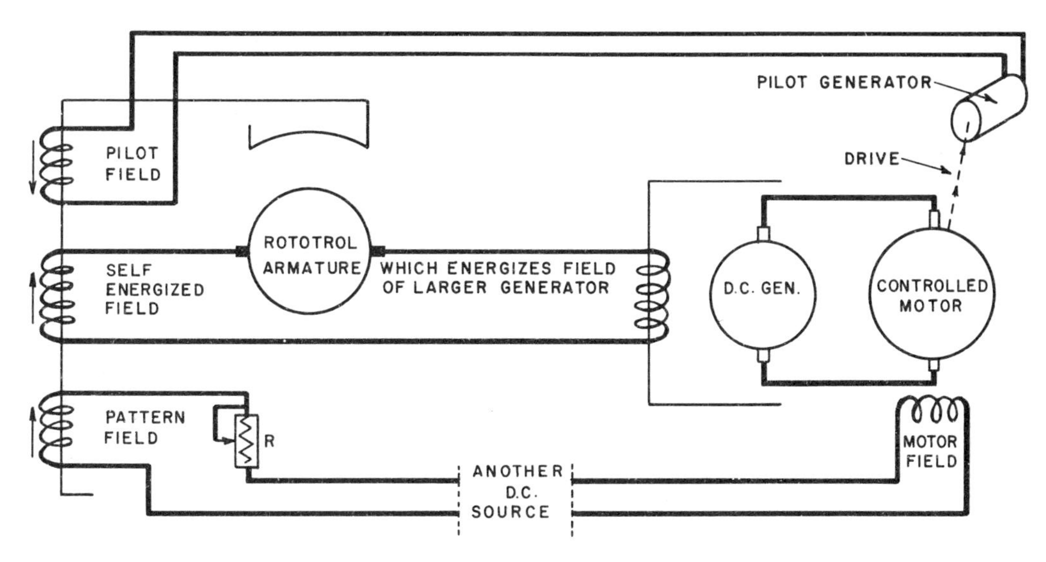

Fig. 24-19 Rototrol Motor Control

To illustrate the behavior of this circuit, suppose the load on the controlled motor is reduced and its speed rises slightly. This increases the output of the pilot generator. Increasing the pilot field causes a decrease in total field in the Rototrol, because the pilot field opposes the other fields. The decrease in total field reduces Rototrol voltage output, which reduces field of D.C. generator, which reduces D.C. generator output. The armature of the controlled motor gets less current, which reduces torque so that the motor speed is restored to its original value. The Rototrol series field remains at its reduced value.

If increased load tends to slow the motor, reduction of pilot voltage temporarily permits an increase in total field, so Rototrol output increases, restoring motor speed. The Rototrol output stays at the higher level as long as the increased motor torque is required, its own series field providing the required field strength after the pilot field is brought up to its normal value.

Armatures of the Rototrol and D.C. generator are driven by any large constant-speed machine. A resetting of the pattern field sets a new speed for the controlled motor.

The Rototrol system is especially desirable in applications that are too specialized and complex to be described here. The pilot field, or pilot fields, can be fed by currents produced by devices sensitive to temperature, position, tension, and so forth. For example, a photo-cell may watch markings on paper going through a press, the photo-cell determines the output of an electronic amplifier, and the amplifier output is used to control the Rototrol field, making any necessary adjustments in speed of the machine.

AMPLIDYNE MOTOR CONTROL

Like the Rototrol, the Amplidyne is a modified D.C. generator, the output of which is determined by controlling currents in the Amplidyne field. Control is so precise that an electric signal as small as half a watt applied to the field will instantly release kilowatts of power.

Let's introduce the operation of the Amplidyne by reviewing the operation of a typical separately-excited D.C. generator. Assume that Fig. 24-20 represents such a generator, delivering full load current of 50 amperes at a terminal voltage of 100 volts, which is 5 kilowatts of power. Separate excitation supplies 100 watts to the field of the generator.

Note that the current in the armature conductors sets up a magnetic field which, in the armature iron, is at right angles to the main field flux. In the Amplidyne, this armature flux is put to work.

In developing the Amplidyne, one aim is the reduction of the field-excitation power. Let's examine the effects of reducing the excitation power in the above example.

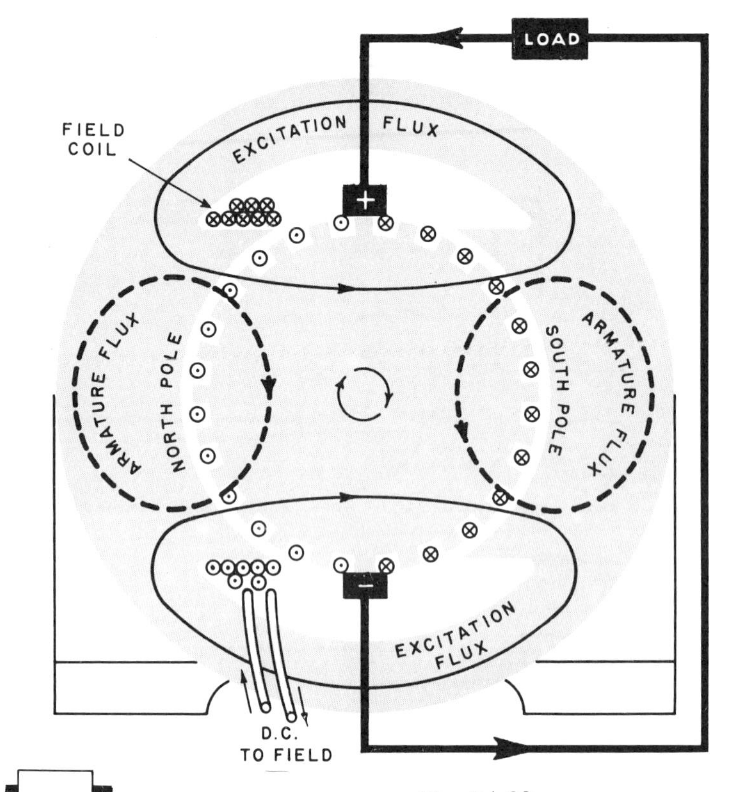

Fig. 24-20

Fig. 24-21

Suppose we reduce it from 100 watts to 1 watt by installing a smaller field winding. This reduced power creates only 1% of the original excitation flux, so the voltage output goes down from 100 volts to 1 volt. At low voltage, the load current is cut from 50 amps to 0.5 amp, which produces only 1% of the original armature flux. We have reduced the power output of the generator to an impractically low value.

We can restore the armature current and armature flux to practically their original values by disconnecting the original load and short-circuiting the brushes, as in Fig. 24-21. The excitation power and flux is still very low, but now this very small field excitation controls the normal rated armature flux.

The next step is to put this idle armature flux to work, and make the armature deliver rated power output.

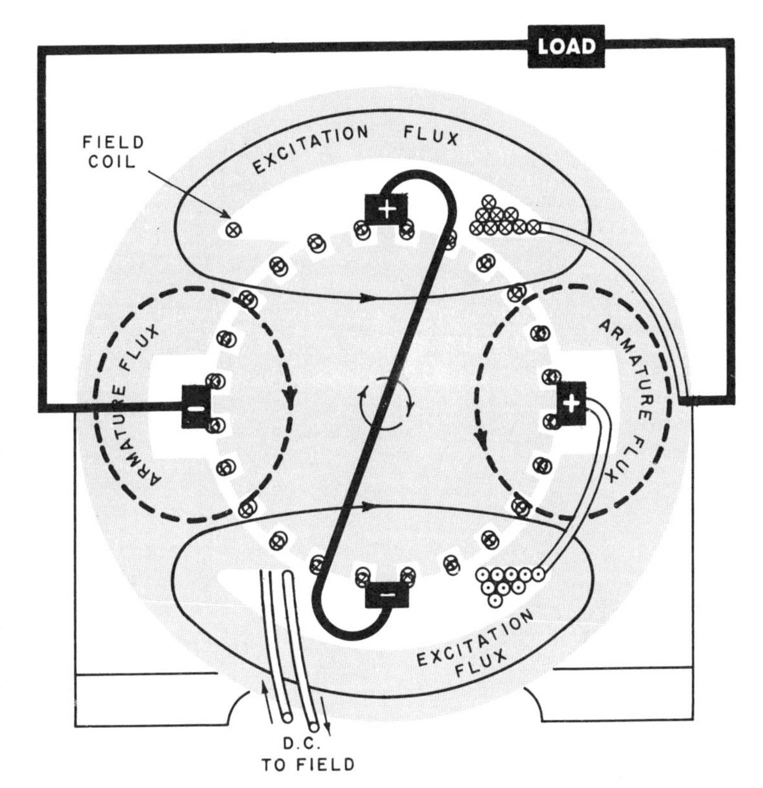

Fig. 24-22

The small field coil at the left produces a small excitation flux as before. This small excitation flux makes possible the generation of a moderately large current in the armature conductors and in the short-circuit between the top and bottom brushes.

This armature current produces the armature flux shown by the closed loops at the right and left. The field-poles have been split to re-locate this armature flux.

In effect, a new two-pole field has formed: The two top halves of the field poles forming the north pole and the two bottom halves, the south pole.

Assuming that this new full-strength field is about the same strength as used in the first illustration, it is possible to generate 100 volts from this armature, provided we locate a pair of brushes in the proper position to pick up this voltage. These two brushes are at the sides of the diagram, connected to the same original load, delivering 100 volts and 50 amps.

This new and additional 50 amp current in the armature would set up its own armature flux, which would be undesirable. Therefore, the load current is passed through a "compensating field" winding in series with the load. (This winding is at the right in Fig. 24-22.) The compensating field flux is equal in strength and opposite in direction to the armature flux due to load current in the armature, hence these magnetic fields cancel, leaving the magnetic field as shown in Fig. 24-22.

Summarizing: A tiny (1 watt) amount of originally-applied field enables a low-voltage high current to be generated in the armature short circuit. This current produces a new flux, at 90° to the original field excitation. This new strong flux enables a high-voltage high current to be generated for the external load. The release of a 5000 watt output is controlled by the very small excitation power of 1 watt.

If the excitation current of the above example is doubled, making the excitation power 4 watts ($P = I^2R$) this results in doubled excitation flux and doubled short circuit current. This doubles the armature flux, and the output voltage increases to 200 volts. Load current increases to 100 amperes. From these figures, we see that an increase in the control input from 1 watt to 4 watts has increased the output, from 5 w to 20 kw.

The range of applications for the Amplidyne are practically unlimited. A few of these functions are:

1. Controlling and regulating speed, voltage, current, and power, with extreme accuracy.

2. Controlling tension and torque to maintain production uniformity in many manufacturing operations.

3. Speeding up acceleration, or deceleration, to increase the production from high-speed machines.

The preceding diagrams showed only one control winding on the Amplidyne field. Several control windings are often used. The output of the Amplidyne may be controlled by using, for its separately-excited control field, current from any or all of the following sources:

1. A pilot generator, sensitive to r.p.m.

2. IR drop across a resistor in a controlled-motor armature circuit, sensitive to changing current requirements of the motor.

3. Current from a steady D.C. source, determined by a rheostat setting.

4. Current from an amplifier, the output of which is, in turn, determined by some element sensitive to temperature, position, stress, flow rate, etc.

The Amplidyne is often used to energize the field of a generator, thereby controlling the output of the generator. The generator drives the controlled motor. The sketch below illustrates, in much simplified form, the application of the Amplidyne in a Diesel-electric locomotive.

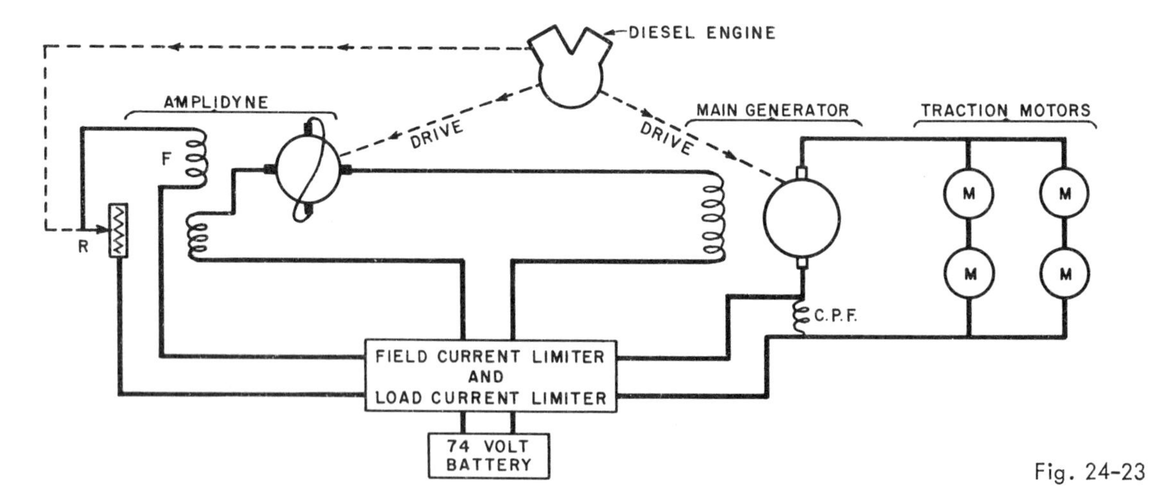

Fig. 24-23

F is the control field of the Amplidyne. R is a load-control rheostat, mechanically coupled to the governor of the engine. Its function is to prevent Diesel-engine overload. C.P.F. is the commutating-pole field of the main generator; the voltage across it, which is proportional to the output current of the generator, is used in the load-current limiting circuit. The operation of these limiter circuits is complex enough to merit nonmention at this point.

The current in the control field, F, of the Amplidyne is only a few tenths of an ampere. The armature of the Amplidyne produces the field current for the main generator, which is less than 50 amps. The main generator, driven by a 1600-h.p. engine, may deliver as much as 3000 amps to six traction motors when starting. At high speed, the current is much less; voltage ranges up to 875.

The term "amplifier" usually reminds us of radios or record-players, but notice that the circuit of Fig. 24-23 meets the broad definition of a "power amplifier" – a device in which a small amount of input power controls the production of a large output power.

Motor-control circuits illustrate the use of the "feedback" principle which is the central idea in machine automation. Referring to the Rototrol circuit used in Fig. 24-19, any tendency to change speed causes the generation of a "signal voltage" which is fed back into the control circuit to automatically make the necessary correction. In the locomotive circuit (Fig. 24-23) a too-high output current produces its own signal voltage which is fed back into the control circuits to reduce the output.

In automated machine operations, D.C. motors may be driven by electronically-controlled rectifiers which get their power directly from an A.C. line. A rectifier is a device that lets electrons through in only one direction, (see Unit 26). For motors of smaller sizes, rectifiers are more convenient than bulky motor-generator sets.

The sketch below shows in only a general way the application of electronic devices in motor controls. Field and armature currents are carried by separate rectifiers, separately controlled, so that any reasonable combination of speed and torque can be obtained. Operator's controls include starting and stopping, and also permit the operator to take over direction and speed control from the "program control." Program control is any system based on punch cards, magnetic tape, or rotating switches that causes the motor to repeat a timed sequence of operations. Pick-ups sensitive to position, pressure, etc., on the driven machine can effect any necessary corrections. (Program control is not limited to rectifier-operated systems; it can be added to other motor-control systems.)

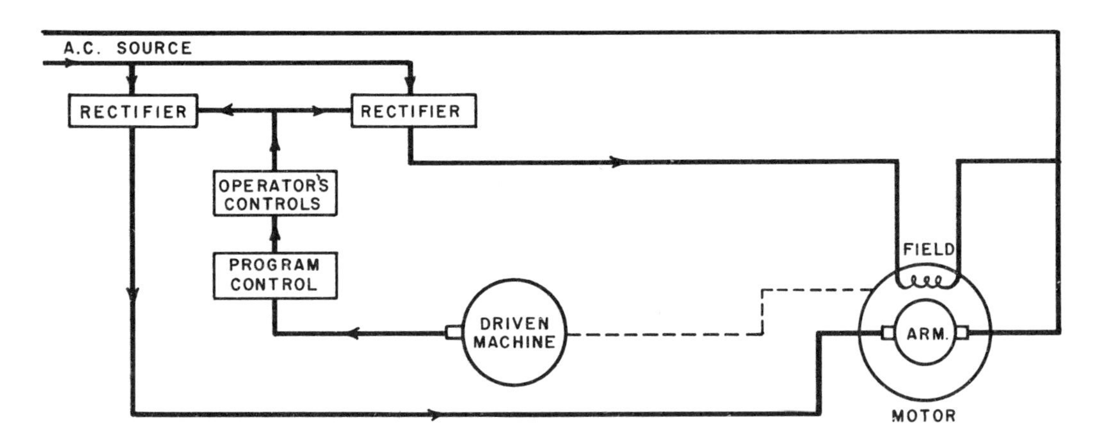

Fig. 24-24

In summary, all of these motor-control systems are ways of using to good advantage the wide ranges of control of speed and torque that are possible with a D.C. motor.

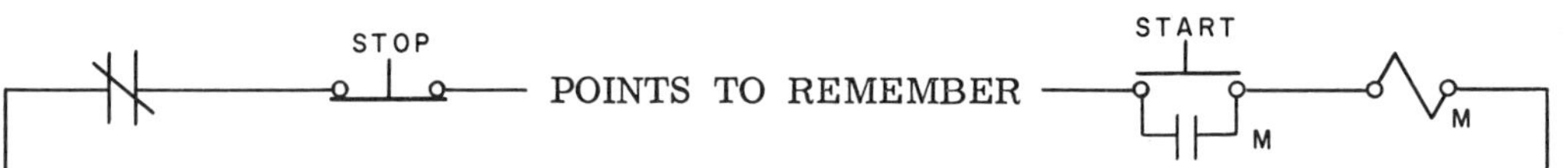

- Panel wiring diagrams show the physical layout of parts and wiring; schematic diagrams show circuit operation.

- Review circuitry and sequence of operations for
  - a. the counter e.m.f. controller.
  - b. the voltage drop acceleration controller.
  - c. the definite time controller.

- Dynamic braking stops a motor by making it act as a generator, converting its rotational energy to electrical energy and then to heat in a resistor.

- Electrical interlocking is a system for insuring that one device be disconnected before interfering or contradictory device is energized.

- Review circuitry, operating principles, and uses of
  - a. the Ward Leonard control system.
  - b. the Rototrol generator.
  - c. the Amplidyne generator.

REVIEW QUESTIONS

1. Explain the difference between a schematic wiring diagram and a panel wiring diagram.

2. A D.C. shunt motor is rated 40 amperes, 115 volts, 5 H.P. Calculate the proper current rating for a heater unit to install in a counter e.m.f. controller to serve as proper running overload protection.

3. a. What is the purpose of starting overload protection?

   b. What size fuses should be used as starting protection for the shunt motor in Problem 2?

4. Explain what is meant by "Dynamic Braking" in motor control work.

5. a. Explain how a wide range of above- and below-normal speeds is obtained by using the Ward Leonard control on a D.C. motor.

   b. What is one disadvantage of this type of control system?

   c. If, in the system shown in Fig. 24-18, Page 292, the efficiency of the A.C. motor is 80%, the efficiency of the D.C. generator is 78%, and the efficiency of the controlled motor is 80%, calculate the overall efficiency of the system. (Disregard losses in rheostats and exciter)

6. Shown below is a schematic wiring diagram of a counter e.m.f. motor controller connected to a shunt motor. Complete the panel wiring diagram to comply with the schematic diagram.

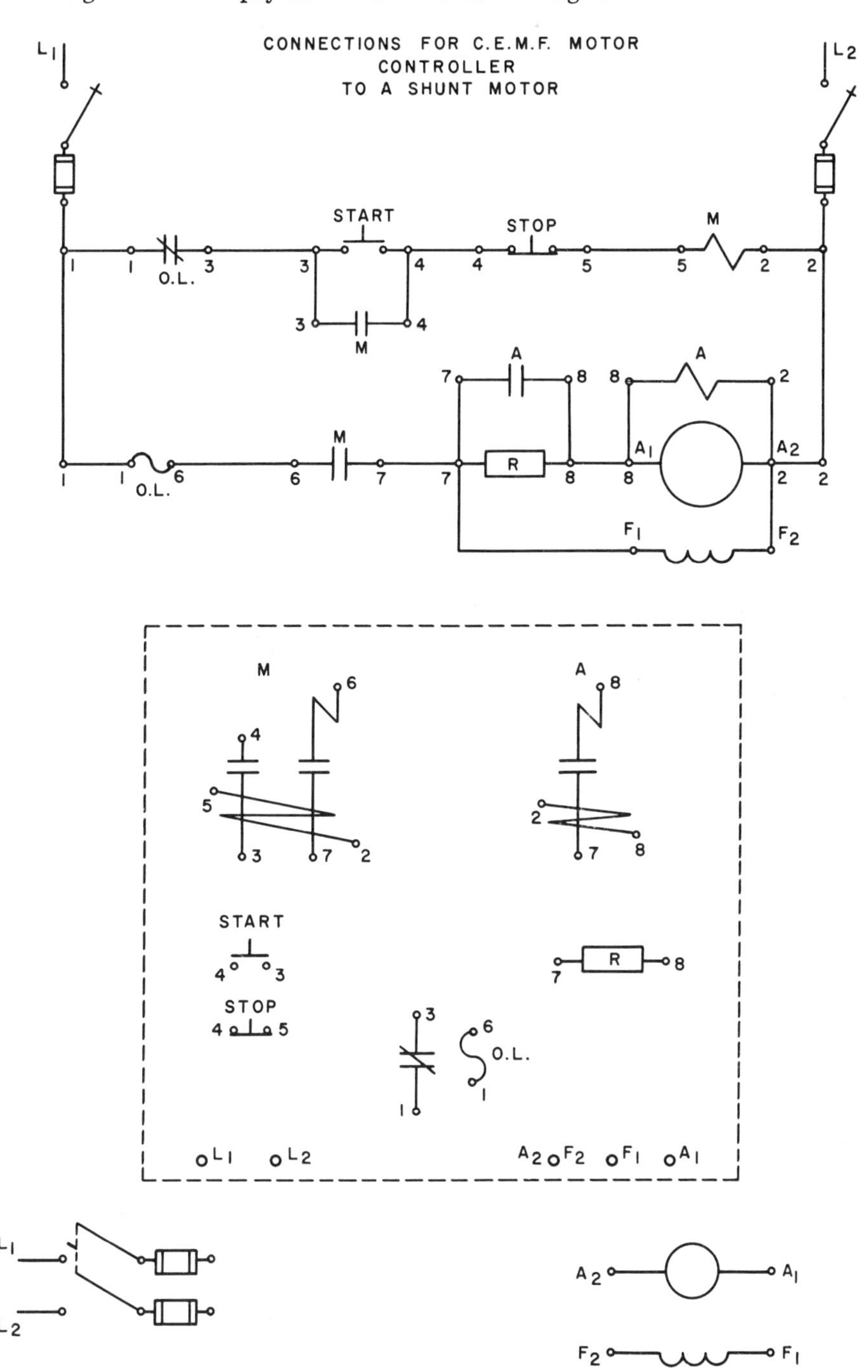

7. The controller shown above is used with a shunt motor rated at 40 amp, 125 volt, 5 H.P. Armature resistance is 0.2 ohm; shunt field resistance is 62.5 ohms. Find the ohmic value of the current-limiting resistor in series with armature so starting current will not exceed 150% of full-load current rating. (Neglect currents in relay coils.)

8. Using the schematic wiring diagram given for the Definite Time Controller, (see Fig. 24-16, Page 290) complete the panel wiring diagram below:

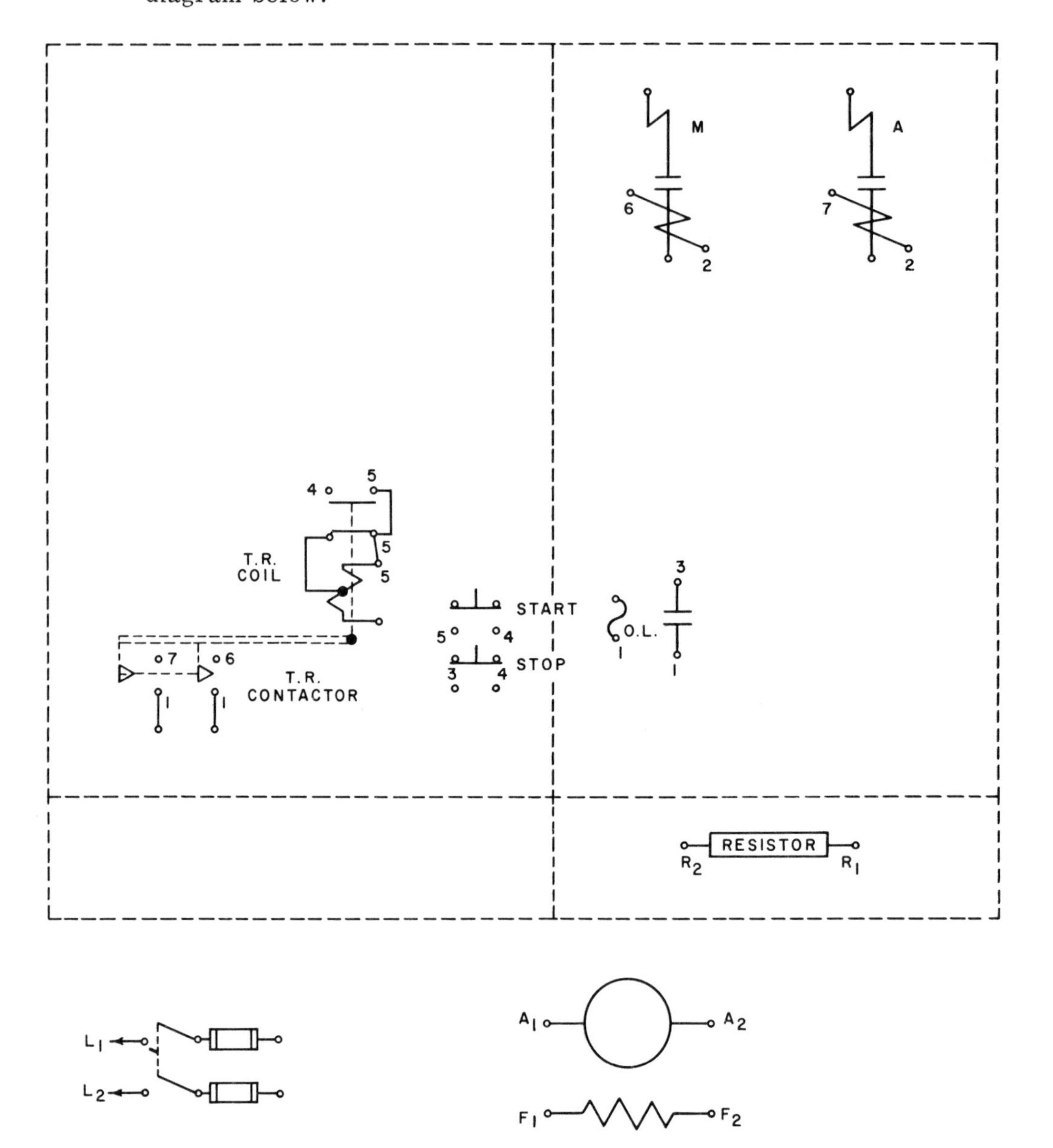

9. Explain what is meant by the term "Electrical Interlocking"?

10. Explain the difference between a conventional D.C. generator and an Amplidyne.

11. List several practical industrial applications for Amplidyne units.

12. List four sources of excitation current used with Amplidyne units in practical industrial applications.

Unit 25 ELECTRIC HEATING AND LIGHTING

When electrons flow through a material, some of their potential energy is used in jiggling the atoms and molecules of the material. The energy of motion of atoms and molecules is what we call heat. In many devices heat production is undesirable, and some care has to be taken to prevent excessive heat production. When heat is desirable, we need only to supply a resistance with the current to heat it, and the equation "watts = I^2R" tells us the rate at which electrical energy is converted to heat. This is a complete conversion of energy: all electrical heating devices are 100% efficient in this energy conversion, though they may differ in how effectively the heat is directed to some useful task.

HEAT FROM CURRENT IN A SOLID RESISTOR

The solid resistor in the most-common heating devices is a coil of nickel-chromium alloy wire. For localized production of small amounts of heat, the ease of control of electrical devices is sufficient reason for their wide use.

Nickel-chromium (nichrome, chromel, etc.) alloys provide a good combination of features: small space requirement, reasonable cost, long life, and freedom from breakage.

To illustrate factors considered in building a heating element, assume that an amateur desires to make a 200-watt heater. According to the table, he can use #26 wire. From watts = volts × amps, the current will be 1.74 amp. From Ohm's Law, R = 65.5 ohms.

Using $$R = \frac{kL}{C.M.}$$

he finds that about 28 feet of wire is needed.

If #24 wire is used instead of #26, a longer piece of wire will be required. The surface temperature of the #24 will not be as high, oxidation will be slower, and the heater will have a longer useful life.

Nichrome Wire Recommendations

Heater Watts (115 volts)	Wire Gage No.
100-200	26-30
200-350	24-28
350-400	22-26
450-500	20-24
550-650	19-23
700-800	18-22
850-950	17-21
1000-1150	16-20
1200-1350	14-18
1400-1500	12-16
2000	10-14

(Adapted from Driver-Harris Co. Technical Catalog, copyright 1958. Nichrome is a registered trademark of Driver-Harris Co.)

Electric stoves often use a heater element consisting of a coiled resistance wire enclosed in a steel tube. The space around the wire, inside the tube, is packed with magnesium oxide or similar filler to electrically insulate the wire from the tube.

"Three-heat" hot plates have two heater elements, controlled by a four-position switch. On the high setting, both elements are in use, connected in parallel to the 115-volt line. On the medium and low positions, the larger or smaller of the elements will be in use individually.

Electric ranges, water heaters and clothes driers operate on a 3-wire system, now to be described.

Three-Wire 120/240-Volt Supply

Assume that a device needs 3000 watts, which can be supplied either by 25 amps at 120 volts, or by 12 1/2 amps at 240 volts. The power loss on the line leading to the device is I^2 times the resistance of the line. Comparing circuits with line-wires of the same size, 25 amps causes four times as much line loss as 12 1/2 amps. The reason for use of the 240-volt system is to keep voltage and power loss on the line reasonable, without the use of excessively large wire.

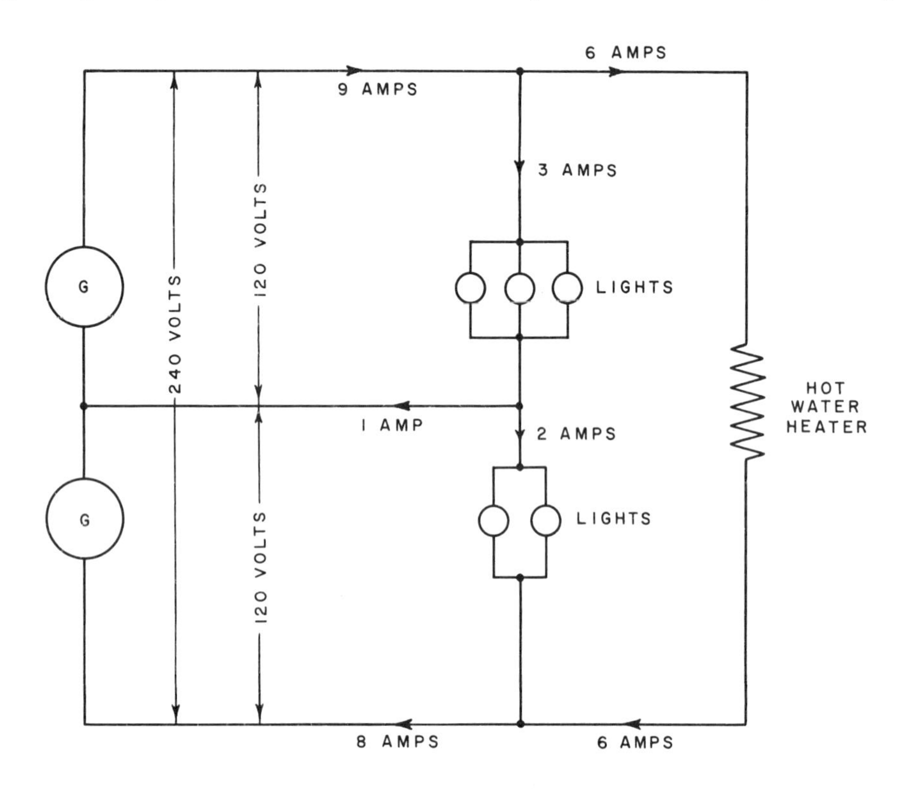

Fig. 25-1 Three-Wire Circuit

To explain the operation of the 3-wire system, assume that we have two generators connected in series, as shown. Each generator develops 120 volts; the two in series give 240 volts. The two "outside wires", at top and bottom in Fig. 25-1, provide the 240-volt supply for ranges and large heaters. The middle wire, in practice, is grounded securely to a cold-water pipe.

A grounded wire is called a "neutral". So grounded, it is at the potential of the earth and eliminates any chance of shock from touching that wire. Also, the maximum voltage between either outside wire and ground is 120 volts, so the danger of shock from contact between a wire and ground is no more than with the 2-wire, 120-volt system.

Further study of the diagram shows that the neutral wire carries only the difference in current carried by the two outside wires, and therefore need not be as large as the outside wires.

The above current- and voltage-relationships hold true, whether the source voltage is D.C. or A.C. In alternating-current work, the above arrangement is termed 3-wire single-phase. It definitely is not to be called three-phase, which is an entirely different arrangement.

Electric Range Circuits

With two voltages (120 and 240) available, a multiple contact switch allows as many as eight different heats to be obtained from various combinations on two different heating elements.

For example, one manufacturer uses a 6-position switch to obtain five heat settings from two heater elements (46 ohm and 59 ohm) in one cook-top unit:

1. Both in parallel on 230 volts: 1150 + 900 = 2050 watts
2. The 46 ohm on 230 volts: 1150 watts
3. Both in parallel on 115 volts: 290 + 220 = 510 watts
4. The 46 ohm on 115 volts: 290 watts
5. Both in series on 115 volts: 125 watts

Kanthal Alloys

The tradename "Kanthal" is applied to a group of alloys containing iron, chromium, aluminum and cobalt. These alloys are useful for heater elements with a high-temperature requirement. Such applications include resistor-type solder irons and cigarette lighters, involving a concentrated heat source, and also high temperature kilns and furnaces. Kanthal in use builds up a very adherent aluminum oxide coating, which resists further oxidation. Various alloys are intended for operation at temperatures from 2100° to 2460° F. A powder-metallurgy product, Kanthal Super, containing molybdenum, silicon, and other metals and ceramics, operates at 2900°F.

Silicon Carbide Resistors ("Globar" Elements)

Silicon carbide is not only an abrasive, but in the form of rods is useful as heating elements. So-called "Globar" heaters, used in kilns and furnaces, are made in lengths from 4 inches to 6 feet; their resistances range from 0.4 to 5 ohms. Operating current, and heat output, is controlled by the use of a multiple-tap transformer as a source, or by the use of series reactors. The resistivity of silicon carbide, about 0.1 ohm per centimeter cube, classifies it among the semi-conductor materials. These resistors are usable for temperatures ranging up to 2800°F.

Resistance Welding

Welding of sheet steel is often done by heat developed by current in the steel itself. Copper electrodes are pressed against the steel, then the electrodes are connected to a low-voltage high-current supply for a short time. The resistance of the steel is small, but I^2R is large enough to weld the metal. After the current is turned off, electrode pressure is maintained briefly, then the work is released. In production machines, the "squeeze-weld-hold-off" cycle and the control of current is accomplished by specialized electronic equipment.

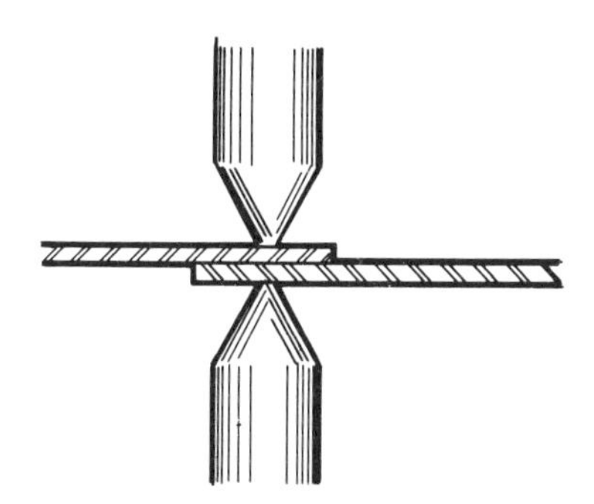

Fig. 25-2 Resistance Welding

HEAT FROM ARCS

Motor-driven D.C. generators supply the power for most industrial arc-welding. Welding imposes a peculiar set of operating conditions on the generator. No-load voltage is about 60 volts. When the arc is struck, voltage has to be reduced greatly, and be restored at once if the arc is extinguished. During welding, the current should remain quite constant, though resistance of the arc varies.

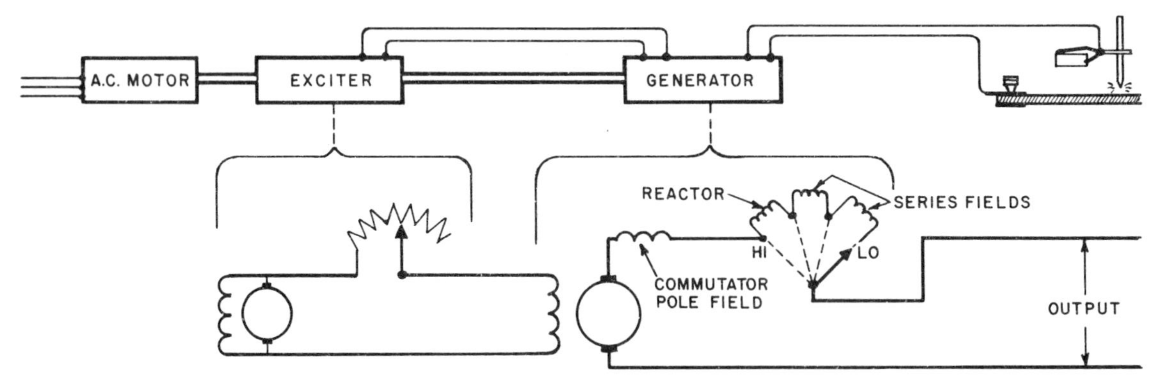

Fig. 25-3 Welding Generator

Fig. 25-3 shows one type of welding generator. The exciter generator supplies a fairly constant, but adjustable, field for the welding generator. The reactor is a low-resistance iron-core coil, the purpose of which is to help hold the output current constant. If current in the coil suddenly increases, an e.m.f. generated in the coil itself opposes the increase; if current starts to decrease, the generated e.m.f. in the coil helps maintain the current, (Lenz's Law). The series field is connected differentially (in opposition) to the field supplied by the exciter, so that the output voltage is desirably lowered if load resistance is suddenly reduced. Instead of the taps as shown above, the series field may be controlled by a diverter rheostat in parallel with it. For high current output, the series field is shorted out.

Arc Furnaces

A large-scale example of heat production by carbon arcs is the use of electric furnaces in the production of alloy steels. In the laboratory, a small, high-temperature furnace may be constructed by surrounding a carbon arc with refractory material.

INDUCTION HEATING

Although induction heating is a strictly alternating-current process, it deserves mention in this unit. If a piece of metal is placed inside a coil which is supplied with high-frequency alternating current, the rapidly-changing magnetic field induces eddy currents in the surface of the piece of metal, thereby heating it. This method is often used in surface-hardening heat treatment for gears and similar machine parts.

COMPARATIVE COST OF ELECTRIC ENERGY

	Heat Content	Assumed Efficiency	Price	B.T.U. per Dollar	
				Purchased	Used
Electricity	3,413 B.t.u./KWH	100%	1.6¢ / KWH	213,000	213,000
Natural Gas	1,000 B.t.u./cu.ft.	83%	9 1/2¢/100 cu.ft.	1,100,000	875,000
Oil	141,000 B.t.u./gal.	80%	17¢ / gal.	830,000	665,000
Coal	12,500 B.t.u./lb.	76%	$24/ ton	1,040,000	791,000

Before drawing too many conclusions from the above chart, one should recalculate costs, using energy prices that apply in his own locality. Other factors to consider would include such items as safety, ease of control, cleanliness, and reliability.

For electric house-heating, the three most-used types of resistance heating devices are (1) ceramic-core wall units; (2) ceiling and floor cable; (3) circulatory fan units. For moderate climates, one should also investigate an electric-motor-driven device called a heat pump. It delivers more energy per dollar than resistance-type heaters do.

ELECTRIC LIGHTING

The first practical electric light to be developed was the carbon arc, followed by the carbon filament incandescent lamp, and then the tungsten filament incandescent lamp. "Incandescent" means glowing due to heat, – white hot.

HOW LIGHT IS MEASURED

The term "measurement of light" may refer to either of two quantities: (1) the intensity of the source, or (2) the illumination on a surface.

The intensity of a light source can be measured in candlepower. For many years this measuring unit was the light of a "standard candle", made of sperm wax of specified size and shape, burning at the rate of 120 grains per hour. This standard was unsatisfactory on several counts. The present standard, adopted in 1948, is based on the light produced by white-hot powdered thorium oxide in a furnace held at 3216° F. The light coming from a 1/60 sq. cm. hole in this furnace is defined to have a source intensity of one candle. This is far more convenient and more accurately reproducible than any candle flame.

The unit of measure for surface illumination was the foot-candle, defined as the illumination on a surface at a distance of one foot from a standard candle. It became desirable to introduce another unit, called the lumen. One lumen is the rate of flow of visible light energy through a one square foot hole at a distance of one foot from a 1-candle light source. If we place a one square foot surface at a distance of one foot from a standard candle, its illumination is one lumen per square foot. One lumen/sq. ft. is the same as a foot-candle. Since the surface area of a sphere = $4 \pi r^2$, a 1-candle source produces 4π lumens.

If a 100% efficient light source could be produced, converting all of its electrical energy into visible light, it would produce 621 lumens per watt. An ordinary 100-watt tungsten lamp has an efficiency of 15 1/2 lumens per watt; fluorescent tube lamps give about 50 lumens per watt.

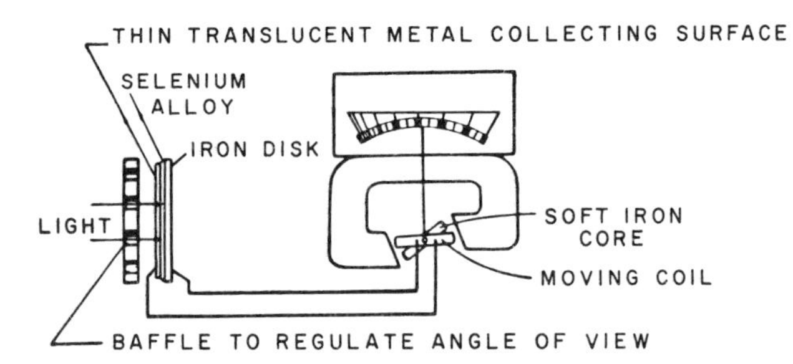

Fig. 25-4

The eye is highly adjustable to changes in illumination. Outdoor illumination may vary from 8,000 or 10,000 lumens/sq. ft. in clear, bright sunlight to 100 lumens/sq. ft. on a dull, dark day, to .03 lumens/sq. ft. on a night lighted by a full moon. Recommended illuminations for artificial lighting vary from 0.5 lumens/sq. ft. for sidewalks to 10 or 12 for classrooms and offices to 25 lumens/sq. ft. for drafting rooms. For ordinary work, illumination is measured by "light meters" which consist of a photoelectric cell and a micro-ammeter which is scaled to read lumens/sq. ft.

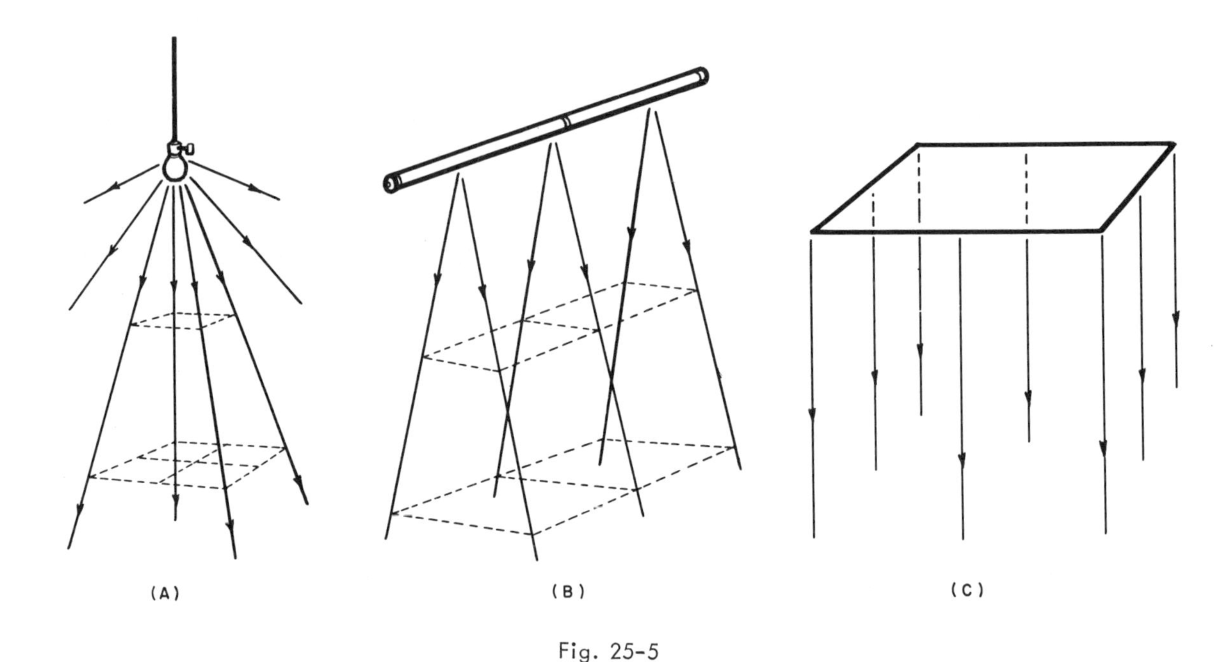

Fig. 25-5

Source, Distance and Illumination

From the geometry of the above distributions of light:

A. Light from a single point source spreads as it radiates, so that the surface illumination is inversely proportional to the square of the distance of the surface from the source. In (A), the light which would fall on a one-foot square surface held 2 ft. below the lamp would cover 4 sq. ft. if allowed to travel twice as far from the source.

B. Light from a line-source, such as a long string of fluorescent tubes, spreads out so that the surface illumination is proportional to the distance from the source. Illumination of surfaces below these two light sources is improved by placing reflecting surfaces above the source.

C. Light from a source which is a flat surface, indefinitely wide in extent, gives an illumination which is independent of distance from the source.

WHAT IS LIGHT?

Light is energy that is radiated by electronic disturbances in atoms. Electrons in an atom can accumulate energy in many ways: from heat, as in a red-hot object; or by being hit by other electrons, as in a gas-conduction tube; or by absorbing energy radiated by other materials. Sooner or later, this absorbed energy is given out. The amount of energy that an electron can get rid of in one burst depends on where the electron is, that is, what kind of atom it is in, and its location in the atom.

The energy is radiated as a wave-like pulse of electric lines of force and magnetic lines of force, which is called an electromagnetic wave. The vibration frequency of these traveling lines of force is proportional to the amount of energy that the electron gave off. Frequencies in the range from 4.3×10^{14} to 7.5×10^{14} vibrations per second affect electrons in our eyes. We call electromagnetic waves in this frequency range by the name of "light."

Waves of a frequency slightly higher than 7.5×10^{14} are called "ultra-violet"; waves in a lower frequency range, from 10^{11} to 10^{14} vibrations per second are called "infra-red", and heat radiation. The term "black light", often used by newspaper reporters who do not know the correct terms, may mean either ultra-violet or infra-red. Ultra-violet and infra-red differ greatly in their effects and uses.

A listing of the applications of electromagnetic waves of various frequencies is given at the right.

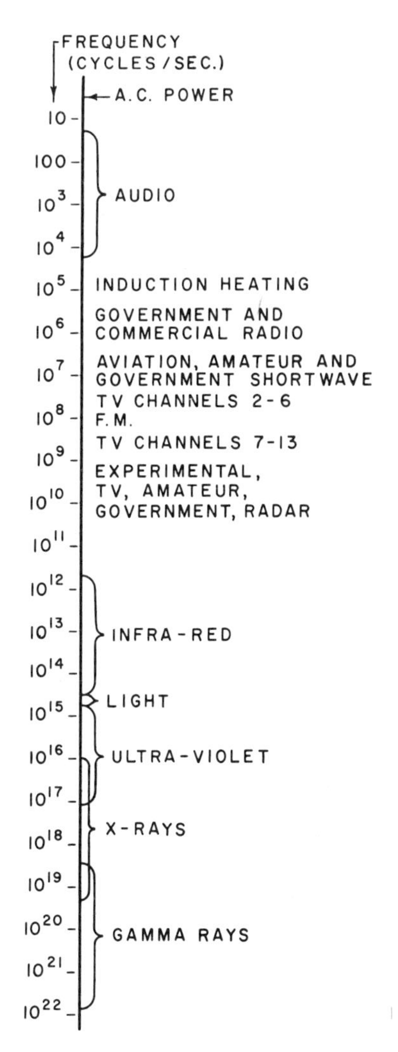

Fig. 25-6 Electromagnetic Spectrum

At low frequencies, only the electrons of the outermost rings of atoms are involved. X-rays and gamma rays are produced by large bursts of radiation emitted by the innermost electrons of atoms.

The speed of travel of all of these electromagnetic waves is the "speed of light", 186,000 miles/sec., provided there is nothing in the way.

COMMERCIAL LIGHT SOURCES

Carbon Arcs

Carbon arc lamps have one particular feature which, in some applications, is a great advantage. That feature is the extremely concentrated brilliance of the source of light. In some types of light projection equipment, such as 35 mm movies, and searchlights, D.C. arcs are still preferred, for the concentrated source of light avoids complexities in the optical system. A few carbon arcs are still in use in street-light installations.

For comparison purposes, here are a few surface-brightness figures (in candles per sq. cm.):

The sun, 160,000; ordinary carbon arc, 13,000; high-intensity arc, 80,000 plus; melted tungsten (6120° F.), 5740; interior of furnace at 3216° F., 60; frosted glass surface of 40 watt lamp, 2.5; filament of tungsten projection lamp, 2100.

Despite the high surface brilliance of the carbon arc, so much of the energy supplied to the arc is converted to heat that its efficiency is low enough (10 to 20 lumens per watt) to help make it unsuitable for general illumination. At the high temperature (about 10,000° F.) of the carbon arc, the radiation includes considerable amounts of ultra-violet. Eye irritation noticed after exposure to arcs is caused by this ultra-violet radiation.

Incandescent Lamps

Considering all of the specialized types of lamps that are manufactured, we find hundreds of sizes and types of tungsten incandescent lamps. The reader may provide his own cross-section diagram of construction by smashing a few old lamp bulbs.

Filament temperature in ordinary (25 w. - 300 w.) lamps ranges from 4200° to 4800° F. At rated voltage average life is 750 - 1000 hours. Efficiencies range from 10.4 lumens per watt for the 25-watt lamp to 19.6 lumens/watt for the 300-watt lamp. A 100-watt lamp rated for 750 hr. life produces over six times as much light as a 25-w., 1000-hr. lamp, for two reasons: larger lamps are more efficient than small ones, and 750-hr. lamps operate at a higher filament temperature than 1000-hr. lamps, thereby producing more light per watt.

Originally, incandescent lamp filaments operated in a vacuum, to prevent oxidation of the filament. 40-watt and larger lamps are now filled with nitrogen at near-atmospheric pressure. The gas pressure retards evaporation of the filament, permitting the filament to be operated at higher temperature, which makes for higher efficiency.

Vapor Lamps — Gaseous Conduction

A variety of inert gases and metallic vapors can be used in more specialized lighting equipment. Most such lamps require some type of auxiliary current-limiting equipment.

Several types of mercury lamps are manufactured, being useful in two areas: (1) the blue light of the mercury arc is an advantage in some photographic work, and in photochemical processes; (2) for industrial general illumination, where color is unimportant, the high efficiency (30-65 lumens per watt) is desirable.

In a few street and highway lighting systems, sodium vapor lamps are used. Rated 180 watts, 10,000 lumens, their good features are long life and high efficiency. The light is orange-yellow.

Small neon-glow lamps (.04 watt to 3 watts), giving an orange-red light, are particularly useful as indicator lamps. Though their efficiency is low, this is not disadvantageous, as they are not intended as sources of general illumination. Their life averages over 3000 hours, and they are unusually reliable in that they fail gradually, having no filament to burn out. The 2-watt NE-34 lamp deserves consideration as a night light for home use.

Similar small argon-glow lamps produce a pale blue-violet light; the ultra-violet that they produce makes them desirable as small-scale ultra-violet sources.

Fluorescent Lamps

The conductor in the fluorescent lamp is mercury vapor, at very low pressure. Current through this low-pressure vapor produces a little blue and violet light, but most of the radiation is invisible ultra-violet. This ultra-violet radiation is absorbed by the coating on the inside of the tube; this coating re-radiates some of the energy at lower frequencies which are visible. The color of light radiated by the coating is characteristic of the coating material itself. Substances which have this ability to absorb radiation and immediately re-radiate energy are called "fluorescent materials" or "phosphors."

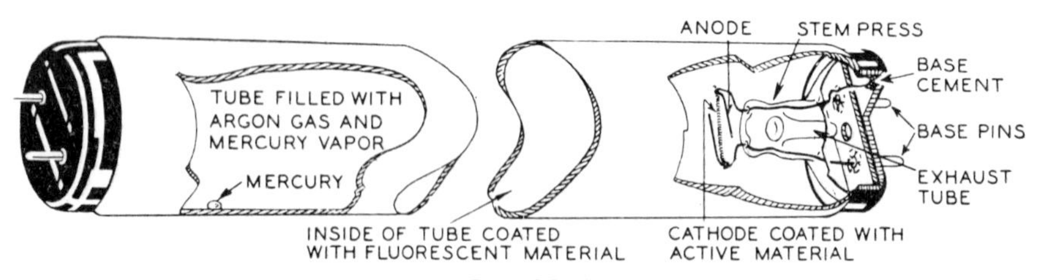

Fig. 25-7

The sketch below illustrates the simplest circuit arrangement for starting and operating a fluorescent lamp.

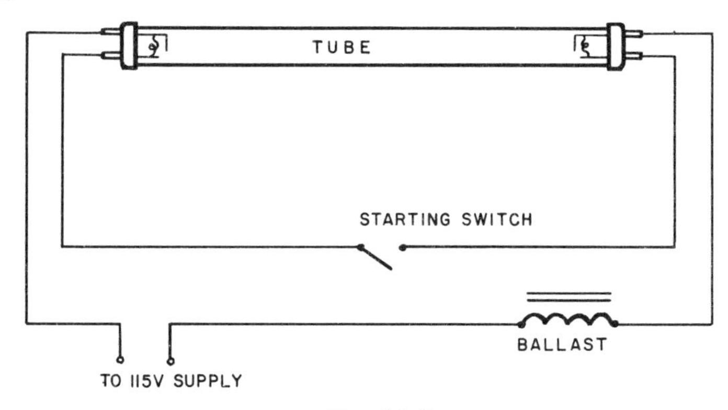

Fig. 25-8

115 volts applied to the above circuit causes no current at first, because the resistance of the tube is too high to permit an arc to start. Closing of the starting switch permits a current through the filaments at the ends of the tube and through the ballast. The ballast, or reactor, is a coil of copper wire on an iron core. Assuming this circuit is operated on A.C., the bouncing magnetic field in the ballast coil induces voltages that hinder the continually-changing current, thus limiting the amount of current in the circuit. Heating of the filaments in the ends of the tube warms the mercury vapor, and electrons are emitted from the hot filament, making the tube ready to conduct. When the starting switch is opened, the collapsing magnetic field in the ballast coil induces a momentary high voltage in the circuit, which starts electrons moving through the mercury vapor, the vapor ionizes, and conduction is under way.

During operation, the voltage across the tube is between 50 and 100 volts, depending on the size of tube. Opposing voltage generated in the inductive ballast coil accounts for the rest of the circuit voltage. The ballast limits current through the tube without causing too great heat production, as would occur if a series resistor were used.

Fluorescent fixtures generally include an automatic starter, shown below:

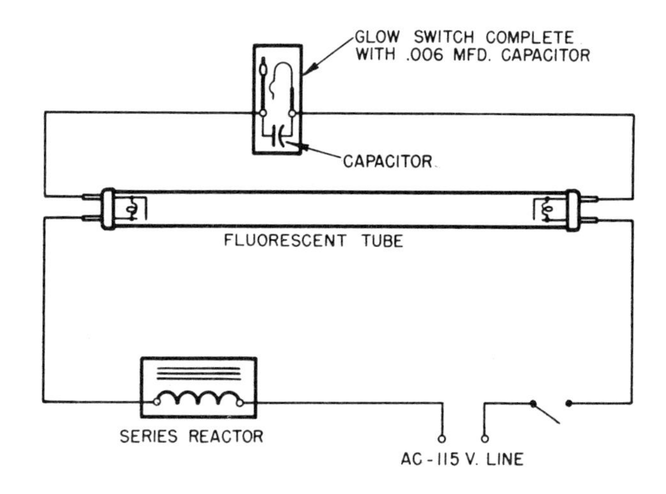

Fig. 25-9 Circuit for Fluorescent Tube

The glow switch replaces the "starting switch" shown in Fig. 25-8. The glow tube is a neon-filled glass bulb, containing a U-shaped bimetallic strip and a fixed contact, normally open. When the circuit is connected to the 115-volt line, current is small due to the high resistance of the glow tube, and there is little voltage drop across the series reactor. Voltage across the glow tube contacts is enough to start a little arc discharge between the bimetal strip and the fixed contact. This arc heats the bimetal, which bends and touches the fixed contact.

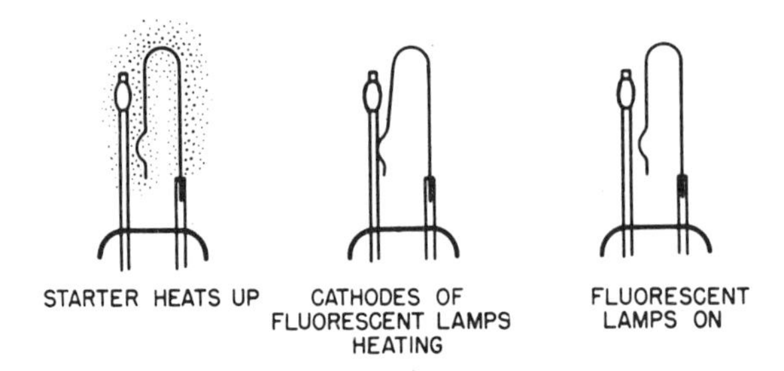

Fig. 25-10 A Glow Switch Starter

Closing of the starting switch has now been accomplished, and the tube filaments are heated. Closing of the contact in the glow tube stops the glow tube arc; the bimetal cools, and the contacts open. At the instant of opening, the inductive voltage kick generated in the series reactor coil starts conduction in the fluorescent tube.

Instant-start fluorescent lamps have a cathode that requires no pre-heating. A special instant-start ballast is used, consisting of an arrangement of coils and capacitors that provides a high-starting voltage, yet limits the current after conduction starts.

SWITCH CIRCUITS

The control of one lamp, or one group of lamps, from two locations, is accomplished by the use of two "three-way" switches.

As indicated in Fig. 25-11, a three-way switch is a type of single-pole, double-throw switch. The movable blade is always in connection with the common terminal. There is no "on" or "off" position marked on the switch, because the common terminal is always connected to one or the other traveler terminal.

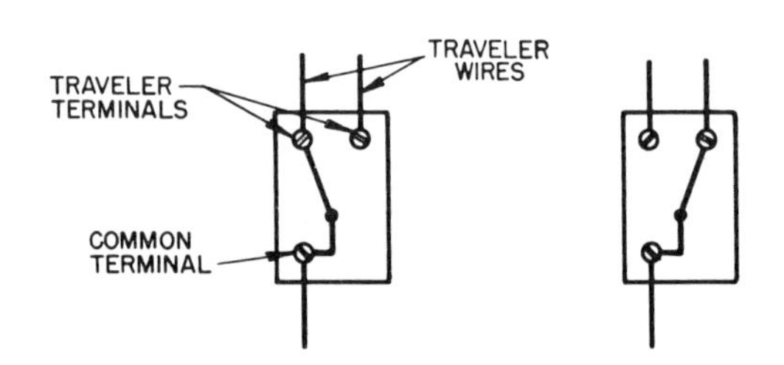

Fig. 25-11 Two Positions of Three-Way Switch

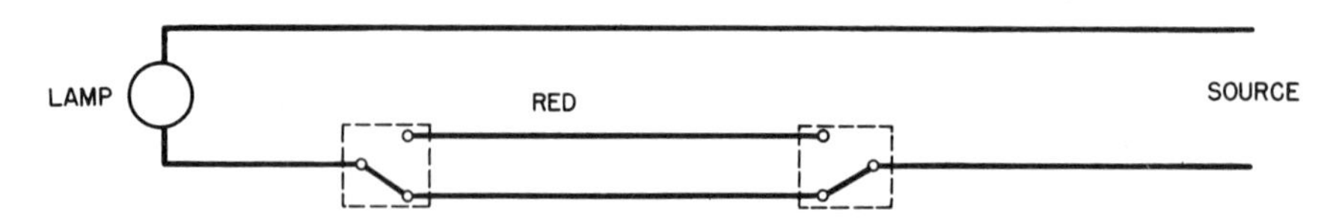

Fig. 25-12 Circuit With Three-Way Switch Control

Fig. 25-12 shows two three-way switches in a lamp circuit. As shown, the lamp is on, and it can be turned off by either switch. When the lamp is off, operation of either switch can again close a circuit to the lamp, using one or the other of the two traveler wires between the switches.

For control of a lamp from three or more locations, another type of switch, called a four-way, has to be put into the circuit between the two three-way switches.

A four-way switch has the same effect in a circuit as a reversing switch. The schematic diagram below (Fig. 25-14) shows lamps controlled from four locations. (A) and (D) are three-way switches. (B) and (C) are two four-way switches, as in Fig. 25-13. Operation of switch (B) converts its internal circuit to that shown in (C); moving the handle of (C) makes its connections like those as drawn for (B). Tracing the circuit through the switches in the diagram, one finds that the circuit is open. Operating any one of the four switches will close the circuit.

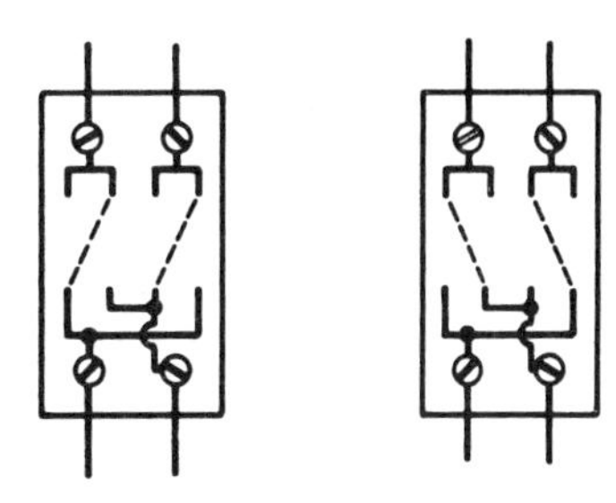

Fig. 25-13
Two Positions of Four-Way Switch

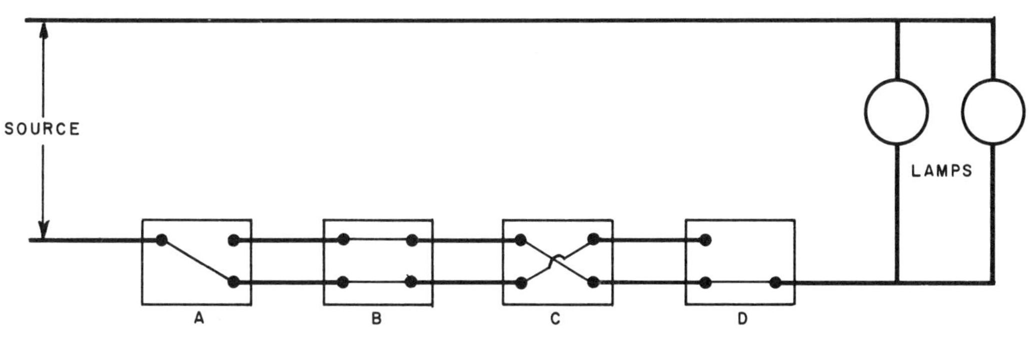

Fig. 25-14

REMOTE CONTROL SYSTEMS

If someone wants a system enabling him to control all of the outlets in his home from each of several different locations, the 115-volt outlets can be turned on or off by low-voltage operated relays. A less expensive wiring installation is secured with the low-voltage system, since there is no need for extra 115-volt cables. Low-cost #18 wire is used, and easily installed.

At each controlled outlet, one 25-volt relay is mounted on the outlet box. The relay contains two coils. A momentary current in the "on" coil closes the 115-volt contacts, which remain closed until a momentary current in the "off" coil opens them.

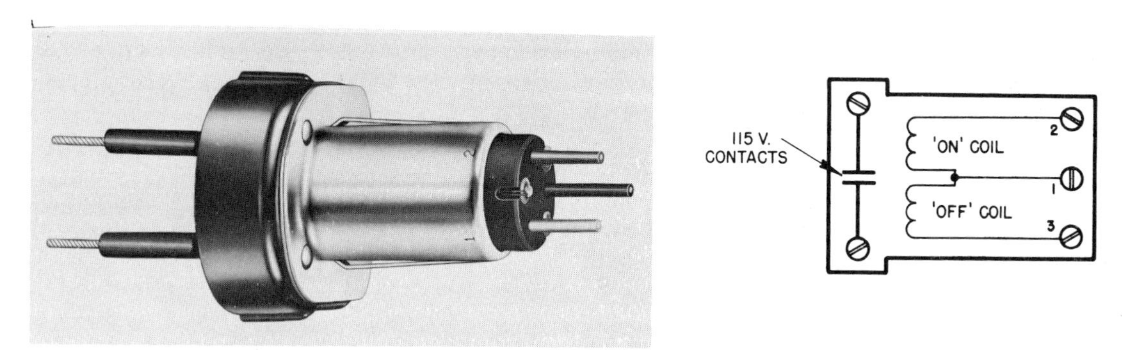

Fig. 25-15 Relay Connections

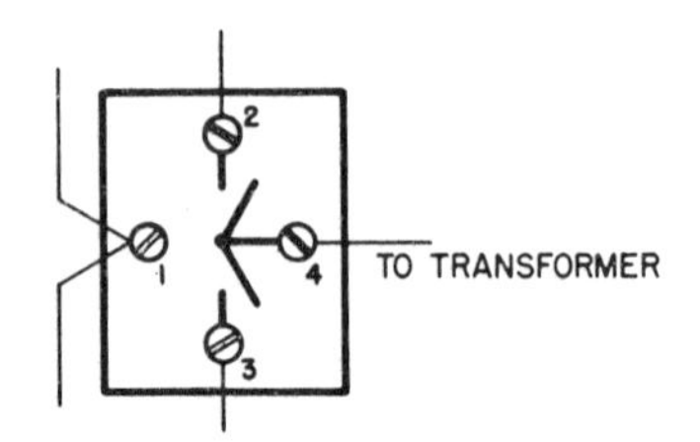

Fig. 25-16 Low-Voltage Switch

The relay coils are operated from a 25-volt transformer by normally-open momentary-contact switches, several of which may be connected in parallel to control one relay.

Such a switch is shown in Fig. 25-16; its connection in the circuit is shown below.

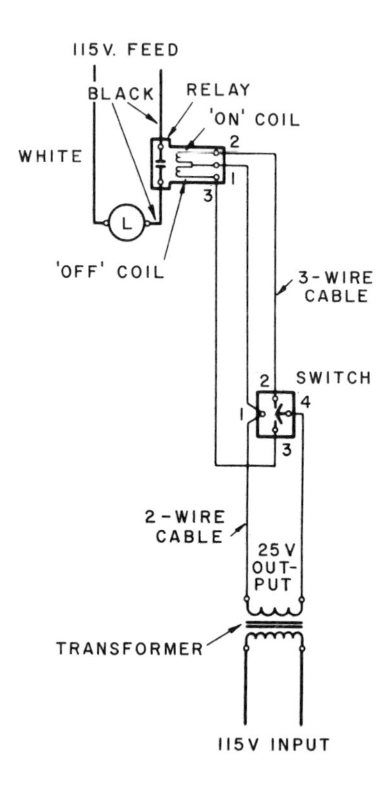

Fig. 25-17 One Light Controlled from One Switch Point

Referring to Fig. 25-17, turning the lamp on is done by momentary contact of switch terminals 2 and 4. Turning it off is done by contact of terminals 3 and 4. As many switches as desired may be wired in parallel with this switch.

Terminals #2 of all the switches are connected together; wire from the 24-volt output leads to terminals #4; all terminals #3 are wired together. Terminal #1 on the additional switches would not be used.

The 2-wire and 3-wire cable shown in the sketch is inexpensive low-voltage low-current wiring.

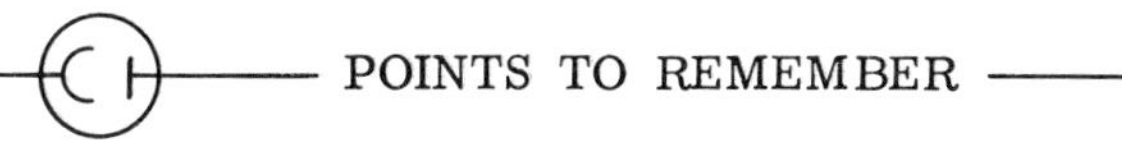

- Resistors are inherently 100% efficient as heat producers.
- Heating rate, in watts, $= I^2 R$.
- The three-wire distribution system is economical of energy and of copper. Current in the neutral wire equals the difference of the currents in the outside wires.
- Resistance welding uses large currents at low voltages; arc welding uses moderate current and voltage.
- An "induction furnace" generates heat-producing alternating current in the metal to be heated.
- Intensity of a source of light is measured in lumens. 12.57 lumens equals one candlepower.
- Intensity of illumination of a surface is measured in lumens per square foot.
- Surface illumination is increased not only by increasing power of source, but also by reducing distance between source and surface, and placing reflecting surfaces behind the light source.
- Light is produced by electron disturbances in atoms. Light is one narrow group of vibration frequencies of the entire electromagnetic spectrum.
- Larger incandescent lamps are generally more efficient than small ones. Fluorescent lamps and mercury arcs are 2 1/2 to 3 times as efficient as incandescent lamps.

REVIEW QUESTIONS

1. Assuming that 10,000 B.t.u. per hour are required to keep a room warm (70°) when the outdoor temperature is 25°, calculate the necessary equivalent rate of electrical heating, in watts.

2. Resistors are connected to a 3-wire system as shown. Calculate the current at each of the lettered points (A, B, C, and D).

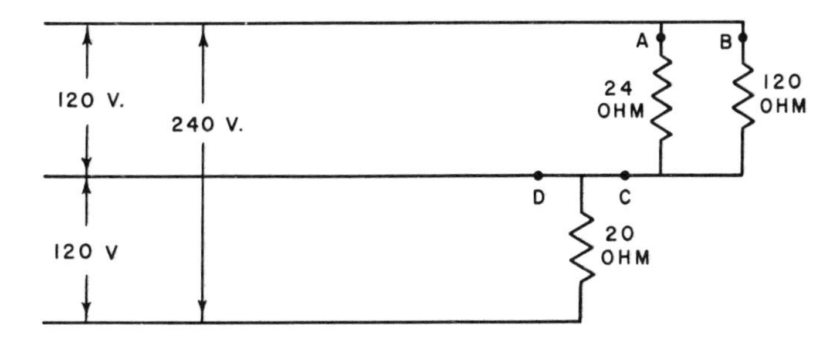

3. Calculate appropriate amount of nichrome wire for a 440-watt heating element.

4. A certain heater element is rated "1600 watts, 220 volts". Calculate its resistance. What will be its watts if operated at 110 volts?

5. Name two units for measuring intensity of a light source. State the numerical relation between them.

6. Name two units for measure of surface illumination.

7. A 25-watt lamp has an efficiency equal to 10.4 lumens per watt. How much light does it produce?

8. A work surface is illuminated by a single incandescent lamp, with no reflector, placed 5 ft. above the surface. If the lamp is lowered so it is 4 ft. from the surface, the illumination on the work directly below the lamp has been increased how many times?

9. State two uses for carbon arc lights.

10. State uses for mercury arcs, sodium arcs, and neon glow lamps.

11. What is a phosphor?

12. Diagram a simple fluorescent lamp circuit.

13. Diagram a circuit for operating a lamp by switches at three different locations.

14. Under what circumstances are remote control relays appropriate?

Unit 26 DIRECT CURRENT FROM ALTERNATING CURRENT

In previous sections where direct current generators were discussed, there was an occasional hint that they may be driven by alternating current motors. A reasonable question is "Why do power companies provide us with A.C., instead of D.C.?" The answer lies in an explanation of energy losses over transmission lines. Direct current must be generated and used at the same voltage; but by the use of transformers, alternating current can be transmitted at high voltage and low current, with less energy loss on the line.

Assume a small city is to be supplied with 10,000 KW, 120-volts direct current from a generating station 10 miles away. The current in the transmission line would have to be 10,000,000 ÷ 120 = 83,000 amps. If the line wires (copper) were two inches in diameter, the line resistance would be 0.275 ohm. In forcing 83,000 amps through 0.275 ohm, the voltage loss on the line (= IR) would be 22,800 volts, so the original generator voltage would need to be 22,920 volts, only 120 of which is usefully delivered. 1,900,000 KW would be wasted in heating the transmission line.

That power loss could be reduced by (1) moving the generating plant to one mile from town, (2) using larger wire, say 3″ diameter, and (3) delivering the energy at higher voltage, say 440. For this new set of conditions, voltage loss on the line is 278. But it may not be necessary to point out the impractical aspects of the above three suggestions.

By using transformers, which efficiently and easily convert one alternating current into another alternating current at a different voltage, A.C. energy can be transmitted without excessive loss. 10,000 KW of A.C. may be delivered at 120,000 volts by a line carrying 83 amps. If the copper wire is only 1/4 inch in diameter, a two-wire line 10 miles long has 17.6 ohms, and IR loss is 83 × 17.6 = 1460 volts, which is trifling compared with the 120,000-volt output. Only 121 KW is wasted in heating the line. The necessary 10,121 KW may be delivered to the transmission line by a transformer, the input of which is 2200 volts, 4650 amps. At the delivery end of the line, the 83 amps at 120,000 volts can be "stepped down" to 2400 volts, 4150 amps, for distribution, and stepped down again to 120 volts by small transformers in each city block.

For direct current, transformers will not work. Transformers generate an alternating current by using the energy of the bouncing magnetic field of another alternating current. If steady direct current is put into a transformer, the output is heat, not electrical energy.

RECTIFIERS

As mentioned before, D.C. motors, welding machines, and electrochemical processes require D.C., which is often supplied by a motor-generator set, that is, a D.C. generator driven by an A.C. motor. D.C. has to be produced near the location where it is to be used.

D.C. can also be supplied, from A.C. sources, by various electronic and semi-conductor devices, called rectifiers. Broadly defined, a rectifier is a device that converts A.C. energy to D.C., but as used, the term "rectifier" generally refers to devices other than motor-generator sets.

ELECTRONIC RECTIFIERS: VACUUM TUBES AND GAS TUBES

The internal circuits of radio receivers, amplifiers, and electronic control systems need a supply of steady D.C. for their operation. This D.C. is often supplied through a type of vacuum tube called a diode rectifier.

The cathode (symbol ⊓) in the tube is a metal sleeve, which is heated internally by current in a tungsten filament. The cathode is coated with a mixture of compounds (barium and strontium oxides) which emit electrons readily when the material is red-hot. These electrons are jarred loose from the cathode by the heat; they float around in the space near the cathode like steam over a pan of hot water.

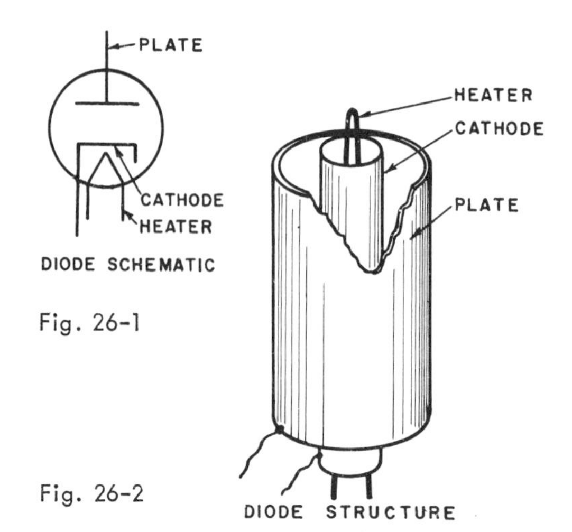

Fig. 26-1

Fig. 26-2

The "plate" of the tube (symbol ⊥) is a larger metal sleeve or box that surrounds the cathode. It is not heated, and in normal use cannot emit electrons.

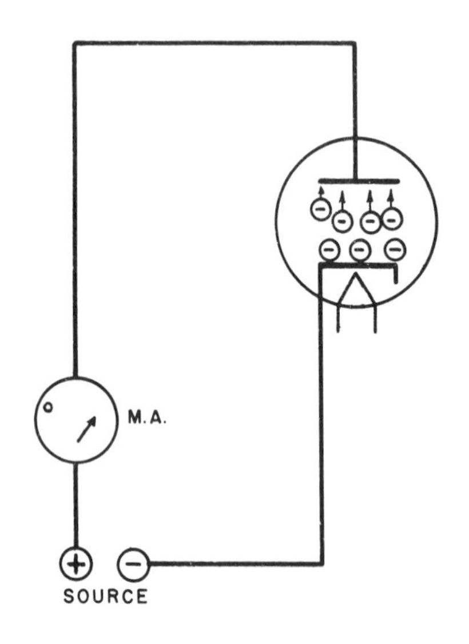

Fig. 26-3

This diode tube is a one-way conductor. When placed in a circuit so that the plate is more positive than the cathode, Fig. 26-3, loose electrons fly from the cathode to the plate. The heated cathode surface maintains a supply of loose electrons. If the plate is more negative than the cathode, Fig. 26-4, there is no current through the tube, because electrons cannot hop off the plate. (For simplicity, the heater circuit is omitted.

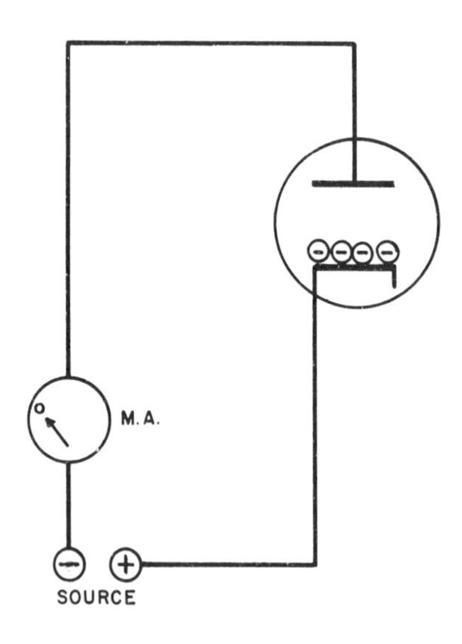

Fig. 26-4

To use this tube as a rectifier, we connect it, in series with the load, to an A.C. line. In Fig. 26-5 the load is represented by a resistor, though the actual load may be something more complex.

For many rectifier applications where a vacuum tube is suitable, a steady direct current, rather than pulsing D.C., is required. To secure a steady D.C. through the load, such as would be obtained from a battery, the diode tube is used to charge a capacitor. At this point, we need to take time to find out more about capacitors.

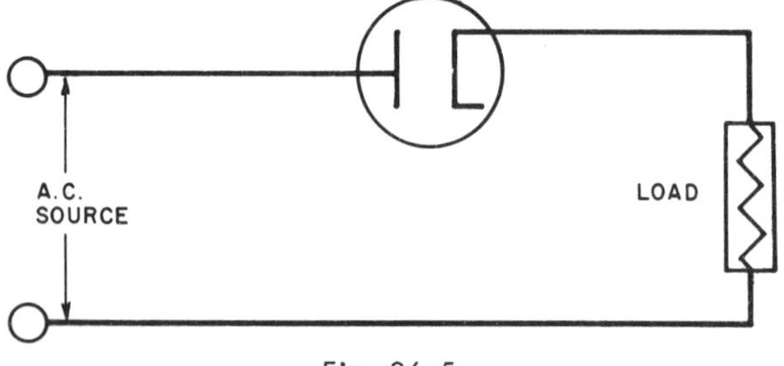

Fig. 26-5

CAPACITORS (or, Electrical Condensers)

By tearing apart a discarded small capacitor from a radio or TV set, one finds that it is usually made of two long strips of aluminum foil, separated from each other by strips of waxed paper, rolled up and covered with wax or plastic. Any two conducting sheets, separated by insulation, form a capacitor.

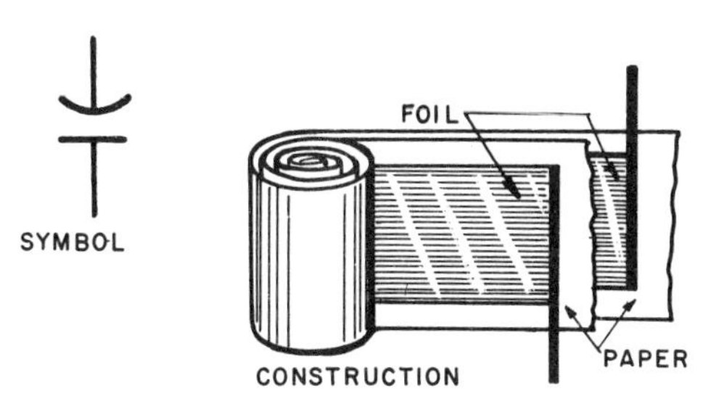

Fig. 26-6

To see how electrons behave in a capacitor, we may compare the capacitor to the water-filled cylinder in the sketch below. The solid piston in the cylinder, held in place by springs, compares to the insulation between the capacitor plates. Assume at the start that the cylinder and pipes are filled with water, to be comparable with the capacitor plates and wires which are filled with their normal number of electrons.

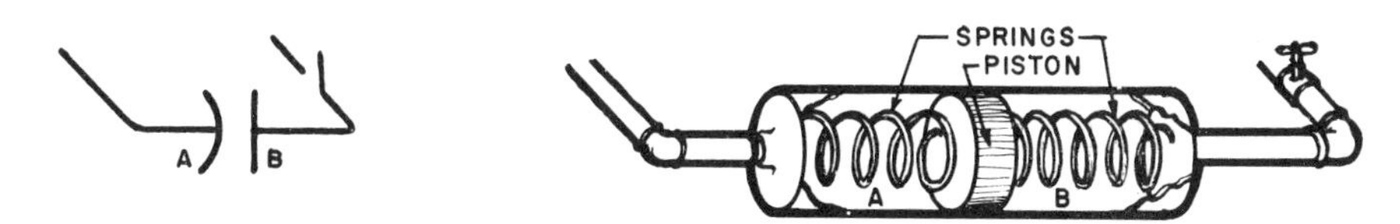

Fig. 26-7

- More electrons can be forced on to plate A, provided that electrons are taken out of plate B at the same time. After this is done, A is charged negatively, and B, with its electron-deficit, is called positive-charged.
- Given a chance, excess electrons will leave A, provided electrons can be restored to B at the same time.
- There can be no steady flow of electrons through the capacitor, but due to electrical attraction and repulsion forces, electrons can be bounced back and forth in the wires leading to A and B.
- If greater potential difference (volts) is applied, more electrons are forced into A and removed from B.
- Amount of electrons is measured in coulombs.
- "Capacitance" is defined as the number of extra coulombs put into A for each volt of pressure that is used.
- If 10 coulombs are put into A when the potential difference between A and B is 5 volts, then the capacitance is 2 coulombs per volt.

- More water can be forced into space A, provided that water is allowed to flow out of space B at the same time. After this is done, A has more than its normal amount of water, B has a deficiency.
- Given a chance, excess water will run back out of A, provided water can run back into space B at the same time.
- There can be no steady flow of water through the cylinder, but due to stretching and compressing of the springs, water can be bounced back and forth in the pipes leading to A and B.
- If greater pressure difference (pounds) is applied between A and B, more water is put into A and removed from B.
- Amount of water can be measured in quarts.
- "Capacitance" corresponds to the additional water forced into A for each additional pound of pressure used.
- If 10 more quarts of water go into A when there is 5 more pounds pressure in A than in B, the capacitance is 2 qts. per pound of pressure.

A one-volt potential difference would put 2 coulombs of extra electrons on plate A of the capacitor above; a 20-volt potential difference would put 40 coulombs of extra electrons on to A. At the same time, an equal amount of electrons has to be removed from plate B. Note that capacitance is the ratio of charge (coulombs) to voltage; it is not simply coulombs.

As stated, capacitance is measured in coulombs per volts; however, the long expression "coulombs per volt" is replaced by the word "farad", which means coulombs per volt. The capacitor in the preceding example is correctly termed a 2-farad capacitor.

$$\frac{\text{coulombs}}{\text{volts}} = \text{farads}$$

The above definition can be used in calculations, for example:

How much voltage is needed to put 20 coulombs of charge on a 0.5 farad capacitor?

$$\frac{20 \text{ coulombs}}{X \text{ volts}} = 0.5 \text{ farads}$$

$$0.5\,X = 20$$

$$X = 40 \text{ volts, Ans.}$$

For commonly-used capacitors, the farad is an inconveniently large unit of measure. Capacitors are usually rated in microfarads (millionths of a farad, abbreviated mfd.). An 8-mfd. capacitor is a 0.000008 farad capacitor.

The formula, $\text{microfarads} = \frac{\text{microcoulombs}}{\text{volts}}$ is useful to answer questions like this:

How much charge is put on to a 20-mfd. capacitor by a potential difference of 120 volts?

$$20 = \frac{X}{120}$$

$$X = 2400 \text{ microcoulombs}$$
or, 0.0024 coulombs

The Capacitor in the Rectifier Circuit

Returning now to the rectifier discussion, let's see how we can use the capacitor to get steady current, instead of pulsing, from the diode circuit:

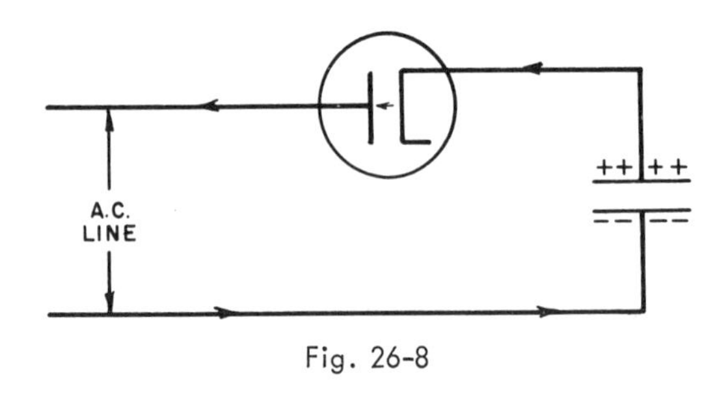

Fig. 26-8

If we connect a capacitor in series with a diode to the A.C. line, charges are built up on the capacitor plates, as shown at the left, when the tube is able to conduct. Electrons are removed, through the vacuum tube, from the top plate of the capacitor, so it becomes positively charged. An equal number of electrons are forced on to the lower plate.

When the polarity of the A.C. line reverses, the line tries to push electrons through the tube from left to right, but they won't go, because the tube will not conduct in that direction. So the top plate remains positively charged. Also, the line tries to pull electrons off the bottom plate, but they won't go, either. They are held there, attracted by the + charge on the nearby top plate. Or, from another view, there is no circuit for them, for the tube temporarily acts as an open switch. So, the capacitor can be charged through the tube, but it cannot be discharged through the tube.

When a load (resistor) is connected in parallel with the capacitor, we find that when the tube is conducting it can supply current to the load while it is charging the capacitor.

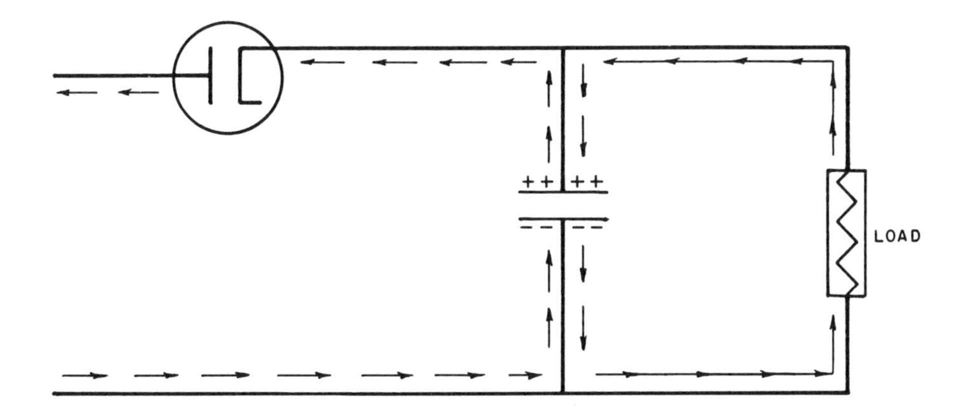

Fig. 26-9

During the time that the tube is not conducting, the stored charge of the capacitor supplies current for the load. Electrons from the negative-charged plate flow toward the load resistor and are attracted toward the positive plate of the capacitor. The arrows in Fig. 26-9 are intended to show pulsing current in the tube and line wires at the left, and to indicate a steady current in the load. In the wires leading to the capacitor, the flow alternates: upward when the capacitor is being charged, downward when the capacitor is discharging through the load.

In order to maintain a continuous current, the capacitor has to be large enough so that its saved-up charge is not all lost through the load during the short interval that the tube is not conducting. Even with a large capacitor, the flow is not truly steady, but slacks off as the capacitor discharges a little and its voltage is reduced.

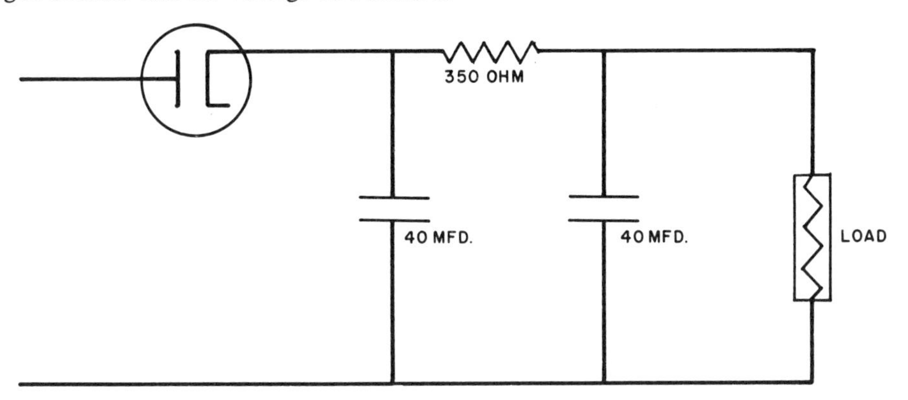

Fig. 26-10

The very-steady voltage required in radio receivers is attained by using two capacitors, arranged as in Fig. 26-10. The two capacitors and the extra resistor are called a "filter circuit." The values given for resistor and capacitor will depend on the current and voltage that the load demands. Similar filter circuits may be used in connection with other rectifying devices. A type of capacitor commonly used in filter circuits is the "electrolytic" capacitor, described on Page A-5 in the Appendix.

In the above circuit diagrams, it was assumed that the cathode was heated indirectly by a current in the heater filament. The heater is electrically insulated from the cathode, so this current is entirely independent of the rectifier action. Commonly, the heater is supplied with A.C. at low voltage, either from a low-voltage winding on a transformer, or by being placed in series with the heater-filaments of other tubes.

Many rectifier tubes use a "directly-heated" cathode, which means that the hot filament itself serves as a cathode. For low (100-300) voltages the filament has an electron-emitting coating. The filament carries both the A.C. which heats it, and the smaller pulsing rectified current. The sketch below shows the filament heated by the output of a center-tapped transformer winding; if there is no center-tap the wire leading from the positive side of the capacitor can be brought directly to either end of the filament.

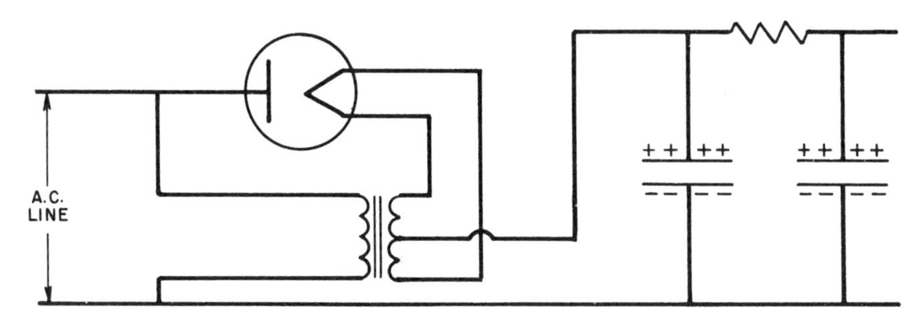

Fig. 26-11

The rectifiers, Fig. 26-11, are called "half-wave" rectifiers, due to the fact that the tube can conduct only half the time. Larger radios, amplifiers, and TV sets often use rectifier tubes containing two plates, which conduct alternately in a "full-wave" rectifier circuit:

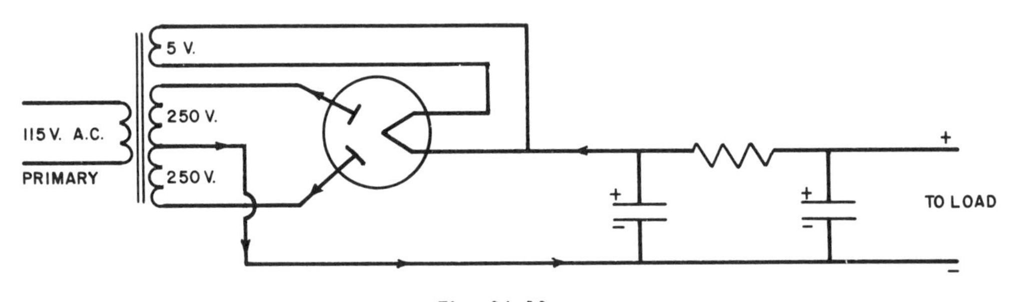

Fig. 26-12

The cathode is heated directly by a 5-volt secondary winding of a power transformer (for such tubes as 5Y3, 5U4G). The two plates connect to the ends of a high-voltage secondary, which ends are alternately + and -. Whichever plate happens to be positive will pick up electrons; their circuit-path is out the center-tap to the negative side of the filter capacitor. An equal number of electrons is withdrawn from the positive side of the filter capacitor. Electrons are given off at the cathode all of the time, going first to one plate and then to the other, but the flow is not steady. Since the A.C. voltage drops to zero instantaneously at the moment of reversal, the current in the wires leading to the first filter capacitor is a pulsing D.C., varying as shown in the graph at the right. To provide steady D.C. for the load, the filter is still necessary.

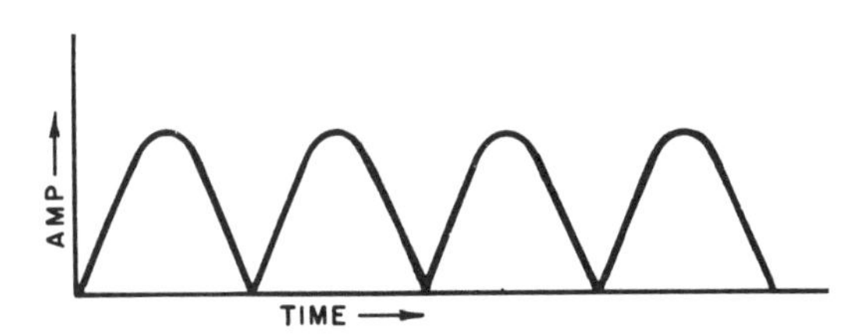

Fig. 26-13 Full-wave D.C.

High-vacuum tubes are particularly useful for rectifying small currents (one amp or less) at voltages from 110 up to several thousand. Their disadvantage is low efficiency, that is, there is considerable power loss in the tube, compared to the total power handled. For small currents, the power loss is small enough in amount to be unimportant, though it may be large in percentage.

GAS-FILLED DIODES

For larger currents (1/2 amp to 75 amp) gas-filled diodes can be used. The gas is usually argon or mercury vapor; helium, neon or xenon can be used. These tubes have higher efficiency than vacuum rectifiers, since ionization of the gas frees electrons that make the tube a good conductor. The potential drop across gas tubes is usually in the range of 10 to 25 volts, and is independent of current. Gas rectifiers are used for rectification at low and moderate voltages (to 440); a few types can be used at higher voltages, to 20,000. Most tubes have directly heated cathodes, some use indirectly-heated cathodes. They may be seen in operation supplying D.C. for a great variety of devices — magnetic separators, magnetic chucks on machine tools, motor-control circuits, etc. These tubes, sometimes called phanotrons, contain gas at very low pressure, about one hundred-thousandth of atmospheric pressure.

One type of gas diode, called Rectigon or Tungar, contains argon at about 15% of atmospheric pressure. This tube is used in battery chargers, and is made in current ratings from 3 to 15 amps. Its tungsten filament requires no preheating, as some phanotrons do. The plate is a graphite disk.

A few gas tubes, called "cold-cathode" tubes, require no current for cathode heating. Conduction starts when high voltage is applied across the tube; ion bombardment heats the cathode after conduction starts. The "OZ4" tube used as a rectifier in old-model automobile radios is of this type.

GAS TRIODES

A triode tube contains a third element, called a grid, placed between the cathode and plate, which acts as a control element. Gas triodes are also called grid-controlled rectifiers, thyratrons, or grid glow-tubes. As shown in the simplified construction sketch below, the "grid" of this rectifier tube is a metal disk with a hole in it, in contact with a surrounding metal cylinder.

The ability of the grid to determine the start of conduction in the tube makes this a highly desirable type of rectifier. It is used in welding controls, automatic motor control circuits, photoelectric relays, and a great variety of control devices.

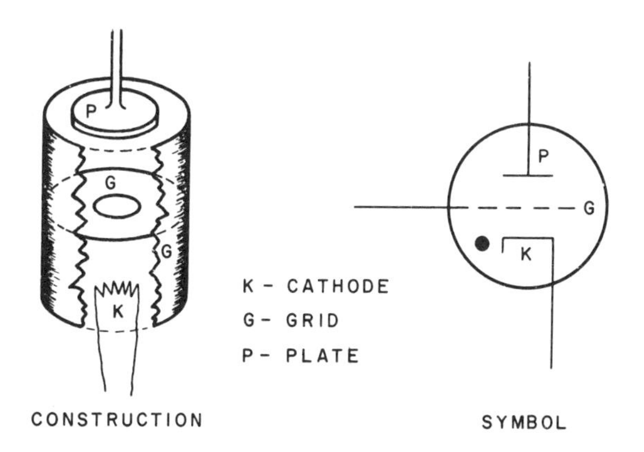

Fig. 26-14 Gas Triode

When the grid of this tube is sufficiently negative, it repels electrons toward the cathode strongly enough so that conduction does not start, even though there is positive voltage on the plate. (The cathode is the reference point with which these positive or negative voltages are compared.) By reducing the negative charge on the grid, conduction can be allowed to start. Once started, so many ions are formed that the grid has no further effect on the electron flow through the tube. If an attempt is made to reduce the current by applying more negative voltage to the grid, the grid collects positive ions which nullify its charge. The grid regains control only after conduction is stopped by a reduction in plate voltage. After conduction stops, positive ions recombine with electrons in less than a thousandth of a second, so a momentary stoppage restores control to the grid.

On this graph, Fig. 26-15, the curve marked "applied plate voltage" shows how the 60-cycle A.C. line voltage builds up to a peak and falls again to zero during one half-cycle (1/120 sec.). If the A.C. line voltage is 113, the voltage rises to a peak of 160 volts, averaging out to produce the same power (I^2R) as 113 volts of D.C. would. The whole numbers on the time scale are placed there merely for convenient reference.

The meaning of the curve "Critical Grid Volts" can be shown by numerical examples: During the time from 0 to 2, the line voltage applied to the plate rises to 56 volts, which of itself is enough to start conduction. Whether conduction starts depends also on the grid voltage. Reading under time "2" on the critical grid volts line we find the value 4.4 negative grid volts. This means that, at time 2, if the grid voltage is any value less negative than -4.4 (0, or -3, or +1), the tube will be conducting. If the grid voltage is more negative than this "critical" value, -4.4, electrons are not allowed to flow. At time 3, when plate voltage has risen to 72 v., the grid must be -5.5 v. or more negative to hold back electrons.

If the grid is held at a constant -6.5 v., conduction will start at time 4.4 in the cycle. At that instant, plate voltage becomes strong enough, 112 v., to overcome the retarding effect of the grid.

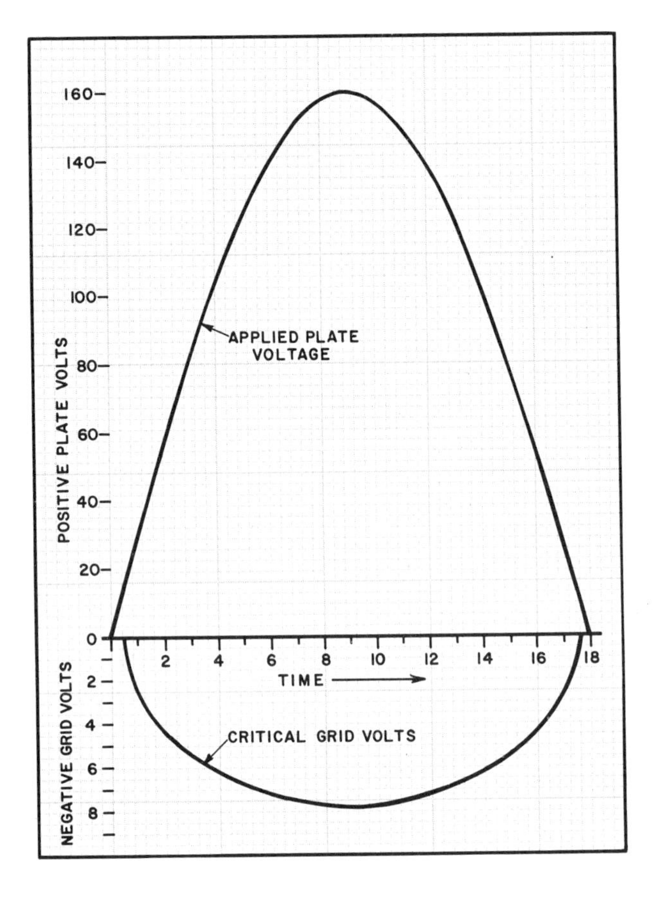

Fig. 26-15 Grid Voltage Control Graph
2A4G Argon Thyratron

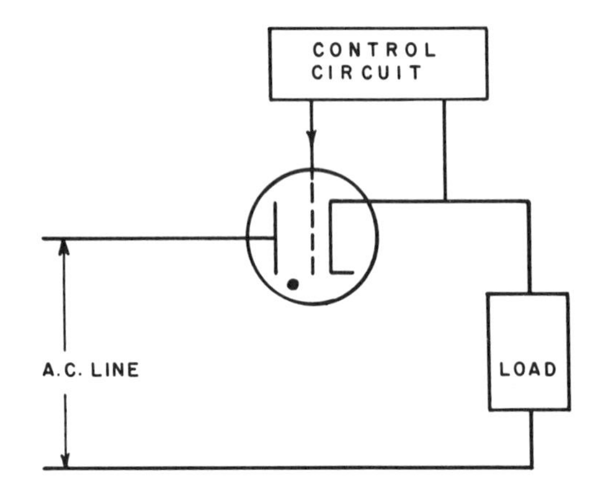

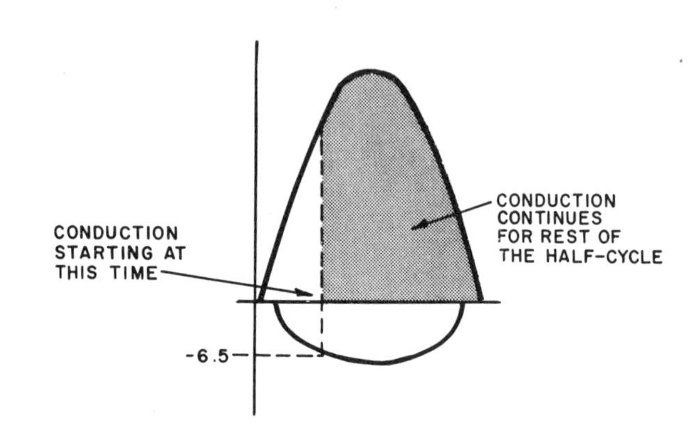

Fig. 26-16

This "trigger action" permits one to determine, by a grid-voltage setting, a time instant during each first quarter-cycle when the tube is to be allowed to conduct, thereby regulating the average current through the tube.

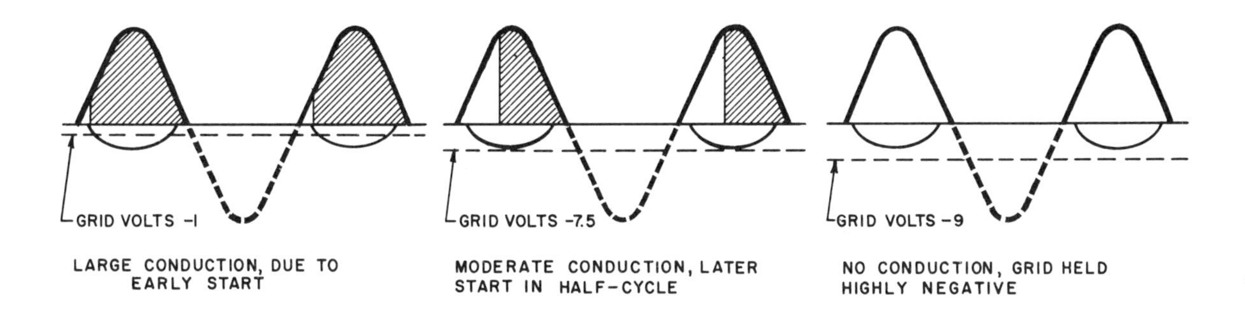

Fig. 26-17

By using a thyratron, current control is accomplished without the large power losses that would occur in series rheostats. Furthermore, necessary adjustments in grid voltage can be made automatically, by tying the grid control circuit into the output of some electronic device that is responsive to changes in light, speed, position, temperature, etc.

Accurate control of current over the entire half-cycle can be achieved by applying an alternating voltage to the grid, the timing of these alternations being adjustable relative to the timing of the A.C. power impulses applied to the plate circuit of the tube.

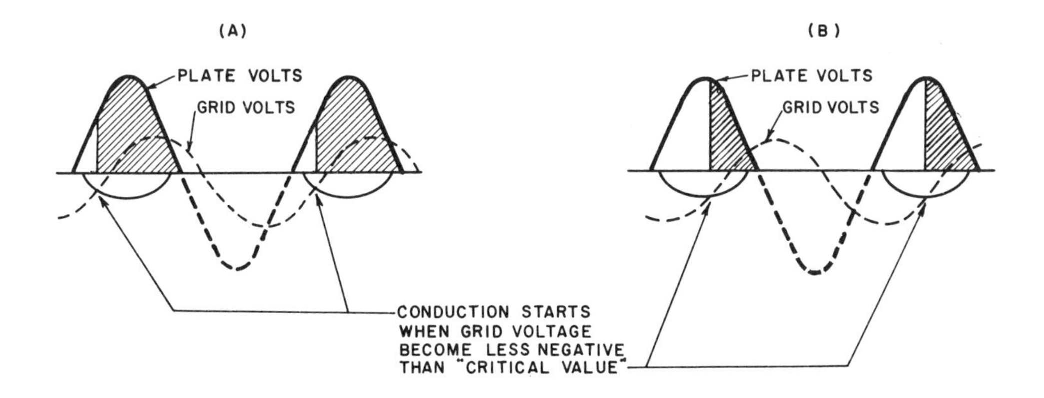

Fig. 26-18 Phase-Shift Control

In "A" above, the grid voltage is nearly in step with the plate voltage alternations. Early in the conduction half-cycle, the grid becomes positive enough to allow conduction to start. Conduction continues for the remainder of the half-cycle, stopping when the plate voltage drops off. In "B", the grid is held highly negative until late in the half-cycle, so conduction starts late in the half-cycle. By putting the grid voltage completely out-of-step with the plate voltage, that is, letting the grid become positive only while the plate is negative, conduction can be cut off entirely.

This method shown in Fig. 26-18, called "phase-shift control", is widely used in automatic control equipment. Full-wave rectified output can be obtained with two tubes.

THE IGNITRON

For currents of hundreds or thousands of amperes, larger than are handled in gas thyratrons, various types of mercury-vapor rectifiers are available.

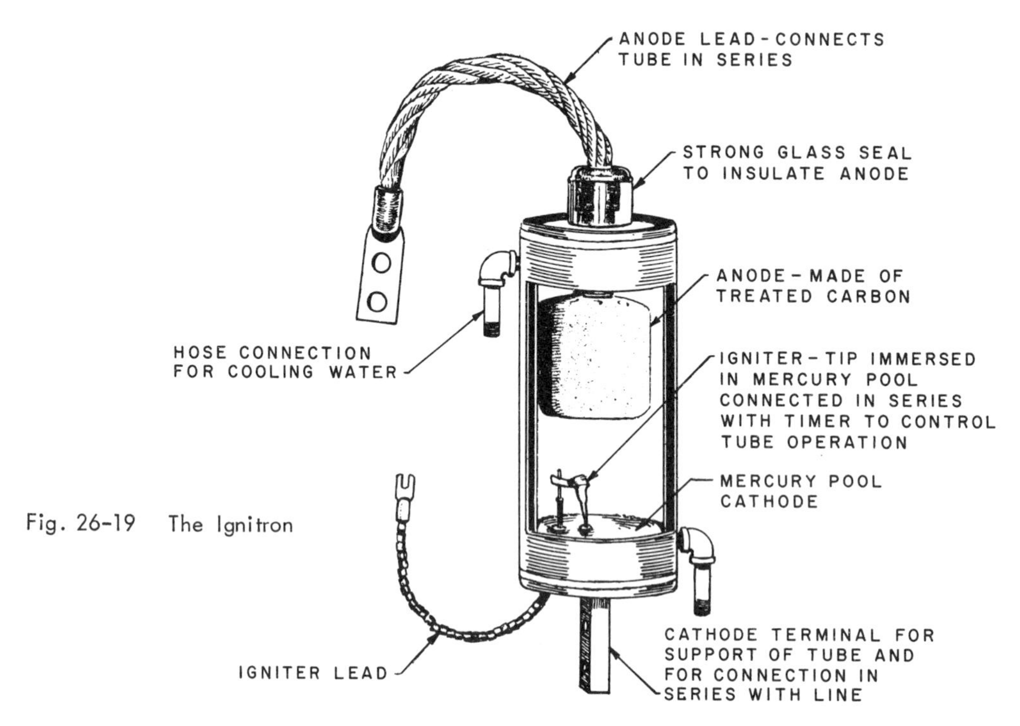

Fig. 26-19 The Ignitron

The Ignitron-type "tube", Fig. 26-19, has a water-cooled steel container. When the applied alternating voltage across the input builds up to about 25, the small ignitor rectifier conducts, forming a small arc where the silicon carbide ignitor electrode dips into the mercury surface. This arc forms ions, lowering the resistance between the mercury cathode and the main anode, so the main conduction stream takes the path from the cathode to the large plate. The voltage drop in this main arc is 15 volts, not enough to maintain conduction through the ignitor rectifier. The main arc continues to the end of the A.C. half-cycle, when conduction stops, then is initiated again on the next half-cycle by the ignitor rectifier.

Ignitrons also can be arranged for full-wave rectification. By using a thyratron as the ignitor rectifier, the ignitron can be made to "fire" at any desired time in the half-cycle, thus achieving accurate control of current without power losses. Ignitrons are used in welding equipment, electrochemical processes, and in D.C. motor drives.

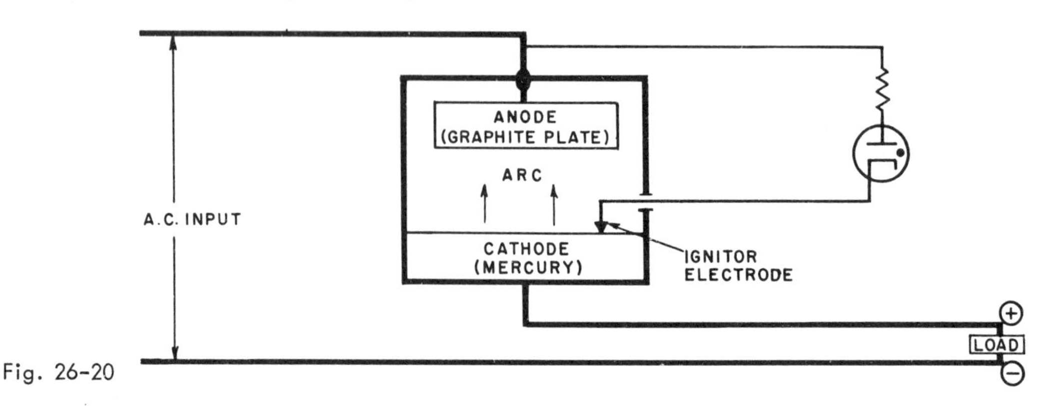

Fig. 26-20

SEMI-CONDUCTOR RECTIFIERS (Dry Disk Rectifiers)

Germanium, selenium, and silicon rectifiers are replacing tube-type rectifiers in many new applications.

Briefly, these rectifiers consist of layers of two different materials in close contact -- materials whose conducting properties permit electrons to flow readily in one direction across their boundary, but with great difficulty in the other direction.

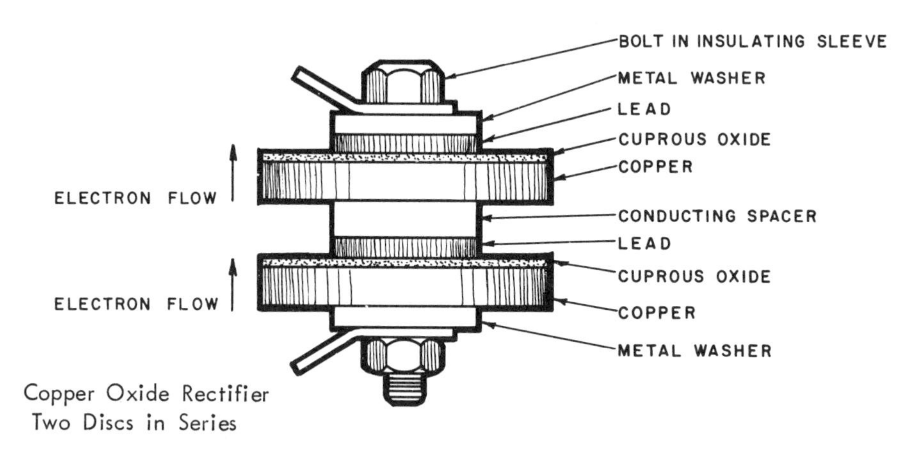

Fig. 26-21 Copper Oxide Rectifier Two Discs in Series

The oldest widely-used dry-disk rectifier is the copper-oxide rectifier. Electrons flow easily from copper into a cuprous-oxide layer formed on its surface. Contact with the oxide is made by a soft lead disk pressed against the oxidized surface. Electrons flow from the oxide into the copper only with great difficulty. Placing several copper-cuprous-oxide disks in series allows the rectifier to withstand more reverse voltage. Copper-oxide rectifiers are likely to be damaged by use at over 150° F.

Fig. 26-22 shows one section or "cell" of a selenium rectifier. Six of these in series form the small selenium rectifier used in some radio receivers. The base plate is iron or aluminum, coated with nickel or bismuth, on top of which a thin layer of selenium is deposited and given a crystallizing heat-treatment. Then a melted alloy is sprayed on to the selenium surface, forming what is called the "counter-electrode". Rectifying action takes place between this counter-electrode and the selenium.

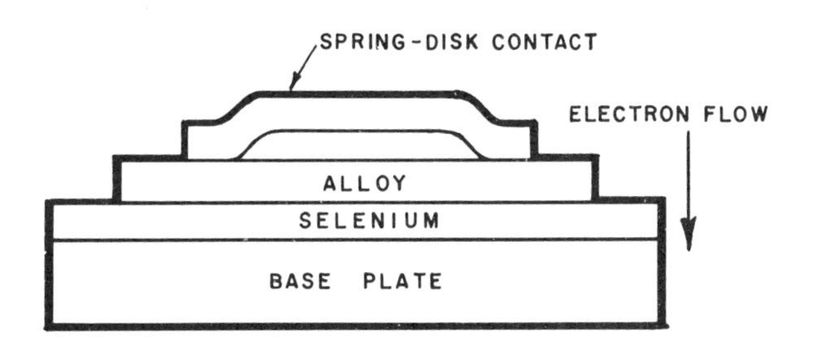

Fig. 26-22 Section of Selenium Rectifier

Two distinct types of germanium rectifiers are manufactured. Tiny germanium "point-contact" diodes have been used for some years to rectify very small currents in electronic equipment. A "crystal receiver" can be built easily, using such a diode as the detector. Germanium "junction rectifiers", similar to selenium rectifiers in general appearance contain thin layers of germanium. On one side of the layer an electron-poor impurity is introduced into the germanium. It is a small, closely-controlled amount. On the other side an electron-rich impurity is introduced, forming a so-called P-N junction in the germanium itself. Electrons flow easily from the electron-rich N area into the P area, but only with great difficulty in the reverse direction.

Selenium rectifiers, as of now, are used in the greatest number of applications -- battery chargers, welders, magnetic equipment, electronic power supply, electroplating, and driving small D.C. motors. Single units are made to carry as much as 100 amps. Germanium junctions (in sizes to 500 amps) feature high efficiency in low-voltage, high-current equipment, such as electroplating.

For full-wave rectification, selenium disks are often stacked in the arrangement shown in the sketch below. Schematically, the full-wave bridge may be drawn as at the right.

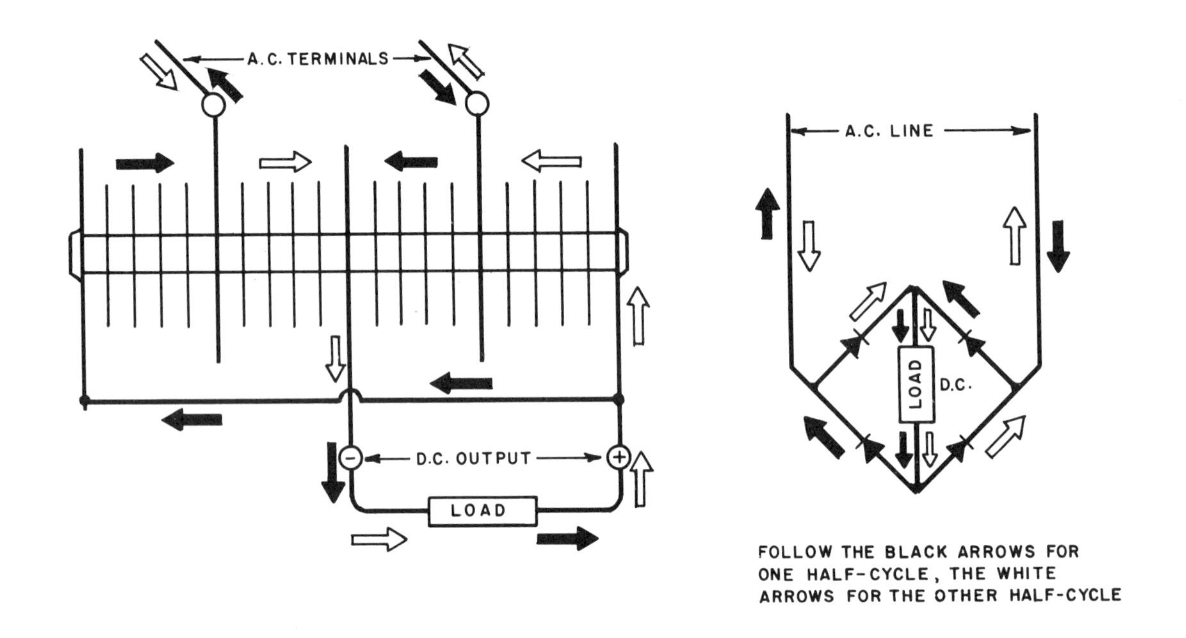

Fig. 26-23

The schematic at the right, above, uses the rectifier symbol, —▶|— In reading diagrams in which this symbol appears, one should first try to determine whether the black triangle points in the direction of electron flow, or in the opposite direction, for both systems are in use. Armed services training-manuals use the triangle pointing in the electron-flow direction, as is done in the sketch above, and as will probably be done eventually in all texts, replacing the older and more confusing symbol in which the triangle represented the anode, the straight line the cathode.

Recent developments in silicon power rectifiers are likely to make silicon the most-used power rectifier in the medium-voltage (50-600) medium-current (1-250 amp) range. Some can be operated continually at 375° - 400° F without damage. They are ruggedly built and offer a great deal of rectifying ability in a small space at low cost. Present uses include high-current electrolytic processes, arc furnaces, general D.C. supply for motors, magnetic equipment, battery charging, and many others.

The recently developed "silicon controlled rectifier" is a compact, reliable and efficient power rectifier to compete with thyratrons in control equipment. It is composed of four alternate layers of P- and N-type silicon. A pulse of current to a third contact, called the gate, starts conduction.

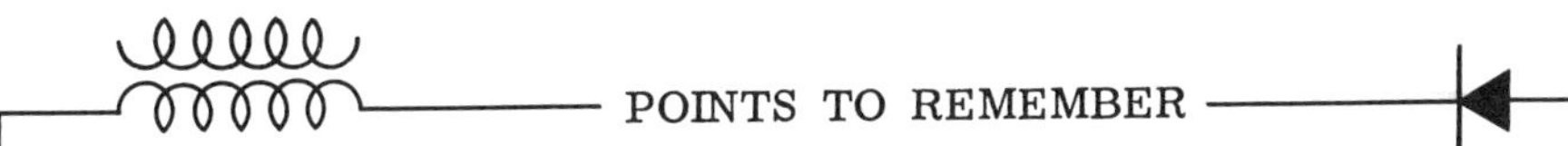

- The reason for use of alternating current in power transmission:
  a. Energy loss on the line is proportional to the square of the current.
  b. Transformers convert power at high amps and low volts to the same power at high voltage and low current, which causes less loss of energy.
  c. Similar transformation of D.C. energy is not yet feasible.

- A.C. can be converted to D.C. by motor-generator sets, or more efficiently by rectifiers.

- Rectifiers include vacuum tubes, gas tubes, and semiconductors.

- In the rectifier circuit, capacitors act as electron-storage devices, helping achieve steady electron flow.

- Grid control allows precise, economical control of tube current in automatic equipment.

REVIEW QUESTIONS

1. Calculate charge on a 20-mfd. capacitor at 400 volts.

2. If the above capacitor is completely discharged in one-tenth of a second, calculate the current.

3. If the above capacitor is completely discharged in one-hundredth of a second, calculate the average current.

4. How much voltage is required to put one-half coulomb of charge on a 500-mfd. capacitor?

5. The power input to a certain A.C. motor is 1000 watts. The motor is 75% efficient. The motor drives a D.C. generator, which is 78% efficient. Calculate the power output of the generator, and the efficiency of the motor-generator set.

6. A.

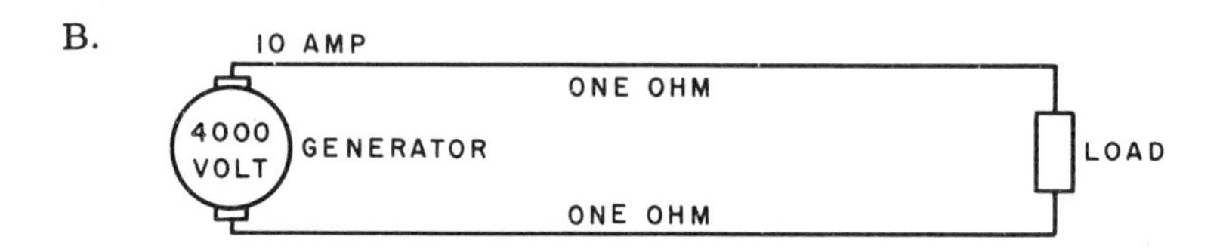

B.

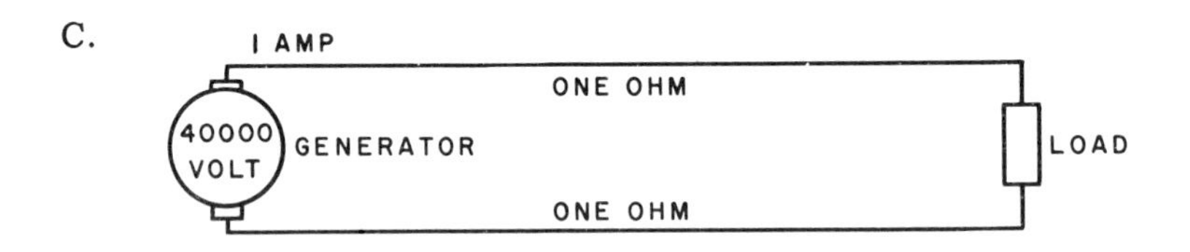

C.

1 AMP
ONE OHM
40000 VOLT
GENERATOR
LOAD
ONE OHM

For each of the above, calculate —

1. power output of generator
2. watts loss on line
3. power delivered at the load

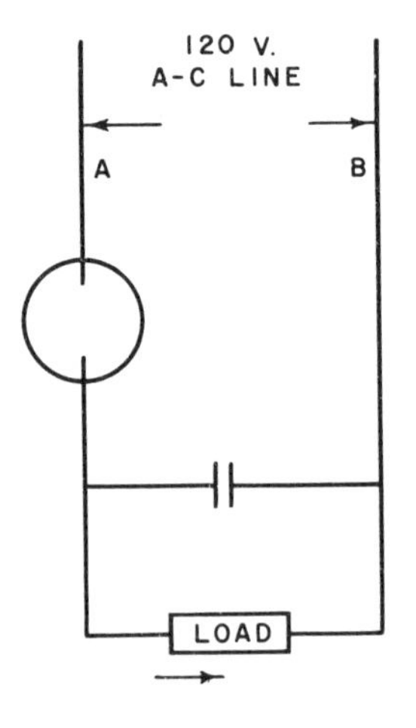

7. a. Add cathode and plate symbols in the circle at the left, to represent a diode so placed that electrons flow through the load in the direction shown.

   b. Mark the charge on the capacitor. Locate plus (+) and minus (-).

   c. Describe what happens when A is plus and B is minus.

   d. Describe what happens when A is minus and B is plus.

8. Diagram and explain a full-wave high-voltage rectifier, operating from a center-tapped transformer.

9. Diagram and explain the operation of a full-wave bridge.

10. Are gases classified as insulators or as conductors?

11. What is a thyratron and what is its use?

Unit 27 SOLVING D.C. NETWORK PROBLEMS

A network is any complex arrangement of resistors or similar circuit elements. At first glance, determining voltages and current in various parts of some circuits may appear difficult or impossible. Like all problems, they are easy after they are solved.

Some circuits can be redrawn so that it becomes apparent that the ordinary principles of series and parallel circuits can be applied, (review Pages 37-38).

Example #1: Given the arrangement of resistors in diagram A at the right, to find the current in each resistor, combine groups of resistors so that the circuit can be simplified.

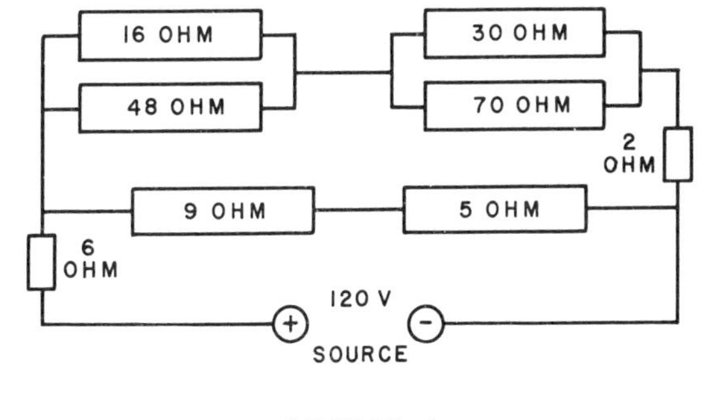

DIAGRAM A

a. Using product ÷ sum, the 16 ohm and 48 ohm in parallel are equivalent to a 12-ohm resistor. Likewise the 30 and 70 combine to equal 21 ohms. The circuit simplifies to diagram B.

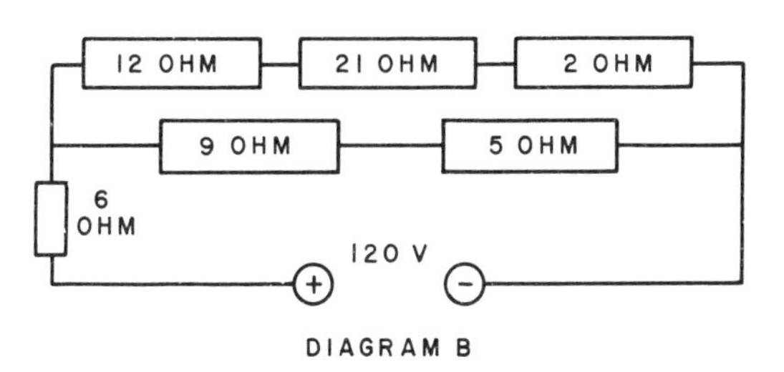

DIAGRAM B

b. The 12, 21, and 2 are in series, and add to 35 ohms. The 9 ohm and 5 ohm = 14 ohm, so the circuit can now look like diagram C.

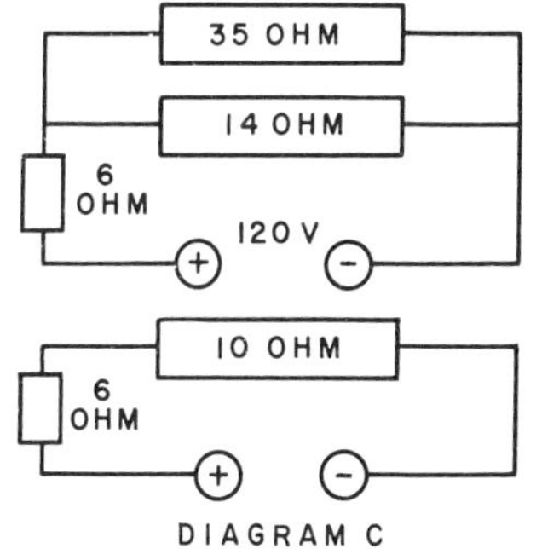

DIAGRAM C

c. The 35-ohm branch is in parallel with the 14-ohm branch. Using product ÷ sum again, the 35 and 14 in parallel are equivalent to a single 10-ohm resistor, which has a 6-ohm resistor in series with it. Therefore, the total resistance of the entire circuit is 16 ohms, and the current in the supply line is therefore 120 # 16 = 7.5 amps.

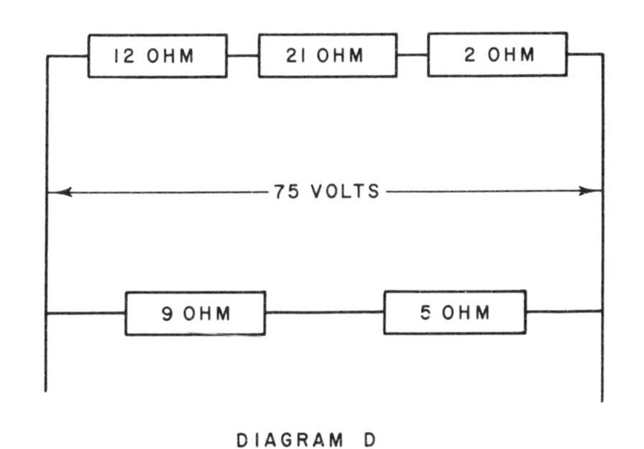

DIAGRAM D

d. This entire 7.5 amp passes through the 6-ohm series resistor, and the voltage across the 6-ohm resistor is 6×7.5 = 45 volts. The voltage applied to the rest of the circuit, represented by the 10-ohm resistance, is 10×7.5 = 75 volts. This 75 volts applies to two parallel branches, diagram D:

$$\frac{75}{35} = 2.14 \text{ amps in upper branch}$$

$$\frac{75}{14} = 5.36 \text{ amps in lower branch}$$

so the currents in the original 9-ohm, 5-ohm, and 2-ohm resistors are found.

The 12-ohm and 21-ohm resistors in sketch D have voltage drops of $12 \times 2.14 = 25.7$ volts and $21 \times 2.14 = 45$ volts. The 12-ohm resistor represents the original parallel combination of 16 and 48 ohms, so the current in the 16 ohm is $25.7 \div 16 = 1.6$ amps, and in the 48 ohm, $25.7 \div 48 = 0.54$ amps. The 21-ohm resistor represents the original 30, 70 parallel combination. The current in the 30 ohm is $45 \div 20 = 1.5$ amps; in the 70 ohm, $45 \div 70 = .64$ amp.

A problem of this type is noted only for its length, and repetition of the use of Ohm's Law. No new principles have been added.

Example #2: Here is a favored brain teaser or catch question that reappears now and then:

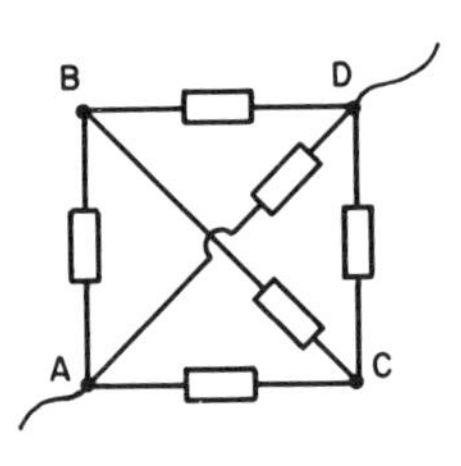

DIAGRAM 2A

Six equal resistors (say 10 ohms each) are connected as shown in diagram 2A at the left. Problem: Calculate the total resistance of the combination, between A and D.

By pulling out the resistor crossing over from A to D, and placing it to one side, the picture becomes diagram 2B.

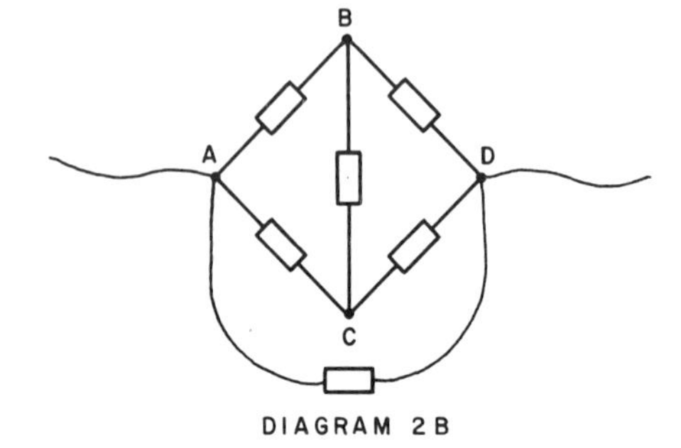

DIAGRAM 2B

The A B C D square may remind one of the Wheatstone bridge arrangement. In this case, it happens that the potential of B equals that of C, since the resistors are equal. In other words, the resistor between B and C will have no current in it, so it may as well not be there. In effect the circuit has become diagram 2C.

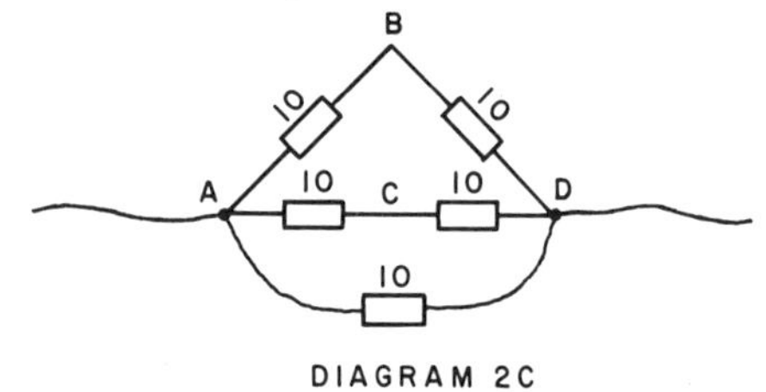

DIAGRAM 2C

Diagram 2C can be solved by methods for a parallel circuit. The two 20-ohm branches are equal to a single 10-ohm branch. This 10 with the original 10 equals a combined resistance of 5 ohms.

Having solved the above, the next question is: Using the same arrangement of resistors as originally given, find the resistance between A and C instead of between A and D.

Is the sketch below a correct rearrangement of this question?

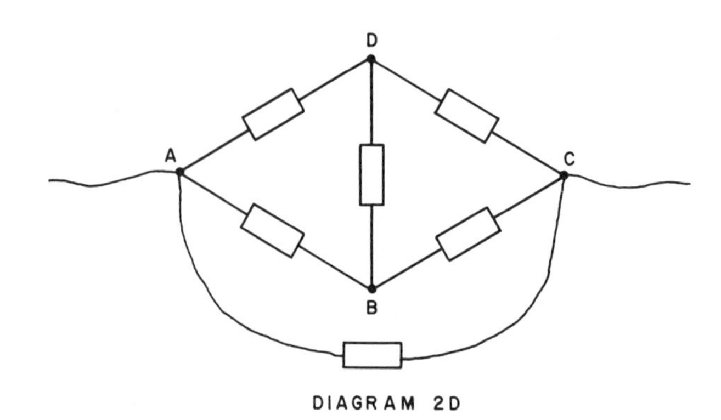

DIAGRAM 2D

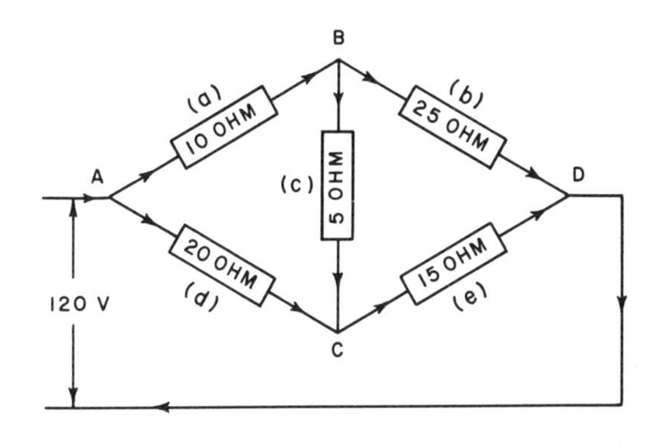

Finding the current in each resistor in an arrangement such as that at the left requires that one use a combination of Ohm's Law, algebra, and common sense.

The common sense principles are these two:

1. The total current coming toward any point in the circuit must equal the total current leaving that point.
2. The total voltage drops along any series path must equal the applied voltage.

The above two statements are called "Kirchhoff's Laws". The first idea we have already used in parallel-circuit problems. The second, we have used in series-circuit problems.

Proceeding to find the currents in the above network, we shall first call the current in the 10-ohm resistor, I_a; in the 25-ohm resistor, I_b; and so on. Using the first of Kirchhoff's Laws, and assuming current directions as shown on the diagram,

At junction-point B, $I_a = I_b + I_c$; or $I_b = I_a - I_c$

At point C, $I_c + I_d = I_e$; or $I_d = I_e - I_c$

From the second "Law" —

Taking electrons through the path A-B-D, $V_a + V_b = 120$

Through the path A-C-D, $V_d + V_e = 120$

Adding voltage drops across the three resistors in the A-B-C-D path, $V_a + V_c + V_e = 120$

The above five equations enable us to find the five unknown currents, using ordinary algebraic methods of solving simultaneous equations. First, we need to substitute for the voltages V_a, V_b, V_c, etc., their IR equivalents, from Ohm's Law. For V_a we substitute $I_a \times 10$, or $10\,I_a$. Making similar substitutions in the three equations just above, we have —

$$10\,I_a + 25\,I_b = 120$$

$$20\,I_d + 15\,I_e = 120$$

$$10\,I_a + 5\,I_c + 15\,I_e = 120$$

In these equations, to simplify them by reducing the number of unknown quantities, we insert for I_b its value $(I_a - I_c)$ and for I_d its equivalent $(I_e - I_c)$. The three voltage equations become:

$$10\,I_a + 25\,(I_a - I_c) = 120$$

$$20\,(I_e - I_c) + 15\,I_e = 120$$

$$10\,I_a + 5\,I_c + 15\,I_e = 120$$

Combining terms and dividing each of the preceding equations by 5:

$$7\ I_a - 5\ I_c = 24$$

$$7\ I_e - 4\ I_c = 24$$

$$2\ I_a + I_c + 3\ I_e = 24$$

We now have three equations and three unknowns. To reduce this to two equations, at the same time getting rid of one unknown, the last equation may be multiplied by 7, becoming

$$14\ I_a + 7\ I_c + 21\ I_e = 168$$

The first equation, times 2, is $14\ I_a - 10\ I_c = 48$

Subtracting the two equations: $17\ I_c + 21\ I_e = 120$

$7\ I_e - 4\ I_c = 24$, above, rewritten: $-12\ I_c + 21\ I_e = 72$

Subtracting again, $29\ I_c = 48$

$$I_c = \frac{48}{29} = 1.655 \text{ amps, call it } 1.66$$

Inserting this value of I_c into $7\ I_a - 5\ I_c = 24$, we find $I_a = 4.61$ amps.

Returning to one of our original equations, $I_b = I_a - I_c$, $I_b = 4.61 - 1.66 = 2.96$ amps.

Inserting the known value of I_c into $7\ I_e - 4\ I_c = 24$, we get $I_e = 4.37$ amps.

And from the original equation $I_d = I_e - I_c$, $I_d = 2.72$ amps.

These five answers may be checked by using them to calculate voltages across each resistor: for the 10 ohms, 46.1 volts; for the 25 ohms, 74 volts; for the 5 ohms, 8.3 volts; for the 20 ohms, 54.4 volts; and for the 15 ohms, 65.5 volts. Adding these voltages for the various series paths, we get results agreeing with 120 volts as closely as can be expected from currents accurate to three figures.

If in our original assumptions about current directions, we had guessed wrong on the direction in resistor C, the answer would have come out -1.655 amps, the algebraic minus sign indicating the reversed direction.

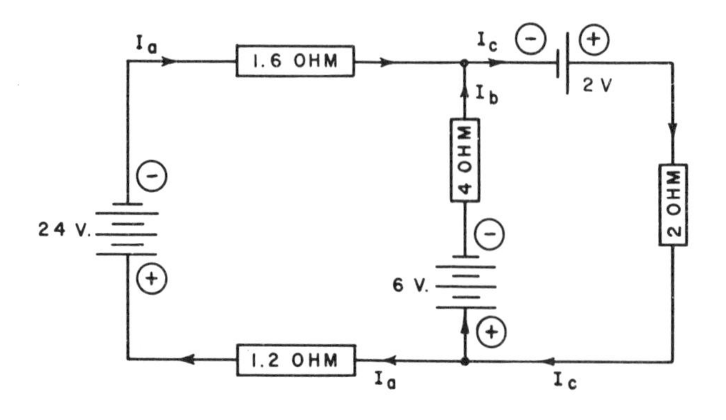

Another example: Given the network of batteries and resistors shown left, find the current in each.

In this circuit there are only three different currents, assumed to be in the directions shown.

The formula, $I_a + I_b = I_c$, takes care of the current.

A voltage equation may be written for the I_a and I_c path. This circuit contains two batteries, the 2-volt battery opposing the 24-volt one, so the effective "applied voltage" is 22 volts.

a. $22 = 1.6\ I_a + 2\ I_c + 1.2\ I_a$

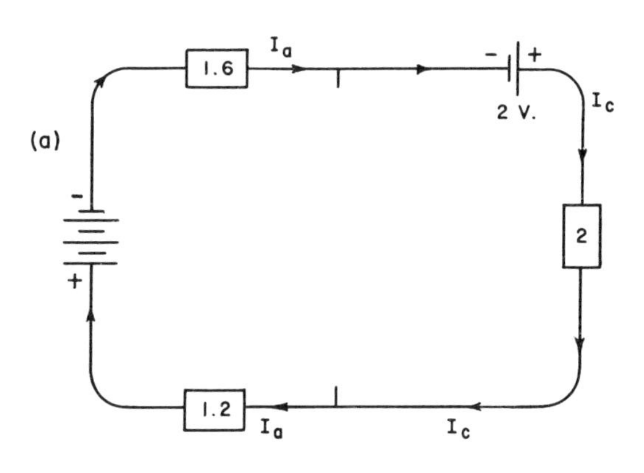

Another voltage equation can be written for the I_a and I_b path, although it appears that no electrons actually take that route.

If we carry an electron from the minus pole of the 24-volt battery around this circuit clockwise, it will be driven by the 24-volts and will be opposed by the 6-volt battery, so that applied voltage is 24 - 6 = 18 volts.

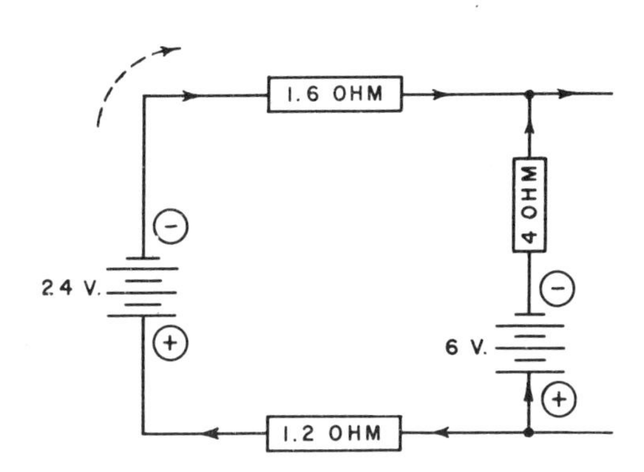

In the 1.6-ohm resistor the voltage drop is 1.6 I_a. This is a loss of potential, comparable to the loss of potential energy of water running down hill. In the 1.2-ohm resistor there is a similar voltage drop, 1.2 I_a.

Carrying our electron through the 4-ohm resistor, in a direction opposite to the assumed current, compares to carrying some water up a waterfall: it gains energy, rather than experiencing a drop in potential. The total voltage drop for the circuit is $1.6\ I_a + 1.2\ I_a - 4\ I_b$.

b. $18 = 2.8\ I_a - 4\ I_b$

To conveniently handle the arithmetic for circuit paths like this one, where there are several voltages, Kirchhoff's second law is sometimes used in this form:

The algebraic sum of voltages around a circuit path is zero.

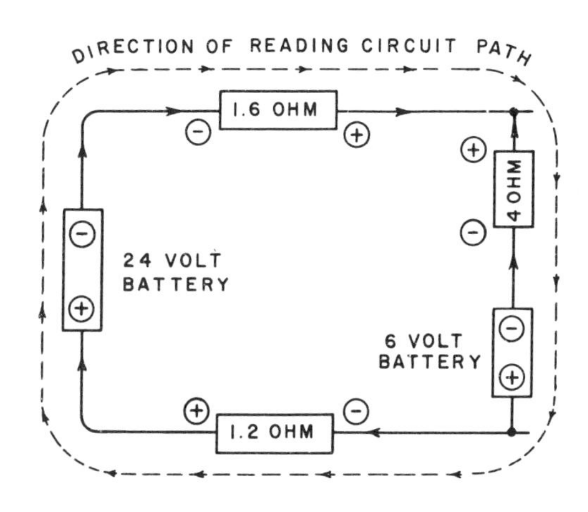

The "circuit path" is any path we choose to follow, whether we think electrons actually complete the path or not.

The arrows on the wiring in this diagram represent assumed current direction. From them, the polarity of each resistor can be found, since electrons flow from the ⊖ end of the resistor toward the ⊕ end. Polarity of the batteries is as given at the start.

To write the "algebraic sum" of the voltages, as we read clockwise around the diagram, give all of the "- to +" items one algebraic sign, and all of the "+ to -" the other algebraic sign.

The "- to +" voltages are the drops across the 1.6-ohm resistor, the 1.2-ohm resistor, and the 6-volt battery. The "+ to -" voltages are the 24-volt battery and the drop across the 4-ohm resistor.

$$\underbrace{1.6\,I_a + 1.2\,I_a + 6}_{\text{"- to +" voltages given the algebraic + sign}} \underbrace{- 24 - 4\,I_b}_{\text{"+ to -" voltages given the algebraic - sign}} = 0$$

This equation simplifies to $2.8\,I_a - 18 - 4\,I_b = 0$, which is equivalent to our previous equation (b), $18 = 2.8\,I_a - 4\,I_b$.

If one had chosen to call all of the "- to +" voltages minus, and all of the "+ to -" voltages plus, the resulting equation would also be correct.

Or, one could say:

> The total of the "+ to -" voltages is equal to the total of the "- to +" voltages.

Returning to the original problem, a third voltage equation could be written, involving the circuit path shown at the right.

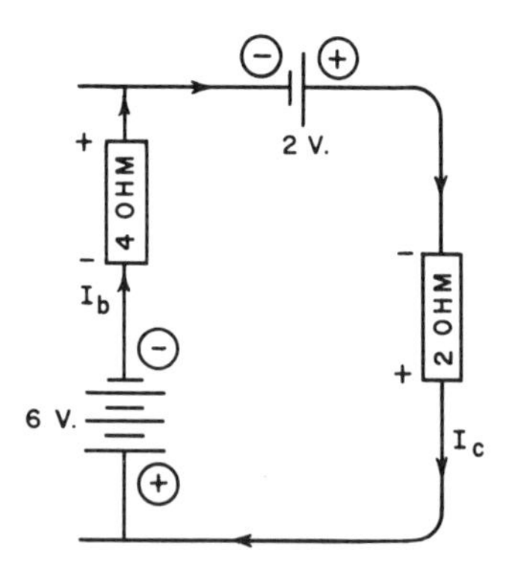

$$\underbrace{\text{Total "- to +" voltages}} = \text{"+ to -" voltage}$$

$$4\,I_b + 2 + 2\,I_c = 6$$

or

c. $$4\,I_b + 2\,I_c = 4$$

We now have one current equation and three voltage equations:

$$I_a + I_b = I_c$$

a. $2.8\,I_a + 2\,I_c = 22$

b. $2.8\,I_a - 4\,I_b = 18$

c. $4\,I_b + 2\,I_c = 4$

Actually, three independent equations are sufficient for finding three unknown quantities, so only two of the voltage equations needed to be written. Equation (c) is the result of subtracting equations (a) and (b).

Rewrite (a), inserting for I_c its equivalent, $I_a + I_b$.

a. $2.8\ I_a + 2\ I_a + 2\ I_b = 22$

$$\left.\begin{array}{ll}(a) & 4.8\ I_a + 2\ I_b = 22 \\ (b) & 2.8\ I_a - 4\ I_b = 18\end{array}\right\} \text{two equations, two unknowns}$$

Multiplying (a) by 2, and adding the two equations gives —

$$12.4\ I_a = 62$$

$$I_a = 5 \text{ amps}$$

Inserting this value into the original equation (a), —

$$2.8\ I_a + 2\ I_c = 22$$

$$14 + 2\ I_c = 22$$

$$I_c = 4 \text{ amps}$$

Since $I_a + I_b = I_c$, $5 + I_b = 4$, and $I_b = -1$ amp

This algebraic minus sign means that the 1 amp is opposite in direction to what we had originally assumed for I_b. No harm has been done by this wrong assumption, and no part of the calculation need be repeated.

POINTS TO REMEMBER

For solving complex circuits:

- Try rearrangement to series or parallel combinations.
- Use Kirchhoff's Laws:
  - Total current toward a point equals current away from that point.
  - Total voltage drops along any series path equal the applied voltage.
  - Or, total of "plus to minus" voltages equals total of "minus to plus" voltages.

REVIEW QUESTIONS

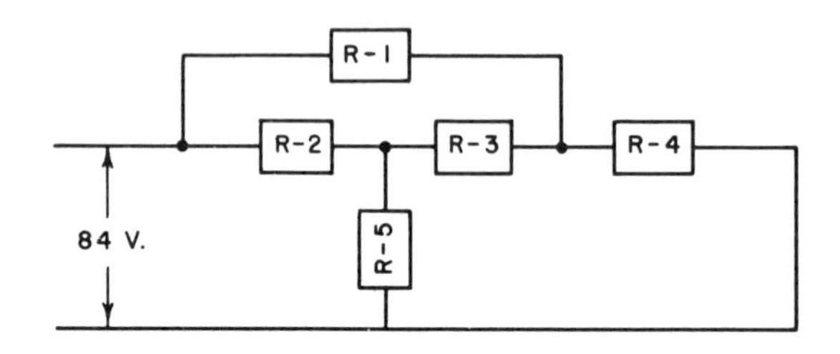

1. Resistors are arranged as at the left. The first four resistors are 6 ohms each, R-5 is 2 ohms. Find current in each resistor; voltage across each resistor.

2. Same arrangement of resistors as above. Line volts is 110. R-1 is 33 ohms, R-2 is 16.5 ohms, R-3 is 55 ohms, R-4 is 22 ohms, R-5 is 11 ohms. Find current in each resistor; voltage across each resistor.

3. A D.C. generator, e.m.f. = 9 volts and internal resistance = 0.15 ohm, is charging two batteries which are connected in parallel. Battery #1 has e.m.f. = 6 volts, internal resistance = 0.1 ohm. Battery #2 has 6-volt e.m.f., 0.2-ohm resistance. Calculate current in each battery and terminal voltage of generator.

4. Determine:

   a. The total resistance of the circuit.

   b. The voltage drop across A-B.

   c. The current in the branch A-D-C.

   d. The potential difference between B and D.

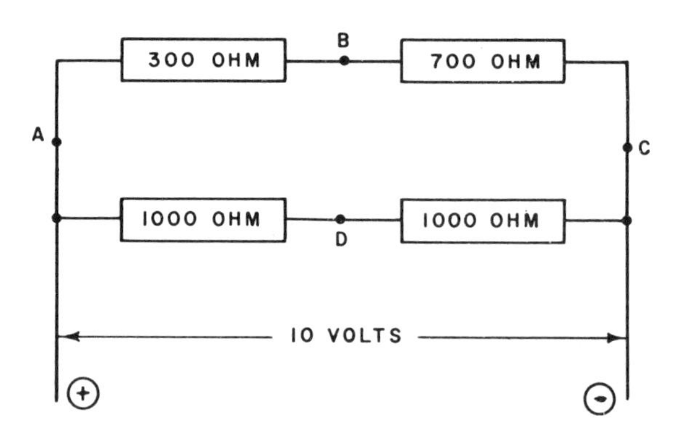

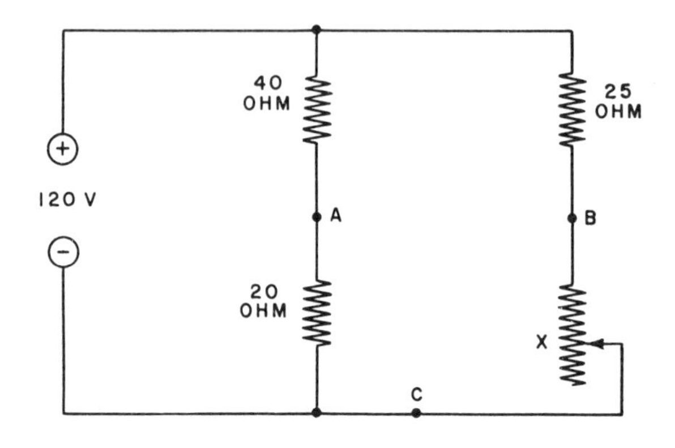

5. This network of resistors is used to produce a certain potential difference between two points, A and B.

   a. How much resistance must be placed at X so that the voltage between A and B is zero?

   b. How much resistance must be placed at X so that A is 5 volts more positive than B?

Appendix

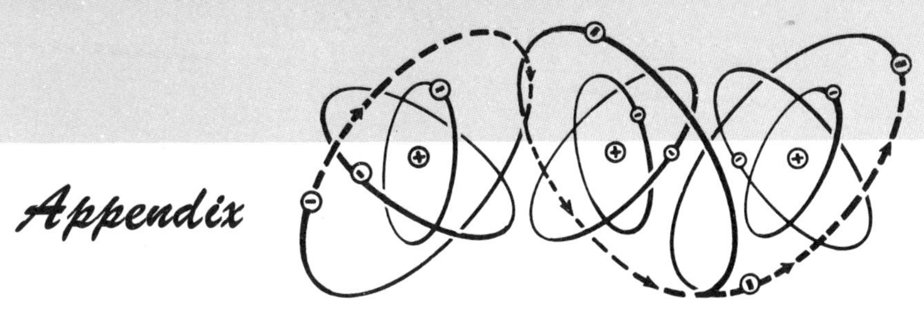

RESISTANCE OF METALS AND ALLOYS

Resistivity in microhm-cm. at 70° F. (Resistance of a centimetercube, in millionths of an ohm.)

To obtain ohms per mil-foot: Multiply the "resistivity" figure as given in table by 6.015

Temperature coefficient given for one centigrade degree.

Metals	Resistivity	Temp. Coeff.	Metals	Resistivity	Temp. Coeff.
Aluminum	2.83	.004	Magnesium (Mg)	4.6	.004
Alumel	33.3	.0012	Manganese (Mn)	5	
Aluminum bronze (90% Cu, 10% Al)	12.6-12.7	.003	Manganin (84% Cu, 12% Mn, 4% Ni)	44-48	.0000
Beryllium	10.		Mercury	95.78	.0009
Bismuth	119.	.004	Molybdenum	5.6	.003
Brass (various comp.)	7. 6.5-8.3	.002	Monel (Cu, Ni)	42	.002
Bronze (88% Cu, 12% tin)	18.	.0005	Nickel	7	.006
Cadmium	7.55	.004	Nichrome (Ni, Cr)	90-110	.0002
Calcium	4.6		Platinum	10	.003
Carbon	3500.	-.0005	Silicon steel (4% Si)	62	
Chromel (Ni, Cr)	70-110	.0001	Silver	1.6	.004
Chromium	13		Steel, var. alloys piano wire	25-100 11.9	.002-.003 .003
Cobalt	9.7		Sodium	4.4	.004
Constantan (60% Cu, 40% Ni)	44-49	.0000	Tantalum	15	.003
Copper, annealed Copper, hard-drawn	1.724-1.73 1.77	.004 .0039	Tellurium	200,000	
German silver (Cu, zinc, 18% Ni)	33	.0004	Tin	11.5	.004
Gold	2.44	.0035	Titanium	50	
Graphite	800.		Tungsten at 3150° F at 5000° F	5.51 60. 100.	.0045
Invar (65% iron, 35% Ni)	81		Uranium	30	
Iron, pure cast	9.7 60.	.005	Vanadium	59	
Lead	22.	.004	Zinc	5.8	.004

AMERICAN WIRE GAGE TABLE

B & S Gage Number	Diameter in Mils	Area in Circular Mils	Ohms per 1000 Ft. Copper* 68° F	Ohms per 1000 Ft. Copper* 167° F	Ohms per 1000 Ft. Aluminum 68° F	Pounds per 1000 Ft. Copper	Pounds per 1000 Ft. Aluminum
0000	460	211,600	.049	.0596	.0804	640	195
000	410	167,800	.0618	.0752	.101	508	154
00	365	133,100	.078	.0948	.128	403	122
0	325	105,500	.0983	.1195	.161	320	97
1	289	83,690	.1239	.151	.203	253	76.9
2	258	66,370	.1563	.190	.256	201	61.0
3	229	52,640	.1970	.240	.323	159	48.4
4	204	41,740	.2485	.302	.408	126	38.4
5	182	33,100	.3133	.381	.514	100	30.4
6	162	26,250	.395	.481	.648	79.5	24.1
7	144	20,820	.498	.606	.817	63.0	19.1
8	128	16,510	.628	.764	1.03	50.0	15.2
9	114	13,090	.792	.963	1.30	39.6	12.0
10	102	10,380	.999	1.215	1.64	31.4	9.55
11	91	8,234	1.260	1.532	2.07	24.9	7.57
12	81	6,530	1.588	1.931	2.61	19.8	6.00
13	72	5,178	2.003	2.44	3.29	15.7	4.8
14	64	4,107	2.525	3.07	4.14	12.4	3.8
15	57	3,257	3.184	3.87	5.22	9.86	3.0
16	51	2,583	4.016	4.88	6.59	7.82	2.4
17	45.3	2,048	5.06	6.16	8.31	6.20	1.9
18	40.3	1,624	6.39	7.77	10.5	4.92	1.5
19	35.9	1,288	8.05	9.79	13.2	3.90	1.2
20	32.0	1,022	10.15	12.35	16.7	3.09	0.94
21	28.5	810	12.8	15.6	21.0	2.45	.745
22	25.4	642	16.1	19.6	26.5	1.95	.591
23	22.6	510	20.4	24.8	33.4	1.54	.468
24	20.1	404	25.7	31.2	42.1	1.22	.371
25	17.9	320	32.4	39.4	53.1	0.97	.295
26	15.9	254	40.8	49.6	67.0	.77	.234
27	14.2	202	51.5	62.6	84.4	.61	.185
28	12.6	160	64.9	78.9	106	.48	.147
29	11.3	126.7	81.8	99.5	134	.384	.117
30	10.0	100.5	103.2	125.5	169	.304	.092
31	8.93	79.7	130.1	158.2	213	.241	.073
32	7.95	63.2	164.1	199.5	269	.191	.058
33	7.08	50.1	207	252	339	.152	.046
34	6.31	39.8	261	317	428	.120	.037
35	5.62	31.5	329	400	540	.095	.029
36	5.00	25.0	415	505	681	.076	.023
37	4.45	19.8	523	636	858	.0600	.0182
38	3.96	15.7	660	802	1080	.0476	.0145
39	3.53	12.5	832	1012	1360	.0377	.0115
40	3.15	9.9	1049	1276	1720	.0299	.0091
41							
42	2.50	6.2					
43							
44	1.97	3.9					

*Resistance figures for standard annealed copper. For hard-drawn, add 2%

WIRES PER INCH TABLE

Gage No.	Wires per Inch S.C.C.	Wires per Inch D.C.C.	Wires per Square Inch (Approx.) S.C.C.	Wires per Square Inch (Approx.) D.C.C.	Wires per Square Inch (Approx.) P.E.	Wires per Square Inch (Approx.) Formvar	Feet per Pound Bare	Feet per Pound P.E.	Feet per Pound D.C.C.
8	7.4	7.1	55	50	58		20	19.8	19.5
9	8.2	7.9	69	63					
10	9.3	8.9	86	78	92		31.8	31.5	31
11	10.3	9.9	108	98					
12	11.5	10.9	132	120	145		50.6	50	49
13	12.8	12.1	166	148					
14	14.2	13.5	206	183	225		80.4	79.4	77
15	15.8	14.8	255	223					
16	17.9	16.5	320	280	358	340	128	126	119
17	20	18.3	400	340					
18	22	21	492	415	572	530	203	201	188
19	24.5	23.5	625	510					
20	27	24.5	770	625	875	800	323	319	298
21	30	26.7	940	750					
22	34	30.2	1165	915	1332	1200	514	507	461
23	37.5	32.2	1400	1070					
24	41.5	35.5	1700	1260	2045	1820	818	805	745
25	45.5	38.5	2065	1495					
26	50	42	2510	1745	3090	2700	1300	1280	1118
27	55	45	3030	2020					
28	60	48.5	3645	2330	4670	4000	2067	2030	1759
29	65	52	4280	2690					
30	71.5	55.5	5060	3050	6860	5500	3287	3220	2534
31	77.5	59	6000	3480					
32	84	62.5	7050	3900	10050	7700	5225	5120	3137
33	90	66	8100						
34	97	70	9400		14250	10500	8310	8160	6168
35	104	74	10800						
36	112	78	12800		20000	14900	13210	12850	7875
37									
38	127	84					21010		
39									
40	143	90					33410		

S.C.C. = Single Cotton Covered

D.C.C. = Double Cotton Covered

P. E. = Plain Enamel

MOTOR FORMULAS

From the fundamental definitions of current and magnetic field strength, the force on a current passing across a magnetic field is equal to:

$\frac{B \times L \times I}{10}$ B is lines per sq. cm., L is length of the wire in cm., I is current in amps, force is measured in dynes

Since — Pounds $\times$ 445,000 = dynes

$$\frac{\text{Lines}}{\text{Sq.in.}} \times \frac{1}{6.45} = \frac{\text{Lines}}{\text{Sq. cm.}}$$

Inches $\times$ 2.54 = cm.

$$\text{Force} \times 445{,}000 = \frac{B}{6.45} \times \frac{I \times L \times 2.54}{10}$$, which reduces to

$$F = \frac{B \times L \times I}{11{,}300{,}000}$$, in which F is force in pounds on a single wire, L is the length (inches) of wire in the field, B is lines per sq. in., and I is amperes.

Torque on one wire is Force (lb.) $\times$ radius (ft.) $T = \frac{B \times L \times I \times r}{11{,}300{,}000}$

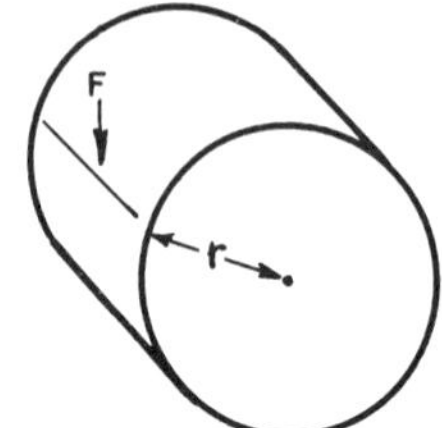

I, the current in a wire, is $\frac{I_a}{m}$;

I_a is the total armature current;

m is the number of parallel paths through armature

Calling the total number of wires Z, the total torque on all the wires is $T = \frac{Z \times B \times L \times I_a \times r}{11{,}300{,}000 \times m}$

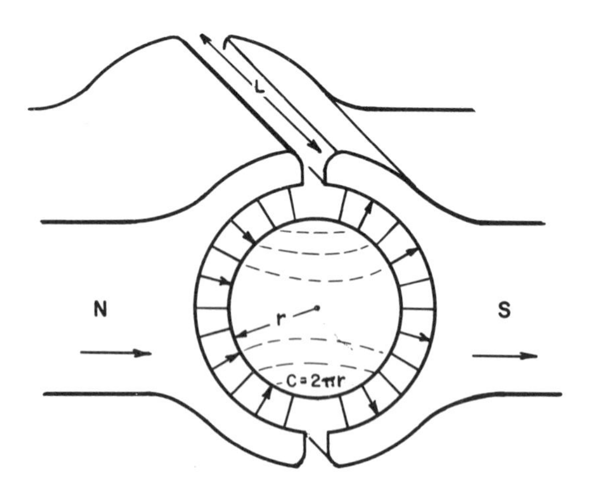

The flux (ϕ) passing through the armature can be found by multiplying the lines per sq. in. (B) by the sq. in. area of half of the cylindrical armature surface (assuming that the motor is of compact construction so that the armature is surrounded by field poles).

The entire curved surface is $2\pi r \times L$ sq. in.; half of it is $\pi r L$.

$$\phi = \pi r LB \text{ (r in inches)}$$

$$\phi = 12\pi r LB \text{ (r in feet)}$$

$$\frac{\phi}{12\pi} = r LB$$

Substituting $\frac{\phi}{12\pi}$ for $r \times L \times B$ in the previous Torque formula, $T = \frac{Z \times I_a \times \phi}{11{,}300{,}000 \times m \times 12\pi}$

$$T = \frac{Z \times I_a \times \phi}{425{,}000{,}000 \times m}$$

T is torque in lb.-ft.
Z is total number of armature wires
I_a is total armature current
m is the number of parallel paths through the armature
ϕ is the flux passing through the armature

THE ELECTROLYTIC CAPACITOR

This capacitor consists of a sealed aluminum can containing a roll of sheet aluminum which is oxidized on the surface. The can is filled with an electrolyte, in either liquid or jelly form.

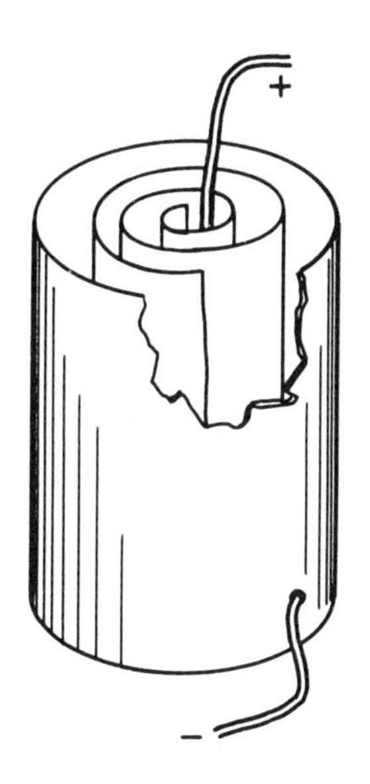

Any capacitor is essentially two separate conductors, separated by an insulator. In the electrolytic capacitor, the roll of aluminum sheet is one conductor, and the electrolyte is the other conductor. The insulator between them is a thin layer of aluminum oxide, formed on the roll of sheet aluminum. The container is in contact with the electrolyte.

An electrolytic capacitor of this type is to be used only in circuits where a D.C. voltage is maintained across the capacitor when in use. To explain how this requirement arises, we need to see how aluminum electrodes behave in an electrolytic solution:

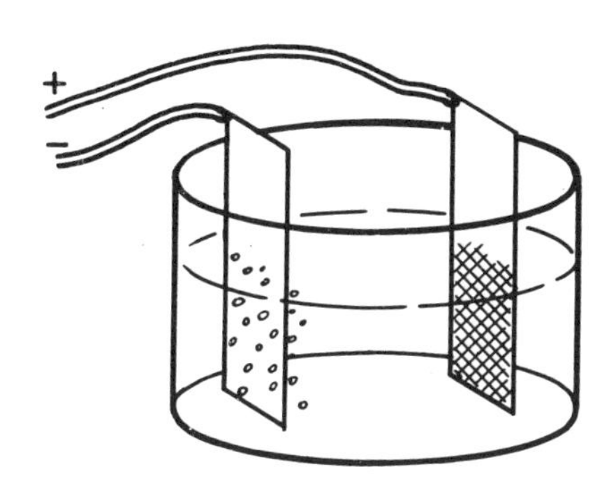

Assume two sheets of plain aluminum are placed in a conducting solution, and connected to a D.C. source. The solution may consist of borax or other salts; or it may consist of mild acids. (Borax is used in the capacitor.) As in many electrolytes, the current causes hydrogen to be released at the negative electrode, and oxygen to be released at the positive electrode. In the electrolytic cell pictured at left, hydrogen gas bubbles away at the negative electrode, having no effect on the negative aluminum sheet. On the positive aluminum electrode, oxygen atoms released either from the water or from negative ions in the electrolyte, combine with the positive aluminum sheet, forming a thin coat of aluminum oxide on the positive aluminum.

(This process of electrolytic oxidation of aluminum is called anodizing. The term "anode" means the electrode where electrons leave the conducting device.

As the above electrolysis process goes on, the resistance of the cell increases, due to the electrical resistance of the aluminum oxide that is forming. However, this is a one-way resistance, that is, if the battery connections were later reversed so that the oxidized aluminum is made the negative electrode, a high current will exist through the cell. Hydrogen from the solution will combine, now, with the oxygen of the oxidized surface, changing the oxide back to aluminum. The one-way character of the resistance may be described this way: Loose electrons can go from aluminum metal into the oxide layer readily; but electrons trying to get from the oxide into the pure metal can do so only with great difficulty.

In the past, this one-way resistance of aluminum oxide has been employed in various crude electrolytic rectifying devices. Some very useful dry-type rectifiers depend on the fact that electrons move readily from a metal into its oxide, but with difficulty in the reverse direction.

Applying this information to the capacitor, as long as a D.C. voltage of correct polarity is maintained across the capacitor, the aluminum oxide insulating film is maintained. Even if the capacitor is subjected momentarily to a high voltage that breaks down the oxide, the insulating layer is rebuilt when the capacitor is again operated at correct voltage. If the capacitor is connected into a circuit with its polarity reversed, it is a conductor rather than a capacitor; current through it decomposes the oxide film and also is likely to produce enough heat to generate steam in the moist electrolyte.

Electrolytic capacitors are particularly useful as filter capacitors in power rectifier circuits, smoothing out the pulsing D.C. voltage. Electrolytics have the advantage of high capacitance in a small space. The capacitance of a capacitor depends, among other things, on the plate area and the distance between the plates. Large plate area makes for large capacitance. By etching (chemical roughening) of the aluminum surface, a large effective area is obtained. The closer the conductors, the larger the capacitance. In the electrolytic capacitor, the conductors (electrolyte and aluminum metal) are separated only by the very thin layer of aluminum oxide.

Electrolytic capacitors for use in A.C. circuits (motor-starting) consist, in effect, of two capacitors in series. Both aluminum sheets are etched and oxidized. As the line polarity reverses, the two oxide layers are alternately responsible for maintaining the insulating effect.

With increasing age, moisture may evaporate from the capacitor, for a 100% perfect seal is difficult. Loss of moisture reduces the amount of useful electrolyte, which reduces the capacitance. When a radio receiver gradually develops a hum or low-pitched buzz (60 or 120 cycle) it is likely that the filter capacitor needs replacement.